Galaxy Series

Olive Stafford Niles   Reading Consultant, Connecticut
State Department of Education. Lecturer in courses
on the teaching of reading, American International College,
Springfield, Massachusetts. Formerly, Director of
Reading, Public Schools of Springfield, Massachusetts;
Member of the Board of Directors, International
Reading Association; Director: High School and College
Reading Center, Boston University.

Elsie Katterjohn   Formerly, Reading Coordinator,
Willowbrook High School, Villa Park, Illinois;
Chairman of the Language Arts Department, Community
High School, North Chicago, Illinois.

THRUST

Editorial direction: **Leo B. Kneer**

Development: **Aloha S. Lawver**
with Donald Abramson,
Ellen Wettersten, and Harold Eaton

Design: **Robert Amft**

Scott, Foresman and Company

3

The authors and editors of *Thrust* acknowledge with gratitude the contributions to this anthology made by the teachers listed below who tried out materials in classrooms and assessed the effect of various selections on their students. Their students helped, too, through their candid comments on the selections they were asked to read.

Mrs. Virginia Briner
Daniel Webster Junior High School, Waukegan, Illinois

Dr. June S. Wilson
The University School, Ann Arbor, Michigan

Mrs. Sheila B. Feigelson
The University School, Ann Arbor, Michigan

Mrs. Florence Meaghan
Franklin Junior High School, Cedar Rapids, Iowa

Mr. Charles Olschefski
Pasteur Elementary School, Detroit, Michigan

Mrs. Margaret Petters
Daniel Webster Junior High School, Waukegan, Illinois

Mrs. Linda C. Roberts
Southern Junior High School, Louisville, Kentucky

Miss DeLite Sharp
Taft Junior High School, Cedar Rapids, Iowa

Mrs. Barbara H. Taylor
Barret Junior High School, Louisville, Kentucky

We also wish to express appreciation to Mr. Raymond Griffin, formerly Principal of the Wadsworth Upper Grade Center, Chicago, and to Mrs. Jeanne Connelly Junker, Principal of the Bryn Mawr School, Chicago, who permitted us to try out selections in classrooms in their schools.

ISBN: 673-04850-0

Copyright © 1975, 1969 by Scott, Foresman and Company, Glenview, Illinois 60025. Philippines Copyright 1975, 1969 by Scott, Foresman and Company. All rights reserved. Printed in the United States of America. Regional offices of Scott, Foresman and Company are located in Dallas, Texas; Glenview, Illinois; Oakland, New Jersey; Palo Alto, California; Tucker, Georgia; and Brighton, England.

CONTENTS

THRUST

5

10 CONSEQUENCES

11 C S S D REVIEW

12 INVENTORY

DICTIONARY ENTRIES on pages 176, 292, 293, 297, 400, 401, 408, and 448 are based on the *Thorndike-Barnhart Advanced Junior Dictionary,* copyright © 1968 by Scott, Foresman and Company.

PICTURE CREDITS:

ILLUSTRATIONS BY:

gam ut (gam′ət), *n.* **1.** t
musical notes. **2.** the majo
anything: *In one minute I r
to despair.* [contraction of

whole series of recognized
scale. **3.** the entire range of
the gamut of feeling from hope
Ied.L *gamma ut < gamma G,*

all summer in a day

by Ray Bradbury

The children could not remember a time when there wasn't rain.

"READY?"
"Ready."
"Now?"
"Soon."
"Do the scientists really know? Will it happen today, will it?"
"Look, look; see for yourself!"

The children pressed to each other like so many roses, so many weeds, intermixed, peering out for a look at the hidden sun.

It rained.

It had been raining for seven years; thousands upon thousands of days compounded and filled from one end to the other with rain, with the drum and gush of water, with the sweet crystal fall of showers and the concussion of storms so heavy they were tidal waves come over the islands. A thousand forests had been crushed under the rain and grown up a thousand times to be crushed again. And this was the way life was forever on the planet Venus, and this was the schoolroom of the children of the rocket men and women who had come to a raining world to set up civilization and live out their lives.

"It's stopping, it's stopping!"
"Yes, yes!"

Margot stood apart from them, from these children who could never remember a time when there wasn't rain and rain and rain. They were all nine years old, and if there had been a day, seven years ago, when the sun came out for an hour and showed its face to the stunned world, they could not recall. Sometimes, at night, she heard them

stir, in remembrance, and she knew they were dreaming and remembering gold or a yellow crayon or a coin large enough to buy the world with. She knew they thought they remembered a warmness, like a blushing in the face, in the body, in the arms and legs and trembling hands. But then they always awoke to the tatting drum, the endless shaking down of clear bead necklaces upon the roof, the walk, the gardens, the forests, and their dreams were gone.

All day yesterday they had read in class about the sun. About how like a lemon it was, and how hot. And they had written small stories or essays or poems about it:

I think the sun is a flower,
That blooms for just one hour.

That was Margot's poem, read in a quiet voice in the still classroom while the rain was falling outside.

"Aw, you didn't write that!" protested one of the boys.

"I did," said Margot. "I *did.*"

"William!" said the teacher.

But that was yesterday. Now the rain was slackening, and the children were crushed in the great thick windows.

"Where's teacher?"
"She'll be back."
"She'd better hurry, we'll miss it!"

They turned on themselves, like a feverish wheel, all tumbling spokes.

Margot stood alone. She was a very frail girl who looked as if she had been lost in the rain for years and the rain had washed out the blue from her eyes and the red from her mouth and the yellow from her hair. She was an old photograph dusted from an album, whitened away, and if she spoke at all her voice would be a ghost. Now she stood, separate, staring at the rain and the loud wet world beyond the huge glass.

"What're *you* looking at?" said William.

Margot said nothing.

"Speak when you're spoken to." He gave her a shove. But she did not move; rather she let herself be moved only by him and nothing else.

They edged away from her, they would not look at her. She felt them go away. And this was because she would play no games with them in the echoing tunnels of the underground city. If they tagged her and ran, she stood blinking after them and did not follow. When the class sang songs about happiness and life and games her lips barely moved. Only when they sang about the sun and the summer did her lips move as she watched the drenched windows.

And then, of course, the biggest crime of all was that she had come here only five years ago from Earth, and she remembered the sun and the way the sun was and the sky was when she was four in Ohio. And they, they had been on Venus all their lives, and they had been only two years old when last the sun came out and had long since forgotten the color and heat of it and the way it really was. But Margot remembered.

"It's like a penny," she said once, eyes closed.

"No it's not!" the children cried.

"It's like a fire," she said, "in the stove."

"You're lying, you don't remember!" cried the children.

But she remembered and stood quietly apart from all of them and watched the patterning windows. And once, a month ago, she had refused to shower in the school shower rooms, had clutched her hands to her ears and over her head, screaming the water mustn't touch her head. So after that, dimly, dimly, she sensed it, she was different and they knew her difference and kept away.

There was talk that her father and mother were taking her back to Earth next year; it seemed vital to her that they do so, though it would mean the loss of thousands of dollars to her family. And so, the children hated her for all these reasons of big and little consequence. They hated her pale snow face, her waiting silence, her thinness, and her possible future.

"Get away!" The boy gave her another push. "What're you waiting for?"

Then, for the first time, she turned and looked at him. And what she was waiting for was in her eyes.

"Well, don't wait around here!" cried the boy savagely. "You won't see nothing!"

Her lips moved.

"Nothing!" he cried. "It was all a joke, wasn't it?" He turned to the other children. "Nothing's happening today. *Is* it?"

They all blinked at him and then, understanding, laughed and shook their heads. "Nothing, nothing!"

"Oh, but," Margot whispered, her eyes helpless. "But this is the day, the scientists predict, they say, they *know*, the sun . . . ."

"All a joke!" said the boy, and seized her roughly. "Hey, everyone, let's put her in a closet before teacher comes!"

"No," said Margot, falling back.

They surged about her, caught her up and bore her, protesting, and then pleading, and then crying, back into a tunnel, a room, a closet, where they slammed and locked the door. They stood looking at the door and saw it tremble from her beating and throwing herself against it. They heard her muffled cries. Then, smiling, they turned and went out and back down the tunnel, just as the teacher arrived.

"Ready, children?" She glanced at her watch.

"Yes!" said everyone.

"Are we all here?"

"Yes!"

The rain slackened still more.

They crowded to the huge door.

The rain stopped.

It was as if, in the midst of a film, concerning an avalanche, a tornado, a hurricane, a volcanic eruption, something had, first, gone wrong with the sound apparatus, thus muffling and finally cutting off all noise, all of the blasts and repercussions and thunders, and then, second, ripped the film from the projector and inserted in its place a peaceful tropical slide which did not move or tremor. The world ground to a standstill. The silence was so immense and unbelievable that you felt your ears had been stuffed or you had lost your hearing altogether. The children put their hands to their ears. They stood apart. The door slid back and the smell of the silent, waiting world came in to them.

The sun came out.

It was the color of flaming bronze and it was very large. And the sky around it was a blazing blue tile color. And the jungle burned with sunlight as the children, released from their spell, rushed out, yelling, into the springtime.

"Now, don't go too far," called the teacher after them. "You've only two hours, you know. You wouldn't want to get caught out!"

But they were running and turning their faces up to the sky and feeling the sun on their cheeks like a warm iron; they were taking off their jackets and letting the sun burn their arms.

"Oh, it's better than the sun lamps, isn't it?"

"Much, much better!"

They stopped running and stood in the great jungle that covered Venus, that grew and never stopped growing, tumultuously, even as you watched it. It was a nest of octopi, clustering up great arms of fleshlike weed, wavering, flowering this brief spring. It was the color of rubber and ash, this jungle, from the many years without sun. It was the color of stones and white cheeses and ink, and it was the color of the moon.

The children lay out, laughing, on the jungle mattress, and heard it sigh and squeak under them, resilient and alive. They ran among the trees, they slipped and fell, they pushed each other, they played hide-and-seek and tag, but most of all they squinted at the sun until the tears ran down their faces, they put their hands up to that yellowness and that amazing blueness and they breathed of the fresh, fresh air and listened and listened to the silence which suspended them in a blessed sea of no sound and no motion. They looked at everything and savored everything. Then, wildly, like animals escaped from their caves, they ran and ran in shouting circles. They ran for an hour and did not stop running.

And then—

In the midst of their running one of the girls wailed.

Everyone stopped.

The girl, standing in the open, held out her hand.

"Oh, look, look," she said, trembling.

They came slowly to look at her opened palm.

In the center of it, cupped and huge, was a single raindrop.

She began to cry, looking at it.

They glanced quietly at the sky.

"Oh. Oh."

A few cold drops fell on their noses and their cheeks and their mouths. The sun faded behind a stir of mist. A wind blew cool around them. They turned and started to walk back toward the underground house, their hands at their sides, their smiles vanishing away.

A boom of thunder startled them and like leaves before a new hurricane, they tumbled upon each other and ran. Lightning struck ten miles away, five miles away, a mile, a half mile. The sky darkened into midnight in a flash.

They stood in the doorway of the underground for a moment until it was raining hard. Then they closed the door and heard the gigantic sound of the rain falling in tons and avalanches, everywhere and forever.

"Will it be seven more years?"

"Yes. Seven."

Then one of them gave a little cry.

"Margot!"

"What?"

"She's still in the closet where we locked her."

"Margot."

They stood as if someone had driven them, like so many stakes, into the floor. They looked at each other and then looked away. They glanced out at the world that was raining now and raining and raining steadily. They could not meet each other's glances. Their faces were solemn and pale. They looked at their hands and feet, their faces down.

"Margot."

One of the girls said, "Well . . . ?"

No one moved.

"Go on," whispered the girl.

They walked slowly down the hall in the sound of cold rain. They turned through the doorway to the room in the sound of the storm and thunder, lightning on their faces, blue and terrible. They walked over to the closet door slowly and stood by it.

Behind the closet door was only silence.

They unlocked the door, even more slowly, and let Margot out.

THE END

↻ **Talking it over**

1. *a.* In what ways is the life of the young people in the story different from the life of people you know?

b. In what ways are the young people on Venus like the young people you know?

2. *a.* Why do the others dislike Margot? Give as many reasons as you can. In what way is Margot herself to blame for the fact that the others don't like her?

b. Why is locking Margot in the closet an especially cruel thing to do?

3. *a.* How do you think the experience with the sun will affect the children's feeling about the rain?

b. How may the experience with the sun affect their attitude toward Margot?

4. There are descriptions in the story that can help you see things very clearly. Find at least two, and prepare to read them aloud to the class.

5. Which of the following statements best expresses the "big idea" the author wanted you to get from this story? Explain your answer.

a. People on Venus behave differently from the way people do on Earth because it rains all the time on Venus.

b. People can be cruel to those they consider "different," but they may not realize the consequences of their cruelty until it is too late.

c. Scientists don't know very much about what life would be like on a far distant planet.

⇄ **Words in action**

Read the Glossary definitions of **concussion** and **repercussion**. Then fill the blanks in items 1-4 with either **concussion** or **repercussion**.

1. If only Jim could make one of his companions hear him! "Help!" he yelled. He could hear the _____ of his voice bounce from one side of the canyon to the other, but that was all. No one answered his call.

2. People may laugh when you slip on a banana peel, but it really isn't funny. You can easily suffer a _____ of the brain from such a fall.

3. Steve knew that if he flunked math there would be _____s at home. His father would make him give up football practice for the rest of the year.

4. Sonic boom can cause a _____ strong enough to break windows.

Read the definitions of **tumultuous** and **resilient** in the Glossary. Choose either **tumultuous** or **resilient** to fill each blank below.

5. A foam rubber mattress is more _____ than one stuffed with straw.

6. "You must learn to be more _____," Lisa's mother told her. "No one likes people who sulk all day because of some little disappointment."

7. The Jazzabelles were given a _____ welcome by thousands of screaming teen-agers.

He was
fascinated
by
the future

Ray Bradbury began writing stories for the fun of it at the age of twelve, and his first published story appeared when he was nineteen. As a boy, he was fascinated with the comic-strip adventures of Buck Rogers and Flash Gordon, and became interested in writing stories about the future.

Today Mr. Bradbury is a very successful writer of science fiction and fantasy. He has published hundreds of short stories, several novels, and many television and radio plays. Some of his best-known stories are set on Mars. His Martians are not monsters or robots, but humans who came from Earth.

The cougar paid no attention to Tom —
he had seen men before.
But he had never seen anything
like Genevieve Trueheart!

john evans

by James McNamee

TOM HAMILTON liked his Aunt Prudence. She taught at the university. Tom's father said she was all brains. Her name was Doctor Prudence Hamilton. When she came to Tom's father's farm in the Cowichan Valley on Vancouver Island, which is part of the Province of British Columbia, she always brought presents. Tom liked her.

From *Over the Horizon and Around the World in Fifteen Stories* by James McNamee. Reprinted by permission of Victor Gollancz, Ltd.

He didn't like her constant companion, Genevieve Trueheart, a dog.

Tom Hamilton was fond of other dogs. He had a dog, a bull terrier called Rusty, a fighter right from the word go. Rusty kept the pheasants out of the garden and the young grain. He worked for a living. Tom couldn't like Genevieve Trueheart. She was good for nothing. She never even looked like a dog. She was a great big soft wheezing lazy wagging monster, a great big useless lump.

Genevieve had been born a Golden Retriever of decent parents and Aunt Prudence had papers to prove it. But Genevieve had eaten so many chocolates and French pastries and frosted cakes that she was three times as wide as a Golden Retriever ought to be. She had the soft muscles of a jellyfish. She couldn't run. She couldn't walk. All she could do was waddle. She was a horrible example of what ten years of living with Aunt Prudence would do to any creature. She looked like a pigmy hippopotamus with hair.

Genevieve Trueheart gave Tom Hamilton a hard time. She followed him. She went wherever he went. She was starved for boys. She never had a chance to meet any in the city. Tom couldn't bend over to tie a boot but her big pink tongue would lick his face. She loved him.

At half-past eight when he finished breakfast and started for school, there on the porch would be Genevieve Trueheart waiting for him.

She wants to go to school with you, Tommy, Aunt Prudence always said.

I think she'd better stay home, Tom always said. It's a mile. That's too far for her.

Take poor Genevieve, Tommy, Aunt Prudence and his mother always said. You know how she likes being with you.

Tom could have said, Why should I take her. When I take her the kids at school laugh at me. They ask, Why don't you send her back to the zoo and get a dog. But he didn't say that. It would have hurt Aunt Prudence's feelings.

On this morning he thought of something else to say. He said, A friend of mine saw a bear on the road. She had two cubs. We'd better leave Genevieve at home. I'll take Rusty.

Rusty has to stay to chase pheasants, his mother said.

What if I meet a cougar? Tom said. A fat dog like Genevieve would be a fine meal for a cougar.

Tommy, stop talking, his mother said.

A cougar can pick up a sheep and jump over a fence, Tommy said.

Tom Hamilton, his mother said, get to school!

So Tom Hamilton went down the woodland road with Genevieve Trueheart panting and puffing and snorting behind him. Twice he had to stop while Genevieve sat down and rested. He told her, Rusty doesn't think you're a dog. He thinks you're a big fat balloon that's got a tail and four legs. Tom said, Genevieve, I hope a car comes on the wrong side of the road and gets you, you big fat slob. He never meant it. He said, I hope we meet those bears. He was just talking. He said, Do you know what I'm going to do at lunchtime, Genevieve? I'm going to give the fried pork liver that I have for you to another dog, to any dog who looks like a dog and not like a stuffed mattress, and your chocolate, Genevieve, I'll eat it myself. This was a lie. Tom Hamilton was honest.

Every kid who went to that school came with a dog. Yellow dogs. Brown dogs. Black dogs. White dogs. Black and white dogs. Black, white, and yellow dogs. Black, white, yellow, and brown dogs. They were a happy collection of dogs, and had long agreed among themselves who could beat whom, who could run faster than whom, who had the most fleas. From nine o'clock in the morning until noon they scratched. From noon until one they looked after their boys. From one o'clock until school was out at three they scratched.

These dogs did not welcome Genevieve. They were not jealous because she was a Golden Retriever and had papers to prove it; they didn't believe an animal with a shape like Genevieve was a dog. A Mexican hairless dog, one of those small dogs you can slip into your pocket, put his nose against Genevieve's nose, and what did she do, she rolled over on her back with her feet in the air. After that, there wasn't a dog who would have anything to do with Genevieve Trueheart.

The kids asked Tom, What's she good for?

Tom knew the answer but he never told them. She was good for nothing.

Boy! she's a ball of grease, the kids said.

She's a city dog, Tom said.

Why don't you leave her at home? the kids said.

Because my aunt gives me a dollar a week to walk her to school, Tom said. A lie.

Boy, oh, boy! a kid said, I wouldn't be seen with her for two dollars a week.

After school, Tom waited until all the others had left. He couldn't stand any more unkind words. He took his time going home. He had to. If he hurried, Genevieve would sit down and yelp. They came to the woodland road. It was like a tunnel. The tall trees, the Douglas firs, the cedars and the hemlocks, all stretched branches over Tom's head. The air seemed cold even in summer. Owls liked the woodland road,

john ewds

and so did tree frogs, and deer liked it when flies were after them, but Tom didn't like it much. He was always glad to get out of it and into the sunshine. Often when he walked along this road he had a feeling things were looking at him. He didn't mind Genevieve too much here. She was company.

This day, Tom knew that something was looking at him. He had the feeling. And there it was!

There it was, all eight feet of it, crouched on a rock, above him, a great golden cat, a cougar, a Vancouver Island panther! Its tail was twitching. Its eyes burned green, burned yellow, burned bright. Its ears were flat against its head.

Tom's feet stopped. His blood and all his other juices tinkled into ice, and for a moment the whole world seemed to disappear behind a white wall. A heavy animal brushed against him, and at the shock of that, Tom could see again. It was Genevieve. She had sat down and, to rest herself, was leaning on his leg.

The cougar's ears were still flat, its eyes burning as if lighted candles were in them. It was still crouched on the rock, still ready to spring.

Tom heard a thump, thump, thump, thump, thump, and he thought it was the sound of his heart, but it wasn't. It was Genevieve beating her tail against the gravel to show how happy she was to be sitting doing nothing. That made Tom mad. If she had been any kind of a dog she would have known about the cougar before Tom did. She should have smelled him. She should have been just out of reach of his claws and barking. She should have been giving Tom a chance to run away. That's what Rusty would have done. But no, not Genevieve; all she could do was bump her fat tail and look happy.

The cougar had come closer. Inch by inch, still in a crouch, he had slid down the rock. Tom could see the movement in his legs. He was like a cat after a robin.

Tom felt sick, and cold, but his brain was working. I can't run, he thought, if I run he'll be on me. He'll rip Genevieve with one paw and me with the other. Tom thought, too, that if he had a match he could rip pages from one of his school books and set them on fire for he knew that cougars and tigers and leopards and lions were afraid of anything burning. He had no match because supposing his father had ever caught him with matches in his pocket during the dry season, then wow and wow and wow! Maybe, he thought, if I had a big stone I could stun him. He looked. There were sharp, flat pieces of granite at the side of the road where somebody had blasted.

The cougar jumped. It was in the air like a huge yellow bird. Tom had no trouble leaving. He ran to the side of the road and picked up a piece of granite.

Of course, when he moved, Genevieve Trueheart, who had been leaning against his leg, fell over. She hadn't seen anything. She lay there. She was happy. She looked like a sack of potatoes.

The cougar walked around Genevieve twice as if he didn't believe it. He couldn't tell what she was. He paid no attention to Tom Hamilton. He had seen men before. He had never seen anything like Genevieve. He stretched his neck out and sniffed. She must have smelled pretty good because he sat down beside her and licked one of his paws. He was getting ready for dinner. He was thinking, Boy, oh, boy! this is a picnic.

Tom Hamilton could have run away, but he never. He picked up one of those sharp pieces of granite.

The cougar touched Genevieve with the paw he had been licking, friendly-like, just to know how soft the meat was. Genevieve stopped wagging her tail. She must have thought that the cougar's claws didn't feel much like Tom Hamilton's fingers. She lifted her head and looked behind her. There can be no doubt but that she was surprised.

Tom was ashamed of her. Get up and fight! he yelled. Any other dog would fight. Rusty would have put his nips in before the cougar got finished with the job. But not Genevieve. She rolled over on her back and put her four fat feet in the air. She made noises that never had been heard. She didn't use any of her old noises.

The cougar was disgusted with the fuss Genevieve was making. He snarled. His ears went back. Candles shone in his green-yellow eyes. He slapped Genevieve between his paws like a ball.

Tom saw smears of blood on the road and pieces of Genevieve's hide in the cougar's claws. He still had a chance to run away. He never. He threw the piece of granite. He hit the cougar in its middle. The cougar turned, eyes green, eyes yellow.

How long the cougar looked at Tom, Tom will never know.

The sweet smell of Genevieve's chocolate-flavored blood was too much for the cougar. He batted her about like a ball again. Tom picked up another piece of granite that weighed about ten pounds, and bang! he hit the cougar right in the face.

The cougar fell on top of Genevieve. Then the cougar stood up and shook its head. Then it walked backwards like a drunken sailor.

And at that moment a bus full of lumberjacks who were going into town rounded the curve. The tires screeched as the driver stopped it, and thirty big lumberjacks got out yelling like—well, you never heard such yelling, and the cougar quit walking backwards and jumped out of sight between two cedars.

What did Genevieve Trueheart do? That crazy dog waggled on her stomach down the road in the same direction the cougar had gone. She was so scared she didn't know what she was doing.

Boy, oh, boy! that's some dog, the lumberjacks said. She just won't quit. She's a fighter.

Yah! Tom said.

She's bleeding, the lumberjacks said. She saved your life. We'd better get her to a doctor.

They put Genevieve Trueheart and Tom Hamilton in the bus.

Boy, oh, boy! the lumberjacks said, a fighting dog like that is man's best friend.

Yah! Tom said.

The bus went right into Tommy's yard and the thirty lumberjacks told Tommy's mother and father and Aunt Prudence how Genevieve Trueheart, man's best friend, had saved Tommy.

Yah! Tom said.

Then Aunt Prudence put an old blanket and old newspapers over the back seat of her car so that blood wouldn't drip into the fabric when she was taking Genevieve Trueheart to the horse, cow, and dog doctor.

Aunt Prudence said, Now you know how much she loves you, Tommy. She saved your life.

Yah! Tommy said.

THE END

Talking it over

1. The people in this story have different feelings about Genevieve.

   a. What does Tom think of her?

   b. Does Tom have good reasons for feeling as he does? Why?

   c. How does Aunt Prudence think of Genevieve?

   d. What could be some reasons for her attitude?

2. Although you are not told so directly, it is clear that Genevieve has *her* opinions, too. How does she feel about Tom? About the other dogs? About the cougar?

3. When Genevieve is brought home, why doesn't Tom tell what really happened? What does this incident tell you about Tom?

4. When the boys at school ask why he doesn't leave Genevieve at home, Tom says that his aunt gives him a dollar a week to walk the dog to school. And yet the author tells us Tom is honest. Do you think he is? Why or why not?

5. How do you explain the title of the story? What is amusing about it?

1. Mr. McNamee, the author of this story, makes it easy for you to "see" the awkward, overfed Genevieve. Instead of saying simply that she is fat, he creates pictures of her fatness by comparing her to things that are bulky or clumsy. For example, he compares her to a sack of potatoes.

With what other objects or animals does he compare Genevieve? List as many comparisons as you can.

2. The cougar's movements are also made vivid through comparisons. How does the author describe:

 a. the way the cat looks as it slides down the rock?

 b. the appearance of the cougar as it springs?

 c. the way the cougar attacks Genevieve?

 d. how the cat moves when hit by Tom's rock?

It began with Lulu Belle

James McNamee lives in British Columbia, the Canadian setting for "G. Trueheart, Man's Best Friend." He farmed and ranched in western Canada for ten years before becoming a freelance writer.

The idea for this story grew out of the author's life with Lulu Belle, an "extra large" dog who was so ferocious in her youth that friends stopped coming to see the McNamees and no mail was delivered on their side of the street for years. The situation changed when Waldo, a tiny orphan kitten, was brought into the house.

"As soon as Waldo's four feet touched the floor," Mr. McNamee recalls, "he hustled over to Lulu Belle and bit her square on the nose." This action, he says, was "like a tugboat squaring off to a battleship. . . . Waldo, a half-pound cat, had successfully taken on a ninety-pound bully!

"In two short years Waldo reduced Lulu Belle to a shivering mass of animal jelly. Lulu Belle is now a mental case. She does not know from what quarter she is going to get it. When the postman comes, and she's lying across the path, he kicks her. She's the most un-dog dog in the neighborhood.

"I said to her once, Lulu Belle, if you're afraid of Waldo, what would you do if you met one of our local cougars?"

For you to read

If you enjoyed this story, you might like James McNamee's short book *My Uncle Joe*.

1

A mouse in her room woke Miss Dowd;
She was frightened and screamed very
loud.
Then a happy thought hit her—
To scare off the critter,
She sat up in bed and meowed.

2

There was an old man of Peru,
Who dreamt he was eating his shoe.
He woke in the night
In a terrible fright—
And found it was perfectly true!

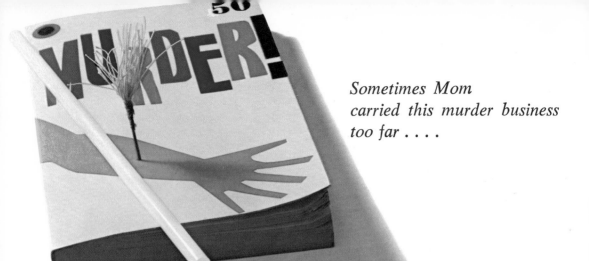

Sometimes Mom
carried this murder business
too far . . . .

INTRODUCING ELLERY'S MOM

by Margaret Austin

MOM IS a good sort, short and kind of pudgy—what Dad calls "a comfortable armful"—and looks like she might belong to the Garden Club, which she does. I guess it's 'cause we've known her all our lives that we don't think of her as Katherine Sanders Mac-Kay, with her name on as many mystery book jackets as Agatha Christie's.

To Dad she's just "Kate," and to us five kids, "Mom." To the town busybodies for a good many years she was "that woman who neglects those poor kids, my, I don't know how the doctor stands it!" Only Mom didn't look at it that way. She said making our own peanut butter sandwiches taught us self-reliance and independence and that

Reprinted by permission of the author.

after being around disinfected neatness all day, it relaxed Dad to come home to a place that was lived-in.

As for Dad, I think he liked Mom being a writer. When he was called out at night, she'd get up and beat out a few hundred words, then when he got home they'd drink coffee and discuss their respective cases.

Anyway, we grew up with Father Brown, Arséne Lupin, and Hercule Poirot the way most kids grow up with Joe DiMaggio, Yogi Berra, and Mickey Mantle. We knew about aconite, the poison, long before we saw aconite, the flower. And not one of us would have eaten a castor bean more willingly than we swallowed castor oil.

'Course, sometimes I think Mom carried this murder business too far.

It's convenient for a mystery writer to have a doctor on tap but it kind of rocked Dad to have her ask, right in the middle of serving scrambled eggs, "Where would you knife a person to have instantaneous death and very little blood?" or have her suddenly come out of a reverie with "I think I'll freeze him to death." What I mean is, it isn't normal conversation.

Then, too, there were the names. She was still getting printed rejection slips[1] when Nicholas (Nick) Charles was born, followed a year later by Hildegarde, both now in college. I was next, then came Ngaio, then Perry, the baby, though he's in second grade now. He got named that by default; Dad tromped on Mom's first suggestions—said the kid would have enough burdens in this vale of tears without bearing "Sherlock," "Philo," or "Nero,"[2] which were Mom's first choices.

Me, I'm Ellery,[3] though mostly everyone says "Ray," me not being the Ellery type.

By the time Perry came along, Mom was well known to the lending libraries. *Murder in the Maternity Ward* came out soon after and the TV sale and reprint checks started piling up, so she hired a housekeeper and Perry never got to learn self-reliance and independence.

Anyway, by the day James Griggs, the chemistry teacher, died, Mom was something of a celebrity around Maplecrest, where we live.

Once I asked Mom if she couldn't get more inspiration living in a city where more exciting things happened than in Maplecrest, which took a sleeping pill sometime in the 1880's.

"My goodness, no!" she replied. "What you need for inspiration is not excitement—it's character. City dwellers don't know five people as well as I know most of the population here. I just ask myself what Ross Hammond would do if his wife started chasing around, and pretty soon I have a story."

Which brings me back to the day Mr. Griggs, the chemistry teacher, died and why I needed to talk to Mom.

Since I'd been at baseball tryouts after school, the halls were deserted when I went to my locker. First, there's the West entrance, which goes out to the parking lot, then the chemistry lab, chemistry classroom, and another classroom, then the bank of lockers where I was assigned—so that I had a position in the dugout,[4] so to say, for what happened.

It started when Miss Dean came out of the chem lab. She turned at the door and trilled, "I'll see you tomorrow night at eight, then?" She listened briefly to someone inside the lab and continued, "No, I'm sure he doesn't suspect anything—it would be terrible if he did!"

She clicked briskly down the hall, stuffing a bright card into an envelope as she came. I wished I could have shrunk into the locker or gone into orbit or something, but I just stood there and said, "Hello, Miss Dean," real original-like.

---

[1] **rejection slips,** brief form letters used by magazine and book publishers telling an author his manuscript is not being accepted for publication.

[2] **Sherlock, Philo** and **Nero** refer to famous fictional detectives: Sherlock Holmes, Philo Vance, Nero Wolfe. Others are Nick Charles, Hildegarde Withers, and Perry Mason. Ngaio (ni′ ō) Marsh is a popular detective-story writer.

[3] **Ellery,** for Ellery Queen, pen name used by two men who have jointly written many mystery stories. A fictional detective by the name of Ellery Queen is also a character in many of these stories.

[4] **position in the dugout,** a baseball term. Ellery had a good view of what went on in the lab, though he himself was not directly involved.

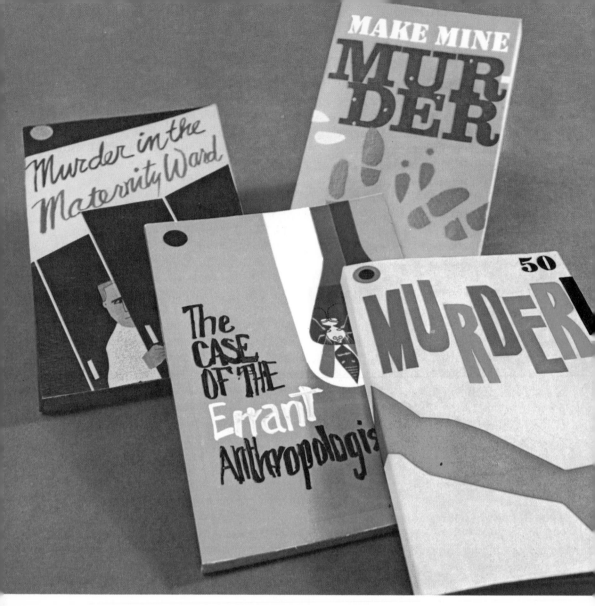

Sure, it startled her, but she recovered quickly, threw me a brief wave, and clicked on. I was shook up enough to dump everything off the locker shelf trying to dig out the U.S. History book, so I said a few short pithy words—not from one of Mom's books—and scooped up a year's accumulation of junk. What with that and getting on the jacket and cap Mom always insisted on my wearing, even if the weather was spring-balmy, it must have been five minutes before I heard Mr. Griggs scream. Men usually yell but this was a scream, like in agony, along with a great thumping and crashing of glass—then silence.

Well, naturally, I raced down the hall but even so, I wasn't the first one there. The principal, Mr. Wilson, pelted through the West door and beat me to the lab by a good thirty feet.

"Stay back, stay back, boy!" he yelled, so I parked in the doorway.

Mr. Wilson was kneeling on the floor in a mess of broken test tubes and crucibles, some of them still leaking unfinished experiments. The principal blocked the view but those were unmistakably Mr. Griggs' long skinny legs. His feet flopped out with one toe pointing to me and the other to the open window across the room. Just looking at those feet, you knew he was dead.

I stood there, peering at the mess until old Smitty, the janitor who's been with the schools for the last century, tapped my shoulder. Then, of course, I moved into the room to let him through.

The principal stood up, pulled a handkerchief from his pocket, and wiped it across his forehead. Now all of Mr. Griggs was exposed. You'd think, with Dad being a doctor and Mom writing about death all the time, that I'd be hardened. But it doesn't look the same in real life as it does in books.

Nobody ever called Mr. Griggs handsome. His eyes kind of bulged, maybe from looking at too many Bunsen burners, his nose hooked under at the end, and his chin slipped toward his Adam's apple. A couple of weeks ago, when Miss Dean started pussyfooting around in quiet corners with him, I sure wondered why.

Sprawled there on the lab floor he was even less appealing. His skin was gray, like rain-soaked paper. . . . Well, let's skip the details.

One thing really fascinated me, though. His shirt sleeves were rolled up and on his left forearm, which had fallen across his chest, there was a small red spot. As I watched, the spot grew bigger and redder. Seemed mighty indecent for a spot to do that on a dead man.

"Smitty," Mr. Wilson said, "clean up this broken stuff before someone is cut. He's dead"—nodding toward Mr. Griggs—"probably his heart, but I'll call Doc Morton." Noticing me, he added like an apology, "His office is right across the street."

"Ray," he went on, almost kindly, "there's nothing we can do. Go on home and try not to think about this."

Well, I can tell when I'm dismissed, so I went outside—but not home. No-sirreebob! I went out to the parking lot, then circled back through the evergreens until I was outside the chem lab window. And was I glad I did! There in the soft earth under the window was a mess of footprints—blurred, like whoever stood there had shuffled around some—but maybe the police could find one clear enough for a cast.

It wasn't long till voices came through the lab window. Coronary attack, all right, Dr. Morton pronounced, and it didn't surprise him one bit, the way Jim Griggs wouldn't listen when he was told to take it easy. More talk, medical stuff, then a discussion of which funeral home to call since the deceased didn't have any relatives in Maplecrest. Dr. Morton said they'd better notify Police Chief Higgins—no business for him but he likes to know what's going on around town.

I got careless and Mr. Wilson spied my red cap above the window sill. A principal has lots of practice reading the riot act to boys—so I blasted off for home and Mom.

The housekeeper said Mom was on the sun porch. 'Course, it's been soundproofed and winterized now for Mom's office, but we still call it the sun porch. Snitching a couple of fresh cookies, I headed that way.

Mom was whittling away at a sheaf

of yellow paper, her fat black pencil moving fast and furiously. The editor must of gotten tough about the deadline on *Make Mine Murder,* the current epic.

"Hello, dear—have a nice day?" The pencil didn't break its flying rhythm.

"Mom, something strange happened this afternoon."

"Don't talk with your mouth full, Ray."

I gulped down the rest of the cookie. "Mr. Griggs died."

"Hmm. That's nice, dear." The pencil still flew.

"Mom," I said loudly, "it might be M-U-R-D-E-R."

That stopped the pencil in mid-flight.

"Ray, there hasn't been a murder in Maplecrest since 1858, when a slave dealer found half the town in the Underground Railroad[5]—and that was more a lynching than murder! Poor dear, you've inherited my imagination, but sit down and tell me all about it."

I told her everything, just the way it had happened.

"But Bob Wilson is engaged to that pretty Clara Dean, isn't he?"

"That's it, Mom! He gave her the ring at Christmas. They're supposed to be married this summer. But for the last couple of weeks she's been sneaking around with Mr. Griggs, and then he dies and Mr. Wilson is right there on the scene!"

"Bob Wilson has always been most coöperative with the PTA. Hmm. What do you think of him, Ellery?" She's getting serious when she starts calling me Ellery.

"For a principal, he's always seemed like a right guy. He was even pretty decent about it when he lifted my peashooter—" Too late. There I stood with a mouth full of size-ten brogan.[6]

"What's this, young man?"

"Aw, Mom, all the gang has them, like everybody had hula hoops a couple of years ago. There's nothing wrong with 'em—we use paper and it doesn't even sting."

"In the future you will tend to your studies and not to shooting paper wads." She kind of snorted. "At girls, no doubt." With that taken care of, she got back to the case.

"Wish they'd called your father. Old Dr. Morton should have retired years ago—he couldn't tell a heart attack from. . ." Her voice trailed off and she got that spark in her eye, like when she's finally worked out the solution to a locked-room mystery. "Ellery, get your father's *Modern Drug Encyclopedia.*"

She whipped through the pages until she found what she wanted, then she scribbled a few lines on a sheet of yellow paper and jammed it in her pocket.

"I still don't see. . ." she murmured to herself. "If he came in the West door, the footprints. . ." Then to me, "Were there screens on that window? No— that's it, of course!"

"Got it solved, Mom?" I asked hopefully.

"Absolutely! Identical to *The Case of the Errant Anthropologist*—stupid of me not to see it immediately. Oh, he was clever and he would have got clean away with it if you hadn't been there.

---

[5]**Underground Railroad.** Before the American Civil War, this was a secret system that helped Negro slaves escape from the South to Canada. The fugitives were smuggled from house to house along the way.

[6]**There I stood with a mouthful of size-ten brogan.** A brogan is a kind of heavy shoe. The remark refers to the expression "to put your foot in your mouth," which means to say something accidentally that will get you into trouble.

Come on, we're going to talk to Chief Higgins—you can be sure he won't see it!" She added generously, "Of course, he doesn't have all the facts, as I do."

It wasn't as plain to me as it was to her, but rather than be classified with the Chief, I pretended to be with it.

She refused a ride on my bike—this wasn't the time, she said, to arrive at the Town Hall on the crossbar of a bicycle. So we walked—it's only four blocks.

Mom bounced along, full of purpose, and I trailed her.

Chief Higgins greeted us cheerfully. He and Mom have gotten to know each other pretty well through the years, what with her having to check on police procedure and such.

"Well, Kate MacKay! This is a pleasant surprise! How's the doctor and the rest of the family?"

With the small talk out of the way, Mom brought the business meeting to order: "Chief, I've heard about Jim Griggs' death at the High School this afternoon. Ray was there when it happened and I think between us we might be helpful to you. I don't mean to be poking my nose into your department, but some facts may have been concealed."

"There isn't a police chief in this country who wouldn't be honored to have the assistance of the most skillful mystery authoress writing today."

Wow!—didn't know the old guy had it in him!

Mom sat there, glowing and smoothing her dress over her knees. Then, armed with his compliment, she told what I'd heard and seen.

The Chief pulled out the bottom desk drawer, leaned 'way back in his leather swivel chair, and stuck his big boots on top of the drawer. You could see by the scratches that this was routine.

When Mom finished my part in the case, the Chief looked puzzled and said slowly, "Yes, that's the way it happened, but I don't see what you're drivin' at."

So Mom gave him the rest.

"Well, I didn't see it either, at first. But did you know Clara Dean is engaged to Bob Wilson? And that she's been two-timing him with Jim Griggs recently—Ellery has seen them together several times. That certainly gives Bob Wilson a motive and he was right at the scene. From the footprints outside the window, I believe he was standing there when Griggs started screaming. He could have run from there to the chemistry laboratory much quicker than Ellery could from his locker.

"All that tied together very neatly but it left the question of how he actually committed the murder—the *modus operandi*,[7] Chief. That baffled me until Ellery let slip about the principal's taking a peashooter away from him. There you have it! The natives of Borneo use blowguns with poisoned darts most effectively and at far greater distances than Wilson was from Griggs. Then, when Wilson reached the body he ordered Ellery to stay back *while he removed the dart*—you'll find a puncture on Griggs' left arm, I'm sure—and pocketed it under the pretense of removing his handkerchief.

"Oh, yes," she finished, "an autopsy will probably show that Quinidine[8] was the poison used." She took the slip

---

[7]**modus operandi** (mō′ dəs op′ ə ran′ dī), a Latin phrase which means "plan of action" or "method of attack."

[8]**Quinidine** (kwin′ i dēn), a medical compound similar to quinine, obtained from the bark of certain trees or shrubs. It is poisonous in large doses.

of yellow paper from her pocket and put it on his desk. "As principal, he could easily unlock the nurse's office at night and take all he needed. If the theft were noticed, it would be reported to him and that would be the end of it —he'd simply 'forget' it. Quinidine gives the reaction and appearance of a heart attack. Another doctor might have been suspicious but, confidentially, you and I both know that Dr. Morton is fighting senility. That is probably why Bob Wilson called him."

No doubt about it, Chief Higgins was jolted. He sat there for a few moments, then carefully took his feet off the drawer, came back to vertical, kicked in the drawer, and put his arms on top of the desk.

"Kate, for a long time now I've been a great admirer of yours. I've read all your books and, frankly, the hero usually figures out the murderer before I do. But this beats anything you ever wrote. It's as logical and tidy, with no loose ends, as any bit of deduction ever was. My hat's off to you."

Mom sat there, flushed and beaming —even more than she did the night the Mystery Writers of America gave her an "Edgar."

"In fact," the Chief continued, "it makes me downright ashamed to tell you that it didn't happen that way at all." Then he added generously, "Of course, you don't have all the facts, like I do.

"First, there wasn't anything between Jim Griggs and Clara Dean—except plans for Bob Wilson's surprise birthday party tomorrow night. The whole faculty were in on it, but those two were getting the present and handling all the details.

"Second, it was Smitty the janitor

who made those tracks in the dirt outside the window—while he was washing it. Bob Wilson had forgotten some Merit Scholarship forms and returned for them—Smitty saw him come straight from the parking lot."

Well, Mom was deflating like a busted balloon.

"Third," the Chief went on, "Jim Griggs did have a heart condition—has had it for several years—but he's kept quiet about it because he didn't want the school board to find out. You're right about the puncture on his arm. Made by an early wasp, though— there's your murderer. Griggs crashed around in the lab trying to kill it. The exertion, plus excitement, plus shock from the wasp's sting, set off the heart attack."

Man! Maybe you think we didn't have a funeral march all the way home! Mom really took it hard, and I forgot my own goof, worrying about her.

When we reached the front porch, Mom plunked into the swing. Like our house, it's old-fashioned, hanging by chains from the porch ceiling, and it squeaked and rattled when she sat down.

I dropped on the steps and made like "The Thinker,"[9] of which Dad has a pair of bookends in his office.

Dad came home soon, and seeing me sitting there he asked, "Why the gloom?"

"There is no joy in Mudville tonight,"[10] I replied.

"What?"

_____

[9] **"The Thinker,"** a well-known statue by the French sculptor Rodin, showing a man sitting with his chin on his hand, looking intently in front of him. Small reproductions are often used as bookends.

[10] **There is no joy in Mudville tonight,** a reference to the last line in the poem "Casey at the Bat" by Ernest L. Thayer: "But there is no joy in Mudville—mighty Casey has struck out."

I told him the whole humiliating story and when I got to the poison he started grinning. "She should have called me," he said. "It would take a harpoon to carry a lethal load of Quinidine."

I threw him a look of pain and said how it was going to ruin Mom as a writer—maybe even give her all sorts of complexes—and just about wreck our family life. So he wiped off the grin.

We both looked down to the end of the porch where Mom still sat in the swing.

Her eyes had that over-the-hills-and-far-away glaze they always get when she's plotting a new novel.

"Who do you suppose," she asked dreamily, "knew about Jim Griggs' heart condition and wanted him out of the way badly enough to leave a wasp in the chemistry laboratory?"

THE END

Talking it over

1. *a.* Why does Mom prefer living in a small town?

b. According to Mom, what was the motive behind Mr. Griggs' "murder"?

2. *a.* What is meant by "jumping to conclusions"?

b. In what specific cases do Ellery and his Mom jump to conclusions?

3. What two clues to the mystery do Ellery and his Mom miss?

4. Why is Chief Higgins' explanation of what happened to Mr. Griggs more accurate than Mom's?

5. How can you tell that Mom is not satisfied with the chief's explanation?

Words in action

Ellery uses some colorful and often humorous language. Sometimes he exaggerates greatly. Sometimes, on the other hand, he uses understatement—that is, what he says is much milder than what he means. Often he makes amusing comparisons.

For example, when Ellery says he "dropped on the steps and made like 'The Thinker,'" he means that he sat on the steps with his elbow on his knee and his chin cupped in the palm of his hand.

What does Ellery mean by the following remarks?

1. "Dad tromped on Mom's first suggestions—said the kid would have enough burdens in this vale of tears without bearing 'Sherlock,' 'Philo,' or 'Nero'. . . ." (page 29)

2. "Maplecrest . . . took a sleeping pill sometime in the 1880's." (page 29)

3. "I wished I could have shrunk into the locker or gone into orbit or something, but I just stood there and said, 'Hello, Miss Dean,' real original-like." (page 29)

4. ". . . so I said a few short pithy words—not from one of Mom's books." (page 30)

5. ". . . old Smitty, the janitor who's been with the schools for the last century. . . ." (page 31)

6. ". . . his chin slipped toward his Adam's apple." (page 31)

7. "Mom was deflating like a busted balloon." (page 34)

8. "Man! Maybe you think we didn't have a funeral march all the way home!" (page 34)

the Raccoon

I began to have an uneasy feeling that instead of Wayatcha's being my pet, I was becoming his.

by Daniel P. Mannix

THE TROUBLE with Wayatcha, a raccoon which I acquired when I was fourteen, was that he had more brains than I did, and quickly found it out. By the time he reached his full weight of twenty-five pounds he was running the household, and everyone—including me—lived in mortal terror of him. A big male raccoon is a formidable animal. A famous bull terrier in Toronto who had defeated every dog

Adapted from *All Creatures Great and Small* by Daniel P. Mannix. Copyright ©1963 by Daniel P. Mannix. McGraw-Hill Book Company. Used by permission.

put into the pit with him was considered to have reached the apex of fighting ability when he killed a boar 'coon half his weight.

The idea of disciplining an animal had never occurred to me. It had never been necessary with my other pets, and I took for granted that all wild animals responded to love and kindness. Not that Wayatcha was vicious; he was simply determined and saw no more reason why he shouldn't always have his own way than would any other spoiled child.

I got Wayatcha when he was still a baby from a grocer who found him one morning in the storeroom. Wayatcha had gotten his head stuck in a jar of applesauce and couldn't get it out again. I took the baby to the loft of our garage-barn and tried to get the jar loose. There has been a great deal written about the marvelous manner in which animals know when you are trying to help them. I've never noticed it. I have yet to see one you didn't have to hogtie before lancing an abscess or washing out a cut, and Wayatcha was no exception. After struggling with him for half an hour and getting badly scratched, I finally had to break the jar. Wayatcha suffered no ill effects from his experience except a terrible bellyache from eating too much applesauce. I spent the next week trying to overcome the little wild creature's timid nature and another two years trying to put the fear of God into him.[1]

Wayatcha tamed quickly—partly because he was young, but mainly because he was lonely. Raccoons stay with their mothers for at least a year after they are born, and I can only suppose that Wayatcha's mother had been killed, forcing the baby to shift for himself. At first he had a hard time understanding how anyone who had treated him so badly (he clearly regarded my efforts to get the jar off his head as a brutal attack) should now be bringing him food. After much mental agony, he managed to take cookies from my hand, although he snarled and ran if I tried to touch him. But he didn't really lose his fear of me until I tried to play a joke on him.

One afternoon while Wayatcha was

sitting on the barn floor beside me eating cookies, I held out a handful of raisins with my fist closed. Wayatcha finished the cookies and waddled over to inspect my fist. He smelled it, located the raisins, and then tried to pry my fingers open with his little black paws. When this did not work, he patted my hand and looked up questioningly. I chuckled to myself and said nothing. Then Wayatcha sat down with my fist in his lap to think it over.

Raccoons are very fond of clams; they open them by a sharp bite at the joint. I had forgotten this trick but Wayatcha had not. A few minutes later he had the raisins and I was getting first aid from a bottle of iodine. That was the end of Wayatcha's backwardness. After that he thought nothing of taking a flying leap at me as soon as I opened the cage door and hanging onto my necktie with one hand while he went through my pockets with the other. If I had known more about animals, I would then and there have begun to discipline Wayatcha. But there are few animals so appealing as a baby raccoon.

Even my grandparents, usually indifferent when not actually opposed to my pets, were delighted by Wayatcha. We were all fascinated at the wonderful manner in which he could use his hands. He was as clever as a monkey at opening doors and uncorking bottles. I honestly believe he could have threaded a needle had he wanted to. It was great fun to think up tricks for him and then see how long it would take him to open a box or drawer. We had a game like "find the thimble" played with a piece of candy. Wayatcha could use his nose instead of the usual "hot" and "cold" helps. Unfortunately, he got so expert

<hr>

[1] **put the fear of God into him,** teach him that he must respect authority or else be punished.

at the game that he played it night and day, even opening drawers and kicking out the clothes just in case somebody had hidden some candy there by mistake.

Then the cook made a serious error. Wayatcha, like all raccoons, had a tidy habit of washing his food before eating it, and he selected the kitchen sink for this purpose. As he ate at all hours he was a nuisance, whining and pulling at the cook's skirts to turn the water on for him. At last in desperation she took fifteen minutes off and taught him the trick of the spigots. He learned at once, but nobody was ever able to teach him how to turn them off again. The natural result was that we had to keep all the bathroom doors locked. Simply closing them did no good, for Wayatcha could handle the doorknobs as well as any human.

I think Wayatcha's greatest pleasure was to go wading in the creek that ran through our neighbors' farm, in search of frogs and crayfish. Wayatcha would walk daintily along the bank until a frog dived into the soft mud. Then he would wade out to where the frog had disappeared and suddenly make a grab in the slime on the bottom. He always washed the frogs carefully; perhaps 'coons have developed their neat habit of washing their food because most of their hunting is done along the banks of streams.

As Wayatcha grew bigger, he became increasingly difficult to control. For a long time he never bit. I would be playing with him in the living room when Wayatcha would decide it was time to go to the kitchen for a light snack. He would start off at a trundling gait which looked clumsy but was surprisingly fast. He was perfectly capable

of opening the icebox and going off with the evening's roast; I therefore had to catch him. Wayatcha would not turn on me, but neither would he desist from his purpose. If I could catch him on the open floor, I could pick him up, put him out of the house, and lock the door. But if Wayatcha managed to get hold of a table leg or one of the water pipes, it was impossible to dislodge him. Even when I was carrying him off, Wayatcha's long arms were reaching out to grab any passing object. Once, while we were passing through the maids' dining room in which the table had been set for supper, Wayatcha managed to clutch a corner of the tablecloth with results terrible to behold.

When he reached his full weight and girth after two years, even picking him up wasn't too easy. The Indians call the raccoon "Little Cousin of the Bear" (the name we use comes from the Indian *Arocoun*), and Wayatcha was very much like a sawed-off grizzly. He was low-slung, powerful, and determined. He didn't exactly struggle when I tried to pick him up—he just kept right on going, and lifting him clean off the floor was a major operation.

When Wayatcha was a cute baby, my grandparents and even the maids were willing to forgive him a multitude of sins.[2] Now, as a big boar 'coon, he wasn't nearly so charming. Still, perhaps surprisingly, the decision to forbid Wayatcha the house was mine, not my grandparents'. I had frankly grown tired of wrestling with this junior bruin and cleaning up after him. Not that Wayatcha wasn't perfectly housebroken—like all 'coons, he was very tidy in

---

[2] **multitude of sins,** part of a saying from the Bible, "Charity covers a multitude of sins." Here it means that everyone thought Wayatcha was so delightful that they didn't mind his naughty tricks.

that respect—but he labored under the delusion[3] that somebody might have hidden food behind the books in the bookcase, concealed something fascinating under the rugs, or left an article of great interest on top of the highest table in a room. By the time Wayatcha had satisfied his curiosity, repairing the damage was a good hour's hard work.

Wayatcha had no intention of being kept outside. He patrolled the house like a sentry, and as soon as anyone opened a door or a maid leaned out a window to shake a mop, Wayatcha was on the spot in a matter of seconds. From then on he was in; no one could close a door or window against Wayatcha when he wanted to exert his full strength.

About this time I began to have an uneasy feeling that instead of Wayatcha's being my pet, I was becoming his. Wayatcha believed in discipline. He wasn't cruel with me, only firm. When I tried to get a collar and chain on him, Wayatcha did not bite; he merely jerked the collar off each time I fitted it around his neck. When I grew more insistent, Wayatcha walked away, and—as I couldn't hold him and put on the collar at the same time—I had to let him go.

Wayatcha was two years old before he ever bit me, and then he did it because he was frightened and confused.

One afternoon I missed Wayatcha. Since finding him was usually no problem (it was avoiding him that presented difficulties), I was fearful that someone had shot him or the village boys had killed him with a club. Suppertime came and still no Wayatcha. After sup-

per, I went out again, this time taking Rags with me. Rags was no friend of Wayatcha's—they had played together when Wayatcha was a baby, but when the 'coon got big he was too rough for the little dog—but I still hoped he might be of some help.

It was almost dark when I saw Rags sniffing at the mouth of a big drainpipe that ran from the garage-barn to the compost pile. I got on my hands and knees and looked up the pipe. I couldn't see anything, but I heard a curious, frightened whining. It didn't sound like any noise Wayatcha usually made. He had a conversational *chur-chur* when we were playing together, a plaintive *er-er-er* when he wanted something, and occasionally at night I would hear him give the typical 'coon's whicker, an almost bird-like note apparently used as a mating call. I couldn't believe that this was Wayatcha, nor could I understand what he was doing up that pipe. Nevertheless, I crawled in to see.

The pipe was so small that I was barely able to worm my way along. I had gotten some ten feet up it when the whining started again, this time running up the scale until it became a shrill scream. It didn't sound frightened any more, only furious. I said "Wayatcha?" doubtfully and put out my hand. I touched Wayatcha's bristly fur neck; as I did so, he sank his teeth into my hand.

The pain was excruciating and I screamed in agony. Then I tried to wriggle backward out of the pipe, but I could only go inches at a time—and meanwhile Wayatcha was following me, biting as he came. I was afraid he'd get me by the face and kept putting up my hands to push him away. Each time I did so, Wayatcha would seize my hand and worry it, growling and hissing.

[3] **labored under the delusion.** Wayatcha was wasting his time when he kept looking for treats that he only imagined were hidden in the house.

By the time I finally got out of the pipe, I was crying with pain and my hands looked as though I'd run them through a meat grinder. Rags was bouncing around outside, barking hysterically. Wayatcha followed me out. He started for me again and I ran. Then he turned on Rags, who promptly and sensibly fled like a leaf on the wind. After looking around him Wayatcha marched off, muttering to himself.

I staggered to the back door, leaving a trail of blood behind me. The cook screamed when she saw me and shouted for Mary Clark, the housekeeper. Mary took one look at me, cried "Holy Saints, Master Dan!" and led me to the bathroom. While she washed my hands, she called to the upstairs maid: "Telephone Dr. Griggs and tell him to come at once. Don't let the Madam know, she'd be that upset!" I sat weeping and watching the blood run out of my mutilated hands until Dr. Griggs arrived. He cauterized the cuts with iodine and then sewed them. Those were the days be-

Howard Mueller

fore Novocain,[4] and I shall never forget the pain. I remember screaming and Mary holding my head while pleading, "Please, Master Dan, the Madam and the old gentleman will hear you!" At last she gave me a twisted washcloth to bite on. I don't know how many stitches the doctor took because toward the last I was delirious.

Of course, when my grandparents saw my hands the next morning they

demanded an explanation. When they heard what had happened, Grandmother wanted to send for a vet and have Wayatcha put down. I begged for his life so passionately that Grandmother finally said, "Well, we'll see," but I heard her stamping upstairs to the phone. Grandfather merely remarked, "Your Cousin Kenneth used to feel that way about horses. One finally killed him. Let me see, was that in ninety-eight or ninety-nine?" I rushed outside to find Wayatcha and hide him.

[4]**Novocain,** a local anesthetic, a medicine used to deaden feeling. It is widely used by dentists.

Wayatcha, however, had taken matters into his own paws and disappeared. He never returned.

Obviously, I should never have crawled up the pipe after Wayatcha, particularly when he was frightened and angry. I have no idea what he was doing up the pipe or why he refused to come out. Possibly dogs had chased him and he had taken refuge there. But my greatest mistake was allowing him to control me instead of controlling him. Once a powerful wild animal learns that he is stronger than his owner he becomes potentially dangerous—an unfortunate fact sentimentalists dislike to admit. Wild animals are frequently extremely rough with their own families. A male 'coon, once the breeding season is over, will half-kill his former mate if he finds her looking for frogs in his favorite pool, and the female will be equally rough with her own cubs once they become old enough to shift for themselves. It is unreasonable to suppose that they would put a human in a different category than their own species.

Disciplining wild animals is a complicated technique. For example, if I had tried to punish Wayatcha by using a whip I would only have infuriated him and forced him to turn on me. Also, raccoons have such thick coats that a blow has very little effect—except to enrage them. What I should have done was put a collar on Wayatcha when he was still fairly small and use a lead-pole. Lead-poles are equipped with a snap on one end which can be opened and closed by a wire leading to the handle. When Wayatcha was heading for the kitchen, I could have snapped the lead-pole to a ring on his collar and held him. If he proved stubborn, I could

have kept him on the lead-pole for several days until he realized that he could neither reach me nor escape. Eventually a habit pattern would form and Wayatcha would have accepted the fact that he had to obey. Restraints of this nature are no more cruel than using a bridle and bit on a horse. If the animal is to live with you, he must learn that he cannot always do what he wants and cannot turn on you whenever he is thwarted or in a bad mood.

At considerable cost, I had learned three important lessons from Wayatcha. First, unless the animal is as happy-go-lucky as the Nikkies, my pet skunks, or as phlegmatic as Claude and Claudette, my porcupines, he cannot be allowed to run wild. He will grow too independent. This is especially unwise if the animal is large enough to be dangerous. He loses all natural fear of man but learns no respect for him. A prime example of such semi-wild animals are the bears in Yellowstone Park—bears that are a constant potential menace to careless motorists.

Second, the animal must be kept under control, but a type of control the animal can understand. A simple "treat 'em rough" policy is no good whatsoever; the technique must be slanted to the species and the individual animal.

Third, you must always be prepared to have a potentially dangerous animal turn on you; not in the sense that the animal is "vicious," but in the sense that a horseman must always be prepared to have a high-spirited horse do the unexpected: The rider can never relax.

I did not know what I was doing when I tried to make a pet of Wayatcha without proper experience. I paid for my ignorance and I fear Wayatcha also paid a higher price, for he had only contempt for humans. But perhaps he returned to the wild and adopted 'coon ways instead of staying near civilization. I certainly hope so.

THE END

Talking it over

1. *a.* When did Wayatcha lose his fear of Mannix?

b. How was Wayatcha's behavior toward Mannix different after this incident?

2. *a.* Why didn't Mannix try to discipline Wayatcha when the animal was still young?

b. When did Mannix first try to discipline him?

c. Why didn't he succeed?

3. *a.* What mistakes did Mannix and other members of the household make in handling Wayatcha?

b. What are some of the things Mannix says they should have done?

4. Which of the following best expresses the "big idea" that is emphasized in this account?

a. Raccoons are clever and interesting animals.

b. To live happily and safely with a wild animal pet, you must teach it to respect you.

c. Wild animals do not make good pets and cannot be trusted.

d. People can learn a great deal by watching the behavior of wild animals that have been tamed.

Wild animals were his playmates

"I have always had wild animal pets," says Dan Mannix. "My father was a captain in the Navy and he and Mother were often away, so I was brought up in my grandparents' home outside Philadelphia—then largely open country. I didn't have many human playmates."

His first pets included rabbits, skunks, and the raccoon he writes about here, but later he had more unusual pets. One of them was an alligator which he kept in the family swimming pool.

In college he studied zoölogy, journalism—and witchcraft. While he was trying to make up his mind about a career, he spent some time working as a magician and a sword-swallower in carnivals. He even established a world record for swallowing the longest sword —23½ inches.

Mannix and his wife Jule have both written books about their adventures with animals. In addition to the book from which this article was taken, Mannix has written about his carnival experiences, about hunting in Africa, and about the slave trade. He has also written many magazine articles, made films, given illustrated lectures about his adventures, and appeared on TV. In 1967 he received the Dutton Animal Book Award for *The Fox and the Hound.*

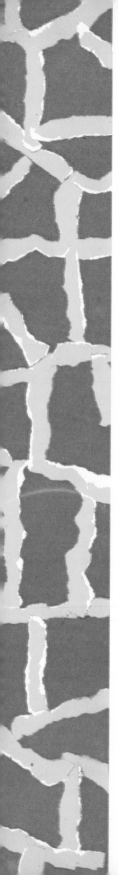

THE GIRAFFE

by Geoffrey Dearmer

Hide of a leopard and hide of a deer
And eyes of a baby calf,
Sombre and large and crystal clear,
And a comical back that is almost sheer
5 Has the absurd giraffe.

A crane all covered with hide and hair
Is the aslant giraffe,
So cleverly mottled with many a square
That even the jungle is unaware
10 Whether a pair or a herd are there,
Or possibly one giraffe,
Or possibly only half.

If you saw him stoop and straddle and drink
He would certainly make you laugh,
15 He would certainly make you laugh, I think,
With his head right down on the water's brink,
Would the invert giraffe,
The comical knock-kneed, angular, crock-kneed,
Anyhow-built giraffe.

20 There's more than a grain of common sense
And a husky lot of chaff
In the many and various arguments
About the first giraffe,
The first and worst giraffe;
25 Whether he grows a neck because
He yearned for the higher shoots
Out of the reach of all and each
Of the ruminating brutes;

From *All Day Long* by Geoffrey Dearmer. Reprinted by permission of the author.

Or whether he got to the shoots because
30 His neck was long, if long it was,
Is the cause of many disputes
Over the ladder without any rungs,
The stopper-like mouth and the longest of tongues
Of the rum and dumb giraffe,
35 The how-did-you-come giraffe,
The brown equatorial, semi-arboreal
Head-in-the-air giraffe.

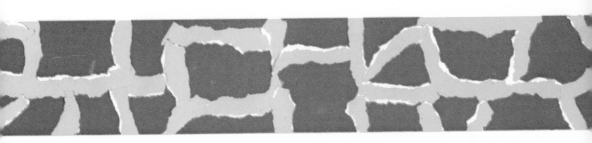

Talking it over

1. What things about the giraffe seem absurd?

2. To what two things is the giraffe compared? Do you think these comparisons are good ones? Explain.

3. What do you like about the poem?

Is the poet saying, then, that the arguments about the giraffe's neck

    a. are mostly sensible, but a few are silly?

    b. are mostly silly, but a few are sensible?

    c. are all very sensible?

    d. are entirely worthless?

2. *a.* The poet also says that the tender leaves which the giraffe likes to eat are out of the reach of the "ruminating brutes." To **ruminate** means to "chew the cud" or to "chew again." What common farm animal ruminates?

    b. The word *ruminate* or *ruminating* has another meaning very much like "chew again," except that this meaning does not refer to a physical process. In the sentence "Sitting in his study, the philosopher ruminated on the strange happenings of the past week," what is meant by *ruminated?*

Words in action

1. The poet says that arguments as to why the giraffe has such a long neck contain "more than a grain of common sense and a husky lot of chaff." **Chaff** means the husks that are separated from grain by threshing; the chaff is considered worthless. **Husky** usually means "big and strong," but as used here it probably means "sizeable" or "large"—as well as "full of husks."

THE MIDNIGHT VISITOR

A one-act play by Elsie Katterjohn based on
a short story by Robert Arthur

CHARACTERS:

Adams, an American secret agent
Fowler, a young American writer
Max, a foreign agent
Henri, a Frenchman

THE SCENE:

*A small, sixth-floor room in a gloomy
hotel in Paris. The room is dark except
for a shaft of light from a partly open
transom above the door to the hall at
stage right. The dim light reveals the
usual collection of shabby hotel-room
furniture. At stage left are two doors:
one at left center is closed and blocked
off by a desk placed squarely against it;
the closet door at lower left is slightly
ajar. At upper center are shabby vel-
veteen curtains that hide all but a narrow vertical strip of the window behind.
Traffic noises from the street six stories
below sound faintly in the background.*

Adapted from a story in *Mystery and More Mystery,* "The Midnight Visitor," by Robert Arthur.
Copyright 1939 and renewed © 1967 by Robert
Arthur. Published by Random House, Inc., and
reprinted with their permission.

THE TIME:

The present. It is nearly midnight.

As the curtains open, a dark figure moves stealthily about the room. He holds a small flashlight which he shines into the closet, among the papers on the desk, and into the chest of drawers across the room. After a moment, footsteps and voices are heard in the hall. Suddenly alert, the dark figure snaps off his flashlight. His form is seen once against the darker black of the window; then he disappears into the closet.

Through the open transom is heard a jingling of keys. As the door opens, Adams is talking. He wheezes as he talks.

Adams (*ushering his companion into the room ahead of him*): Of course you are disappointed! You were told that I was a secret agent, a spy—that I deal in espionage and danger. You wanted to meet me because you are a writer—and young and romantic. (*He presses a light switch inside the door. When the stage is lighted, Adams is seen to be very fat and his wrinkled business suit is badly in need of cleaning. He looks anything but a secret agent.*) No doubt you expected mysterious figures in the night, the crack of pistols, maybe even drugs in the wine. (*Closing the door, he chuckles at the embarrassment of his guest, a good-looking, neatly dressed young man who seems more boyish than his 28 years.*)

Fowler: No, not really. Well—(*with a self-conscious laugh*) a couple of mysterious figures, maybe.

Adams (*tossing his battered hat onto the bed*): Instead, you have spent a dull evening in a second-rate music hall with a sloppy fat man.

Fowler (*protesting*): Oh, it wasn't so bad.

Adams: And do I get messages slipped furtively into my hand by dark-eyed beauties? On the contrary, all I get is one ordinary telephone call making an appointment in my room. Admit it, my friend, you have been bored.

Fowler: No, not bored—just a bit—

Adams: Ah yes, you are completely disillusioned. An evening wasted and you have nothing to write about—not even a small paragraph to put into that notebook of yours. (*Fowler looks at notebook he is still holding in his hand, smiles sheepishly, and puts it into his pocket.*) But take cheer, my friend. After all, this is Paris. You may yet see some drama tonight.

But come—see my view—even from a shabby hotel room on the sixth floor it is still quite a view. (*He walks to window and pulls open the draperies a few more inches. The night presses blackly against the glass.*) Oh, too bad, the fog is even thicker now. But still you can make out the Eiffel tower in the distance there. (*chuckling*) Even a foggy night in Paris is better than a clear night in Des Moines, no?

Fowler (*taking a few steps toward the window and glancing only briefly at the distant view*): Mr. Adams, excuse me if I am prying, but—you mentioned—well—that phone call. . .

Adams: Ah, Mr. Fowler, you are observant. Very observant. And such devotion to your work shall not go unrewarded. Was that phone call important? Yes, my friend, it was very important. That is why we have cut short a bit our evening on the town, and why, in fact, I have brought you back here with me. Perhaps I will show you that I do not waste my time completely. Yes, the call had to do with a certain paper—a very important paper—for which several men have risked their lives. You shall see this paper presently. It will come to me here in the next-to-last step of its journey into official hands. (*confidentially*) You realize, of course, that I could not let you witness this event if it were not for your uncle's very persuasive letter. But how can one disappoint a dear old friend? (*closing the draperies and returning to a position down center*) Some day soon this paper may well affect the course of history. Now in this thought there is drama, is there not?

(*Suddenly the door to the closet opens and out steps a man with a small automatic in his hand. He is slender, not very tall, and his rather pointed features suggest the crafty expression of a fox.*)

Adams: Max!

Max (*speaking with an indefinable European accent*): Good evening, Mr. Adams.

Adams (*wheezing*): Max, you gave me a start! I thought you were in Berlin. What are you doing here? (*He backs away.*)

Max: I was in Berlin, yes. But I, too, had a telephone call—earlier in the week. So here I am. I will have your weapon, please. (*Adams puts on a look of innocence.*) Your gun, please, which I know you are never without. Give it to me. (*Adams shrugs, hands over gun he takes from shoulder holster. Fowler looks amazed, not having suspected that Adams was armed.*) Thank you. Now—the report—(*Again Adams pretends innocence.*) The report on our new missiles that is being delivered to you tonight? (*with exaggerated politeness*) We merely thought it would be safer in our hands than in yours.

Adams: But—even I didn't know until the phone call tonight—(*He smiles weakly, then shrugs.*) Well, you always were known for your timing—

Max (*with a tight smile*): Just so. Please sit down. We may as well be comfortable. You, too, young man. (*He shrewdly appraises Fowler, who remains standing, still dazed at the turn of events.*)

Adams (*backs to armchair at center stage and sinks down heavily*): Max, I just can't get over your being *here*. (*to Fowler*) As you may have gathered, Max and I have known each other a long time. In fact, I might say (*glances at Max*) we are old business associates. (*Fowler smiles nervously, nods.*) Max, I'm sorry not to be more hospitable, but I can't say I am exactly happy to see you. The last time we met—two years ago, wasn't it? In Geneva? (*Adams is obviously playing for time.*) I was expecting you then—but now—why, I don't even have comfortable accommodations to offer you—certainly nothing like that delightful little villa in Geneva. You remember it— the one with the stained glass windows and the balconies?

Max: Yes, I recall your hospitality at that villa—including the gendarmes.[1] Thank you! But this room will serve for our transaction.

---

[1]**gendarmes** (zhän'därmz), police. *French.*

Adams: Oh, well, I suppose the quarters (*indicating room*) are adequate, but really, the management here is impossible! (*to Fowler*) I was assured—*assured* that this hotel was safe, and yet this is the second time in a month—the *second* time, mind you—that somebody has gotten into my room off that confounded balcony!

Max: Balcony? No (*taking key from pocket and holding it up*), I used a passkey. I did not know about the balcony. It might have saved me some trouble had I known.

Adams (*in surprise and irritation*): A passkey? A passkey! Well, that is the limit. Max, I'm truly annoyed. I expected the balcony, but a passkey— why, this is ridiculous. At least the balcony called for a little ingenuity. The ironic thing is that it is not even my balcony. It belongs to the next apartment. (*glancing toward Fowler*) This room, you see, used to be part of a larger unit, and that door there (*indicates sealed door*) used to connect with the living room. *It* had the balcony, which extends under *my* window, too. You can get onto it from the empty room two doors down—and someone did, last month. Nothing was lost that time—but the management promised me they would block it off. (*Shrugs wearily.*) But they haven't done it. No matter, I guess—

Max: As you say, no matter. (*Glancing at Fowler, who stands stiffly a few feet from Adams, Max waves the gun with a commanding gesture.*) Please sit down. (*Fowler perches on edge of bed.*) We have a wait of half an hour at least, I think.

Adams: Thirty-one minutes. The appointment was for twelve-thirty. (*moodily*) I wish I knew how you learned about that report, Max.

Max (*smiling, but only with his mouth*): I may say, the interest is mutual. We would like to know how the report was gotten out of our country. However, no harm has been done. I will have it back.

(*There is a sudden rapping on the door. Fowler jumps.*)

Max (*sharply*): Who—?

Adams (*calmly*): The gendarmes. I thought that so important a paper as the one we are waiting for might well be given a little extra protection tonight—from the police.

Max (*in an angry whisper, flourishing the gun*): You—! (*Bites his lip uncertainly as the rapping is repeated.*)

Adams: What will you do now, Max? If I do not answer, they have instructions to enter anyway. The door is unlocked. And they will not hesitate to shoot. (*Max starts toward closet door.*) Nor will they neglect to search the room. You would be quite a prize for. . . .

Max (*interrupting in a sharp whisper*): Quiet!

(*His face twisted with rage, Max has been glancing about the room. He abruptly changes direction and backs swiftly toward window at upper center. The gun in his right hand is still leveled at the other two. With his left arm, he reaches behind him and pushes open the window. Then he swings his left leg over the sill. The street noises are louder now.*)

Max: Don't move till I'm gone! You have outsmarted me this time—but we haven't seen the last of each other, I think! (*smugly*) So thoughtful of you to inform me of this convenient exit. Au revoir![2]

(*The rapping on the door becomes louder, more insistent.*)

Henri (*from outside*): M'sieu![3] M'sieu Adams!

(*Max, who has twisted his body so that his gun still covers the fat man and his guest, grasps the window frame with his left hand and then swings his right leg up and over the sill. He pushes free with his left hand and drops out of sight.*

Adams' body relaxes visibly. With seeming casualness, he goes to the window and closes it, then crosses the room and opens the door.)

Adams: Ah, Henri—

(*A waiter enters with a tray on which are a bottle and two glasses.*)

Henri: Pardon, M'sieu, the cognac[4] you ordered for when you returned. (*He sets the tray on a small table and deftly uncorks the bottle.*)

Adams: Merci, Henri. (*Hands him a coin.*)

Henri: Merci, M'sieu. (*He leaves.*)

Fowler (*staring after him, stammering*): But—the police—

Adams: There were no police. Only Henri, whom I was expecting.

Fowler: But the man on the balcony—Max—won't he—?

Adams: No, he will not return. (*He reaches for the bottle of cognac.*) You see, my young friend, there is no balcony.

(*Fowler stands frozen as the meaning of this last statement sinks in; then he*

dashes to the window, flings it open, and looks down. Among the street noises that filter up through the open window, an ambulance siren rises and grows steadily louder.*)

Adams (*filling the glasses*): Come, have your drink. Maybe now, after all, you have something to write about.

(*He raises his glass as the* CURTAINS CLOSE.*)

Talking it over

1. The word *suspense* means "anxious uncertainty"—feeling excited about what is going to happen next. Where in this play did you feel the greatest suspense?

2. *a.* In what part of the play does Mr. Adams best show his ability as a secret agent?

   b. In what ways is his personality well suited to his work?

3. What comparison does the playwright use to tell you the kind of person Max is? What does this comparison tell you about Max?

4. *a.* Why is a shabby hotel room used as the setting for the play, rather than a better room?

   b. Why is midnight a good time for a mystery to be staged?

5. *a.* Why is it important for Max to exit from the room exactly as described in the stage directions?

   b. With what sound effect does the play end? What does this tell you?

---

[2] **au revoir** (ō rə vwär′), goodbye; till we see each other again. *French.*

[3] **M'sieu** (mə syoe′), monsieur, the French word for "mister" or "sir."

[4] **cognac** (kōn′yak), a kind of French brandy.

THE MIDNIGHT VISITOR / 51

Sure enough—bear tracks!
Here was Wilbur's chance to get even
with his smart-aleck city cousin.

THE
BEAR
HUNT

by Gene Caesar

IT WAS the day before Thanksgiving. We were figuring on our relatives arriving by noon—Uncle Walter and Aunt Stephanie and Cousin Marion. I didn't especially like any of them then, but I'd been waiting for them ever since summer, thinking up ways I could fix Marion. Because my cousin, who wasn't a girl but a boy with a girl's name, really invited fixing. He wasn't even a full year older than me, and he was smaller at that. But he dressed and

acted like a miniature minister and went around talking like a school-teacher. I'd never heard him laugh, and I'd never seen him scared. I didn't care whether he laughed or not, but after that time in August when he'd made a fool of me in a diving match, I'd have given anything to see him scared.

"You been studyin' hard on some-thin' all mornin'," Dad said. "What you up to, Wilbur?"

"Nothin'," I insisted carefully, be-cause for some strange reason he seemed to like my cousin and take his side all the time. "Just thinkin' maybe

Reprinted (slightly abridged) by permission of the author and *Boys' Life*, published by the Boy Scouts of America.

I'd take Marion rabbit huntin' this afternoon."

"You doubtless got somethin' else in mind. You remember, boy, your cousin ain't had all the nat'ral advantages you got. How'd you like to live in a *Detroit* apartment, hafta look for a park somewheres just to set your foot on the ground? I know Marion's a cold one, but you give him a chance for once! You hear me?"

After Uncle Walter's new car had pulled into the yard, we ate lunch. Aunt Stephanie worried and fussed for an hour or so about how dangerous hunting could be, but Marion and I got ready anyway. Aunt Stephanie insisted, though, that Marion wasn't to touch firearms and in her opinion boys ought to be able to have just as much fun outdoors and enjoy nature and all that without shooting guns. Marion didn't even stick up for himself. It seemed to me that with him, agreeing with grownups was a way of pretending he was one of them.

"Walter! You forgot the hand warmer," Aunt Stephanie suddenly remembered. "Go get it."

"Hand warmer!" I acted real polite and curious. "Is it somethin' like a bed warmer?"

"It's carried in the coat pocket, so it should help keep the chest warm as well," she explained. "We just bought it. I should think that, living out in the cold so much, you'd have one too, Wilbur."

"No, ma'am," I told her sadly, and all the time Uncle Walter was carefully following the directions on the package about filling and lighting the thing, I stood close and asked fascinated questions like "What'll they think of next?" pretending not to see the look Dad was

giving me. Finally I ducked back to my room. "I almost forgot to bring my compass!" I gasped. "It's a long way out to the brush piles, too—clear across the west pasture."

Dad cleared his throat in a way then that meant if I didn't shut up and stop putting on an act it wouldn't be rabbits I'd get that afternoon, so I just waited quietly until Marion and his hand warmer were all ready. Then I led the way along the fence and on across the open fields to the edge of the scrub oak Dad and I were clearing. At the first mound of brush, I searched the snow for tracks.

"There's a bunny in there now," I told Marion. "If your hands are warmed up enough, you get up on top and jump up and down real hard. I'll get him when he runs. I'd jump him out myself and let you do the shootin', 'cept you mustn't touch firearms."

I lifted the old 20-gauge to my shoulder and held it there, but I wasn't really waiting for any rabbit. I was waiting for Marion to go crashing down through the sharp-clipped oak branches. I didn't really want to see him get hurt. I just wanted him to yell or cry and get that frozen look off his face. But he ruined it by walking around the brush pile first.

"If those are the tracks of the rabbit entering," he told me, "then these are the tracks where the rabbit left."

"No," I argued. "There must be two bunnies in there."

He shook his head firmly. "Those tracks are the reverse of these."

He had me there, so I shrugged and went on to check a half-dozen brush piles before I found one that really had a rabbit in it. Then I lifted the shotgun and waited again. "Come on," I said to Marion. "Jump him out o' there."

He stared at the mound of branches a moment, then simply pulled a long stick from the edge. Instead of climbing up, he merely poked and prodded a few times. The rabbit went out the other side, and I didn't see him until he was far out of range.

"I wish we had a good beagle," Marion surprised me by saying.

"What do you know about rabbit hounds?" I demanded skeptically.

"Oh, I've read a lot about them, from the library, mostly." His voice suddenly turned close and confiding. "If I could keep a dog, I'd know just the kind I'd want. Did you see the article last month in—"

"Up here," I reminded him, "a fella doesn't hafta read books and magazines to find out about huntin'."

"No, I suppose not." His voice had turned back cold again. "But I don't really think this is a very sporting way to hunt rabbits—forcing them out of their lodges."

Now every fellow I know jumped rabbits out of brush piles. Probably every farm kid who ever lived jumped rabbits out of brush piles. And my city cousin didn't think it was sporting. But I went on trying to be nice to him.

"All right, we'll go after some big white rabbits," I suggested happily and agreeably, because all at once I was getting a new idea. I'd take him back to the big swamp, where there weren't any paths. I'd slip off somehow and leave him lost there until he got so frightened he started shouting for help. Then I'd find him and tell him to stop acting like a baby. "They can run twice as fast as reg'lar rabbits, and they don't hole up in brush piles, so goin' after them oughta be sportin' enough."

Motioning for him to follow, I started on through the oak ridges. Suddenly, halfway through the scrub oak, I grabbed Marion's arm and pointed. Directly across a clearing ran a series of big tracks—some almost round, others like a barefoot human footprint. There was no mistaking that trail. And all at once I realized this was my chance. It was perfect! "Bear tracks!" I gasped.

"Honestly?" He sounded fascinated. "I've never seen them before."

"Shhh!" I hissed, lifting my shotgun like we could expect a charge at any moment and trying to see his face out of the corner of my eye. Fascinated wasn't the way I wanted him to sound. I was just bluffing, of course. I'd seen bear tracks in our woods before, and I'd asked Dad why didn't he take his deer rifle and follow them. He'd explained that the only time a bear goes wandering around in winter is when he wakes up hungry. Food is hard to find then, and it takes a lot of it to fill him up, so he walks maybe twenty or thirty miles in a single night. There might be bear tracks in our woods, Dad had told me, but chances were the bear that had made them was somewhere in the next county. All of which suited me fine, since I didn't particularly want to meet any bear. All I wanted to do was throw a scare into Marion. "If you're 'fraid to come along," I offered hopefully, "you can follow our tracks back easy enough. But I gotta hunt this bear down and shoot him!"

"Why?" he wondered.

"Why?" I gave him the look you give a little kid asking something silly. "'Cause it's dangerous havin' hungry bears prowlin' around in winter. This bear could break into our barn tonight and kill every cow we got. Or even worse. Maybe some kid'll be goin' to school and not have any gun along, and this bear'll be lyin' up waitin' for him. This isn't the *Detroit* zoo where they feed the bears reg'lar, you know!"

I turned away from him and began following the tracks in a crouch with the gun ready. But instead of heading for home like I wanted him to, he stayed right with me, nonchalantly dragging along the stick he'd used for poking the rabbit out. "Why don't you get your father, then?"

"There ain't time now. If you're scared, you can go back."

"If what you say is true," he argued, "neither you nor any other twelve-year-old boy would be hunting a bear without having your father along."

"Listen! Up here a fella has to do things like this. A fella has to grow up in a hurry up here."

"Those tracks are probably a week old, Wilbur."

"It snowed yesterday, didn't it?" I reminded him. "This bear trail's so hot, it's smokin'!"

"Besides," he pointed out knowingly, "whatever size shot you're using for rabbits isn't going to kill any bear unless you're right on top of him."

I was so surprised that he knew about such things that I almost couldn't think of an answer. "I know it," I explained, "but there's no time to go back, so I'll have to take him at close range, no more than twenty feet or so. All that worries me," I turned his smartness right back on him, "is what you'll do, seein' a bear close up for the first time. Our only chance is to take him by surprise. So try to walk quieter and stop bangin' that stick."

"You're making more noise than I am, Wilbur," he argued right back.

It was clouding over again as we crossed the last ridge, with the swamp-edge cedars dark green just ahead, and I made the hardest try yet at frightening Marion into turning back. "When he charges us," I whispered, "I'm gonna hafta shoot for bone and break him down, then put a finisher in him. This is just a single-shot gun, so I'll hafta load up again on the spot." I took a shell and stuck it between my teeth.

"How do you know this?" he demanded.

"I been bear huntin' ever since I was a kid," I muttered.

"Humph!" he said.

I turned my back on him and pushed on through the cedar boughs. I was still certain the bear was somewhere in the next county, but not quite certain enough to like the idea of following his trail much farther. I'd counted on Marion getting scared and giving up, so I could go on and just sit down out of sight for an hour or so, then come back and tell him the bear had escaped me.

"If you're gonna break out screamin' or get in my way or anything, I don't want you along," I snapped at him. "A wounded bear at close range'll prob'ly drive a city kid like you right out of his mind. I don't want any trouble."

"I can keep this up as long as you can."

Raging because he wouldn't quit and let me quit, I rushed along that wandering track as fast as I could force my way through the swamp. In great rambling arcs, I followed its twists and turns. I was getting deeper into that labyrinth of marsh and water and tight timber than I'd ever been before, but I didn't worry too much about it at

first, because we could just track ourselves out easy enough.

But the wind kept rising until it was
making a sound like a train going by
in the distance, blasting us with gusts
of fine snow now. I knew what I had to
do—give up and turn back. But each
time I was about to stop, I winced at
the thought of what he would say and
the knowing look he'd have on his face.
So I kept right on following that track.

I was taking a shortcut across a pothole when it happened. I'd probably
crossed a dozen of the frozen little
snow-covered ponds, and I never
thought to wonder why the bear had
circled this one. His trail was plain and
clear in the trampled marsh grass of the
slope beyond, and I was just heading
straight for it when the ice suddenly
gave way beneath me. My shotgun
went flying out of my hands, and I fell
sideways and sank completely under.
The shock was like nails being driven
right through me. The water was so
cold it seemed to burn. I got my head
up and tried to stand, but, although the
pothole wasn't more than a yard deep,
there was soft muck underneath, and I
was scared sick as I kept sinking on
down.

"Get hold of this!" I heard Marion
yell, and I twisted frantically about until I could grab his rabbit-poking stick.
While he braced himself and pulled
hard, I got one foot free at the bottom,
then the other. Falling forward and
breaking more ice, I scrambled on up
the snow of the bank.

"Are you all right?" he wondered,
crouching beside me, and for once the
grown-up sound of his voice was good
to hear. He'd fallen through behind me.
He was soaked, too, up to his waist
anyway.

"Yeah," I told him, trying to keep my teeth quiet, but I was a long way from home all right. The wind was stabbing through my wet clothes everywhere. I knew I had to do something, to get warm somehow, but I was too numb to think straight. I just watched as Marion went after the shotgun, cautiously raking it in bit by bit with his stick, then carrying it over. "What'll we do now?" he wondered. "Get out of the wind and get a fire going somewhere." We'd freeze before we could get back to the house.

I was wondering if he could possibly be as cold as I was and still talking so calmly. Forcing myself to my feet, I led the way back to a thick stretch of cedars. The wind was screeching, and the snow was like white fog by the time we got there, but we forced our way on until we found a tiny clearing where the boughs almost met overhead. There was plenty of deadwood around, but I could hardly hold onto my knife as I began whittling some sticks. Making a fire seemed an almost impossible job from the first, and it seemed completely impossible when I dug what was left of the matches from my pants pocket. All but two had their heads scraped off, and even though I blew on one for a long time and tried to be as careful as I could about scratching it, it just fell apart too.

"Oh, no!" I moaned. I was afraid even to try the one that was left, and I didn't have to bother asking my cousin if he had any—one look at his face and I knew he didn't. I don't know how long we just crouched there without saying anything, each of us waiting for the other to admit that all we could do was go ahead and make a try at getting home through a storm in wet clothes.

But suddenly Marion was fumbling in his coat pocket, then sliding his new hand warmer out of its little cloth sack.

"Something must burn in it to make it warm," he reasoned. "Let me try."

I gave him our last match and then bit off my breath as he pressed its head tight against a woven-wire thing that had to be some sort of wick. The burst of flame came so fast it surprised us, and Marion looked as nervous as I felt, guarding the match in his cupped hands. But then the sticks I'd whittled caught. Our fire sputtered for a long time, hissing on the snow, but all at once it flared up, and we both began piling dead branches on. At last we could just crouch close and soak up that wonderful heat.

After a while we thought to get our boots and shoes off and wring out our socks. We propped them up on sticks, and my jacket too, then just tried drying the rest of our clothes on us, keeping that fire roaring and staying as close to it as we dared.

"You know?" Marion suddenly decided. "It's nice here!"

I was surprised to hear him say it, but he was right—it was nice there.

"Yeah!" I agreed, and there was more I had to say, even if I couldn't look at him while I said it. "It was all my fault. I wasn't really huntin' any bear, just tryin' to get you scared. The bear that made those tracks is prob'ly somewhere in the next county."

He could have said a lot of things, but he didn't.

"I never really been bear huntin'," I stumbled on, in a hurry to get it all out. "The only live bears I ever saw were the ones that come to the township dump at night and you go watch 'em from the car with the headlights on. And even the tourists see those."

"I'd like to see them sometime," he offered.

"All that stuff about a bear eatin' our cows or attackin' some kid—I never really heard of one doin' anything like that around here. I got it out of a movie called *Black Rogue* or *Black Terror* or somethin' like that. All that business about shootin' for bone to break him down and then puttin' a finisher in him —it was from the same movie. I never really hunted anything but rabbits and partridge, and most o' the time I miss a partridge when one flies up. You can't even hunt deer up here till you're four-teen, not even if your dad wants to let you. It's the law."

Marion didn't let the silence last long enough to get uneasy. "By the time you're fourteen," he suggested, "maybe my mother won't be so afraid of guns, and I can come up here deer season."

"Sure, it'd be great!"

We were by that fire for two or may-be three hours, and if it was like magic to be comfortable and warm after go-ing through the ice of that pothole, it was even more so to be comfortable with my cousin, to feel so warm toward him, after the way things had been such a short time earlier. We talked and talked, and I think he told me things he'd never told anyone else, because that's just what I was doing. Then all at once we realized that the wind was letting up and the air was clearing.

We put out our fire, and I picked up the shotgun and led the way on to the next open swale. I can still remem-ber the way everything looked in the dead silence—fresh with new whiteness that lay unbroken on the ground and frosted every tree. It was a funny feel-ing but a good one—like all that had

ever happened had been erased, chalked out, with time starting over again—and right then I could laugh about the fool thing I'd done as though it had hap-pened years earlier when I wasn't old enough to know better.

But then I remembered something else that had been erased, and I didn't feel so good, because I had to admit to Marion that, with our tracks gone, I wasn't sure of the way back.

"You brought your compass," he re-minded me.

"Yeah." I'd brought it only as a joke. "But I don't know which way we came after we got into the swamp. I just went where that bear trail went."

"Aren't there any landmarks we could look for?"

I shook my head. "It's just a big tangle. One pothole or rise looks just about the same as another." I tried to keep my voice as calm as his.

"Well, let's think about it a minute." He marked a patch of snow with his stick. "Say this is the house, and this is north. Which way did we start out?"

I drew what I could for him with the shotgun butt. "West across the pasture, then north through the woods. But the swamp makes a big elbow here, and it goes on and on for miles. We could be anywhere in it."

"Where's the road? And what's over here?"

"Way south." I drew it in, too. "And this is the big woods between our farm and— Wait a minute." I was relieved to be the one having an idea for a change, even if he'd made me think of it. "If we just head southeast, it looks to me like we'll hafta come out some-place where I'll know where we are!" I tested the idea by drawing lines from every possible spot we could be, and

they all hit the farm or the road or the woods. "Yeah!"

We started right out, checking the compass every fifty yards or so. We'd been hiking for maybe a fast fifteen minutes when we pushed into a thicket and ran directly into the giant footprints of the bear again.

"Look!" It was spooky there in the failing light. A cold tingling began climbing my spine.

"This can't be where we came in." Marion said the same thing I was thinking. "Our tracks would be here, too. Do you suppose these were made *after* the storm?"

All at once I didn't have to suppose anything. Because in the shadowy line of brush ahead, a big piece of the shadow moved.

"He's there!" I gasped. "Right there!"

"Where?" He acted like he half thought I was making things up again.

"Shhh!" I turned and tried to make him see I really meant it.

Then suddenly he did see, and the old frozen look on his face melted fast. His eyes got big behind the glasses, and his mouth came open like he was trying to say something and couldn't. I was almost too frightened to turn and look, but even more frightened not to—and there was the bear, standing up facing us.

I remembered the shotgun in my hands, but I couldn't even get it to my shoulder. My arms were heavy and dead. I really felt more like running than shooting, but right then I couldn't do either one.

"You b-b-better not miss!" Marion stuttered. I'd wanted to scare him, and I'd sure done a good job—almost as good as I'd done on myself. "This stick isn't v-v-very sharp."

There was an abrupt snapping and crashing. Like a great black dog shaking itself after a bath, the bear sent snow and branches flying as he fought his way clear of that tight, tangled thicket. I could see all of him then, and he seemed the size of a horse—a giant dark shape blotting out everything.

The shotgun went off by itself in my hands. A patch of snow a few feet in front of the bear's forepaws exploded. He let out a snorting, woofing sound, whirled to one side, and padded off.

We stood there silent for a long time, and we didn't say much of anything when we finally thought to keep going. It was long past supper time when we got home, of course, and once again I was glad to have Marion along. He did all the explaining, and he did it just right. He didn't lie about anything, but he left out everything that made the whole mess my fault.

I knew Dad would get the real story out of me later. But that evening he let it stand the way Marion told it, because Aunt Stephanie was upset enough already.

I got along fine with Marion after that and I guess Aunt Stephanie did some backsliding on her notions, too, because Marion did come deer hunting with us later, just as he'd hoped, and season after season after that. And before long, of course, we could joke about our bear hunt and admit to ourselves that the bear wasn't charging us, just trying to get away, and probably twice as scared as both of us put together. But even so and even now, if I look back on that Thanksgiving holiday when snow was whiter and bears were bigger, I find myself laughing and shuddering at the same time.

THE END

Talking it over

1. *a.* Why does Wilbur act the way he does toward Marion?

   b. In what ways does Wilbur consider himself superior to Marion?

2. What does Marion do or say to show Wilbur that he isn't so ignorant of "country knowledge" as Wilbur thinks he is?

3. What makes Wilbur confess that the bear hunt was phony, and apologize to Marion?

4. What do you learn about Marion from:

   a. his reaction to Wilbur's confession?

   b. his explanation to their parents as to why the boys returned home late?

5. How are the two boys changed by their experiences during the bear hunt?

Words in action

Words do not always mean what they seem to mean. The tone of a person's voice may reveal his true feelings more clearly than the words he uses.

In reading, too, you try to "hear" this tone in order to understand what someone really means. Keep the entire situation in mind and try to "get inside the skin" of the speaker.

Look again at page 53, beginning with Aunt Stephanie's mention of the hand warmer. What is Wilbur really thinking when he makes these comments?

1. I stood close and asked fascinated questions like "What'll they think of next?"

2. "I almost forgot to bring my compass!" I gasped.

3. "If your hands are warmed up enough . . . ."

Prepare to read this section aloud, letting your voice indicate Wilbur's true feelings.

GOOD BOOKS TO READ

GAMUT

Charlie the Lonesome Cougar,
by Mark Van Cleefe

Jess Bradley finds a tiny cougar cub abandoned in the Cascade Mountain forests. He takes it home to save its life and finds, as a result, that some changes come in his own life. (Four Winds, 1968, 80 pages)

The Cinnamon Hill Mystery,
by Lorrie McLaughlin

The girls aren't looking forward to having their cousin William spend the summer with them. It will be boring to have to entertain a boy, they think. But William brings his entertainment with him. Soon the old house in the country is alive with his ideas, centering on his "invention." William seems to see into problems and understand how to involve others in solving them. (Crowell, 1967, 234 pages)

Let's Go, Yaz,
by Robert B. Jackson

This is the story of a fine young athlete, highly successful in basketball and then in baseball. It takes Carl Yastrzemski through his boyhood and up to 1967, the season in which he became a sensation in the sports world. (Walck, 1968, 54 pages)

Prisoners in the Snow,
by Arthur Catherall

When Toni and Trudi, twins who live high in the Austrian mountains, see a pilot bail out of his burning plane, their first thought is to help him. But when the plane crashes into a mountain and starts an avalanche that threatens their home and their lives, they have problems of their own. (Lothrop, 1967, 128 pages)

The Weightless Mother,
by Norman Bell

With everything going wrong in the Flippin household that morning, Mrs. Flippin reaches for what she thinks is an aspirin bottle. But the pills she takes are experimental ones made by her husband, a space scientist. He has been planning to produce weightlessness in monkeys. The whole nation becomes involved in what happens to Mrs. Flippin and the family dog. (Follett, 1967, 144 pages)

The Year of the Jeep,
by Keith Robertson

Cloud Selby wants to own a jeep. To do so, he must earn the money himself. His successful ventures for accumulating funds include catching bats to sell to a biologist. (Viking, 1968, 254 pages)

M E

The Canyon Castaways,
by Margaret C. Leighton

It has always seemed easier to do things the way the other kids suggested, so Jill Gay has never developed any self-confidence. Here she is caught in a spot where death threatens the lives of children for whom she expected to be only a baby-sitter, and survival depends on what she and a rescued college boy can do to preserve life and attract help. (Farrar, Straus, 1966, 150 pages)

A Man of the Family,
by Elizabeth Burleson

The one thing Speck wants is to be as much of a man as his father and brothers are. He is tired of being the baby of the family, held back from a full share in the ranch activities because he hasn't been well. This is the story of his struggle for acceptance. (Follett, 1965, 189 pages)

Star Island Boy,
by Louise Dickinson Rich

Larry has been a state kid all his life. Living in one foster home after another, he has built a shell around his feelings, for experience has taught him that people want a state kid only as long as they need the money the state pays. He has not meant to like Star Island, but he does; and as summer approaches and he thinks his life there is over, he has to try to do something about it. (Watts, 1968, 160 pages)

Wolfskin,
by Lillian Pohlmann

Johnny Clemens arrives in Alaska in 1898 with his father, who is heading for the gold fields. Motherless Johnny has been living with an aunt and uncle in San Francisco and would have preferred to stay there; but his father feels the Alaskan experience will be good for both of them. Before they can reach the gold fields, Johnny's father dies of a heart attack. The boy is befriended by an Indian and goes to work for a Russian family to earn his passage money home. (Norton, 1968, 143 pages)

The Year of the Raccoon,
by Lee Kingman

Everybody else in the family is talented, but Joey feels he is nothing at all and that his family thinks so, too. What is he going to do after high school? He can't decide. During the year of the raccoon, in which he learns what it means to make a pet of a wild animal, Joey makes a start toward understanding himself and his importance in the family. (Houghton, 1966, 246 pages)

PRESSURE

The Barrel,
by Ester Wier

By the time Chance Reedy is twelve, he has lived in seven foster homes. Then the Child Welfare Agency learns he has a brother and a grandmother living in the Florida swamps. Chance finds that even with relatives a person can be under pressure to prove his courage and worth. (McKay, 1966, 136 pages)

Katrina of the Lonely Isles,
by Margaret Ruthin

Inhabitants of a small island in the Faroe group rescue a crew from a Russian ship that has gone aground and will sink when the tide rolls in. Olaf, a main figure in the rescue team, is badly injured. Only plasma and surgery can save his life—and these are available only on the abandoned ship. Katrina, Olaf's twin, pleads with the ship's doctor to save him, but the ship's captain forbids the doctor to return to the endangered craft. It becomes a question, then, of either disobeying a superior officer or letting Olaf die. (Farrar, Straus, 1965, 162 pages)

The Mystery of Mound Key,
by Robert F. Burgess

Sandy has taken an old telescope from his dead uncle's sea chest. He and his friend Jib think the markings on the scope may be a map. When Mr. Scanlon, the uncle's former partner, buys all the dead seaman's mementoes, the boys are sure he must be looking for the scope. With the aid of an old sea captain, the boys set out to try to follow the map and possibly to find an old treasure. From this point they struggle against dangers that include the merciless Scanlon and his hired killers. (World, 1966, 187 pages)

Queenie Peavy,
by Robert Burch

Queenie imagines that her troubles will be over when her father gets out of prison. In the meantime, she responds to other children's teasing by behaving as badly as possible. Her father returns, but the results are not what Queenie expected. (Viking, 1966, 160 pages)

Shadow on the Water,
by Robinson Barnwell

The summer between eighth grade and high school is one of sadness and worry for Cammie Rutledge. She has become aware of problems disturbing her brother and her sister, and the shadow of a breakup between her parents threatens to destroy the closeness that has made home such a happy place. (McKay, 1967, 216 pages)

CONSEQUENCES

The Black Pearl,
by Scott O'Dell

At sixteen, Ramon Salazar is a partner in his father's pearl business in Mexico, but most of his work is in the office. Determined to dive for pearl oysters with the men from the fleet, he has an Indian teach him how without his father's knowledge. He dives in a spot that the Indian says is ruled by the Manta Diablo, a huge sea monster. In the misfortunes that beset the family afterward, Ramon can think of only one solution. (Houghton, 1967, 140 pages)

The Bushbabies,
by William Stevenson

Jackie Rhodes hates to leave Africa when her father's work as a game warden ends. She is somewhat comforted by permission to take her pet bushbaby out of the country with her. Aboard ship, she suddenly realizes that she hasn't brought the necessary papers to make the animal's trip legal. On impulse, she dashes down the gangplank, finds Tembo, her father's assistant, and begs him to help her take the bushbaby to a safe place to release it. The ship sails without her—and then the girl and the African must face many hardships and dangers in the wild country of Kenya. (Houghton, 1965, 278 pages)

Children of the Ark,
by Robert Gray

Reminding us that Noah's Ark was built to save animals, the author of this book challenges us to save wild creatures again—this time from a flood of human beings and the kind of civilization they have created. He gives examples of animals that are now extinct because mankind has been thoughtless or selfish, and he warns that unless many people take a hand in changing things, many more animals will be forever lost. (Norton, 1968, 120 pages)

The Mystery of the Old Musket,
by Patience Zswadsky

Jim Brady's great-great-great-great-grandfather is thought to have acted as a spy for the British in the American

Revolutionary War, and 200 years later the Brady descendants are still scorned by the townspeople. Can anything be done to clear a man so long dead? (Putnam, 1967, 128 pages)

Police Dog,
by Roderic Jeffries
When sheep and lambs are killed near the home of Police Constable Barry Trent, suspicion points to his dog, Caesar, an Alsatian trained to track criminals. The animal is to be destroyed, but first Caesar is needed for one more job. (Harper, 1965, 147 pages)

NECESSITIES

Hold Zero!
by Jean Craighead George
The town has done everything possible to supply activities for young people, but the high-school boys in this story want to do something on their own—something that adults don't plan and supervise. They devise a wonderful hideaway on an island, and then build a rocket. When an adult learns of the dangerous project, trouble sets in. (Crowell, 1966, 161 pages)

Lapland Outlaw,
by Arthur Catherall
In the Arctic regions of Europe live the Lapps, whose lives depend on maintaining a large herd of reindeer. When Jouni Sarris is badly burned and is flown away to a hospital, his sixteen-year-old son Johani and his daughter Anna, with one faithful herdsman, are left to protect the herd against a trader's plan to steal the animals by pretending to have purchased them. (Lothrop, 1966, 160 pages)

A Racecourse for Andy,
by Patricia Wrightson
The five boys had played together all through their childhood, with Andy a favorite of all. But gradually it became obvious that Andy was going to remain childlike. Mike, Terry, Matt, and Joe are still his friends. They take him around with them and protect him from people who might tease him. The four normal boys have a favorite game: pretending they own large public properties such as the Public Library or the town hall. Andy wants to be like the others, but he has trouble thinking of something to own. Then one day he has a chance to "buy" a race track for $3.00. (Harcourt, 1968, 156 pages)

Second-hand Family,
by Richard Parker
Giles Willis is used to the British orphanage in which he lives. But he hasn't cared much about the foster homes that have taken him in from time to time. He doesn't look forward to joining the Maxwells, either. The adjustment to life with them is even more difficult than some of the other situations have been, but he finds himself surprisingly interested in the Maxwells. (Bobbs-Merrill, 1966, 114 pages)

Tomas Takes Charge,
by Charlene J. Talbot
For many nights, Papa has not come home, and the neighbors are planning to turn Tomas and Fernanda over to the New York City Welfare Department. Both children are afraid of the change. Tomas finds a boarded-up apartment in an old building and the two move in. Then Tomas takes over the job of finding food and other necessities. (Lothrop, 1966, 191 pages)

2

Word Attack

Context   C S S D

Structure   C S S D

Sound   C S S D

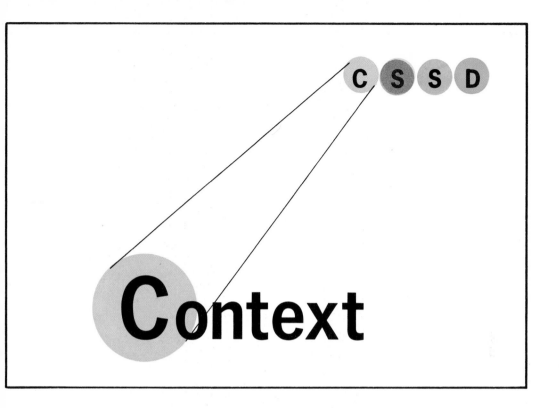

LESSON ONE: What context clues are

Picture the following movie scene:

> A ship at sea has struck an iceberg. The ship is leaning far to one side. Lifeboats full of people are being lowered into the water. The captain is shouting orders and officers are dashing back and forth.
>
> "Mr. Johnson," the captain shouts, "has **wireless** received any answer to our SOS?"
>
> "From the *Queen Anne,* sir, but she's ninety miles away."
>
> "Keep sending! As long as there's power!"

You may not know that the British call a radio a wireless, but the word *wireless* doesn't give you any trouble. You see where the action is taking place, you see what is happening, and you hear all of what is said, not just the word *wireless*. Because of what you see and hear, you know the meaning of a word that might otherwise have no meaning for you.

Several years ago, when the space program was just getting started, Americans watched TV and listened to newsmen explain what was going on. As they saw scenes like the following and heard the announcers' words, no one had to explain *launching pad*, *space suit*, *lift off*, or *capsule*.

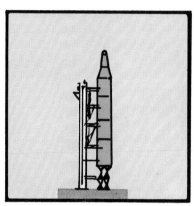

"The Atlas rocket is in place on the **launching pad.**"

"Captain Glenn, wearing his **space suit,** has just arrived."

". . . five, four, three, two, one, **lift off!**"

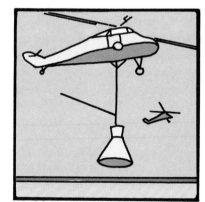

"The **capsule,** Freedom 7, has just been lifted aboard the U.S.S. . . . ."

Just as you can often figure out the meaning of words you hear, you can also learn to make pretty good guesses at what many unfamiliar *printed* words mean. For one thing, pictures in books sometimes supply the same kind of help that TV pictures and movies do. Here are some passages that contain words you may never have met before. How do the pictures help?

One man, in a red nightcap, with his **cutlass** in his mouth, had even got upon the top and thrown his leg across . . . .

From *Treasure Island*

Up from the grass before him flew a **covey of quail**.

From *"The Old Dog"*

When you see these pictures, you are quite certain what a cutlass is and what a covey of quail is. But in many kinds of printed material you do not have help from picture clues as clear as these. More often, clues to the meaning of a printed word are given by other words in the passage rather than by pictures.

Although you may not know the words in bold type in the following passages, you can certainly tell what they mean.

A. Aunt Bess had gifts for all of us when she came back from her trip to India. She brought my mother a **chatti,** a heavy pottery jar.
B. Hiccups are not usually thought of as a serious **affliction,** but there are cases where hiccups have caused death.

In example A, the words after *chatti* tell you exactly what a chatti is. In example B, it is difficult to say which words tell you what *affliction* means; but the whole passage gives you enough information so that you are pretty sure that *affliction* means "illness" in this sentence.

The surrounding information that helps you figure out the meaning of a word is called **context,** or sometimes **context clues.** You can learn to use context clues on a printed page just as easily as you use context clues when words are spoken.

EXERCISE I. Using context clues in reading

Part A

1*a*. Unlike the hot, steamy jungle of the Congo, the desert of North Africa is hot and _____.

What does context tell you about the missing word? It tells you that the word describes the climate of a desert. Context also tells you that the desert is UNLIKE the hot, *steamy* jungle. Together, these clues are enough to tell you that the missing word is *dry* or a synonym of *dry*. Write *dry* after number 1*a* on your paper.

When you come to a word you don't recognize, you can sometimes figure out what it means just as you decided what word would fill the blank space. Here is the same sentence as above except that a word is supplied in place of the blank. But it is a word that you may not know.

1*b*. Unlike the hot, steamy jungle of the Congo, the desert of North Africa is hot and *parched.*

If you don't know what *parched* means, the same context clues which told you that *dry* was correct in the blank tell you that *parched* means "dry." Write *dry* after number 1*b* on your paper.

Continue writing the word that fills the blank or has the same meaning as the word in bold type in the remaining twelve items.

2*a*. The American _____ is known as "The Stars and Stripes" and "Old Glory."

2*b*. The American **ensign** is known as "The Stars and Stripes" and "Old Glory."

3*a*. The gunshot injuries the President received were so deadly that the doctors' best efforts to save him were _____.

3*b*. The gunshot injuries the President received were so deadly that the doctors' best efforts to save him were **unavailing**.

4*a*. As the disease spread among the natives, fewer and fewer of them reported for work in the fields. The English plantation owners, however, thought the natives did not wish to work; they said the natives were _____.

4*b*. As the disease spread among the natives, fewer and fewer of them reported for work in the fields. The English plantation owners, however, thought the natives did not wish to work; they said the natives were **indolent.**

5a. A Civil War surgeon was faced with some horrible decisions. In those days a seriously wounded leg had to be cut off to stop the infection from spreading. And the only thing the doctors could use to _____ the pain was whiskey.

5b. A Civil War surgeon was faced with some horrible decisions. In those days a seriously wounded leg had to be cut off to stop the infection from spreading. And the only thing the doctors could use to **alleviate** the pain was whiskey.

6a. In most tropical countries, it is the custom to take an afternoon nap. The midday sun makes the temperature so _____ that working is almost impossible.

6b. In most tropical countries, it is the custom to take an afternoon nap. The midday sun makes the temperature so **torrid** that working is almost impossible.

7a. King John felt that his crown entitled him to a number of special _____. The nobles, however, did not agree that simply because he was king, John should have such power over them.

7b. King John felt that his crown entitled him to a number of special **prerogatives.** The nobles, however, did not agree that simply because he was king, John should have such power over them.

Part B

Although context clues are very useful, they are not perfect. Consult the Glossary now to see whether the clues in the sentences above all led you to the correct meaning of the words in bold type. If they did not, write the correct meaning on your paper.

LESSON TWO: Two kinds of context clues

So far in this section you have met two kinds of context clues. In one situation, the author stops to explain the meaning of a word he has used. He wants to use this word, but he thinks you may not know what it means, so he tells you directly. In the other situation, the passage gives you enough information so that you can guess the meaning of an unknown word, even though the author doesn't make any special effort to explain it.

Part A

Here are some examples in which an author stops to explain the meaning of a word.

1. Every time the boys were told to report for practice on Saturday morning, David's mother called to say that David was sick. The coach finally got fed up and angrily replied that he would not stand for **malingering**—pretending to be sick—in order to get out of practice.

2. The little French girl's father is the **concierge** for a large building. A concierge is about the same as a janitor or caretaker in America.

3. The chief logger went ahead of the work crew. After **girthing** the trees, or measuring them around as he would measure a person's waist, he marked those he wanted to have cut down.

Notice that in each of these cases the author seems to be trying to teach you a new word. He could have left the new word out and simply put the definition in its place. For instance, in the first example the author could have steered clear of the word **malingering:** ". . . The coach finally got fed up and angrily replied that he would not stand for the boy's pretending to be sick in order to get out of practice."

The same is true of the second and third examples. State examples 2 and 3 without using the words *concierge* and *girthing*.

Part B

Most of the time, however, when you run across a word you don't know you will find that the author has not explained it directly. Here are some examples of the second kind of context clue—clues that come from the general information in the passage.

4. As the enemy pushed forward, the captain began to search for ways to escape. Terrified, he realized that the enemy had surrounded his men, and there was no **egress.**

5. As far as Sandra was concerned, the best part of having a school basketball team was the pep assembly on the day when the team played. The cheerleaders and the band really stirred things up. Then the principal did what he could to appeal to school spirit. But the highlight was always Coach Alexander. His speech was so **fervid** that he drove the kids nearly wild.

6. On each holiday weekend, the happy plans of hundreds of Americans lead directly to their death. Traffic accidents kill as many as 700 people; drowning may kill 50 more; nearly 100 more meet with other kinds of accidents and die. This holiday **carnage** has been one of the greatest concerns of the National Safety Council.

From reading example 4, did you guess that *egress* means "way out" or "exit"?

What information in examples 5 and 6 gives you an idea about the meaning of *fervid* and *carnage?*

Check these words in the Glossary. Were the meanings you arrived at close enough so that you understood the sentences where the words appear?

EXERCISE II. Recognizing context clues

Read the following paragraphs, paying special attention to the words in bold type. From the context, you should be able to figure out a good enough meaning so you will understand the passage.

> People usually think of Europe in **medieval times,** the olden time of kings and castles and knights in armor, as a place where honor came first and where all knights were brave and honest. It is hard to imagine a man in shining armor committing an **ignoble** deed.
>
> But the legends of the Middle Ages are not without villains. **Modred,** a nephew of the famous King Arthur, was as **guileful** a man as you could have the bad luck to turn your back on. And even as King Arthur lay dying, another of his trusted knights **succumbed to** greed and tried to trick the king so that he could get the king's famous sword.

Write the answers to the following questions on your paper. After each answer, write "directly defined" if the author has told you the meaning. If you have to depend on the meaning of the passage in general to help you understand the word, write "general meaning."

1. What do the words **medieval times** mean?
   (a) the present   *(b)* the days of your grandfather
   (c) a time in the far past   *(d)* a time of evil

2. What does **ignoble** mean?
   (a) honest   *(b)* shameful   *(c)* difficult   *(d)* humorous

3. What or whom does the name **Modred** refer to?
   (a) a place where Arthur stays   *(b)* a river
   (c) Arthur's wife   *(d)* a relative of Arthur

4. What does **guileful** mean?
   (a) double-crossing   *(b)* brave   *(c)* honest
   (d) chicken-hearted

5. What does **succumbed to** mean?
   (a) fought off   *(b)* paid no attention to
   (c) became happy because of   *(d)* gave in to

LESSON THREE: Using common sense with context clues

Read the passage below. After it, there are three explanations, each one telling how a person might think about the context to figure out the meaning of the word in bold type. Which one of these people is using good sense?

A

One of the jobs of a U.S. Customs agent is to make sure that shippers are telling the truth about the number of things they are sending into this country. If the label says "50 Swiss clocks," it's easy enough to open the crate and count the clocks. But it's not that easy when the label says that a crate contains 24 live monkeys.

Of course, monkey crates are like cages, so the customs agent can look right in. But as he tries to count, the monkeys scurry back and forth so that he doesn't know which ones he's counted and which ones he hasn't. The experienced agent knows the **futility** of trying to be exact; he is satisfied if there seem to be as many monkeys as the label says there are.

1. The first person thinks: "The monkeys must look funny as they dash around while the agent tries to count them. *Futility* probably means 'fun.'" (NOTE: Does the passage stress the humor of the agent's problem? Substitute *fun* for *futility* and the sentence reads, "The experienced agent knows the *fun* of trying to be exact; he is satisfied if there seem to be as many monkeys as the label says there are." What is wrong with this statement?)

2. The second person thinks: "The passage tells how important it is to check to see that things are labeled honestly when they enter our country. *Futility* probably means 'necessity.'" (NOTE: This passage does stress checking for honesty in labeling, but when you substitute *necessity* for *futility* the sentence reads, "The experienced agent knows the *necessity* of trying to be exact, so he is satisfied if there seem to be as many monkeys as the label says there are." What is wrong with this sentence?)

3. The third person thinks like this: "The passage says that while it is easy to count clocks, it is very difficult to count live monkeys. An experienced agent (one who has probably tried to count monkeys in the past) is satisfied if the number seems to be

about right. *Futility* probably means 'uselessness.' " (NOTE: Are all the statements in this description true? If you substitute *uselessness* for *futility* the sentence reads, "The experienced agent knows the *uselessness* of trying to be exact; so he is satisfied if there seem to be as many monkeys as the label says there are." If a thing is useless, would you try to do it? Does the agent try to count the monkeys?)

The third person is the only one who has used the context clues in passage A in a sensible way.

Now read passage B and the three explanations which follow it. Which is the one sensible explanation of the way the context clues should be used? Be ready to discuss what is wrong with the other two explanations.

B

It was not that the queen was cruel. It was simply that she was not fit to rule. She did not understand her people, and she was not interested in their problems. While she lived a life of luxury and pleasure, her tax collectors robbed the poor. Young men were seized by her soldiers and taken away from their homes and their work to serve in the army. Judges sent their enemies to prison for crimes that were never committed. At last the people could no longer stand such injustice. Not all the armies in Europe could have stopped the **insurrection** that followed.

4. This passage is about a queen who lived for luxury and pleasure. In the end there is an insurrection. *Insurrection* must mean "a celebration" or "a party."

5. The passage is about injustice. When the people could no longer stand it there was an insurrection. *Insurrection* must mean "the adoption of a set of just laws."

6. All the wrongs mentioned in passage B lead up to an insurrection. You know that events like these would ordinarily lead to rebellion. *Insurrection* must mean "rebellion" or "uprising."

EXERCISE III. Defining words from context

As you read the following paragraphs, pay close attention to the words in bold type and the clues that help tell you the meaning of the words.

One of the medical mysteries that still **stymies** doctors is, of all things, hiccups. Doctors know what hiccups are—that is, they know which nerves are affected—but they don't know what starts them. More important, they don't know how to stop them.

Hiccups that last only a few minutes cannot be thought of as a very serious disease. As a matter of fact, a short-lived attack is often the cause of laughter rather than dread. But when a **chronic** attack occurs, it is not a laughing matter.

Can you imagine hiccuping for three years? There is a case on record where a woman suffered a three-year **siege** of hiccups. It is hard to imagine a case worse than that. But some cases of hiccups have been worse: hiccups have resulted in death. The mayor of an Illinois town died after three weeks of **unrelenting** hiccups. A Montana policeman **expired** after a six-month attack.

There are probably few diseases for which there are so many home "cures" as there are for hiccups. People have tried freezing their ears, wishing on teacups, holding cold pennies to the backs of their necks, and holding their earlobes while spinning around. You have probably tried holding your breath while counting to ten. Some "experts" have **advocated** holding your breath while counting to a hundred, or even to a thousand.

Select the correct meaning for each of the following words as it is used in the passage above. Test your choice by substituting the definition for the word where it appears in the passage. If your choice is correct, the sentence will make sense and will fit in with the meaning of the whole passage. Be ready to tell what context clues led you to the correct definition and which clues told you that the other three definitions in each set are wrong.

1. **stymies**   *(a)* pleases   *(b)* teaches   *(c)* puzzles
   (d) terrifies

2. **chronic**   *(a)* long-lasting   *(b)* sad   *(c)* funny
   (d) short but severe

(cont.)

3. **siege** *(a)* prolonged attack *(b)* short attack *(c)* period of freedom *(d)* delight

4. **unrelenting** *(a)* not active *(b)* pleasant *(c)* never letting up *(d)* peaceful

5. **expired** *(a)* was cured *(b)* sickened *(c)* became sad *(d)* died

6. **advocated** *(a)* forbade *(b)* advised *(c)* ignored *(d)* passed out

LESSON FOUR: Words that context does not define

You have probably noticed that getting the correct meaning of a word from context clues is easy at times and difficult or impossible at other times. Some words seem hard simply because you do not see all the clues. But don't blame yourself if you can't guess the meaning of each strange word you meet. There are times when context doesn't tell you much. Through practice, you can learn to tell when context is helpful and when it isn't. For example, what words would fit in the blanks in the following passage?

> The courtroom was crowded with people anxious to hear the testimony of the chief witness for the defense. They certainly were not prepared for what they saw. Everyone in the room was _____ to discover that the witness was a fourteen-year-old boy. The life of the defendant depended on whether or not the jury believed this boy. When he took the stand, everyone could tell he was very _____.

In order to make sense, the first blank in the passage must be filled with a word that tells how the people reacted to the age of the witness. What would your reaction be to the fact that a very important witness, a witness whose testimony could save a man's life, is only fourteen?

The second blank in the passage must be filled with a word that tells about the boy. Is it possible that he was polite? Is it possible that he was bad-mannered?

Here the context doesn't give you any clue as to how the boy behaved, or how he felt. He might have been bold, shy, brave, frightened, relaxed, or nervous.

EXERCISE IV. Recognizing the limitations of context

Read the following passage and decide whether there are context clues to tell you the meaning of the nonsense words in bold type. Write the answers to the questions on your answer sheet.

> Ankara is the capital of Turkey. It is a lovely city. Its **massals** are smooth and wide, its sidewalks are broad. Shops, hotels, and restaurants line the busy **massals**. There are parks; there is a university; and there is a famous **solamus**.

1. What could the nonsense word **massals** mean?
   (a) churches   *(b)* streets   *(c)* cemeteries   *(d)* people

2. Which of the following things might a **solamus** be? There may be more than one good answer.
   (a) factory   *(b)* palace   *(c)* statue   *(d)* fountain

3. Which word is not explained by the context — **massals** or **solamus?**

What you should know about context clues

1. The surrounding information that helps you figure out the meaning of a word is called **context.** You use context clues in one way or another every day—as you watch TV or movies, as you listen to others speak, and as you read.

2. Sometimes writers explain words directly, but more often you must figure out the word yourself by using information in the passage and by applying common sense.

3. Context doesn't always help you. When it doesn't, you must ask someone to explain the unfamiliar word or you must consult a dictionary.

In the next word-attack lessons you will review other ways of getting the meaning and pronunciation of words that seem unfamiliar. But you should always start by looking for context clues. And when you think you have figured out the meaning of a word by using other methods of word attack, you must try it out in context again to see if it makes sense there.

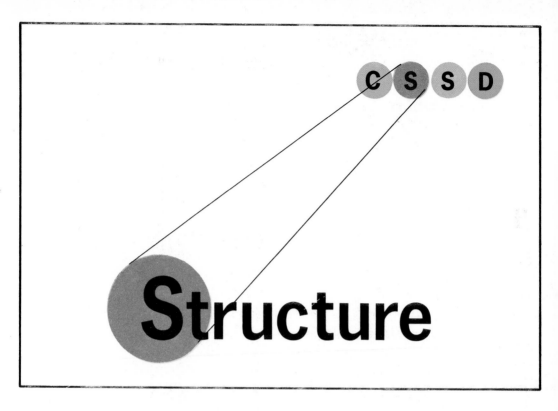

LESSON ONE: Recognizing word parts

Professor Yardly stared at Matt Johnson. "Don't tell me you ran away from a python! Why, they're *nonpoisonous* and almost never attack humans. What did you run for?"

"I guess you've never seen a python," Matt replied.

When you can divide a word that seems unfamiliar into familiar parts, you often find that you know the word. And even if you don't recognize it, the parts you know usually provide clues to the meaning and pronunciation of the word as a whole.

In this part of the Handbook, you will work with three different kinds of word parts: prefixes, suffixes, and root words.

EXERCISE I. Familiar word parts

Part A

On a piece of paper, write the word part that appears in all three words of each list below.

1. transaction
   transplant
   transform

2. bewitching
   bewitch
   witchcraft

3. freedom
   kingdom
   officialdom

4. horsemanship
   manpower
   postman

5. dullest
   brightest
   soonest

6. viewpoint
   previewed
   review

7. reheat
   reload
   refurnish

8. refinement
   settlement
   investment

9. subhuman
   submarine
   substation

Part B

The following questions refer to the parts you wrote in Part A. There is more than one answer to every question.

1. Which of the word parts, like *trans-* in list 1, always appear at the beginning of the word?

2. Which of the word parts, like *-dom* in list 3, always appear at the end of the word?

3. Which of the word parts, like *witch* in list 2, may appear at the beginning, middle, or end of the word?

4. Which of the following are words?
   ment   witch   dom   est   view   trans   man

What you should know about word parts

Many words contain smaller parts that you know. Some of these parts always appear at the beginning of words (for example, *sub-*); others (for example, *-dom*) always appear at the end of words. Some of the parts are words that can stand alone. When you learn how words are built from smaller parts, you are learning about word **structure.**

LESSON TWO: Root words and compound words

Below are three lists of words. Divide the words in lists 1 and 2 into meaningful parts. How are the word parts in list 1 different from the word parts in list 2? Can the words in list 3 be divided in a similar way?

List 1	List 2	List 3
eyeglass	uneasy	license
double-park	darkly	fetch
stronghold	helper	smooth
grindstone	inhuman	scene
dishcloth	subway	rural

Words like *jump, frost, divide,* and *cool* are **root words**. You cannot take away any part of a root word and still have a word related in meaning to the root word. Which list above contains only root words?

A **compound word** is made by combining two or more root words. Which list above contains only compound words?

How are the words in list 2 formed? You will work with words of this kind in a later lesson.

There are many compound words that don't mean exactly what you might expect from combining the meanings of their parts. You must think about the passage where the word appears as well as the meanings of the parts.

> When the Civil War ended, the **railroad** began to move West. It was the beginning of the end for the **stagecoach** lines. Ben Holliday, the **kingpin** of the **Overland** Stage Company, sold his line to a rival in 1866.

Notice that both *railroad* and *Overland* mean what you would expect from knowing the meaning of their parts.

What does *stage* suggest to you? Do you think first of something that has to do with a theater? Does this meaning of *stage* help you understand *stagecoach?*

Consider the meaning in this sentence: "He cleaned the garage in three *stages.*" Now can you see where the *stage* in *stagecoach* comes from?

What does *kingpin* probably mean in this passage? Which part of the word, *king* or *pin,* gives you the better clue to the meaning?

Many compound words make you use your imagination to arrive at their meaning.

EXERCISE II. Compounds—structure and context clues

Part A

If you simply combined the common meanings of the root words that make up the following compound words, what would the compounds mean?

1. headstrong
2. leatherneck
3. featherbrain
4. cartwheel
5. bedrock
6. gooseneck
7. heartbreak
8. headline

Part B

When the words appear in context the real meaning becomes clearer. What do the words from Part A mean in the sentences below?

1. Ron insisted on pitching even though his arm had been injured. If he hadn't been so *headstrong*, our team might have won the game.

2. You might think the marines are called *leathernecks* because they're so tough, but this name grew out of the fact that the marine uniforms once had leather collars.

3. The toast was burned, the cocoa was bitter, and the oatmeal was lumpy. Janice may be smart in school, but in the kitchen she is a *featherbrain*.

4. Hands on the floor, legs in the air, the acrobat ended his act in a whirl of rapid *cartwheels*.

5. The construction workers dug through sand, loose stones, and clay till they struck *bedrock*.

6. Andrew arranged his bedroom furniture so he could bend the *gooseneck* lamp toward the desk for study, or toward the bed when he wanted to read himself to sleep.

7. The students sat staring ahead, some with tears in their eyes. Mr. Abrams knew that they had already heard the *heartbreaking* news.

8. Alan began to read with interest when he saw the *headline* **SCHOOL BOARD EXTENDS SUMMER VACATION.**

LESSON THREE: Root words and prefixes

Part A

    a. Juan made it his habit to visit his workers during the lunch rest period; the men always made him feel welcome.

    b. Juan made it his habit to visit his co-workers during the lunch rest period; the men always made him feel welcome.

    c. Juan made it his habit to visit his co-workers during the lunch rest period; the men always made him feel un-welcome.

1. In sentence *b*, what word has been changed to make this sentence different from sentence *a*? Write the word on your paper and draw a circle around the added part.

2. How does the meaning of sentence *b* differ from the meaning of sentence *a*?

3. In sentence *c*, what word has been changed to make it different from sentence *b*? Write the word on your paper and draw a circle around the added part.

4. How does the meaning of sentence *c* differ from the meaning of sentence *b*?

Part B

The following questions refer to the word parts that you circled in answering questions 1 and 3.

5. Where was a word part added—at the beginning, the middle, or the end of the word?

6. What does the new part do to the meaning of the word to which it is added?

    The kind of word parts that you circled are called **prefixes.** Words made up of a prefix plus another word are called **derivatives** because they are derived from, or formed from, another word.

EXERCISE III. Negative prefixes

Among the prefixes you see most often are those that carry a negative meaning. They mean "not," "wrong" or "wrongly," "bad" or "badly," or "the opposite of." In this exercise you will review some of these prefixes.

Part A

Choose the word that correctly completes each sentence. Be prepared to explain why you selected the one you did.

1. The school rules provide that students will be penalized for _____ at classes.
   attendance   nonattendance

2. Upon _____ of a five-dollar membership fee you will be entitled to use the swimming pool.
   payment   nonpayment

3. Mr. Friedman thinks Frank is too _____ to be put in charge of all this expensive baseball equipment.
   responsible   irresponsible

4. The baby scrawled _____ lines on the paper.
   regular   irregular

5. All your answers on the quiz must be _____ if you are to get an A.
   correct   incorrect

6. Because the bridge he usually used was closed, Mr. O'Connor had to take a(n) _____ route to work.
   direct   indirect

7. Someone must have given Jerry wrong _____ about the time of the picnic, for when he arrived at the park with his lunch, no one was there.
   information   misinformation

8. If the uniforms are _____, you are apt to get the wrong size.
   marked   mismarked

(cont.)

9. Since this was Mrs. Lopez' first traffic offense, the policeman gave her only a warning ticket for —————— parking.

legal   **illegal**

10. Bob's handwriting was so —————— that Mrs. Burns couldn't tell whether his answers were right or wrong.

legible   **illegible**

11. We thought Wanda was —————— to leave the party without some kind of explanation.

polite   **impolite**

12. Tony can control the younger children at camp because he is quite —————— for his age.

mature   **immature**

13. We were so mixed up we were —————— to find even the main highway.

able   **unable**

14. The school board voted to build a new fire escape at Kennedy School because the old one is no longer ——————.

safe   **unsafe**

Part B

15. List seven prefixes that carry a negative meaning.

16. The prefixes *im-*, *il-*, and *ir-* are all forms of the prefix *in-*.

   a. Which spelling is used before root words that begin with the letter *r?*

   b. Which spelling is used before root words that begin with the letters *m* and *p?*

   c. Which spelling is used before root words that begin with the letter *l?*

EXERCISE IV. Prefixes with more than one meaning

On your paper, write the derivatives printed in bold type in the sentences below. Circle the prefix in each one. Then answer the questions to show that you understand what the derivative means.

I

1. If Greg is the most **inexpert** guitar player in town, is he likely to be a member of the school combo?

2. If the road up the mountain is **impassable** for cars, will those who want to go up have to walk?

3. If Public Health officers at international airports question only **incoming** passengers, does this mean they question only those who are entering the country?

4. If a man is **imprisoned**, is he out of prison?

5. Does the prefix *in-* or *im-* have the same meaning in **inexpert** and **impassable** as it does in **incoming** and **imprisoned**?

6. What does the prefix *in-* or *im-* mean in **incoming** and **imprisoned**?

II

7. If our basketball team is **unbeaten**, did we lose last night's game?

8. If Beth made herself a dress completely **unaided**, did she do all the work on it herself?

9. If Mrs. Sims has finished **unpacking** her suitcase, is the suitcase filled with clothes?

10. If six-year-old Benny can **unbutton** his overcoat by himself, should he need help with it when he arrives at school?

11. Does *un-* have the same meaning in **unsafe** as it does in **unbutton**?

12. What does *un-* mean in **unpack** and **unbutton**?

EXERCISE V. Other familiar prefixes

Study the groups of phrases below, noting the prefixes in bold type. Think about what each prefix means. Then decide which prefix should go in the blank in each numbered sentence.

anti-aircraft guns
antiwar demonstrations
antibiotic for an infection

preheated oven
Hollywood movie **pre**view
prepay the postage

rebind the torn library books
recopy the arithmetic assignment
replay a favorite record

transcontinental plane
heart **trans**plant
transpolar route to the Orient

international peace conference
interplanetary space travel
interschool basketball tournament

bargains at the **super**market
Superman's amazing powers
superspeeds of over 100 m.p.h.

1. Dr. Martin Luther King, Jr., devoted his life to bringing about _____racial understanding.

2. The District Attorney hopes that his _____crime crusade will help cut down the number of muggings and burglaries in this town.

3. The first permanent _____atlantic cable, by which messages could be sent between the United States and England, was completed in 1866 by Cyrus Field.

4. Michael liked the life in the army so much that he decided to _____enlist when his two-year term of service was over.

5. Janie and Tom couldn't have met here just by accident; it must have been _____arranged.

6. Henry can't take any kidding because he's _____sensitive.

LESSON FOUR: Root words and suffixes

I

A **laugh** was heard somewhere in the back of the school-room. The teacher looked sternly at the class and said, "We'll see if this still seems so **laughable** after school!"

But then suddenly the teacher himself **laughed** when he saw the quick change of expression on the face of the **laughing** boy.

1. What part is the same in all the words in bold type? What is the root word?

2. Which boldface word describes the boy? What letters have been added to the root word to form this word?

3. Which boldface word describes a situation? What letters have been added to the root word to form this word?

4. Which boldface word tells what someone did? What is the ending on this word?

Word parts that are added to the end of words are called **suffixes.** Words formed with prefixes or suffixes are called **derivatives.**

As you saw in the example paragraph, when a suffix is added to a root word, the word can fit into a different situation, or do a different job in the sentence: "Joe doesn't like to **read.** He thinks there are very few **readable** books."

Like prefixes (*un-*, *anti-*, and so on), suffixes add to or change the meanings of root words. What does *readable* mean? Could you use *readable* in place of *read* in the sentence "Joe doesn't like to read" and still make sense?

Sometimes a word contains more than one suffix: "The teacher suddenly realized the **laughableness** of the situation." How many suffixes are in **laughableness**? How many suffixes have been added to **laugh** to make the word **laughingly?**

II

If you're not old enough to remember the days when the family gathered around the radio in the evening, you probably have no idea how important the **narrator** was in a radio play. Many of the things that you see happening in a TV drama had to be explained through **narration** in a radio play. Often the play began with the **narrator** telling the story as if he were reading it from a book. At some point his voice would fade and the voices of the actors would be heard as they acted out a part of the **narrative.**

All the words in bold type above are based on the root word **narrate**, meaning "tell a story."

5. Write the boldface words on your paper. Circle the suffixes. How is the spelling of **narrate** changed when a suffix is added?

6. Which boldface word means "act of telling a story"?

7. Which means "person who tells a story"?

8. Which means "the story itself"?

If Nick, instead of giving up, would think about the meaning of what he's reading and then would look for parts that he can recognize in *estrangement*, he would probably figure out this word rather easily. He would guess that *-ment* at the end is probably a suffix. The root word, then, might be *strange*. A moment's thought would tell him that Susan and Eleanor are indeed acting like strangers toward each other, so his analysis makes sense. The *e-* at the beginning, he should guess, is probably a prefix. *Estrangement* must mean something like "a feeling of being strangers."

Don't assume that a long word or a strange-looking word is hopelessly difficult. Very often it turns out to be a derivative whose parts you know. Always see if you can break up a long word into parts that you recognize. If these parts suggest a word meaning that makes sense in context, your analysis is probably correct.

EXERCISE VI. Using structure and context clues

1. dissimilarity
2. featherstitch
3. mistrial
4. embitterment
5. shaky

6. windswept
7. shapelessly
8. unconsciousness
9. readmitted
10. interlocking

In this exercise you will analyze the ten derivatives listed above. On a piece of paper, draw the two charts shown below. Make Chart 1 big enough so you will have plenty of room to write word parts in the boxes. Each chart should have ten rows of boxes, one for each word.

Chart 1

ROOT	PREFIX	SUFFIX
1. *similar*	*dis-*	*-ity*
2.		
3.		
4. *etc.*		

Chart 2

	YES	NO
1.		
2.		
3.		
4. *etc.*		

Analyze each numbered word into the parts from which it is built. Write these parts in Chart 1. The first word is done for you.

You might begin by looking for a suffix or suffixes. (One of the words has more than one suffix.) Next, look for the root word, remembering that the spelling of a root word may change slightly when a suffix is added. If you decide that a word is a compound—formed by combining two root words—write both root words in the box labeled "Root." Finally, see if a prefix was added to the root word.

When you have analyzed a word into its parts and decided how it should be pronounced, check your decision by reading the word in context in the sentence on the next page that has the same number. If you think you have figured out the word correctly from its structure, check the corresponding "Yes" box in Chart 2. If you were wrong, or couldn't come to any decision, check the "No" box.

Here are sentences using the ten words you have analyzed.

1. The **dissimilarity** between the two boys of the same family surprised everyone.

2. Around the edges of the blanket my grandmother had worked an elaborate **featherstitch** design.

3. The murderer escaped punishment for the time being because the judge declared a **mistrial**.

4. The principal's announcement that Field Day had been canceled sent everyone into a mood of **embitterment.**

5. After his bone-shattering ride on the old horse, Terry felt **shaky** for several hours.

6. The hill where our house stood was so **windswept** it seemed a miracle the roof hadn't blown off.

7. Mr. Grant's suit was a limp gray affair that hung **shapelessly** on his thin frame.

8. Maybe if he lay perfectly still and pretended **unconsciousness** the nurse wouldn't take the blood sample today.

9. You can't be **readmitted** to school until your doctor signs a statement saying you are completely recovered.

10. Sandra was thrown out of the car when the **interlocking** parts of the buckle on the seat belt gave way.

What you should know about word structure

Many longer words are either compounds or derivatives—that is, they are made up of several parts which combine their meanings.

A **compound** is formed by combining two or more root words:

A **derivative** is formed by adding a prefix, or a suffix, or both, to a root word:

If you know what all the parts of a long word mean, you can usually figure out what the whole word means. Sometimes you can even get a good idea of the meaning of a compound or a derivative from the context plus the meaning of just one part of the word.

When you come to a long word that seems unfamiliar, look for familiar parts. By adding together what you know about word parts and what you can guess from the context, you can unlock the meanings of many words.

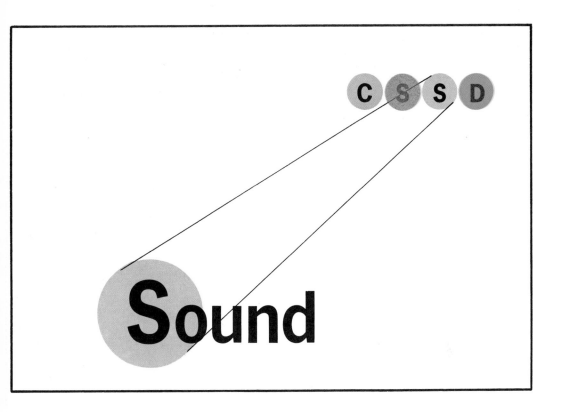

LESSON ONE: Recognizing words through spelling clues

See if you can read this paragraph, even though parts of some words have been blocked out:

Suddenly Bud noticed that someone had left the key in the l   . There was, after all, a way to es   ! He glanced back over his sh   r at the sleeping figure on the floor. Was he a co   d to sneak off like this? Well, it wasn't his resp   b   ity to look after Mr. Mills. At this time yest   he'd never even heard of the old man. Still, Bud couldn't help feeling a little gui   as he turned the   y in the lock. He opened the door as qu   t   as he could. At that moment a scr   m r   b   d through the empty corridor.

You were probably able to figure out all the words except the last one. *Reverberated* is probably not a word you have heard or used very often.

Any word you know well—a word that you use in speaking and have often seen in print—is easy to recognize in reading if you think about the meaning of what you are reading (the context) and about the sounds of a few of the letters in the word. These clues usually tell you immediately what .the word is.

You may, however, be stopped by a word like *reverberate.* If you have never said or even heard the word, you will have to use a dictionary to find out how to pronounce it. But if you have said or heard the word—even if you don't recognize it the moment you see it—you can often figure it out. The spelling of the word usually provides clues to the way it is pronounced.

For example, suppose you come across this sentence: "The pilot was in trouble during the final **phase** of the flight." If you don't immediately recognize the word *phase,* its spelling should suggest these ideas:

1. It is probably a one-syllable word.
2. The final *e* is probably silent and the *a* is probably pronounced like the *a* in *shape.*
3. The letters *ph* are probably pronounced like the *f* in *fat.*
4. The *s* is probably pronounced either like the *s* in *yes* or like the *z* in *breeze.*

If you have heard the word *phase,* you should recognize it from these clues, and then you will know which sound the *s* stands for.

In earlier grades you probably learned many principles or clues like these to help you pronounce letters and combinations of letters. The lessons that follow will review a few of the most useful clues.

LESSON TWO: Sounds represented by consonant letters

I

Jeff decided to **write** a story about the house the local people **called** Morbid Manor. He had heard a lot of **talk** about the **supposedly** haunted **"castle"**; even the older people who **should** have **known better** than to believe in **ghosts** said they felt **doubtful** and **frightened** when they came near the spooky old place.

1. In *write,* the letter *w* is not sounded. Which consonant letter or letters are not pronounced in each of the other words in bold type?

II

A **police car** rounded the **corner** leading the **circus** parade. We **could** hear the **music** of the band with its **cymbals clanging,** trumpets blaring, drum thumping. A **clown** in a **scarlet cape** followed, pretending to be frightened by a tom **cat** being led on a leash by the "animal trainer."

2. Pronounce the boldface words in paragraph II. Do you see that the letter *c* may represent either the *s* sound of *son* or the *k* sound of *kite*? Take each *c* in the boldface words in turn and tell which sound is heard.

3. On a piece of paper, write the letter which comes immediately after each *c* that is pronounced like *s*.

4. Write the letter which follows each *c* that is pronounced like *k*.

5. Using the information you wrote in 3 and 4, fill in the blanks in the statement below. You may want to write the complete statement in your notebook for future use.

"The letter *c* usually stands for the *s* sound when it is followed by the vowel __, __, or __. When *c* is followed by any other letter, or when it is the last letter, it usually represents the __ sound."

(cont.)

III

The **savages** of the **region** moved about like **gypsies.** When we looked for a **jungle village** I had seen a few days earlier, we found that it had disappeared as if by **magic.** Only a **mangy dog** remained.

I **greeted** the animal with the question "Where did everyone **go**?" You won't believe this, but he seemed to **shrug** his shoulders.

6. What two sounds does the letter *g* represent in the boldface words in paragraph III? Take each of these words in turn and tell which sound of *g* is heard.

7. On your paper, write the letter which comes immediately after each *g* that is pronounced like *j*.

8. Write the letter which follows each *g* that is pronounced as in *go*.

9. Using the information from 7 and 8, complete the statement below:

"The letter *g* usually stands for the *j* sound when it is followed by the vowel __, __, or __. When *g* is followed by any other letter, or when it is the last letter, it usually represents the *g* sound of *go*."

IV

The science club did not have **enough** money to **purchase** supplies for all the **worthy** projects suggested. Some of the boys wanted to buy **sheep** heads so **they** could study the brain. **Others** wanted **chemistry** sets. Still others wanted a camera to study **photography.**

10. In each boldface word in paragraph IV there is at least one two-consonant combination, like the *th* in *the*, which represents only one sound. The two letters together stand for a sound that is different from what you would expect to get from adding the separate sounds together. What other combinations of two consonants that stand for only one sound do you find in the boldface words?

LESSON THREE: Sounds represented by vowel letters

Although there are more than three times as many consonant letters as vowel letters, vowels cause more pronunciation problems.

Pronounce the words in each numbered row below. How many different sounds do you hear for the underlined vowel letter in each row? What two words in the row have the same vowel sound?

1. p<u>a</u>rt   l<u>a</u>me   h<u>a</u>rm   d<u>a</u>re   t<u>a</u>ll   f<u>a</u>t

2. p<u>e</u>ck   h<u>e</u>rd   h<u>e</u>   t<u>e</u>nt

3. h<u>i</u>de   b<u>i</u>d   p<u>i</u>t   st<u>i</u>r

4. sh<u>o</u>t   c<u>o</u>rn   n<u>o</u>   p<u>o</u>rt

5. cl<u>u</u>b   b<u>u</u>rn   <u>u</u>se   r<u>u</u>le   b<u>u</u>t

6. sl<u>y</u>   st<u>y</u>le   ugl<u>y</u>   g<u>y</u>m

Which of the following statements is correct?

A. A vowel letter can stand for more than one sound.

B. A vowel letter can stand for only one sound.

EXERCISE I. The spelling of vowel sounds

Say these words to yourself:

<u>e</u>ve   s<u>ea</u>t   n<u>ee</u>d   f<u>ie</u>ld   k<u>ey</u>   mach<u>i</u>ne

Is the sound represented by the underlined vowel letters the same in all these words? Are all the underlined letters the same?

Pronounce the words in each numbered row below. On a piece of paper, write the word in each row that does NOT have the same vowel sound as the first word in the row.

1. **age**   aid   break   weigh   all

2. **strike**   tie   fry   fit   guy   fight

3. **all**   straw   threw   bought   fault

4. **go**   code   boast   toe   throw   out   cold

(cont.)

5. **pool**	flew	blue	snow	rude	group	fruit
6. **bird**	fur	her	car	earth	word	
7. **join**	boy	show	coil			
8. **out**	frown	ought	cloud			
9. **book**	pull	bought	should			
10. **care**	wear	fair	ear			

Which of the following statements is correct?

A. There is only one way to spell each vowel sound.

B. Different spellings may represent the same vowel sound.

LESSON FOUR: Clues to vowel sound in one-syllable words

Lesson Three and Exercise I showed you that you can't be sure of the vowel sound even in a short word by simply looking at the vowel letter or letters. But there are spelling clues in most words that tell you what the vowel sound probably is. These clues have to do with the way the vowels and consonants are arranged in the word—the **spelling pattern** of the word.

Here is a one-syllable word with only the vowel and the letter BEFORE the vowel showing: ba⬛. Can you tell what the word is? It could be *bail, badge, barge, ball,* or any of dozens of other words.

Can you hear that the *a* stands for a different sound in each of these words: *bail, badge, barge, ball?* Does the *b* before the *a* give you any clue as to which sound the *a* represents?

Here are some one-syllable words in which only the vowel and the letters AFTER it are showing:

⬛at   ⬛ance   ⬛arve   ⬛ain   ⬛air

Pronounce the part of each word that shows. Did you have much trouble deciding how to pronounce these word parts? What does this tell you about where to look for spelling clues to the way a vowel is pronounced?

On the following pages is a review of a few of the most useful spelling clues that tell you how to pronounce vowel letters. As you go over these clues, keep in mind that whenever the term "consonant" is used, it means any consonant letter except *r*. The letter *r* affects the pronunciation of vowels in special ways that will not be discussed here.

I

A.   LAME   PETE   HIDE   VOTE   USE

1. Pronounce the words in row A. Do you hear the long or the short sound of the vowel?

2. How many consonant letters appear between the single vowel letter and final *e*?

Clue 1

V C + silent *e*

Clue to the (**long/short**) sound of the vowel.

crane   rope   rice   tune

II

B.   DANCE   TENSE   SINGE   LODGE   BULGE

3. In the words in row B, do you hear the long or the short sound of the vowel?

4. How many consonant letters appear between the single vowel letter and final *e*?

Clue 2

V C C + silent *e*

Clue to the (**long/short**) sound of the vowel.

mince   dodge   trance

C. CLAIM   SAY   BEAK   TEA   SEEK   TOAST   OATS

5. In the words in row C, do you hear a long or a short vowel sound?

6. What pairs of vowel letters appear together in these words?

7. Which vowel is pronounced in each case?

Clue 3

V V

In a one-syllable word, the vowel combinations *ai, ay, ea, ee,* and *oa* usually represent the (**long/short**) sound of the first vowel letter.

hail   may   seat   green   roast

LESSON FIVE: Hearing syllables

Most words that are hard to recognize in reading are words of more than one syllable. The clues to vowel sound presented in Lesson Four can also help you pronounce these longer words. In order to use these clues, you must know what syllables are, and how accent works.

Part A

Say the names of the six objects pictured. How many vowel sounds do you hear in each name?

1. binoculars   2. pyramid   3. igloo

4. sombrero   5. toboggan   6. parachute

Each word part that contains a vowel sound is called a **syllable**. There is only one vowel sound in each syllable. How many syllables do you hear in the name of each object pictured?

Part B

1. How many syllables do you hear in the words *lion* and *tiger*? How many vowel letters appear in these words? Does each vowel letter represent a vowel sound?

2. How many syllables do you hear in the words *baseball* and *stockade*? How many vowel letters appear in these words? Which vowel letters are silent?

3. How many syllables do you hear in the words *baboon* and *cocoa*? How many vowel letters appear in these words? Which pairs of vowel letters represent only one vowel sound?

Part C

Which of the choices in parentheses makes the sentence below a true statement?

"The number of syllables in a word (**is/is not**) always the same as the number of vowel letters in the word."

LESSON SIX: Hearing accent

Whenever a word has more than one syllable, it is pronounced with more emphasis or stress on one of the syllables. This stress is called **accent**.

Try saying *basket* by emphasizing *-ket*. Does it sound right? Now try it with the emphasis or stress on *bas-*. Does this sound right? The emphasized or stressed syllable is the **accented syllable**. Which is the accented syllable in *basket*?

Try *report* the same way. Which is the accented syllable?

EXERCISE II. Identifying the accented syllable

Part A

Go back to Lesson Five, Part A. Copy the words that appear beneath the pictures. Say each word to yourself and then write 1, 2, 3, or 4 after the word to show which syllable is accented. The first one will look like this: 1. binoculars, 2

Part B

Write the following words on your paper. After each word, write the number of syllables it contains. Circle the vowel letter or letters in the accented syllable. The first word will look like this on your paper: 1. paj(a)mas, 3

1. pajamas	4. opposite	7. relative
2. masculine	5. mechanical	8. hesitate
3. guidance	6. difficult	9. emergency

LESSON SEVEN: Clues to vowel sound in two-syllable words

The spelling clues you used to pronounce one-syllable words will also work in pronouncing **accented** syllables in longer words.

The chart below summarizes the clues you studied in Lesson Four. Review the clues and look carefully at the example words in the right-hand part of the chart. It may help you remember the clues if you connect each one with a particular word.

CLUE	VOWEL SOUND	EXAMPLE WORDS
1. V'C + silent *e*	long	remote, invade, grateful
2. V'C C + silent *e*	short	convince, advance, tensely
3. V V' ai, ay, ea, ee, or oa	long sound of first vowel in pair	repeat, complain, boastful, proceed, repay

EXERCISE III. Applying clues in two-syllable words

All the words listed below have two syllables and are accented on the second syllable. Copy the words in a list on a piece of paper. Circle the vowel letter or letters in the accented syllable. Study the arrangement of vowels and consonants in that syllable. Then write the spelling pattern from the chart that tells you how to pronounce the vowel. (Words 1 and 2 are done for you.) Finally, say the word to yourself, listening to the vowel sound.

1. rev(e)ng(e) V'CC + e
2. rem(ai)n VV'
3. giraffe
4. eclipse
5. redeem
6. invite
7. offence
8. stampede
9. release
10. indulge
11. refuse
12. betray
13. parole
14. entreat
15. refrain
16. trapeze
17. canteen
18. enclose

LESSON EIGHT: Other clues to vowel sound in two-syllable words

I

A. CAPTIVE   HELMET   MILLION   HOBBY   HUSBAND

B. DEMAND   PERCENT   INSIST   UNLOCK   DEDUCT

1. Pronounce the words in row A. Which syllable is accented?

2. Do you hear the long or the short sound of the vowel in the accented syllable?

3. How many consonant letters follow the accented vowel?

4. Pronounce the words in row B and answer the same questions.

Clue 4

V' C C

Clue to the (**long/short**) sound of the vowel.

brack′et   ex cept′   dis′mal

II

C. VACANT   LEGAL   CIDER   ODOR   CUPID

D. GRAVEL   LEGEND   FIGURE   MODEL   STUDY

5. Pronounce the words in rows C and D. Which syllable is accented?

6. Copy the words in a list on a piece of paper. Circle the vowel letter in the accented syllable.

7. After each word, write the number of consonant letters that follow the vowel letter in the accented syllable.

8. Pronounce each word again. Write LONG after the word if you hear the long sound of the vowel in the accented syllable. Write SHORT if you hear the short sound of the vowel.

Now you should have on your paper all the information you need to uncover another clue to vowel sound. Choose the words that will correctly complete the clue.

Clue 5

V' C V

Clue to (**the long/the short/either the long or the short**) sound of the vowel.

crit′ic   com′ic   ri′val   mo′tor

EXERCISE IV. Applying clues to vowel sound in longer words

In this exercise you will practice applying Clues 4 and 5 to words of three syllables.

First, study the chart at the top of the next page which summarizes the clues. Then write the numbered words in a list on a piece of paper. Say each word to yourself. Circle the vowel letter in the accented syllable. After the word, write the spelling pattern that tells you how to pronounce the vowel in the accented syllable. The first one is done for you.

CLUE	VOWEL SOUND	EXAMPLE WORDS
4. V'C C	short	disaster, captivate, surrender
5. V' C V	either long or short	elephant, numerous

1. president V'CV
2. revival
3. occupy
4. difficult
5. memory
6. customer
7. crucify
8. decision
9. companion
10. amusing
11. committee
12. deliver
13. umbrella
14. potato
15. invention

LESSON NINE: Special clues to pronunciation

A	B	C
famous	precious	cautious
glamorous	gracious	infectious
poisonous	delicious	superstitious
generous	vicious	nutritious

1. Pronounce the words in list A. Do you hear that all four words sound the same at the end? What is the same in the way they are spelled?

2. Pronounce the words in lists B and C. In list B, how is the part spelled -cious pronounced? What part of each word in list C sounds just like -cious?

D	**E**	**F**
action	expression	fusion
station	dimension	vision
conviction	admission	conclusion
question	depression	decision

G	**H**
facial	essential
racial	partial
special	initial
social	residential

3. Pronounce the lists of words above. Listen to the sound at the end of each word. Which lists would you group together according to the way the words sound at the end? In list F, can you hear that the blue part has one slight difference in sound from the blue part in D and E?

The chart below summarizes the clues to pronunciation that are illustrated in lists A through H.

SPELLING	PRONUNCIATION	EXAMPLE WORDS
ous	əs	enormous, humorous, mischievous
cious, tious	shəs	suspicious, flirtatious
tion, C + sion	shən	education, portion, pension, mansion, procession
V + sion	zhən	occasion, division
tial, cial	shəl	essential, presidential, social, special

3

Inferences

LESSON ONE: Getting information indirectly

1. Is the boy in this picture happy or unhappy? How can you tell?

2. Judging from his clothing, what do you guess the boy has been doing?

3. Which team do you guess he plays on—the home team or the away team?

4. What detail in the picture suggests that this particular loss is probably more disappointing than any other defeat during the season?

5. Why is the boy kicking at the banner?

The details in this picture have been carefully chosen to tell a story. You don't need to ask the artist to explain his drawing. By studying the visual clues—the details you can see in the picture—you can "read" what the artist is saying. This illustration might go with the following paragraph:

> Bill kicked in anger and frustration at the bright banner with its mocking words, "Go Owls!" Across the field, fans of the visiting team were still congratulating one another on their victory. On Bill's side, the Owls' rooters walked slowly away, their postures like his, their shoulders drooping in disappointment. He glanced down at his uniform, stained with mud and grass in evidence of the fight he had put up. But behind him, the scoreboard held its merciless message: "Home Team 21, Away Team 22." Homecoming parties would be quiet affairs that evening.

Although the writer of this paragraph doesn't tell you right out what has happened, he gives you enough clues so that you know. How do his clues compare with those used by the artist? Which words in the paragraph tell you the following?

1. The boy is very unhappy.
2. His team has lost the game.
3. The game was an important one for the school.
4. The boy is a member of the team.

The author of the paragraph could, of course, have given you the same information more directly: "Bill was very unhappy. The football team on which he played, the Owls, had lost their homecoming game by a score of 22 to 21."

Here the author tells you outright what he wants you to know. In the longer paragraph, however, he forces you to read closely and add up the clues to form your own conclusions.

Most writers use both approaches. You may find a statement like "George was very vain." Or you may be told: "George paused for a second time before entering the house to catch his reflection in the darkened window. He ran his hand admiringly over his carefully combed hair." In the second case, you are expected to figure out for yourself that George is vain. You **infer** it from his behavior. Conclusions drawn from clues of this kind are called **inferences.**

You make many inferences every day. If you are talking to a friend on the phone, and you hear a certain musical theme in the background, you infer that your friend has been watching such-and-such a TV program.

What might you guess if you came home and saw the dining-room table covered with a tablecloth and set with your mother's best china?

When your sister uses her most polite tone while talking on the telephone, what do you infer about the person at the other end of the line?

LESSON TWO: Getting information about characters

Frequently an author does not tell you directly such things as what a character is like, what he is thinking, or even how he feels. Instead, he gives you this information indirectly in details of action, conversation, appearance, and thoughts.

For example, when you read, "The woman laughed merrily," you are likely to conclude that she was amused or happy about something. If you read, "Matt set his jaw firmly, took a deep breath, and strode forward with an air of determination," what do you infer about Matt?

EXERCISE I. Making inferences about characters

Part A

Read the paragraphs and answer the questions.

I

Margaret's heart beat painfully. She picked up a pencil, then dropped it, so moist and unsteady were her fingers. The sound of it rolling down her desk jarred against the smooth voice of a classmate reading the paper she held firmly and proudly. Margaret prayed that the bell would ring before it was her turn.

1. List Margaret's physical reactions. What feelings do these suggest?

2. Where is this scene taking place?

3. Why does Margaret feel the way she does?

II

"Get away, Carlos!" Dino yelled roughly to his younger brother. "We don't want no babies tagging after us!"

Carlos' mouth quivered, though he bit his lips and drew them tight. In spite of himself, a sob jerked in his chest. To hide his face, he stooped and picked up a small piece of wood. "You're mean!" he shouted, and threw the wood at Dino. He rubbed his eyes to keep from crying, but they filled and the tears spilled over.

4. Describe Carlos' feelings. Why is he trying not to cry?

Part B

The way a character acts toward other people or toward animals can tell you a good deal about him.

III

It seemed to him that each day really began at evening, when he was done with his work and could have some time for the spaniel.

He worked slowly, patiently, first teaching the dog obedience. He taught Derry to come to him, to walk at heel, and to sit at his feet without jumping on him. After each lesson he lay on the ground and let the dog run about as he pleased. . . .   From "Choice of the Litter" by Roderick Lull

IV

There was no warmth of feeling between the dogs and the man, even though in this northern country the man was helpless without them. The dogs were the man's slaves, and the only communication they ever received from him were stings of the whiplash and harsh threats to use the whip. The dogs did not snarl as he approached, but their yellow eyes flickered momentarily in a way that might have disturbed a more sensitive man.

5. Which one of the following statements might the character in III make about training a dog? The character in IV?

   a. "Both discipline and affection are important."

   b. "You have to show a dog who is master. You have to beat him to keep him in line."

   c. "A dog should be given complete freedom to do what he wants if he is to learn to love his master."   (*cont.*)

6. What tells you that the man in III is fond of his dog? How can you tell that he is considerate of the dog and his feelings?

7. What words can you suggest to describe the man in III?

8. The dogs in IV probably obeyed the man because
   a. they loved their master and wanted to please him.
   b. they knew they would be rewarded.
   c. they were afraid of the man.

9. Judging from his treatment of the dogs, how would you describe the man in IV? Why does this man own dogs?

Part C

In the next paragraph, the author tells something important about a family by describing their surroundings.

V

Their home was scantily furnished, but shone with cleanliness. There was something attractive in its almost bare simplicity. Some of the furniture had obviously been made of boxes. And some of it appeared to have come from the town dump. But every piece was mended, painted, waxed, and polished. . . .

Adapted from "The Strangers That Came to Town" by Ambrose Flack

10. Is this family probably rich or poor?

11. Although no one in the family is mentioned specifically, what else can you guess about them?

12. How would you expect the members of this family to be dressed?

Part D

In the next paragraph, the appearance of a character reveals many facts about him.

VI

A soiled shirt of unbleached homespun linen was open in front, revealing a hairy, fleshless chest and two powerful collarbones. From the broad bony shoulders hung a pair of long, skinny arms, the longest I had ever seen and probably also the strongest. The hands were huge, big-veined, knotted, bruised, and cracked. The shirt sleeves were rolled above the sharp elbows and the back of the hands was bleached to a dull gold.

13. What does the description of the man's hands tell you about the kind of life he has probably led?

14. What might the words "fleshless," "bony," and "skinny" suggest about the man's life?

15. Why might the hair on the man's hands and arms be "bleached to a dull gold"?

LESSON THREE: Getting information about setting

"Phil and Sally and the other teen-agers arrived at the beach around ten in the morning." In this sentence, the author tells you directly where and at what time of day a scene will take place.

"There was a damp salt smell in the air, but there were human smells, too: scents of suntan oils and skin lotions and sun-baked bodies, cooking smells of frying hamburgers from open-air stands, the aroma of fish browning on the grills of the day's most fortunate fishermen."

Does the author tell you right out where and when this scene takes place? What clues, however, suggest the place? What suggests the general time of day?

EXERCISE II. Inferring time and place

Use the author's clues to infer facts about setting in the examples below.

A

The night was unusually warm. The slowly rising moon outlined giant shadows on the ground and cast a yellow glow on corn shocks and pumpkins in the field. Over everything hung the pungent smell of burning leaves.

1. What time of year is described in paragraph A? What tells you?

B

A bell rang and the green arrow indicated "up." I crowded into the front, holding my breath as the door slid shut. As I glanced in back of me, I saw others standing very straight, trying to shrink themselves into smaller size. One woman who was carrying several large packages was sandwiched between two very talkative women who leaned first in front of her and then behind her to continue their conversation. With a strange sensation of having left my stomach behind, I realized we had started upward. Our trip was quick, but I was relieved when the heavy door slid open again and I stepped out onto the observation tower.

2. What is described in paragraph B? How can you tell?

C

The year Sarah turned fourteen, most of the country was still uncharted wilderness. Only thirteen colonies were populated, and those only thinly. The few roads that crossed this new country were hardly more than trails. Visitors sometimes came from England, and Sarah listened in fascination to their stories about the magnificent affairs at the court of King George III. Still, things that happened three thousand miles away could not help but seem remote and unreal to the girl.

3. What period in history is referred to in paragraph C? Where did Sarah live?

D

The crowd roared as the men in red scattered to set up their defense against the green-clad Southerners. But from that time on, Bill was aware of the noise only as a muffled background for what was taking place on the floor. The captain stepped into the center circle. The big ball flashed into the air. As the Southerner tapped the ball, the other men in green dashed into their carefully planned play.

4. Where does this scene take place? What is being described?

To understand the characters and situation in the opening sections of this story, you must use your skill at making inferences.

From **The Torn Invitation**[1]
by Norman Katkov

AT FIFTEEN in the spring of his sophomore year at Hamilton High School, Harry Wojick was as big as a college senior, a long, thin, big-boned left-hander, who could anchor a leg on first base and stretch halfway to the bull pen for a bad throw from his shortstop.

Now, in the waning daylight, he turned into Glover Street toward his home, his arms swinging as he moved onto the unpaved road. For a few feet he ran easily, bringing his knees up high, until, without warning, he stopped short and bent low to field the imaginary ball cleanly, beating the runner by a mile. He straightened up, grinning in the half darkness, blushing a little from the applause at the brilliant play he had made.

Harry Wojick came off the street onto the sidewalk. He passed the four-family flat in the middle of the block. He passed the empty lot and beyond it the condemned building with all the windows long since broken, and then he turned into the cement walk which ran the length of his house.

1. What seems to be one of Harry's strong interests?
2. From the appearance of the neighborhood, what can you guess about the financial condition of Harry's family?

The windows were raised in the kitchen and he smelled the roast. He smelled the asparagus for the roast and the fried potatoes with onions that nobody made like Ma, and he was suddenly terribly hungry after the three hours of baseball practice.

When he came into the kitchen, Theresa Wojick turned from the stove, smiling at her son, rubbing her hands on her apron as she walked to meet him. She held him at the elbows, examining him carefully, her face warm and her eyes gentle, welcoming him as though he had returned from

---

a long and perilous journey. She was a tall woman with large, capable hands and black, unkempt hair shot through with gray. She held Harry and she said, "Hello, my little son. Will you eat supper?" joking with him as always.

3. What is your impression of Mrs. Wojick? On what details is it based?

4. What are Mrs. Wojick's feelings toward her son? What tells you?

5. Can you infer anything at this point about how Harry feels toward his mother?

He put his cheek to hers, noticing again the redness of her chapped hands. She could try to do something about it, he said to himself, as she released him, remembering the mothers of his teammates who lived on Livingston Drive and Harding Boulevard and scattered through Maple Heights. They were mothers with manicures and they were thin—and their hair was always set just right.

6. With whom does Harry compare his mother? Which kind of mother does he seem to think is superior?

7. In what ways are the neighborhoods Harry is thinking of probably different from his own?

Harry went to the sink to wash and, turning, saw the table set for three.
"For Frankie Thomas," his mother whispered, looking at her son. "His mother is gone again till half the night, and leaves cold cuts. Boy like Frankie to eat cold cuts," she whispered. "You call him, Harry."
"Why can't she learn to speak English?" he asked himself savagely, turning away. "She's been here long enough!"

8. Why has Mrs. Wojick invited Frankie to dinner?

9. What effect does Mrs. Wojick's speech have on Harry?

Harry walked through the short hall and stood under the arch which led into the living room. "Hey, Frankie," Harry said. "Come on and eat." Harry whistled shrilly and came back into the kitchen.
He pulled the chair out and held it suspended off the clean, bare floor, his fingers tightening on the wood. There, next to his plate, was the white, square envelope, and atop

it, covered by a transparent sheet of thin paper, was the embossed invitation.

Harry looked at his mother, who had her back to him, busy at the stove. He heard Frankie coming through the house and knew it was Frankie's work, *knew* it. He moved the chair at last and sat down and, without touching it, his hands holding his knees, he read the invitation from the faculty of Hamilton High School to an open house in honor of all the students' mothers.

It was for tomorrow.

Harry knew *that*, all right. Had known it for ten days and had kept it secret. He looked up as Frankie sat down across the table.

10. How does Harry feel when he sees the invitation? What actions reveal his feelings?

11. How do you know that Harry had not wanted his mother to know about the invitation?

Harry's mother was sitting between them, and as she handed her son the roast she said, "I asked Frankie maybe he has this invitation, Harry. I heard by Celusik, the grocery man, about this open house. Must be open house for junior, senior mothers."

Harry was busy with the roast. "It's for everyone," he said, watching the roast. "Didn't you get one, Ma?" He turned toward his mother. "They mailed them out," Harry said, remembering now that morning when he had waited for the postman on the corner, taken the envelopes from him, searched for the square white one, and had torn it, scattering the pieces in the empty lot before running home and dropping the rest of the mail in the black metal box beside the door.

"Maybe they make a mistake," his mother said.

She reached for a thick slice of the rye bread she baked herself and held it flat in her left hand. She buttered it completely and thickly and brought it to her mouth, taking a large bite, and Harry wanted to leave the table and this house. He remembered the homes on Maple Heights to which he had been invited, where they called it dinner and ate in a dining room with tablecloths; where George Sidley's mother sat at one end of the table and broke her bread piece by piece, buttering it lightly and eating it slowly.

Mrs. Wojick turned to Harry, smiling at her son. "You eat, Harry. Big ballplayer must eat good," she said.

12. What do you infer about Theresa Wojick from each of the following?

    a. Her words and actions toward her son

    b. Her concern for Frankie

    c. Her appearance

13. *a.* List three things about his mother that disturb Harry greatly. Is Harry thinking about his mother's inner qualities, or is he concerned only with outward appearances?

    b. What does Harry's opinion of his mother suggest about *him?*

14. *a.* Why does Harry avoid looking at his mother when he asks her if she received an invitation?

    b. Why did Harry tear up the invitation? On what do you base your opinion?

15. In what way may Harry's opinion of his mother change as the story progresses?

What you should know about making inferences

Sometimes writers present important information indirectly. For example, instead of telling you right out how a character feels or what he is thinking, an author may expect you to **infer** it from what the character says or does. Information about time and place in a story, or about what happened earlier, may also need to be inferred.

When you are reading a long story, you must continually make **inferences**. You may find as you go along that your original conclusions need to be changed. Usually only a few things about a character are revealed in any one part of a story. You may need to see a character in various situations before you can decide what kind of person he really is.

Before drawing any conclusion, be sure you have a good reason for it. An inference should be based on evidence.

4

Purpose

LESSON ONE: Why you need a purpose in reading

SAM: Hey, Tom, where you going?

TOM: Uh—I dunno. Mom wants me to get something for her—I forget what.

SAM: That sure sounds crazy! How do you know what direction to go? What you gonna look for when you get there? You won't even know when you're there!

TOM: Well, uh—I just thought I'd start walking. . . .

Almost everyone would agree that Tom is acting pretty stupidly. Probably no one would really start off on an errand like that. But students often begin reading an assignment without any idea of what they are looking for.

When you know what you are looking for—what you need to learn or find out—you have a **purpose** for your reading. You know what to pay special attention to, and what you can pass over without trying to remember. Purpose has a great deal to do with the way you read.

How would you read this week's TV schedule if you wanted to see what movies were being shown during the week? What would you do differently if you were looking for tonight's eight o'clock movie on Channel 7?

For what purpose might you read each of the following?

1. A comic book
2. Directions for building a model car
3. A story you choose from the library
4. A newsmagazine
5. Billboards along the highway

How carefully would you read in each case?

LESSON TWO: Using assignments to help set purpose

When you select your own reading material, you usually have a purpose in mind. You may read a magazine to find information about stock cars, or a book of jokes for a few laughs. In school, however, reading is assigned. You often do not select it yourself.

Perhaps your teachers have you write your assignments in a notebook. Suppose a page in your assignment notebook looks like this:

Eng. – "The Red Door," p. 39. Read to see how character of Joy changes in story.

Health – Read pp 75–82. Learn glands that have to do with digestion of food.

Science – Read section 4b, "How do heating and cooling change materials?" → answer self-testing questions.

What details of the reading in health will you try to remember particularly? Which character in "The Red Door" will you pay special attention to? How carefully will you read the science assignment? Do you expect to read it slowly or fast? Why?

When you are given an assignment, listen for specific directions like these:

"Look for the three main causes of the war."

"Watch how the conversation in the story shows you what the characters are like."

"Be prepared for a quiz on the characteristics of reptiles."

In addition to such directions, think about what has been said in the last few class discussions. For example, if you have been talking in English class about how an author gives clues to help you understand his characters, look for these clues in the next story you read.

To set a purpose for assigned reading, use directions from the teacher and clues from earlier class discussions.

LESSON THREE: Using pictures and titles to help set purpose

Terror in the Old House
by Beverly Black

Suppose this title and picture are the first things you see as you open a magazine. Probably you wonder:

1. What is the "terror" in the old house?
2. Who are the boy and girl in the picture?
3. Why are they hiding?
4. Are they alone in the house?
5. Who is the person coming up the sidewalk?
6. Will he get into the house?
7. Is he going to harm the children?

Now suppose the title of the story were "The Day We Ran Away." In this case, what questions would come to mind?

What different questions would you ask if the title were "Uncle Fred Returns"?

The following picture might appear in a factual article.

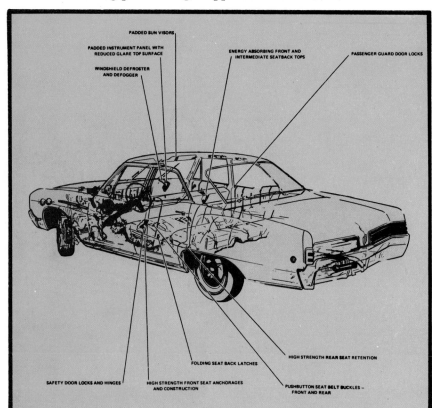

What might this article be about? What questions come to mind when you study the picture?

What would you expect to learn from this article if its title were "Why Can't We Make Cars Safer?" If the title were "Why Cars Cost So Much"?

Setting a purpose for reading is often the same as setting up questions to be answered as you read. Both the title and the pictures in a story or an article can help you think of questions to guide your reading.

EXERCISE I. Using pictures

Write at least two questions suggested by each of the following three pictures:

EXERCISE II. Using titles

Often there are no pictures to suggest questions. However, the title alone may be helpful.

Someone reading a selection with the title "The Girl Who Swam the Channel" might ask questions like these:

1. Who was the girl?
2. What channel did she swim?
3. Why did she want to do it?
4. How did she get ready?
5. Did she have difficulties on the way? If so, how did she meet them?
6. What happened afterward?

Part A

Suppose you are about to read an article titled "The Best Advice I Ever Had." What questions would you ask

1. about the person giving the advice?
2. about the person receiving the advice?
3. about the advice itself?

Part B

Write at least two questions suggested by each of the following titles:

4. "The Case of the Missing Ticket Stub"
5. "When Niagara Falls Stood Still"
6. "The Family Nobody Wanted"

LESSON FOUR: Using the opening paragraph to set purpose

A

"Before you grind your next cockroach under your heel, spare a thought for this little fellow who is one of the most remarkable creatures alive. Of all the creatures that existed 200 million years ago, only the cockroach has survived almost unchanged. While the dinosaurs perished and all other creatures had to undergo considerable change in order to survive, the cockroach went on living as it had always done. This most primitive of all winged insects was, right from the start, perfectly fitted for its particular and peculiar way of life."

Adapted from *Aramco World*

1. What would you expect an article beginning with this paragraph to be about?

2. What questions are suggested by:
   a. the description of the cockroach as "one of the most remarkable creatures alive"?
   b. the fact that *only* the cockroach has survived 200 million years almost unchanged?
   c. the statement that the cockroach is "perfectly fitted for its particular and peculiar way of life"?

B

"He did not have tremendous speed. He was not a natural-born hitter or ball hawk. Worst of all, he had a lame arm. Yet Tyrus Raymond Cobb was the greatest ballplayer of them all. What he possessed, and to a superlative degree, was determination."

From "My Most Unforgettable Character," by Fred Haney. *Readers Digest*, June 1964.

3. What sport is involved here?

4. What characteristic of Ty Cobb's do you expect will be stressed?

5. What would you want to know about the author of the article?

The paragraphs quoted above show you that the opening paragraph of a factual article, along with its title, often (a) tells you what the selection will be about, and (b) gives you a basis for asking purpose-setting questions.

The opening paragraph or paragraphs of a story also can give you important clues you will want to follow up as you read. Here is the opening paragraph of "The Nest," from the next unit:

> "Jimmy was fourteen. He was listening to his mother tell him, in her kindly, measured speech, why she didn't want him to go on the hike; and his clear gray eyes were clouded with sullen rebellion."

Even from this short paragraph you learn certain things. There is a disagreement between Jimmy and his mother, and it has to do with a hike. The mother seems to be a patient, kindly person, but Jimmy doesn't like what she is saying.

The paragraph also makes you wonder—why doesn't the mother want Jimmy to go on the hike? Will it turn out that she is right about the hike? Will Jimmy do as she wants? And what kind of "nest" is meant in the title?

A third help in establishing your purpose is reading the opening paragraph, along with the title, to discover what a selection will probably be about and to find further question-raising clues.

EXERCISE III. Using the opening paragraph (factual material)

Read paragraph A. Decide what the complete article will probably be about. Then write a set of questions suggested by the opening paragraph. Do the same for paragraphs B and C.

A

> "Adapting to life in the tropical bush of West Africa provides some exciting moments, occasional despair, and a few unexpected rewards. It requires a constant struggle to overcome loneliness, the discomforts, and a climate which even ten years ago was referred to as 'the white man's grave.'"

From "Life Under 160 Inches of Rain," by
Aileen V. Barwood. Science Digest, October 1963.

1. Subject: (What will the article be about?)

2. Questions: (What questions will probably be answered?)

B

"Bumper-to-bumper crashes have become a major traffic problem. In heavy city traffic, many such collisions are noisy but minor—they damage nerves and dignity more than they damage cars. But even a 'minor' rear-end collision can sadly damage a budget. And on the high-speed freeways there is virtually no such thing as a 'minor' rear-end collision. Almost every such accident is a spectacular and tragic crash often magnified by a chain-reaction effect involving a long column of cars."

From "Keep Your Bumpers to Yourself," by Arthur R. Forster. *American Youth,* September-October 1962.

3. Subject:

4. Questions:

C

"In a quiet back street in Paris stands a somber, four-story, gray stone building. The main gate is a sturdy affair, painted dull green, fitting flush to the thick wall. On it is a brass plate engraved with the letters ICPO. Behind the door in hundreds of thousands of files are the secrets of the world's international criminals."

Adapted from "Crime Busters International" by David Lewis. *Elizabethan,* May 1965.

5. Subject:

6. Questions:

LESSON FIVE: Using headnotes to help set purpose

He whirled, knowing that gunfire
would burst from the shadow . . . .

Imagine you have just opened your literature book to the story assigned for homework. These words are printed in special type at the beginning of the story. They catch your eye immediately. What is their purpose? What would you expect to find out by reading the story?

In *Thrust,* there are not only interest-catching titles and illustrations, but also headnotes that tease your imagination.

EXERCISE IV. Using headnotes and titles

Read each headnote and title below. (All are from later selections in *Thrust*.) For each one, write two questions that you think the story might answer.

1. *Fear grabbed Jamie—*
but he couldn't go back.
The dizzy heights of the tower
urged him to keep climbing.

The Way Up

2. *He was probably the only man*
in the history of Texas
who deserved hanging more
after he was hung than before.

Necktie Party

3. *At a difficult time in Randy's life,*
his best friend was an

Orphan Pup

4. *Millie felt a strange terror.*
With a word or a nod she could strike
a final staggering blow.

Millie

5. *"You know what my old man told me*
about your old man? . . . that he
was a drunken bum!"

The Old Cardinal Spirit

LESSON SIX: Making a survey to set purpose (factual material)

The headnote alone, the title, an illustration, or an opening paragraph alone is not always enough to suggest useful guiding questions, particularly if the material to be read is long. However, taking a quick look at all these parts of a selection (and usually at the closing paragraph as well) should get you off to a good start. This is called making a **survey.**

Here are the parts of an article you would use in a survey.

*A drop into the raging torrent meant
instant death . . . but he was*

Blondin, the Man Who Could Not Fall
by Colin Bulman

In 1859, two crowds, amounting to about 25,000 people, were gathered on the banks of the river just below the deafening roar of the Niagara Falls. Between the banks of the river and 160 feet above the rapids, just about a hundred yards from the actual falls, was stretched a seemingly slender rope 1100 feet long. The crowds were watching amazed and in stony silence, for in the middle of the rope, balancing precariously, was the solitary figure of a man. . . .

Blondin crossing the Niagara in 1859 Eating his dinner on the rope
at the Crystal Palace, 1861

But his fame rests on his ability as a tightrope walker—as the man who could not fall.

From *Elizabethan* Magazine, September 1964.

1. Judging from the headnote, title, and illustrations, what will this article be about?

2. Read the opening and closing paragraphs. What does Blondin do for a living? What hint is there that he may do other things, too?

3. What suggests that he was a well-known person at the time of the Niagara Falls stunt?

4. What have you learned about his skill?

5. What reason might the author have for beginning his article with a description of Blondin walking above the falls?

As you see, a preliminary survey of an article can give you a fair amount of information. Under what circumstances might you decide to stop here and read no further? Under what circumstances would you decide to read the entire article?

EXERCISE V. Making a survey

1. Make a preliminary survey of the article "Chimp Girl":
   a. Read the headnote and title.
   b. Look at the pictures on the next two pages and read what is printed under them—the picture captions.
   c. Read the first and last paragraphs of the article.

*A young woman makes startling
discoveries about apes!*

Chimp Girl

When you laugh at the antics of a chimpanzee in the zoo, do you ever have the uncomfortable feeling that the chimp is laughing at you, too? Well, he probably is, says a young woman scientist who has spent over three years in the East African jungle watching chimpanzees.

(cont.)

Wild chimpanzees use stems as tools to fish termites out of a nest. The apes strip the leaves from twigs, and break off the ends if they become bent. Insects, considered tasty by the chimps, cling to the stems when they are withdrawn.

A wild chimpanzee gets a handout of ba-nanas from Jane Goodall. At first, chimps ran if she came near them.

Emulating Linus of the "Peanuts" cor strip, a chimp clutches a blanket he l just stolen from camp.

"David Graybeard," the only wild chimp that would allow Miss Goodall to touch him.

When Jane Goodall came to Washington, D.C., to relate her experiences studying wild chimpanzees in East Africa, she made friends with Lulu, a baby chimp from the National Zoo.

. . . .

Miss Goodall has been interested in animals since childhood, when she tried her mother's patience after official bedtime by taking worms to bed to watch them crawl. Her continued interest has been fortunate for the world of science, for her careful studies have led to significant discoveries about the behavior of chimpanzees.

2. On the basis of your survey, write two questions that you think the article will answer.

3. Now turn the page and read the entire article. When you have finished reading it, check to see whether you found answers to the questions you wrote.

A young woman makes startling discoveries about apes!

Chimp Girl

WHEN YOU laugh at the antics of a chimpanzee in the zoo, do you ever have the uncomfortable feeling that the chimp is laughing at you, too? Well, he probably is, says a young woman scientist who has spent over three years in the East African jungle watching chimpanzees.

Twenty-nine-year-old Jane Goodall, an English scientist, thinks the chimps looked down on her as "an inferior creature—like a baboon."

Since 1960, Miss Goodall has been studying a community of primates in "chimpland," the 30 square miles of forested valleys and treeless ridges of Tanganyika's Gombe Stream Game Reserve. She worked under grants from the National Geographic Society. Her almost superhuman patience has allowed her to record for science many aspects of chimp behavior that were unknown.

Miss Goodall observed several chimpanzees sucking water from a natural water bowl in a tree trunk. When the apes had gotten as much as possible this way, they picked up crumpled leaves. They dipped the leaves in the remaining water and sucked the liquid from them.

Incredibly, Miss Goodall also saw chimps use leaves as napkins to wipe sticky hands after eating. One female who slipped in the mud cleaned off the soil with a handful of leaves.

In recent months, she has gathered new evidence of chimpanzees' close family ties. In the wild, a mature female has a baby roughly every two or three years. She suckles the youngster and keeps it with her in the nest at night until it is about three years old.

Three-year-olds may leave their mothers for short periods. Six-year-olds often leave the family circle for two or three days at a time.

"One of the first times that a young male left his family for a day we were lucky enough to see the reunion," Miss Goodall recalled. "His small sister put her arms around his neck, and he went up to kiss his mother—a little peck on her face."

Miss Goodall's most significant find to date was the discovery that chimps fashion and use crude implements—the beginnings of tool use. The apes devise simple tools from twigs to aid in fishing out termites, a chimpanzee delicacy, from their earthen nests.

Miss Goodall also found that chimps influence one another's behavior by vocal calls. She has identified twenty distinct sounds that they make in different situations.

When excited, chimps sometimes throw objects. Miss Goodall has observed male chimps picking up and hurling large stones with an underhand motion. Once, a male threw small stones overhand at a nearby baboon.

Miss Goodall was the first scientist to observe that chimpanzees eat small animals as well as their usual plant and insect diet.

Three or four chimps raided Miss Goodall's tent regularly. Their favorite loot was blankets, which they enjoyed sucking just as a small child sometimes does. At one time, her camp was down to its last two blankets.

They also stole eggs and young chickens. To top it all, one seized a handful of paper money and ran off chewing it. He didn't know this was the last of the "banana money" used to buy fruit for the apes.

Miss Goodall has found that chimps show as much individuality as man himself, and she gives them names to fit their personalities.

"David Greybeard" has an exceptionally calm disposition and an air of natural dignity. He is the only chimp that allows Miss Goodall to touch him. He greets her with a friendly "Hoo!"

Miss Goodall has been interested in animals since childhood, when she tried her mother's patience after official bedtime by taking worms to bed to watch them crawl. Her continued interest has been fortunate for the world of science, for her careful studies have led to significant discoveries about the behavior of chimpanzees.

What you should know about purpose-setting

A good reader reads with a purpose. He knows what he is looking for.

If reading is assigned, your purpose may be set for you by the teacher. You can also set your own purpose by thinking of questions to be answered as you read. To help you think up purpose-setting questions to guide your reading of a story or an article, use the headnote, the title, the illustrations, and the opening paragraph.

5

Do you find that you often have to

...prove you're someone worth knowing?

...live down mistakes?

...learn to see things in a different light?

...decide for yourself what others

once decided for you?

...protect your family as they have

protected you?

And because you are often alone,

do you sometimes feel lonely?

As you read this unit, perhaps

you will discover: "It's about ME!"

This time Jimmy was going to do things <u>his</u> way!

THE

NEST

by Robert Zacks

Reprinted by permission of the author. Slightly abridged and adapted.

JIMMY was fourteen. He was listening to his mother tell him, in her kindly, measured speech, why she didn't want him to go on the hike, and his clear gray eyes were clouded with sullen rebellion.

"All right, Mom," he said in the controlled voice he had learned from his parents. "If you say I can't go, then I can't, can I?"

Mrs. Swanson said gravely, "You make me sound like a dictator, Jimmy."

"Well, you are, kind of, aren't you?" said Jimmy coldly. "I have to do what you say."

His mother winced a little. She bit her lower lip and considered this.

"It isn't as simple as that," she said, pushing her mind with some difficulty toward coping with the point Jimmy had made. She smiled a little, however, in pleasure at such evidence of Jimmy's growing power to analyze a situation. "My decisions are made for your own good, Jimmy."

He misunderstood her smile. He thought she was relegating him to his position as a child. All his parents seemed to do these days was figure out how to hem him in. "Jimmy, you mustn't—"

The words, the restrictions, they wrapped around him like tentacles of an octopus, crushing in on his chest so he couldn't seem to breathe.

He was on his feet, yelling, the controlled, polite speech lost in his bursting anguish for freedom. "Everything is for my own good. Everything! But you aren't telling me the truth. You know why you don't want me to go on the hike? Because of Paul. You just don't like him."

He sucked in his breath, almost sobbing, shocked at himself and yet glad.

Mrs. Swanson had an unhappy look. The Swansons were a happy family; but these days a strange restlessness had come into it.

"No," she admitted. "I don't think Paul is good for you. I don't like your associating with him."

Jimmy said, all his heart and soul in his words, "I like Paul. He's my best friend."

"His father is a drunkard," said Mrs. Swanson quietly. "And Paul came out of reform school, didn't he? He stole from a candy store—"

"He's *nice!*" cried Jimmy, pain in his voice. "And he isn't a crook. He made a mistake. He told me what happened. He was showing off. And now nobody will be friends—"

"But he's formed a gang already, hasn't he? I've heard about it."

"It's just a club, that's all," said Jimmy. "And—and I'm a member. The club is running the hike."

"We won't discuss it further." Mrs. Swanson's voice was suddenly like steel. She stood up. She hesitated, pitying him, and tried to soften it with logic. "Remember, Jimmy, every time we've disagreed, it turned out I knew what I was talking about."

But he didn't listen further. Jimmy turned and blindly ran off the porch across the lawn toward the meeting place at Briggs' Drugstore.

After three blocks he slowed down, panting, his face set with fury. The habit of thinking, encouraged by his parents at every opportunity, began to function.

" 'I know what's best for you. I know what's best for you.' That's all I ever hear!" muttered Jimmy.

To his reluctant mind sprang memories. The time he insisted he could swim to the raft. Mr. Swanson had curtly said no, he couldn't risk it. Jimmy had raged, with his father quietly letting him run down. Then his father had told him to go ahead, but that he'd swim next to him.

Jimmy's throat strangled suddenly at the memory: the water was constricting his windpipe dreadfully, his eyes were bulging, his legs and arms numb with exhaustion from the too-long swim. And then the wonderful, strong, blessed arms of his father turning him on his back, pulling him back to shore—

It was confusing. Jimmy shook his head in bewilderment. Suddenly he felt uncertain, the rebellion drained out of him.

Paul was waiting for him at the drugstore with a stillness upon his face as he leaned against the glass front. He was about fourteen, with dark hair and bright dark eyes. He wore dungarees. Jimmy saw, when he came closer, traces of tears on Paul's cheeks.

"Well," said Paul fiercely, "let's go."

Jimmy stared. "Where's everybody?"

"They changed their minds," said Paul, hate in his voice.

The two boys looked at each other, and Jimmy understood. It made fury grow in him, it made him want to hit somebody. All those parents had stopped the gang from going with Paul because he was once in a reform school.

Paul said, his voice odd, "Maybe you can't go either?"

Jimmy looked deep into Paul's eyes. His heart beat fast with friendship and loyalty. "Don't be a jerk. Come on," he said cheerfully.

Paul's face changed. The hate seeped away, leaving sweetness and humbleness. He flung an arm over Jimmy's shoulder happily.

"Your—your mother doesn't care if you go, huh?" he said.

Jimmy swallowed. Paul needed this so badly. So very badly. Paul had no mother at all. And his father just didn't like looking at the world without Paul's mother, and was always drunk.

"Nah," said Jimmy. "She—she even said I should bring you to supper, afterwards. What shall I tell her, huh?"

Paul turned ashen, then flushed a deep scarlet. "Sure," he muttered. "Be glad to."

"I got to call her," said Jimmy numbly. "Just a minute."

Jimmy went into the drugstore and called his mother. He told her in a choking voice he was going on the hike, just he and Paul, and he didn't care how mad she got. "Nobody else came," he shouted into the telephone, "because all the mothers—" He was unable to go on for a moment. Then he finished, "I'm bringing him to supper afterwards, Mom. I said you asked him."

He hung up before she could answer.

They had a wonderful day. Wonderful. It was May, and the leaves on the trees were chartreuse and new. They went six miles out of town. They watched chipmunks skitter. They lay on their backs and stared at fleecy white clouds changing shape. Paul's face showed his contentment. His eyes were dreamy.

But Jimmy, in one cloud, saw the stern face of his mother.

But Mrs. Swanson's face, when she greeted Paul, wasn't stern at all. She looked uncertain as she studied his wistful, shy smile. Jimmy knew, of course, that his parents would wait until later to lecture him. They never made a scene before other people.

Throughout supper, Mr. Swanson

was very friendly to their guest. But Jimmy could see that at the same time his father was carefully studying Paul. And Paul, never knowing, thinking they'd wanted him, had invited him, glowed and showed the side of his personality that Jimmy liked.

After they'd washed the dishes (at Paul's suggestion), Mr. Swanson nodded to Paul. "Come on, Paul," he said. "I'll show you my tool shop."

As Paul eagerly followed him down the basement steps, Mrs. Swanson touched Jimmy's shoulder. Jimmy's heart thudded as he reluctantly lingered behind. He turned and glared in defiance.

"I don't care," he whispered. "Nobody else came. I couldn't—"

"Jimmy," she said softly, and bent and kissed him. "I'm proud of you, Jimmy. You did the right thing at the right time."

"But you said—" faltered Jimmy. "I mean—"

Her eyes were very bright. "I was wrong," she said steadily. "This time I was wrong. You were right. He's a nice boy, I think."

She turned away, patting his cheek as she did so.

At first, joy filled Jimmy. Joy and pride. *I'm the one who's right,* he thought, dazed. *My mother was wrong. Actually wrong. She admitted it.*

And then came a queer and frightening sense of loss, as well as of gain. It was like being alone, high up on a precipice where the footing was slippery with moss. Jimmy felt he had to be careful of each step. He had always been sure, even in his anger, of being able to depend on the wisdom of his father and mother. They'd always been right.

But not any more. Now they *might* be wrong. And Jimmy would have to decide. THE END

⟳ **Talking it over**

1. *a.* What are Mrs. Swanson's objections to Paul?

b. Which of these has Paul had no control over?

c. Jimmy defends Paul by saying, "He told me what happened. He was showing off." Why do you suppose Mrs. Swanson does not pay attention to this argument?

d. Mrs. Swanson's final words on the subject are: ". . . every time we've disagreed, it turned out I knew what I was talking about." Is she probably speaking the truth? Explain. How do her words tie in with the end of the story?

2. The other boys who were supposed to go on the hike were not at the meeting place when Jimmy arrived.

a. What was their excuse to Paul for not going on the hike?

b. What does Jimmy believe is the real reason the other boys are not going?

c. What does Jimmy do at this point? Why?

3. Which of the following inferences could be made from the story? Be ready to explain your answers.

a. Jimmy and his mother often have loud arguments.

b. Jimmy usually obeys his parents. *(cont.)*

c. Jimmy has decided to go on the hike before he arrives at the drug store.

d. Although Jimmy enjoys the hike, he is troubled by his decision to go.

e. Paul makes a good impression on Mr. Swanson.

f. Jimmy will never again listen to his parents' advice.

4. Reread the description of the way Jimmy reacts when his mother admits she was wrong and he was right (page 143). Describe Jimmy's feelings.

5. Why is "The Nest" a good title for this story?

⇌ **Words in action**

1. What is the same in the words *restrict* and *constrict?* What does this suggest to you about these two words?

2. Look up *constrict* and *restrict* in the Glossary. Which word would be the better synonym for *squeeze?*

3. The difference in the meanings of *constrict* and *restrict* is the difference between what a rubber band does and what a fence does. What does each of the following do, constrict or restrict: a noose, elastic cuffs, prison walls?

4. Restricting doesn't always involve using a fence or other physical means. What restricts your behavior at school, on the playground, at the movies?

5. Which word in parentheses is right for each sentence below?

a. The rules (constrict, restrict) the number of visitors.

b. The snake called a boa (con-strictor, restrictor) kills its victims by squeezing them to death.

c. The water was (constricting, restricting) his windpipe.

d. His mother's (constrictions, restrictions) seemed to keep him from having any fun.

He had to battle

Robert Zacks says, "I turned full-time writer after battling against five older brothers and a sister and my father and mother. They said I shouldn't even dream of such nonsense, and they forced me into the field of accounting, which I hated. Not only that, but a short-story instructor at college laughed in scorn when I told him that I wished to sell stories to a certain national magazine. He informed me that he had been a reader of manuscripts for that publishing firm and he knew they would never accept my writing.

"Well, the very first story I ever sold was to that magazine. And, strangely enough, it was about an accountant. So I guess the accounting wasn't wasted."

Robert Zacks has sold many stories since his first success. A number of them are about young people.

When dealing with adults,
remember two things:
1. Always use your head.   2. Never use your head.

THIRTEEN

by William Dodge

Part 1

THIRTEEN is one of the nicest ages I have ever been. I used to think that being young was nice, too. Now, when I look back on things, I know I would never want to be young again.

For instance, once when I was eleven, Mother took me to the movies. She ordered a half-price ticket for me, and

the woman at the ticket booth put up an argument. She said I was too tall to be eleven and should pay the full price. Mother said I was only a little boy and she wouldn't pay it. She called the manager. He looked up at me and agreed with the ticket lady. He shouldn't have done that. My mother is a woman of "many" words and she used them all. She wanted justice. The ticket lady wanted her money, the manager wanted peace, and I wanted to drop dead.

But this is all in the past. Now, at thirteen, I buy the tickets, and I don't try to get my mother in for half price, either.

There are a lot of things that never happen any more, now that I am thirteen. Nobody tells me what kind of haircut to get. I never hear, "Tell the barber this" or "Tell the barber that." My head now belongs to me. Crew cut or down over the ears, it's all mine.

At home these days, I am called Bill or Billy, never "Honey Boy" or "Little Man." Not even "Angel Child."

I spilled a big gob of cement on the rug last week, and Mother got really mad. I didn't get swatted or sent to my room. She just stamped her foot and raved about "sloppy men" and "impossible male creatures," just the same as she does with my father.

At thirteen a boy can walk down the street with a girl without everybody he knows making fun of him. Girls may not be as nice as regular people, but they're fun to be with, except those who talk real loud and try to look sophisticated. The ones who smile a lot and don't show off are really much nicer.

At thirteen, I can watch any TV show or read any book I please. Yes, I like being grown-up. In fact, I finally gave away my cowboy hat and my six-shooters.

Today I am a man!!!

Part 2

Being thirteen has certain problems that only another thirteen-year-old would understand. The biggest, I think, is learning how to get along well with adults. I have found that when dealing with grown-ups, it is wise to remember two things:

1. Always use your head.
2. Never use your head.

For instance, one day just before supper, my mother sent me to the store for a loaf of whole-wheat bread. They didn't have any whole-wheat. When I told my mother, she said, "Well, what kind did you get?" I told her I didn't get any. She looked at me as if I were some kind of imbecile. "For goodness sakes," she said, "if they didn't have whole-wheat, you should have got something else! Why don't you use your head?"

Not long after that, she sent me for some red oilcloth. The store didn't have any, so I bought seven yards of purple. I thought it was pretty. My mother didn't. She said, "Who ever heard of purple oilcloth in a red kitchen?" I told her I was only trying to use my head. But she said, "Well, don't! And in the future, if you can't get what I send you for, don't get anything!"

See what I mean?

There are other things that seem strange, too. If my father goes out for the evening, he tells me to "look after" my mother and sister. But if the family goes out, and I want to stay home, my father won't let me. He doesn't feel comfortable if I'm home alone. That means I am old enough to "look after" my mother and sister but not old enough to "look after" myself! Figure that out.

Another problem is what you should do when you trip over the cat and land with your head in the refrigerator, causing a large lump to appear above the right eyebrow.

In such a case, your father could feel free to explode with a few choice words.

Your sister could shed enough tears to dampen the whole room. Your mother could, and probably would, do both. But you? You are thirteen and can't do anything! You are too young to cuss, and "big boys" don't cry. So you just stand there looking more stupid than usual.

But in spite of all this, I still think thirteen is a wonderful age!

Part 3

Usually, my home is the most peaceful spot on earth. I am part of a very average family consisting of a sister, age fourteen, a father, age thirty-nine, and a mother, with brown hair.

We get along very well together and I would like nothing better than to keep it that way.

Occasionally, though, my peace of mind is completely shattered, and I feel like packing up my other shirt and moving to the wilds of Africa, or Siberia, or even Jersey City. The cause of my distress is a visit from my cousin, a five-year-old named Walter.

I hate to admit that I can become so upset by a mere child, but you must remember that Walter is no ordinary child. He is more like an army tank running amuck in the petunias.

Unfortunately, Walter visits often— sometimes for a whole week. Mother loves to have him. She thinks he's cute. I can't agree. What is "cute" about a kid in coonskin cap splashing around in a bathtub full of water and singing at the top of his lungs, "Daveeee, Davy Crockett"? And what is "cute" about a kid that just stares at you all the time? No matter what I do, he gazes at me with those great big cow eyes of his.

Yesterday was the absolute limit.

When I got to the breakfast table, Walter was already sitting there, slurping his oatmeal. I tried to eat, but he gazed at me so hard that I felt uncomfortable. I finally yelled for Mother and told her I couldn't stand the brat another minute. Walter looked up at me with a big, toothless grin—as though I had said something clever. I was just about to yell, "Get lost!" when my mother interrupted. "Can't you see he adores you?" she said. "Why, it's almost hero worship."

It was my turn to stare at *her*. I couldn't say a word! What was there to say?

I went upstairs and quite casually looked into my mirror. For the first time I noticed the lines of my strong, determined chin, and my high, masterful forehead. "Hero, huh?" I said to myself, and although I wasn't sure if a hero looked as stupid as I do at times, I *was* sure of one thing. It's really nice to have a child around the house. Especially an intelligent kid like Walter.

THE END

Talking it over

1. *a.* In Part 1, Bill, the person telling the story, discusses some advantages of being thirteen. Which of his examples remind you of experiences you have had?

b. What other advantages could you add to the examples mentioned in Part 1?

2. *a.* Summarize from the examples in Part 2 a major drawback of being thirteen.

b. According to Bill, who creates this problem?

c. Can you recall times when you had the same problem?

3. *a.* In Part 3, Bill discovers that his five-year-old cousin, Walter, looks upon him as a hero. What inference can you make about how this discovery affects Bill's opinion of himself?

b. In what way does it change his opinion of Walter?

Words in action

What does the narrator mean by *young* in the sentence "I used to think that being young was nice, too"?

Some people think that a man under fifty is too young to be President. What do these people mean by *young*?

Sometimes the meaning of a word depends on who is using it. Notice the expression in bold type in each sentence below. In one column on a piece of paper, write what this term means to the narrator in "Thirteen," and in another column write what you think the same words mean to people like your parents or teachers.

1. "Yes, I like being **grown-up**."
2. "Today I am a **man!!!**"
3. "I hate to admit I can become so upset by **a mere child . . . .**"
4. "Especially an **intelligent** kid like Walter."

"I wish it were all over," Larry's father thought.
"Even if he'd lost. . ."

Just Try To Forget

by Nathaniel Benchley

ARTHUR Dobson held open the door of the school gymnasium for his wife, then followed her in. The smell of steam heat and liniment and disinfectant was the same as it had been twenty years before, and he could hear the scurrying, pounding feet of basketball players, punctuated by the sharp *tweets* of the referee's whistle. It never changes, Dobson thought. Every smell

and every sound is still the same. He led his wife past the basketball court, then through another door and up a short flight of steps to the gallery above the swimming pool.

The room was of white tile and glass brick, and it was steaming hot and echoed hollowly with a noise of its own. Dobson and his wife sat down behind a railing overlooking the pool, and Dobson took off his topcoat and put it on the seat beside him.

"I'm getting nervous already," his

wife said. "Do you think they have a chance?"

"All I know is what Larry said," Dobson replied. "He didn't seem to think so."

"I don't really care, so long as Larry wins his race," she said. "I think he'd die if he didn't win it, with you here, and all."

"*He* can't win it or not win it," said Dobson. "He's in the two-hundred-yard relay, so there are three others with him."

"I know, but still . . ." His wife took off her coat, and peered down at the green, transparent water of the pool. "It looks awfully long, doesn't it?" she said.

Dobson looked at the pool, and estimated that he could swim about one length—maybe two, if he took it easy. "Long enough," he said.

Two lanky, muscular figures wearing the bright-blue trunks of the rival school walked out of a door at one end of the pool and dived flatly into the water, hitting it with a double crack, like pistol shots. Then more boys in blue trunks came out and followed them, until the whole squad was swimming up and down the length of the pool. At the diving board, two boys took turns doing unbelievably complicated dives, and Dobson and his wife watched them with a kind of uneasy respect.

"It looks as though Larry were right," Dobson said after a while. "They look pretty good."

"I know," said his wife. "Much too good."

Then Larry's team, wearing red trunks, appeared and dived into the water and swam up and down the pool. At first, Dobson had trouble recognizing his son among the twisting, thrash-ing bodies. The boys all swam alike, with long, powerful strokes, and they made insane-looking, bottoms-up turns at either end of the pool.

Dobson thought back on the summer, many years ago, when he had had some difficulty teaching Larry to swim. As long as Dobson held him, he would splash and paddle gleefully, but the minute Dobson took his hands away he would become panic-stricken and sink. It wasn't until children younger than he had begun to swim that Larry, without any help from his father, took his first strokes.

He's certainly improved since then, Dobson thought. I had no idea he could swim this well. Even last summer, he wasn't swimming like this. Then Dobson looked at the others, in the blue trunks, and they seemed to be swimming just a little better. I guess it always looks that way, he thought. The other guys always look frighteningly good, even if they aren't. But this time they *are* better—there's no getting around it.

When the warm-up was over, the two teams retired, and the officials began arranging their lists and checking their watches. It was the final meet of the season, the letter meet,[1] and the gallery was full of spectators, both students and adults. From below came the sounds of more spectators, who were standing or sitting along the edge of the pool beneath the gallery, and the whole place hummed and echoed and rang with noise.

Dobson removed his jacket, put it next to his topcoat, and loosened his tie. He fought down an urge to light a

---

[1] **letter meet,** last contest of the season. A boy taking part is awarded an athletic letter whether or not he has been in any other event all season.

cigarette, and locked his hands together in his lap. His wife reached across and clutched them briefly, and her hand was cold and wet. He smiled at her. "It's no good worrying now," he said. "Larry's race isn't until the very last."

There was a patter of applause as the rival team, wearing blue sweat suits, filed out and took places on benches set in three rows at the shallow end of the pool. A moment later, the air was shattered with cheers and whistles as Larry's team, in red sweat suits, came out and sat beside them. Presently, two boys from each team peeled off their sweat suits and dived into the pool, then pulled themselves out, shook hands all around, and waited, nervously flapping their arms and wrists. Dobson looked at his son, who was sitting on the back row of benches, staring straight ahead of him and chewing a thumbnail. I wish I hadn't come, Dobson thought. I wish I'd made up some excuse to stay at home. He remembered a time when he was young and his father had come to watch him play football, and he had spent the entire miserable game on the bench. Parents should stay away from athletic contests, he told himself. They ought to be barred by law. Larry continued to chew his thumbnail, and Dobson felt sick.

A manager with a megaphone announced the first event, which was the fifty-yard free-style race, and gave the names of the contestants. The starter pointed a blank pistol upward and told the boys to take their marks. There was complete silence as they stood in a row at the edge of the pool, gripping the rim with their toes. The starter said, "Get set," and the boys crouched, their hands on a level with their feet. There

was a pause. The pistol banged, and after what seemed to Dobson like an unnaturally long wait the boys shot forward, cracked into the water, and churned off down the pool.

The crowd shouted and called and cheered and chanted, and the noise swelled to a roar as the swimmers reached the far end of the pool, made their frantic, ducking turns, and headed back for the finish line. They were almost indistinguishable in the boiling spray, but the two in the farthest lane, the ones in the blue trunks, pulled steadily ahead in the final yards, and finished first and second. Dobson settled back in his seat.

"That makes the score eight to one already," he said to his wife. "This is going to be murder."

But Larry's team placed first and third in the next event, and first and second in the one after that; and somehow, unbelievably, they managed to gain a slight lead. It was never a big enough lead to be safe, and at one point the score was tied, and Dobson saw and pitied the agony of the one boy in each event who failed to score. Some drooped forlornly in the gutter, some cried, and some had to be helped from the pool by consoling teammates, who said futile things to them and patted them on the bottom while they dragged themselves to the benches. As the final event came closer, Dobson looked more often at his son, and it seemed to him that Larry was getting smaller and paler with each race. I wish he'd swum first, Dobson thought. I wish it were all over, so he wouldn't have to wait like this. Even if he'd lost, I wish it were all over.

The diving took a long time, with each of the four contestants doing six dives, and the next-to-last event was the medley relay race, which Larry's team won, putting them ahead, 37-30. When the score was announced, Dobson's wife gave a little shout and grabbed him. "We've won!" she cried. "They can't possibly catch us now!"

"It looks that way," Dobson replied with a certain amount of relief. "It certainly looks that way."

A student behind him touched his arm. "No, sir," he said. "They can still tie us. The last race counts seven points, and there's no score for second."

"Oh!" said Dobson.

He saw Larry and his three teammates strip off their sweat suits, jump into the water, then climb out, shake hands, and stand around fluttering their hands and breathing deeply. The boys from the other school did the same, and they looked big and unnaturally husky. They didn't seem as nervous as the boys on Larry's team.

The noise from the crowd was such that the manager had to, shout three times for quiet before he could announce the event, and when Larry was announced as swimming third in the relay, Dobson had an odd feeling at the sound of the name. His wife slid her hand into his. "I don't think I'm going to be able to watch," she said. "You tell me what happens."

The first two swimmers took their marks, and a tense silence hung until the crack of the gun. Then, as the swimmers leaped out at the water, the spectators came to their feet and shouted and cheered and stamped, and the noise grew and swelled until Dobson couldn't hear his own voice.

The swimmers thrashed down the pool and then back, and the one in red trunks was slightly ahead as they touched the starting line and two more swimmers sprang out. Dobson didn't watch the second boys; all he saw was Larry, who had moved up to the starting line, breathing in deep gulps, his eyes fixed glassily ahead of him. An official squatted beside Larry's feet, and Larry crouched lower and lower as his teammate in the pool approached him. The red-trunked boy was leading by about two yards when he reached the edge, and it seemed to Dobson that Larry was in the air and in the water at almost the same instant. Then Dobson's throat closed and he couldn't make a sound, but beside him his wife was screaming and pounding the rail, her voice all but lost in the growing pandemonium.

Larry finished his lap three or four yards ahead, but as the last two swimmers raced down and turned, the one in blue trunks began to gain. He closed the gap slowly, and the members of both teams crowded around the finish line, jumping and beckoning and bellowing, and then the red-trunked boy put on a final, frenzied spurt and held his lead to the finish line. Larry and his teammates spilled into the water, hugging one another and falling down and shouting, and the blue-trunked boy clung to the gutter, exhausted and miserable.

Dobson sat back and looked at his wife. "Wow!" he said. And she laughed.

Down below, members of both teams clustered around the officials, and then, suddenly, the ones in blue leaped into the air and shouted, and Dobson saw a boy in red trunks hit the water with his fist. There was some commotion, and a lot of noise from the crowd, and Dobson was unable to hear distinctly what the manager said through the

megaphone, but he caught the words "Thirty-seven to thirty-seven."

Unbelieving, he turned to a student in the crowd. "What happened?" Dobson asked. "I couldn't hear."

"We were disqualified," the student answered sourly. "Dobson jumped the gun."

For almost a full minute, neither Dobson nor his wife said anything. Then he put on his coat and helped her on with hers, and as they walked slowly down the stairs she took his arm. "What are we going to say to him?" she asked in a small voice. "What *can* we say?"

"I wish I knew," he replied. "I wish I knew."

They went out to the car, and stood beside it while they waited for Larry. Dobson's mind was a jumble of things he wanted to say, but even as he thought of them they seemed inadequate, and he knew that none of them would do any good. He thought of going in and seeing Larry in the locker room, and then quickly decided against it. I guess it's best to wait out here, he thought. He'll come out when he wants to.

After what seemed like an hour, Larry came out of the gym and walked slowly toward them. His hair was wet and slicked back, and his eyes were red —possibly from the chlorine in the pool, Dobson thought, knowing that wasn't the reason. Without a word, Larry opened a door of the car and dropped into the back seat. Dobson got in front, and, after a moment's hesitation, his wife got in back with Larry.

"Do you want to drive around for a while?" Dobson asked as he started the engine.

"Whatever you say," Larry replied. "I don't care."

They drove through the streets of the town and then out into the bleak, snow-spotted country. For several minutes nobody spoke, and then Dobson cleared his throat. "Would you like me to tell you something?" he asked.

"Sure," said Larry, without enthusiasm.

"When I was in school, I wanted to play baseball," Dobson said. "More than anything else, I wanted to make the baseball team. The only trouble was I wasn't good enough. I got in a couple of games as a pinch-hitter, and once they let me play right field, but I dropped the only fly that came my way, and they yanked me out." He looked into the rear-view mirror and saw the incredulous expression on his wife's face. He continued, "The last game in my senior year—the letter game—we were behind four to three in the ninth inning. We had a man on third, and the coach sent me in to bunt down toward first. On the first ball pitched, I tried to bunt, and the ball hit my thumb and broke it. Technically, I was eligible for a letter, but I never collected it. I couldn't look at any of the team again."

Larry laughed shortly. "I never heard about that," he said.

"I didn't tell many people," Dobson replied, with another look into the rear-view mirror. "But what I'm getting at is that these things are horrible when they happen—you think you'll never live them down—but sooner or later it gets so you can bear to think of them again. It may take a long while, but eventually it happens."

Larry was quiet for a minute. "I guess I was just trying too hard," he said, at last.　　　　　THE END

↻　**Talking it over**

1. *a.* What does Arthur Dobson remember from his own school days as he waits for the first race to begin?

　b. What is Larry probably thinking as he chews his thumbnail?

　c. How does Arthur Dobson feel about parents attending contests in which their children compete?

　d. If you were in a contest of some kind, would you want your parents to be present? Explain.

2. *a.* What are Mr. Dobson's feelings toward the boys who lose the earlier races?

　b. How do their teammates treat the losers?

　c. How do Larry's teammates probably act toward him after the meet? Why?

　d. How does Larry probably feel as he gets ready to meet his parents?

3. *a.* Why would some fathers become angry at the officials who ruled against a son of theirs?

b. Why would some other fathers become angry with their sons?

c. From Arthur Dobson's reactions, what inferences can you make about the kind of man he is?

4. *a.* How do you know that Mrs. Dobson has never heard the story of why her husband did not collect the baseball letter he had earned?

b. Why is he telling the story now?

Words in action

A person might know the meaning of the words *jump* and *gun* and still not know what the boy in the story means when he says, "Dobson jumped the gun." What does this expression mean? Was a gun actually involved at this point?

The word *jump* appears in several such phrases. What is the meaning of the expression in bold type in each sentence below? If you aren't sure, look in a dictionary under *jump.*

1. The criminal **jumped bail.**
2. The hobo **jumped a train.**
3. The train **jumped the track.**
4. The prospector **jumped a claim.**
5. The convict **jumped at the chance** for parole.

It really happened

" 'Just Try to Forget' was nothing but straight reporting," Nathaniel Benchley recalls, "except that it didn't happen to our son. He was on the swimming team at his school, and we saw the incident happen as described, and later thought how horrible it must have been to be the parents of the boy who jumped the gun. So the story is true up to the end of the meet, and is guesswork from there."

Regarding parents watching their own children in competition, Mr. Benchley says, "The strain is too great for aging hearts. When our son's turn came to race that night, I couldn't watch; I went out and walked around the gym."

Mr. Benchley formerly worked as a reporter on a big New York newspaper and on *Newsweek* magazine. He is now a free-lance writer.

Achilles Deatheridge

by Edgar Lee Masters

"Your name is Achilles Deatheridge?
How old are you, my boy?"
"I'm sixteen past, and I went to the war
From Athens, Illinois."

5 "Achilles Deatheridge, you have done
A deed of dreadful note."
"It comes of his wearing a battered hat,
And a rusty, wrinkled coat."

"Why, didn't you know how plain he is?
10 And didn't you ever hear
That he goes through the lines by day or night
Like a sooty cannoneer?

"You must have been half dead for sleep,
For the dawn was growing bright."
15 "Well, Captain, I had stood right there
Since six o'clock last night.

From *The Great Valley* by Edgar Lee Masters. Published by The Macmillan Company 1916, 1944. Reprinted by permission of Ellen C. Masters.

"I cocked my gun at the swish of the grass,
And how am I at fault
When a dangerous looking man won't stop
20 When a sentry hollers halt?

"I cried out halt, and he only smiled
And waved his hand like that.
Why, any Johnnie could wear the coat
And any fellow the hat.

25 "I hollered halt again, and he stopped
And lighted a fresh cigar.
I never noticed his shoulder badge,
And I never noticed a star."

"So you arrested him? Well, Achilles,
30 When you hear the swish of the grass,
If it's General Grant inspecting the lines,
Hereafter let him pass."

Talking it over

1. What clues to time and place do you find in the poem?

2. *a.* Who is Achilles Deatheridge?
   b. To whom is he talking?

3. *a.* What "deed of dreadful note" is Achilles guilty of?
   b. Was Achilles a good soldier?

A lawyer who wrote poems

Edgar Lee Masters was born shortly after the Civil War and lived until after World War II. He was a successful Chicago lawyer who began writing poetry for his own pleasure. He is most famous for a book of poems called *Spoon River Anthology.*

Fear grabbed Jamie —
but he couldn't go back.
The dizzy heights of the tower
urged him to keep climbing.

The Way Up

by William Hoffman

SITTING in the back row of English literature class, Jamie looked through an open window toward a rounded silver water tower which poked up through the woods like a great metal tulip. The tower had recently been painted and appeared immaculate in the spring sunlight. Tubular steel legs were hidden at the bottom by newly greening oaks, sycamores, and poplars that bordered the rear grounds of the suburban Richmond High School.

Jamie had made no brag. He had not even spoken the evening he was at Jawbone's house, loafing in the basement playroom with the others.

"Look at Jamie's," Jawbone said. Jawbone was a dark, wiry boy of eighteen who had a jutting chin. He wanted to go to West Point. He stuck a finger on Jamie's picture in the new yearbook. Under the names of the others were accomplishments—teams, organizations, trophies.

"Not even the Glee Club," Nick said, lying on a sofa, his legs hanging over

the arm rest at one end. He was a blond Italian whose father owned a fancy restaurant downtown.

"They'll never know you been here," Alf said. Alf, the top student, was a heavyset, shaggy boy who'd won his letter in baseball.

More sensitive than the rest, he was immediately sorry. He reached across a chair to punch Jamie's arm. Jamie dodged and smiled, though smiling was like cracking rock.

They meant the remarks goodnaturedly. Still, the words made him see what his relationship to them was. He had gone through four years of high school without leaving a mark. He had ridden with them daily, shared their secrets, and eaten in their homes. They considered him a friend. But they expected nothing from him.

At first he was resentful and hurt, as if betrayed. Next he had fantasies of heroic derring-do on the basketball court or baseball diamond—because of his smallness he didn't dream of football glory any longer. After the fantasies, he tried to think of projects. Finally he came up with a plan.

He had spent a lot of time working out details. He was now merely waiting for the right day—or rather night. Recently there had been rain and blustering weather. Even when the sun shone, the wind gusted. This afternoon, however, as he sat in English literature class, Jamie saw that the treetops barely quivered.

His eyes kept returning to the silver water tower. Other students had attempted the climb. A few inventive ones had gone up as far as the catwalk around the fat belly of the tank, where they had painted skulls and crossbones. A sophomore had lost his nerve halfway and got stuck. The Richmond rescue squad had coaxed him down like a kitten from a light pole. The boy had been so ashamed he had tried to join the Army. Nobody had ever made it to the stubby spike on the crown.

Mr. Tharpe, the principal, understood the tower's temptation and had ordered the ladder above the catwalk taken off. He had also directed that the ladder up the leg be cut high above the ground. Lastly, he had made climbing the tower punishable by expulsion.

The toughest problem was getting from the catwalk to the crown. As the tank served only the school, it wasn't large, but without a ladder the rounded sides appeared unscalable. Jamie concluded that he needed a light hook which could be thrown fifteen to twenty feet.

He found what he wanted in a Richmond boating store—a small, three-pronged, aluminum anchor. Along with the anchor he bought fifty feet of braided nylon line that had a thousand-pound test strength. He also purchased a hacksaw. The clerk packed the things in a strong cardboard box, and as soon as Jamie reached home he hid them in the back of his closet.

He assembled other equipment as well—tennis shoes, a pair of light cotton gloves, a sweat suit which would keep him warm in the night air yet allow him to move freely, a billed cap, a small flashlight with a holding ring, and a sheath knife to fasten to his leather belt.

Twice he scheduled attempts on the tower. The first night a thunderstorm washed him out. The second, the moon was too bright, increasing the risk that he would be seen.

Delay made him uneasy. He felt that if he didn't go soon, he might lose his nerve.

The bell rang. He went to his locker and then left the building quickly. He wanted to get away without the others seeing him, but Alf called his name. Alf ran down the sidewalk. He adjusted his glasses.

"Want to shoot baskets?" he asked, making an imaginary hook shot. He held up two fingers to indicate a score.

"No, thanks," Jamie answered, moving on.

"You're getting pretty exclusive lately," Alf said.

"I've always been exclusive," Jamie told him, hoping it sounded like a joke.

He spent the afternoon working around the house. He cut the grass and spread some of the lawn fertilizer his father had stored in the garage. When he had a chance, he went up to his room and again checked his equipment. The check was just nervousness. He knew his equipment was right.

After dinner, as he was sure they would, his parents went next door to play cards. He and his brother David were left in the house. David was a year younger, although already heavier than Jamie. He had been asked to come out for football and liked to flex his muscles before a mirror.

Jamie sat at his desk and pretended to study so he wouldn't be questioned. He listened to sounds of the night coming through the open window. There was some wind, but not enough to worry him. The sky was cloudy.

When David went down to the kitchen for a sandwich, Jamie undressed, put on the sweat suit, and pulled pajamas over it. He kept his socks on. He slipped his belt through slots in the leather sheath of the knife and buckled it around his waist. Hearing David approach, Jamie got into bed.

"You sick?" David asked, surprised.

"Just sleepy."

"You look kind of queasy."

"I'm okay."

David watched TV and did his exercises before coming to bed. Jamie listened, as he had for weeks, to the pattern of his brother's breathing. In practice, Jamie had got up several times and moved around the dark room. Once David had waked. Jamie had explained he was after another blanket.

David breathed softly. When he was completely asleep, his mouth opened and he wheezed slightly. Jamie heard the wheezing now. Still he did not move, although he wanted badly to start. He lay on his back, eyes open, waiting for his parents.

They returned at eleven. He heard them in the kitchen. Finally his mother came to his and David's room. Jamie smelled her perfume. She bent over them, lightly adjusting the covers. He kept his eyes shut until she went out.

As soon as she was gone, he swung his legs out of bed. He stood, listening, but David's breathing did not change. Jamie walked to the closet, slipped off his pajamas, and sat on the floor to pull on his tennis shoes. He tied the laces in double knots.

He put on his baseball cap and fastened the large, red bandanna around his neck. The bandanna, too, was part of his plan. He had bought it in a Richmond ten-cent store. For some time he had been carrying it to school and whipping it out to be seen by Jawbone, Nick, and Alf. Though no name was on it, people would identify it as his— the right people, anyway.

Lastly he worked his fingers into the cotton gloves, gathered the hacksaw and aluminum anchor, and tiptoed to the window. It was already half raised. Earlier in the week he'd rubbed soap along the metal tracks to prevent squeaking.

The window slid up noiselessly. He unsnapped the screen and lifted it out. David turned in his bed but did not wake. Jamie climbed onto the window ledge, lowered his equipment to the ground, and stepped down to the grass of the back yard. He stood still and listened. David did not stir. Jamie replaced the screen without hooking it and picked up his equipment.

Crouching, he ran—not fast enough to wear himself out, but with the easy lope of a distance runner. He carried the anchor in his right hand, the saw in his left. The damp grass of neighboring yards brushed his feet softly. He stayed in the shadows.

On reaching the high school, he cut behind the main building and headed toward the athletic field. When he was almost to the other side, a dog snarled close behind him. He was afraid that if he continued running, the dog might jump him. He turned and ducked behind a pile of canvas tackling-dummies.

The dog leaped out of the dark, its hair bristling, its teeth bared. Jamie talked softly, holding his hands at his sides so as not to excite the boxer. The animal circled, sniffed, and growled.

"King!" a voice from the field house called. It was Carver, the watchman—an erect, dark figure outlined against a door. "Here, boy!"

The dog sprang off toward the field house. Jamie pressed against the ground. Carver leaned over to pat the boxer.

"What's out there?" he asked, turning on his long flashlight. The light brushed across the dummies. Jamie held his breath. Carver talked to the dog. Finally the flashlight went out, and Carver entered the field house. The door slammed.

Jamie pushed up and sprinted. He wanted to be well away in case the boxer was still loose. His arms pumped. By the time he reached the woods, he was winded. There was no use even starting up the tower unless he was fresh. He rested against a tree.

When his breath steadied, he walked on through the woods. He didn't need his flashlight. Clouds had slid away from a sickle moon, which laid a pale sheen on his path. He stopped once to be certain nobody was following.

He walked out of the woods to the tower and under it. Though the tank wasn't large, it was high and seemed to float like a balloon. The silver skin shone eerily. The steel legs were like those of a giant insect poised over him. He touched the steel and kicked a cement footing to rid himself of the sensation. The tank was simply a water tower which could be climbed.

He didn't hurry. Hurrying might tire him. Methodically he unwound the line from the anchor. He looped the saw onto his belt. He adjusted his cap. Standing away from a leg of the tower, he swung the anchor around his head like a lasso and let fly at the ladder.

The hooks missed by inches. The light anchor clanged against tubular steel, which reverberated like a gong. The sound was loud—loud enough, perhaps, to alert the watchman or the family who lived in a board-and-batten house nearby. Quickly Jamie picked up the anchor, swung it, and threw. A prong clattered over a rung.

He had practiced rope climbing. Two or three afternoons a week he had pulled himself to the I-beam at the top of the gym where ropes were attached to swivels. He had learned to go up without using his legs. Basketball players had stood around to watch, impressed that anybody so slight could climb so well.

"You're turning into a regular Atlas," Nick had said.

Jamie had already tied knots every five feet along the nylon line in order to have a better grip on it. He fingered the line and pulled. As he looked up, he felt doubt. The line was thin, the tower great. He jumped before he had time to think further.

Climbing made him feel better. He reached the bottom of the ladder and easily drew himself onto it. He stopped to loosen the anchor. He wrapped the line around the anchor's shank and hooked it over his left shoulder.

He stepped up slowly. He was attempting to pace himself for the distance. He looked neither up nor down. Doing so might cause dizziness. He narrowed his eyes and tried to see no more than his own gloved hands closing over rungs.

After what seemed a long while, he glanced up to get his bearings on the catwalk. He was disappointed at how far it was above him. He estimated that he had come only a quarter of the way. His excitement was giving him a false sense of time.

He kept on. When he again looked up, he had climbed not quite halfway. His breathing was noisy, and he rested. As he clung to the ladder, he thought how easy it would be to go back now. Nobody knew he was here. He could go down and slip into his bed without ever being missed.

He was angry at himself for considering it. His trouble was thinking too much. To block the thoughts, he stepped up, determined to reach the catwalk without stopping again.

He climbed until his arms and legs ached. He sucked at air. He did not raise his eyes lest the distance to the catwalk discourage him. Occasionally a light wind gusted against his face and chest—not hard enough to worry him, but sufficient to slow his step.

His head banged steel. The blow frightened and pained him and he clutched at the ladder. The catwalk door was right over him, its heavy padlock swinging from his having hit it.

He put his right leg through the ladder and hooked the foot over a rung to keep from falling in case he lost his balance. He unbuckled his belt to get the hacksaw. Because of the awkwardness of his position, he had to work slowly. His left hand held the lock, his right the saw.

Cutting was more difficult than he'd anticipated. He had to rest and wipe sweat from his face. When the metal finally snapped, he flung the saw from him. It was a long time hitting the ground.

He threw the padlock down, too, glad he had on gloves in case an investigation checked fingerprints. He raised a hand to the trap door and pushed. The thick iron squeaked but gave only a little. He stepped up another rung in order to hunch his shoulders and the back of his head against it. The door rose, teetered, and fell to the catwalk with a loud clang.

He climbed the rest of the way up the ladder, swung off it to the catwalk, and, holding the railing, closed the trap door. As he straightened to look out over the dark land, he had his first real sense of how high he was. Instinctively, he pressed against the tank. He edged around the catwalk until he faced the school. Lights from houses were faint and twinkling, and he saw the skyline milkiness of Richmond itself.

He grinned, thinking of Alf, Nick, and Jawbone. They wouldn't believe it! They were lying down there, warm in their bunks. He waved a hand over them.

He turned to the tank. He was still a good fifteen feet from the top. As he calculated the distance, a cloud passing over gave him a feeling that the tower was falling. Space shifted under him. He grabbed at the tank.

Leaning against it, he considered tying his bandanna to the railing on the school side. In the morning everybody would see it. Going up this far was certainly a victory, and people would be impressed.

He took off the bandanna and hesitated, fingering it. For tying the bandanna to the railing he might be temporarily honored, but if he was the first to reach the top, he would be remembered for years.

He retied the bandanna around his neck and unwound the nylon line from the anchor. In order to throw to the top of the tank from the proper angle, he had to lean out and flap his arm upward. He forced his thigh hard against the railing. Holding the anchor from him, he threw.

The anchor thumped on top of the rounded tower but slid back when he pulled the line. He jumped to keep from being hit. He stumbled and almost fell. Fear surged in him.

He rested against the tank. When he was calmer, he again threw the anchor. He made half a dozen tries, but each time it came sliding back. He didn't have quite the angle he needed to get the anchor to the crown where the spike was. There was simply no way to do it. He had to tie the bandanna to the railing and climb down.

Another idea nagged him. He shook his head as if he'd been asked. He didn't want to step up onto the railing. He'd be crazy to do it. He could, of course, use part of his line to tie himself. Thus if he slipped, he wouldn't fall far.

He wrapped the nylon line twice around his waist. He knotted the middle section to one of the upright supports of the railing.

Cautiously, like a performer mounting the high wire, he stepped up onto the pipe railing. He rested a hand against the tank so that any fall would be toward the catwalk. His left foot dangled. Though his body wished to bend, he straightened it. He was sweating, and the anchor was wet in his grip. He blinked to clear his eyes, being careful not to turn his head toward where he might look down.

He hefted the anchor, and with a gentle, looping motion arched it over himself. The anchor slid back and struck him in the side of the face. Standing on the railing, he was unable to dodge. His head throbbed and ached. He touched his cheek, and his hand came away bloody.

He pulled the anchor up from the catwalk. This time he didn't throw it directly over him. When he tugged on the line, the anchor came down. He felt weak and sick.

He balanced the anchor, tossed it, and jerked the line. The anchor did not come back. He jumped to the catwalk and pulled. The anchor held.

He couldn't be certain it was caught on the spike. Perhaps a hook tip was in a seam or had snagged a bolt. He hung all his weight on the line, drawing up his feet to do so. Next he untied the line from the railing support. He dried his hands on his sweat suit and wiped his mouth.

With a great effort, he pulled himself up. When he reached the rounded curve of the roof, he worked his hands under the line that his weight stretched tight. Nausea pumped through him as he bruised his knuckles on the steel. Grunting, he made a final thrust of his body and lay flat against the slope.

His heart beat hard. He sweated, yet felt cold in the gusting wind. He raised his head to look at the top of the tower. Two prongs of the anchor had caught the spike.

He crawled up. Because of the slope and his tennis shoes, he could have done it without a line. He lay on his side as he took off the bandanna. He tied the bandanna high on the spike. He tested to make certain the bandanna would not blow loose.

To go down, he merely let his body slide against the steel. He braked himself by gripping the line. His feet jarred against the catwalk. He hated leaving his anchor, but he knew of no way to pull it free. With his knife, he cut the line as high as he could reach. He wound what was left of it around his body and opened the trap door.

As he put a foot on the ladder, a gust of wind caught his cap and blew it off. He snatched for the cap but missed. It fluttered dizzily down and down and down. He couldn't stop looking. The cap seemed to fall forever. He felt the pull of space. He'd tumble the same way if he slipped. He began to shake. He was too weak to climb down that great distance. He backed off.

Fear ballooned in him, and he shook harder. He couldn't stop thinking of the boy who'd gotten stalled halfway up and needed the Richmond rescue squad. The terrible disgrace of it—the sirens, the people gathered around, and the spotlight swinging up. The police would call his parents.

Yet he was unable to force himself to the ladder. The grip was gone from his fingers, and his body was limp. He might climb down a few steps and not be able to hold. He had the sensation of falling, like the cap, of cartwheeling end-over-end to the ground. He lay flat on the catwalk, his face against steel strips. He was shaking so badly that his temple knocked against the metal.

He gave himself up to fear. As if his mouth had a life of its own, yells came out. He couldn't stop the sounds. He shouted for help. He screamed and begged in a rush of terror.

The wind carried his voice away. Even if he was missed at home and searched for, nobody would think of looking on the tower. He'd have to lie on the catwalk all night. . . . No, he couldn't! With his flashlight he signaled toward the school. There was no response from the watchman. Jamie kept yelling until his voice became faint and hoarse. He wept.

The fright in him was gradually replaced by exhaustion. He lay panting. He felt the heat of shame. He thought of Alf, Nick, and Jawbone seeing him like this. He thought of his parents. Like a person gone blind, he groped for the trap door.

This time he didn't allow himself to look down. Instead he rolled his eyes upward. His fingers measured the position of the hole, and he lowered a trembling foot to a rung. As if decrepit, he shifted his weight onto the ladder.

He went down a step. He was holding the rungs too tightly, and his sweating hands made the steel slippery. He felt the pull of space behind him. His breathing was rapid and shallow. He moved the way a small child would, using the same foot first on each rung.

He closed his eyes. His body functioned with no direction from him. He was a passenger cowering inside.

He rested, hanging his armpits over the ladder and leaning his forehead against the steel. For an instant he was drunkenly comfortable. He wobbled on the ladder, almost letting go. He caught himself and cried out.

Again he started down. In the endlessness of his descent, he didn't believe he would ever get to the bottom. His hands would fail, and he would drop off. He imagined his body curving to the ground.

He stopped on the ladder, not understanding. The fact that his foot swung under him and found no support meant nothing. He believed his tiredness had tricked him. A second time he put out the foot. Like one coming from a cave into sunlight, he opened his eyes and squinted. He saw the dark shapes of trees. He was at the base of the ladder. Lying under the tower was his cap.

Wearily, even calmly now, he untied the line from his waist and knotted it to the bottom rung. He wrapped the line around his wrists. He slid down, but he was too weak to brake himself effectively. The line burned his skin. When he hit the ground, he fell backwards. He lay looking at the silver tower shining above him.

Using one of the tubular steel legs for support, he pulled himself up, staggered, and stooped for his cap. He turned to get his bearings before stumbling into a jogging run. At the trees he wove to a stop and again looked at the tower. He shuddered.

He breathed deeply. Straightening, he entered the dark woods with the step of a man who wouldn't be hurried and walked back toward the house.

THE END

Talking it over

1. What does Jamie hope to accomplish by climbing the water tower?

2. *a.* What possible problems does he foresee in connection with climbing the tower? How does he plan to meet each one?

b. What inference about Jamie can you make from the author's description of these careful preparations?

3. *a.* Several times before he reaches the top of the tank Jamie almost gives up and turns back. Why? Could he have prepared himself ahead of time to deal with this problem?

b. What makes him nevertheless keep climbing?

c. What scares Jamie after he has reached the top and is on his way down? Why does he feel the greatest terror at this point, when he has already accomplished what he set out to do?

4. Explain whether in your opinion Jamie's climb will earn him the admiration of his friends.

5. The title "The Way Up" could refer to several different things in the story. Explain as many different meanings of the title as you can.

⇄ Words in action

1. Which of the following words from "The Way Up" are compound words? Before answering, you may want to review Lesson Two in the section on Word Attack/Structure (pages 82-83).

smallness	downtown	nausea
sunlight	cowering	playroom
Jawbone	yearbook	basketball

2. In which of the following words is *cat* a root word?

catalog	catty	cattle
catcall	catfish	catchup
	catwalk	

Advice to Travelers

by Walker Gibson

A burro once, sent by express,
His shipping ticket on his bridle,
Ate up his name and his address,
And in some warehouse, standing idle,
He waited till he like to died.
The moral hardly needs the showing:
Don't keep things locked up deep inside—
Say who you are and where you're going.

 **Talking it over**

1. *a.* What did the burro have locked up deep inside?

    b. How did this come about?

2. Who are the travelers referred to in the title?

3. Put the advice into your own words.

From *The Saturday Review* (May 5, 1956). Reprinted by permission of Hastings House, Publishers, Inc.

*At a difficult time in Randy's life,
his best friend was an*

orphan pup

by Mitchell F. Jayne

THEY killed a wolf the other day down where I used to live. I read the item in the county weekly that the folks send. I thought immediately of Lonesome.

I know that it couldn't be Lonesome, though, because I've been in the wildlife department here for three years, and it's been seven years since I last saw him. Wild things just don't live that long.

The paper said that the wolf was big, but thin, and it had made the mistake of raiding a poultry yard in its desperation. I imagine it was raising cubs somewhere in Troublesome Hollow, because the wolves in that part of the country are never seen unless there is a drought or a bad winter or something else that prevents them from getting their natural food.

It set me to remembering the warm spring day I found Lonesome.

I came upon him in the woods on the way home from school. I was sixteen then, and I guess I had trudged back and forth from school along that same forest path several hundred times.

I had just passed the old cedar tree that marks the start of Troublesome Hollow, when I heard a low, oddsounding whine. I stopped and looked

Abridgment by permission of the Lenniger Literary Agency.

all around, and after a little searching I found what had made the noise. It was a pup of some sort, with a funny-shaped head and dark fur, and the most appealing blue eyes I had ever seen. I tried to pick it up, but the little thing was frightened and ran off a little way. I kept clicking my tongue and whistling and calling, but it would just crouch with its nostrils twitching wildly and run when I approached.

Finally I outran it and picked it up. I sat down in the grass and put the pup between my legs and stroked it until its growls subsided, trying to figure the thing out. I knew that some people just turned dogs loose in the woods to die, and this idea was foremost in my mind. The pup shook itself and looked around, and finally tried the edibility of my pants leg. I teased it with my book strap and it was delighted, stalking the strap with narrowed eyes and fat belly close to the ground.

The fact that the animal was a wolf came to me like a faceful of cold spring water. I had been looking at it from the standpoint of a dog, and suddenly the pointed ears, furred on the inside, the large feet, the dark, solid-colored fur, and the blue eyes all added up to one thing.

I can still feel a part of the confusion I felt then, when I think of it. I know

I got to my feet and the pup shrank back from my height. I backed up a few steps and it whined again, deep in its stomach, sharing my confusion. However, when I walked a little way, it trotted after me and whimpered, and I picked it up and stuck it in the neck of my sweater. I picked up my books carefully, so that I wouldn't scare it, and started home.

It was an odd feeling that the wolf pup gave me, one I can't even explain now. I only know that it was wild and so was I.

Mine was a lonely wildness, like the forest hollows in January when the ice glistens and the woods are frozen and silent. I was an orphan, and had been ever since I was five years old, when both of my parents were killed in an automobile accident. I suppose I would have been a lonely, overly-sensitive child anyway, but the horror of the accident was so firmly impressed upon me that I retreated completely into an unemotional shell.

Carl and Bea, my foster parents, took me immediately, and, like most childless couples, gave me all the heartfelt love and sympathy such people have stored up. I, in turn, loved them, and I think they always realized it, although I never said much outwardly to prove it. They did everything possible to make up for the thing that had happened to my childhood, but there just wasn't any way to push me into a world I resented and feared. At sixteen, normally a noisy and exuberant age, I was a polite, backward, soft-spoken boy.

I don't suppose that I had ever been much excited about anything. The excitement I felt, however, on that afternoon when I headed home with the wolf cub in my sweater, I can still feel today in recollecting it. All the way home I had been preparing what I would say. In the end, I simply handed the tousled cub to Bea. "It's a wolf," I said. "I found him down in the woods toward Troublesome Holler."

My foster mother cuddled the frightened cub in her careful hands and stroked it between the eyes. It was a baby of sorts, and babies were her weakness. I could see by her eyes that I had one person to persuade instead of two.

Carl had seen too many of the lean, rough-coated killers that are wolves to be much impressed with the innocent appearance of a young one, and he was too much a farmer to forget how many of his geese and turkeys had fallen to its ancestors. He took the cub from my mother and scratched its diminutive chops doubtfully.

He looked at me quizzically, but his eyes were kind. "Well," he finally grunted, "the neighbors will think that I've gone plumb crazy, but I guess you can keep it. Mind you keep it away from the chickens, though!" he added, as I gathered up the cub to leave, in great fear that he might think better of his decision.

I named him Lonesome, but I think that no one but myself understood why. The name reminded me of the way he looked when I first found him, and I guess it carried a little of the feeling of the wild that the cub represented to me. And in a way, lonesomeness was my own quiet pattern of life, of which the wolf was a symbol to me.

For the first few weeks Lonesome was shy, suspicious, and nervous. When a door slammed or something was dropped, he would shrink together like a mouse that hears the voice of an owl, and always he ran to me for protection.

It was painful to both of us when I left for school in the morning, and the day was only bearable for me because of the wonderful excitement of anticipation that started in after the noon recess and built up all afternoon, until at last I could break away from my schoolmates and run all the way home.

I told no one at school about the wolf. I had no close friend to tell and, because of my uncomfortable shyness, was unable to bring myself to make a friend for that purpose. My schoolmates seemed noisy and silly to me.

But soon school was out and I was able to solve the problem of sharing Lonesome by having no one to share him with. I was less alone with the cub than I had been among my high-school class, I felt, and I spent all my energy in devising things I could do for him.

I bought him a forty-foot chain and drove a post in the back yard. Carl, to show me his interest, erected a twenty-by-twenty-foot pen around it. I played with Lonesome so much, leading him around the fields and down to the barn to hunt mice, that he never lacked exercise, and never paced his pen, like most wild things.

But the wolf was wild. It showed in his eyes as he grew, the way it shows in the eyes of a hawk. He would lie, motionless as a gray rock, watching the chickens as they scratched in the grass around his pen. He soon found that if he left a portion of his food uneaten, the birds would come into the pen to eat it. It was fearful to watch him wait, long after a cat would have lost patience, to let a bird walk near enough to his still form so that he could be sure of it.

He played like a pup, but yet always with a subtle difference. He chewed on gloves and slippers, and chased moths that got through the screens; puplike, he cocked his head at every unfamiliar noise. But unlike a dog, he hid or buried everything he chewed. With the saving instinct of his ancestors, he always buried everything he couldn't eat at one meal, although I always fed him enough for two pups his size twice a day.

As the spring turned to summer and summer chilled with fall, Lonesome grew a powerful, lean body to match his long head. His eyes turned from blue to gray, and then to that clear amber I shall always remember. They were a hunter's eyes, fierce and hypnotic. The dark fur faded to a neutral gray, splotched with dark guard hairs on his back and shoulders. His blunt, kittenish muzzle lengthened and grew powerful, until he could take a hambone between his great back teeth and splinter it into shreds with a few crunches.

He would come at my whistle, but that was the only thing I was able to teach him. Most dogs learn with food, but food was always desperate business with Lonesome, despite its abundance.

One winter night he howled for the first time, and the sound was lonely— a desolate, frightening thing that made me sit up in bed with goose flesh pimpling my arms. The wolf was undergoing some timeless change in which I wasn't included, and the full meaning of what I had done in bringing him home began to come to me in all its enormity.

That year, the last year of high school, brought a change in my own life that overshadowed Lonesome for a while—I began to grow up. I met a girl and began to attend social gatherings. I slicked my hair down and bought my first suit. I began to take a real interest in the world which went on outside the quiet farm, and to study seriously. A great loneliness in my soul was being pushed away, and the knowledge that people liked me began to crack the shell I had built around myself in my childhood. I drove the car to school, became a 4-H Clubber,[1] and brought girls home to see the farm.

I still kept a corner of myself for Lonesome, though.

During that last school year, Lonesome and I would go each morning for a run in the fields. He was nearly grown now, with a rug-thick pelt and incredible muscles. Lean and darkly feathered, his legs lifted him in effortless jumps of ten feet or more when he ran. And when he started a rabbit, I had to release the chain and let him catch it to keep my arm from being wrenched out of joint. I don't think that either of us ever knew more joyful times than those early-morning runs when the snow lay smooth and bright on the hay field and the cold air carried our breath in clouds.

The time flew, and one day, entering the yard from school, I saw the green spikes of daffodils around the gate, and realized with a start that spring was almost here. For many weeks I had been wrestling with the problem of what I would do when school was over. At school all the talk was of college. Although a lot of my friends weren't going, I found that I

had a great desire to learn more, to reward in some way the two people who had given part of their lives to raising me.

Carl and Bea had wanted to do things for me, but Carl had worked hard for his security, and I had no intention of asking him to send me to college.

As it happened, however, I didn't spend a long time wondering how to manage the problem. That same evening at supper I could see by my foster father's open face that he had something on his mind.

"Randy." He cleared his throat uncomfortably. "Your dad was a smart man with a good education, and he planned for you to go to college, come time for it. Your ma and I, we want you to go too."

Carl toyed with his fork and looked at me with a little apprehension and continued, "That is, if you're a mind to."

I looked for a moment at the kind face of this man who had been a father to me for twelve years, at his rough hands and the worn bib overalls.

"I've thought about going, Dad," I said finally, "but I thought I'd try to find work first so that I could pay for my board and tuition. That way, it wouldn't run you and Mom short."

Carl understood me. "Money doesn't enter into it," he said quickly and with some relief. "Your dad had enough insurance to send you, and the money's put away for you. But your ma and I— that is, I mean, Bea and I—we'd like to send you. It wouldn't put us out any. We want to."

And thus it was settled. I graduated from high school, and my folks sat in the audience and clapped without a dry

---

[1] **4-H Clubber.** The 4-H Club is a national organization of young people living in rural areas. The 4-H Clubbers learn agriculture and home economics. The four H's stand for Head, Heart, Hands, and Health.

eye between them. I was proud, but not just for me. I applied to the university at Farmington for courses in wildlife, and settled down to work all summer on the farm. It was a good summer and a good life.

There was, of course, only one thing that dimmed my anticipation for college—Lonesome. There was no real affection in the wolf's heart for anyone but me. Only I could take him out in the meadows in the early morning for a run, letting him use his caged muscles for a little space of freedom.

Bea knew how I felt, and she promised that she would care for Lonesome. But I knew in my heart that no one would or could care for him as I had, for they weren't me. His days would be a listless eternity of waiting, chained to a dusty post, for the bright hours of my vacation. I knew, now, that I had done a selfish and thoughtless thing in keeping him. I had robbed him of what was his and given him in return a handicap and the terrible chain of ownership.

Carl suggested that I sell him, and I did put an ad in the county weekly. But I was disgusted with the people who wanted him—one for a plaything, another for a novelty to lead in the streets. I disliked least a trapper, who wanted the wolf for an honest reason— to train his wolf dogs to fight.

After I had told him no, like the rest, and stood watching his old truck rattle off, leaving a yellow dust that blew against my face, I saw at last what I would have to do. For the first time in weeks I felt at ease with myself. Freedom, for Lonesome, would probably mean death. He had known only humans, and wouldn't know that he must fear them. But death is sometimes a small thing, and wild things live with it always.

That evening in my life is very clear to me now, and I recall every moment of it. I went out to the wolf's enclosure, unsnapped Lonesome's chain, and let him lead me from the yard. We followed the silver curve of the meadow, the wolf hunting erratically, moving boltlike to catch a mouse, listening to sounds I couldn't hear while I waited. We moved on and entered the woods. We walked for miles, Lonesome eager and excited at this new hunting, investigating every new smell. We walked until there were no sounds of the farm except the chirping crickets.

I was almost surprised to find myself climbing the ragged ridge of Troublesome Hollow; I had lost all track of time or distance in the magic of that summer night. We stopped, Lonesome and I, on a pine-strewn crest and listened to the quiet woodland spring that trickled somewhere below us. I sat down, and the wolf turned to look at me, his nose twitching in a silent analysis of the night scents. The moon peeped through the pines, and down the hollow I heard a screech owl laugh cruelly at a mouse.

I don't know how long I sat there. I scratched the wolf's jowls and ran my hand over his lean muzzle and between his eyes, feeling the wildness, the live spirit pulsing beneath my hand.

I think I talked to him a long time, and I'm sure he listened, for he looked at me the whole time.

"I borrowed you, Lonesome, and I needed you," I said finally, "and if I've done wrong, at least I loved you." I unsnapped his chain.

I waited, leaning against the fragrant trunk of the tall pine long after

he had gone. Then, without willing my voice to speak, I heard myself say, "Good-by, Lonesome." In my mind I could see the wolf, head turned back, his amber eyes questioning. I thought I heard a short, plaintive whine, almost like the whimper I had heard the day I found the dark bundle of wildness under the cedar tree, and then silence.

I walked the long way home slowly, and never once did I look behind me.

THE END

↻ **Talking it over**

1. *a.* What need does Lonesome satisfy for Randy?

b. How do most young people satisfy this need?

2. While speaking of the first summer when he had Lonesome, the narrator says, "I was less alone with the cub than I had been among my high-school class, I felt, and I spent all my energy devising things I could do for him."

a. What eventually overshadows the boy's desire to be with Lonesome?

b. What is happening to Lonesome at this same time?

c. Is it good or bad for Randy when he and Lonesome grow apart as the story progresses?

3. When Randy decides to leave the farm and go to college, he realizes that he will have to part with Lonesome.

a. What is there about freeing Lonesome that bothers Randy?

b. What other possibilities does

Randy consider? Why does he reject each of them?

c. Explain whether Randy does the right thing in freeing Lonesome.

Each boldface word in the sentences below is a homograph. Find the correct definitions in a dictionary.

1. He scratched the puppy's tiny **chops.**
2. Waiting all afternoon for the news is hard to **bear.**
3. The wolf had a rug-thick **pelt.**

⇄ Words in action

If you wanted to reword "The pup was *stalking* the bird," you might say, "The pup was *sneaking up on* the bird."

How would you reword this sentence: "We need another *stalk* of celery"?

Are you surprised that what seems to be the same word has two completely different meanings? The fact is that you are dealing here with two completely different words that just happen to be spelled the same. Words like these are called **homographs.** If you look in a dictionary, you will find the two words entered separately. Such entries are always followed by a small number such as you see here:

stalk¹ (stôk), **1.** stem or main axis of a plant. **2.** any slender, supporting or connecting part of a plant. A flower or leaf blade may have a stalk. **3.** any similar part of an animal. The eyes of a crawfish are on stalks. *n.*

stalk² (stôk), **1.** approach (wild animals) without being seen or heard by them: *The hunters stalked the lion.* **2.** pursue (an animal or a person) without being seen or heard. **3.** spread silently and steadily: *Disease stalked through the land.* **4.** walk with slow, stiff, or haughty strides. **5.** a haughty gait. **6.** a stalking. 1-4 *v.*, 5,6 *n.*

If a word you are looking up in a dictionary is followed by such a number, and the definitions in the first entry you see don't make sense in context, look for other entries above or below it that are spelled the same.

He raised a wolf pup

Mitchell Jayne actually raised an orphan wolf pup, but unlike Randy, who was a teen-ager, Jayne was married and had two children at the time. The pup slept with the children and played with them and the family's dogs. Like Lonesome, however, Jayne's wolf was never without a certain amount of wildness. When it became apparent that the wolf was dangerous to callers, Jayne reluctantly gave him to a wildlife refuge. Later, Jayne went to the refuge to see if the wolf remembered him. The wolf was gone, vanished into the woods. It was then that Jayne wrote "Orphan Pup."

Dog, Midwinter

by Raymond Souster

This dog barking at me now—
do I really bother him
or is he acting out
the old faithful watch-dog routine?

Or (and I hope it's this)
is he so lonely locked up
in the snow-filled yard that the sight
of another living thing stirs him?

For I can truly say
I'm as lonely now
as you, dog, so
speaking for both of us
bark your crazy head off.

Talking it over

1. *a.* What one word expresses the feeling that this poem is about?

   b. How does the dog help the speaker in the poem?

2. For a while, Randy in "Orphan Pup" has somewhat the same problem as the speaker in this poem. What does Lonesome do for Randy that is different from what the dog in the poem does for the speaker?

From *The Birds and the Beasts Were There.* Reprinted by permission of the author.

Eleanor Rigby

by John Lennon and Paul McCartney

Ah—look at all the lonely people!
Ah—look at all the lonely people!

Eleanor Rigby
Picks up the rice in the church where a wedding has been,
5 Lives in a dream.
Waits at the window,
Wearing the face that she keeps in a jar by the door.
Who is it for?

All the lonely people, where do they all come from?
10 All the lonely people, where do they all belong?

Father McKenzie
Writing the words of a sermon that no one will hear,
No one comes near.
Look at him working,
15 Darning his socks in the night when there's nobody there.
What does he care?

All the lonely people, where do they all come from?
All the lonely people, where do they all belong?

Eleanor Rigby
20 Died in the church and was buried along with her name.
Nobody came.
Father McKenzie,
Wiping the dirt from his hands as he walks from the grave.
No one was saved.

25 All the lonely people, where do they all come from?
All the lonely people, where do they all belong?

Talking it over

1. Describe Eleanor's loneliness.

2. Describe Father McKenzie's loneliness. How does his feeling about his lonely situation seem to differ from Eleanor's?

3. *a.* When do the paths of Eleanor Rigby and Father McKenzie cross?

b. Explain whether either of these people has left a mark on the other one's life.

c. Has either one had much effect on other people in general? Give evidence from the poem.

4. How does the loneliness here differ from that in "Orphan Pup" and "Dog, Midwinter"?

They're Beatles

John Lennon and Paul McCartney met when they were teen-agers in Liverpool, England. After helping one another learn to play guitar, they began to appear as a rock-'n'-roll act. Over several years they added members to their group and lost members until, eventually, the group was made up of the four young men who became famous throughout the world as the Beatles.

Lennon and McCartney have written the lyrics to many of the songs the Beatles perform and record. "Eleanor Rigby" is one of these lyrics. John Lennon has also written two books of humorous verse and prose.

SHOW BUSINESS

*"Although I had traveled ten states
and played over fifty cities by the time I was four,
I never felt I was without a home. . . ."*

I WAS BORN in Harlem on December 8, 1925. My father was the lead dancer in Will Mastin's *Holiday in Dixieland,* a vaudeville[1] troupe in which my mother, Elvera "Baby" Sanchez, was a top chorus girl. Good jobs were scarce so she remained in the line until two weeks before I was born. Then, as soon as she was able to dance, she boarded me with friends in Brooklyn, and continued on the road with my father and the show.

[1]**vaudeville,** a kind of entertainment that was popular from about 1900 until the 1930's, when talking movies took its place in the public favor. Vaudeville consisted of a series of acts (dancers, singers, comedians, acrobats, magicians, etc.) much like a TV variety show.

My grandmother, Rosa B. Davis, came out from Harlem to see me and wrote to my father, "I never saw a dirtier child in my life. They leave Sammy alone all day so I've taken him with me. I'm going to make a home for that child."

I heard my father call my grandmother "Mama" so I called her Mama, and this was appropriate because by the time I could speak I thought of her as that.

Mama was housekeeper for one family for twenty years, cooking, cleaning, ironing, and raising their children and me at the same time.

One day she returned to the nursery school at which she'd been leaving me. The nurse was surprised. "We thought you were on your job, Mrs. Davis."

WAS MY HOME

by Sammy Davis, Jr.,
and Jane and Burt Boyar

"Something told me get off the street-car and see what you're doing with my Sammy. Now I find you put these two other children in his carriage with him and you got Sammy all scrooched up in a corner of his own carriage. I bought that carriage for Sammy. Paid cash for it. Now you got him so he can't stretch out in his own carriage. Get those kids out of Sammy's carriage."

She began taking me to work with her. On her days off she took me to the park and put me on the swings. Nobody else could push or touch me.

When I was two-and-a-half, my parents separated. My mother joined another traveling show, and my father came home to get me.

"Sam, this child's too young to go on the road."

"Mama," he said, "I'm his father and I say he goes on the road. I ain't leaving him here so's Elvera can come in and take him away. 'Sides, I want my son with me."

When the train moved into the tunnel and I couldn't see Mama anymore I stopped waving and settled back in my seat. My father started taking off my coat, my leggings, and my hat. "Where we goin', Daddy?"

He smiled and put his arm around me. "We're goin' into show business, son."

Our first stop was the Pitheon Theater in Pittsburgh. I was backstage with my father all day, but at night he left me at the rooming house with a chair propped against the bed and often I didn't see him again until the next afternoon. Will Mastin came in every morning, bathed me in the sink, and made my breakfast, Horlick's malted milk, which he mixed with hot water from the tap. We were great friends. He spent hours making funny faces at me and I loved making the same faces right back at him. One afternoon I was in the dressing room playing with the make-up, trying to use the powder puffs and tubes and pencils on my face the way I always saw my father and Will doing it. Will was watching me. "Here, let me show you how to do that." I sat on his chair while he put blackface on me. Then he took a tube of clown white, gave me the big white lips, and winked, "Now you look like Al Jolson."[2] I winked back.

He snapped his fingers like he'd gotten an idea, and sent for our prima donna[3] who sang "Sonny Boy." "Next show," he told her, "take Sammy onstage, hold him in your lap, and keep singing no matter what happens."

As she sang, I looked over her shoulder and saw Will in the wings, playing our game, rolling his eyes and shaking his head at me and I rolled my eyes and shook my head right back at him. The prima donna hit a high note and Will held his nose. I held my nose, too. But Will's faces weren't half as funny as the prima donna's so I began copying hers instead: when her lips trembled, my lips trembled, and I followed her all the way from a heaving bosom to a quivering jaw. The people out front were watching me, laughing. When we got off, Will knelt to my height. "Listen

to that applause, Sammy, some of it's for you." My father was crouched beside me, too, smiling, pleased with me. "You're a born mugger,[4] son, a born mugger." He and Will both had their arms around me.

When we arrived at our next town Will began giving out meal tickets to the troupe. Once an act had its name up on a theater, there were restaurants in show towns that would give food on credit. They'd issue a meal ticket for a week's food and we'd settle with them on payday. Will gave my father his ticket and then put one in my pocket. "Here you are, Mose Gastin. You got a meal ticket coming to you same as anyone else in the troupe."

I took it out of my pocket and held it. "Okay, Massey." I couldn't say Mastin. Why he called me Mose Gastin or where he got that name I don't know.

Between shows I'd stand in the wings watching the other acts, like *Moss and Fry, Butterbeans and Susie, The Eight Black Dots,* and *Pot, Pan & Skillet.* At mealtime, I'd sit with my father, Will, and the other performers, listening to them talk show business, hearing about the big vaudeville acts that played the Keith "time."[5] Keith was far over our heads. Shows like ours played small time like TOBA and Butterfield[6] but there was no end of stories to be heard about the great acts who worked the big time.

We always rented the cheapest room

---

[2]**Al Jolson,** a popular singer of the 1920's and 1930's who usually appeared in blackface make-up and sang songs glorifying the old South.

[3]**prima donna,** a female opera star. In show business the term is used, sometimes humorously, to refer to any female singer with top billing.

[4]**mugger,** a comic performer whose specialty is making funny faces.

[5]**Keith "time,"** a big-time circuit. Vaudeville shows traveled from one theater to another in a set pattern, or circuit. In "big-time" the circuits included the best theaters, and the performers received high salaries and did only two shows a day.

[6]**TOBA and Butterfield,** small-time circuits. Performers received low salaries, worked three shows a day, and played at poorer theaters.

we could find, and my father and I shared the bed. He'd turn out the light and say, "Well, good night, Poppa." Then I'd hear a scratching sound. I'd sit up, fast. "What's that, Daddy?"

"I didn't hear nothin'."

The scratching would start again. I'd be suspicious. "Lemme see your hands."

"Fine thing when a kid don't trust his own daddy." He'd hold both hands in the air and I'd lie down, watching them. The scratching would start again.

"Whatsat, Daddy? Whatsat? Lemme see your feet, too."

He put his feet in the air along with his hands. "Now how d'you expect a man to sleep like this, Poppa?" The game was over then and I'd snuggle in close to him where it was safe.

We were playing the Standard Theater in Philadelphia when he said, "Good news, Poppa. There's a amateur dance contest here at the theater day after we close. Course, there's sixteen other kids'd be against you. And all of 'em older'n you. You suppose you c'd beat 'em?"

"Yes."

I was only three but I'd spent hundreds of hours watching Will and my father work, and imitating their kind of dancing. They were doing a flash-act[7]—twelve dancers with fifteen minutes to make an impression or starve. The other kids in the contest were dancing in fox-trot time but when I came on, all the audience could see was a blur— just two small legs flying! I got a silver cup and ten dollars. My father took me straight over to A. S. Beck's shoe store and bought me a pair of black pumps with taps.

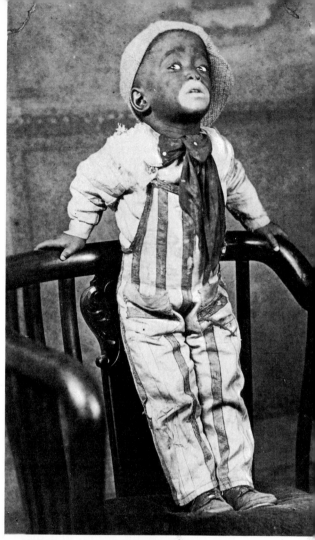

[7]**flash-act,** usually the opening act of a show. The act's rapid tempo is intended to capture the interest of the audience.

We hung around Philadelphia, hoping to get booked, but our money ran out and my father had to call Mama for a loan. She told him, "That's no life for Sammy if you gotta call me for money. I'm sending you fare to bring him home."

He told Will, "Guess she's right. This ain't no life for a kid. Trouble is, I can't bring myself to leave him there and travel around without him now. I'll just have to get me a job around home doin' somethin' else." I saw tears in my father's eyes. "I'll always wanta be in show business, Will. It's my life. So anytime you need me, just say the word."

Massey picked me up and hugged me. "Be a good boy, Mose Gastin. And don't worry. We'll be working together again someday."

Mama was waiting up for us when we got home. I put on my shoes and ran into the front room to show them to her. My father proudly explained how I'd won them. Mama turned on her player piano and I did my routine. She smiled. "My, oh my! You're a real dancer now." She shook her head at my father. "You buy him shoes when you don't have money for food. I always knew you was smart."

My father left the apartment every morning and came back at dinner time, but after a week he was still without a job. "I couldn't bring myself to look for nothin' outside of show business, Mama. I'll do it tomorrow. I really will."

But each day it was the same thing. He was spending his time hanging around backstage with the dancers at the Odeon Theater. When he came home he'd just stare out the window, shaking his head. "I can dance circles around them guys. I'm over them like the sky is over the world, and they're making $150 a week."

Before I was born he'd driven cabs in New York, shined shoes, cooked, pulled fires[8] on the Erie Railroad, and run an elevator at Roseland Dance Hall. Then he'd won some Charleston[9] contests, met Will, and from then on there was only one way of life for him.

One night he looked over and saw Mama and me dancing. That was the first thing that brightened him up. "Mama, just what do you call what you're doin' with him?"

"We're doin' the time step."[10]

He laughed. "That ain't no time step."

Mama snapped back. "Maybe so, but we like it. And if Sammy likes it, then anything to make him happy."

I couldn't stand the way he was laughing at me. I tried harder to do it the way he'd shown me but he kept shaking his head. "He can do some tough ones and can't do the easiest of all. Here, lemme show you again." He did a time step. "Now you do it." I tried to copy it. "You ain't doin' nothin'." I kept trying harder and harder but I couldn't get it right. He said, "Here, looka this." He showed me his airplane step and some of the really hard steps I'd seen him and Will do in the act. "Some day maybe you'll be able to do that too, Poppa." Then he went back to the window.

I heard Mama laughing excitedly. "Look at your son flyin' across the floor."

I was doing a trick of his with one hand on the floor, the other in the air and my two feet kicking out in front of me. He snapped out of his melancholy and almost split his sides laughing. The harder he laughed the harder I kicked. He bent down and put his face right in front of mine. "Betcha I can make you laugh, Poppa." He made a very serious face and stared at me. I bit my lips and tried desperately to keep a straight face, but that always made me die laughing.

He lost interest in me again and went back to the window, staring at the

---

[8]**pulled fires.** Extensive maintenance work had to be done on steam engines at the end of each run. Men who removed the burning fuel from the fire box so the engine could cool were said to "pull fires."

[9]**Charleston,** a dance popular in the 1920's.

[10]**time step,** one of the first basic tap dancing steps learned by beginning tap dancers.

street, leafing through an old copy of *Variety*[11] which he'd already read a dozen times. Suddenly he smacked the arm of the chair and stood up. "Mama, I'm wiring Will to send me a ticket. I'm in the wrong business here."

She snapped, "You ain't in *no* business here."

"Maybe so, but it's better to go hungry when you're happy than to eat regular when you're dead. And I'm good as dead out of show business."

A few days later a letter arrived Special Delivery from Will. My father pulled his suitcase out from under the bed. I ran to the closet for my shoes and put them in the suitcase alongside his. He took them out and I held my breath as he stared at them, balancing them in one hand. Then he slapped me on the back, put them in the suitcase, and laughed. "Okay, Poppa, you're comin' too."

Holding hands we half-walked, half-danced toward Penn Station, smiling at everybody.

"Where we goin', Daddy?"

"We're goin' back into show business, Poppa!"

We rarely remained in one place more than a week or two, yet there was never a feeling of impermanence. Packing suitcases and riding on trains and buses were as natural to me as a stroll in a carriage might be to another child. Although I had traveled ten states and played over fifty cities by the time I was four, I never felt I was without a home. We carried our roots with us: our same boxes of make-up in front of the mirrors, our same clothes hanging on iron-pipe racks with our same shoes under them. Only the details changed, like the face on the man sitting inside the stage door, or which floor our dressing room was on. But there was always an audience, other performers for me to watch, always the show talk, all as dependably present as the walls of a nursery.

We arrived in Asheville, North Carolina, on a Sunday, and Will gave everybody the day off. We were doing three-a-day,[12] from town to town, so most of our troupe spent the time catching up on sleep, which was also the cheapest thing they could do. I wasn't tired so I wandered into the parlor of our rooming house. Rastus Airship, one of our dancers, was reading a paper, and Obie Smith, our pianist, was rehearsing on an upright.[13] I started doing the parts of the show along with him. Rastus left the room and came back with Will and my father and I did the whole hour-and-twenty-minute show for them, doing everybody's dances, singing everybody's songs, and telling all the jokes. People were coming in from other rooms and from the way they were watching me I knew I was doing good. When I finished our closing number, Will said, "From now on you're going to dance and sing in the act." My father picked me up, "That's right, he is," and carried me around the room introducing me to everybody we'd been living with for the past year. "This is my son. Meet my son, Sammy Davis, Jr."

She was much prettier than any of the girls in our show. I started to shake hands with her but she knelt down and

---

[11]**Variety,** a weekly newspaper devoted to show business, especially movies, stage, and TV.
[12]**doing three-a-day,** performing in three shows a day, as was customary in small-time vaudeville.
[13]**upright,** a type of piano.

hugged me and when she kissed me her eyes were wet.

"You cryin'?"

She touched her eyes with a handkerchief. "I'm happy to see my little boy, that's all."

My father told me this was my mother and that I wouldn't be doing the show that night so I could spend time with her. Then he left us alone in the dressing room.

I looked up at her. "I can dance."

"No kidding. Let's see."

I did one of my father's routines but she started crying again.

"Don't you like the way I dance?"

"Darlin', I love everything you do. I know that dance and you did it real good. As good as your daddy."

That was more like it. I did half our show for her. Then we went outside and she held my hand while we walked.

"You like show business, Sammy?"

"Yes."

"You happy?"

"Yes." From the moment we'd left the theater all I could think of was my father and Will would be doing the show without me.

She asked, "How'd you like a nice ice-cream soda?"

"No, thank you."

We came to a toy store. "Let's go in and buy you a present." I didn't want a present. I just wanted to get back to the theater, but she bought me a ball. Outside, she said, "Let's see you catch it, darlin'." I'd never done it before and I put my hands up too late and it hit me on the cheek. It didn't hurt but it scared me. I just watched it rolling away.

"Get it, Sammy."

"I don't want it." I was sorry as soon as I'd said it.

We walked a few more blocks. "Is there anything you'd like to do?" I didn't tell her, but she understood.

I ran ahead of her into the dressing room. My father was putting on his make-up. "You do the show yet, Daddy?"

"Nope. You're just in time."

I ran for my costume. My mother started to leave but I grabbed her skirt. "Don't go."

Each time I turned toward the wings I saw her watching me and smiling. She liked me and I hadn't even done my tricks, yet. When I went into them I could only see her out of the corner of my eye, but she wasn't smiling anymore. I wasn't able to turn around again and when I got off she was gone.

My father picked me up. He was hugging me very tight, patting my back, as he walked toward the dressing room. "Your mother had to leave, Poppa. She said to tell you she loves you."

For no reason I could understand I started to cry.   THE END

Talking it over

1. *a*. Who was the person Sammy called Mama?

   b. Which of Mama's actions showed how she felt about Sammy?

   c. Judging from the things Mama said to Sammy's father and the way she said them, what do you think her feelings were toward him?

2. You can also infer from their actions what other people in this story were thinking and feeling.

a. Why did Will Mastin give Sammy a meal ticket?

b. Could Sammy's father afford the dancing shoes he bought for him? What does this purchase tell you about Sammy's father?

c. Why did Sammy's father read a copy of *Variety* a dozen times?

d. Why did Sammy put his shoes in his father's suitcase?

e. Why did Sammy's father introduce him to people who had already known him for a year? By what name did he introduce Sammy?

f. Why did Sammy's mother buy him a ball? Why did Sammy let the ball roll away?

He made the big time

The talents which earned Sammy Davis, Jr., a place in small-time vaudeville at the age of three have won him world fame as an adult.

When The Will Mastin Trio (Sammy, his father, and Will Mastin) broke into "big time," Sammy was only twenty-one, but he gave outstanding professional performances as a singer, dancer, drummer, actor, comedian, pantomimist, and impressionist. Since that time, Sammy has played in clubs and theaters all over the United States and in London and Paris as well. He has starred on television, in movies, and on the stage; his recordings have sold millions of copies.

However, more is needed to account for Sammy Davis, Jr.'s success than talent alone. In his autobiography, *Yes I Can,* Sammy tells how he was able to overcome prejudice, the loss of an eye in an automobile accident, and other obstacles that threatened his career.

⇄ **Words in action**

Words often have a special meaning among people in a particular trade or profession. What do the following expressions mean to people in the occupations named?

1. **line:** dancer, telephone operator, printer, salesman, railroad engineer
2. **mugger:** actor, policeman
3. **wings:** actor, airplane pilot, house builder, politician
4. **get booked:** actor, policeman

Beginning of Wisdom

by Rachel Field

Every time they laughed and praised her,
she was betraying Ma and the rest. . . .

ORA LARRABIE stayed still as long as she could hold the wonder to herself. Ever since yesterday it had warmed her from the inside out, like a glowing coal, and now, because of it, she had waked before any other sleeper in the tent stirred. It would not do to disturb them, especially Vida May and Loretta, sleeping one on either side.

Cautiously Ora inched herself up and stared about the tent and the familiar humped shapes. Pa breathed heavily beside Ma in the folding camp bed. The baby scarcely showed at all in the orange crate within easy reach of Ma's hand. On the mattress opposite she could see the three boys sprawled —Ed's feet poked out of the covers, Frank face down on his crossed arms, and Jason curled like a tow-headed squirrel between them.

"I've got to get out of here," Ora

decided, "or I'm like to let out a whoop and wake the whole lot. Mustn't do that."

Silent as a fish she slid from between the sleepers, felt along a row of pegs, and found her dress. A button caught in her hair, and she was careful to dislodge it without disturbing the curlers Vida May had helped her fix last night. Her hands counted them over to make sure not one had come loose. To touch them was reassurance that she had not dreamed about the invitation to Hester Burt's party.

The baby whimpered, and Ma reached out to him in her sleep, as Ora ducked under the canvas to meet the morning.

The government camp[1] was not yet roused to activity, but here and there a

---

[1] **government camp.** During the Great Depression of the 1930's, thousands of families poured into California seeking work. But since California also suffered from the Depression, there were few jobs or places for the newcomers to live. The federal government therefore built camps for them.

thread of smoke pushed out of a black arm of pipe from some tent. Over by the outdoor washtubs next to the nearest Sanitary Unit a woman was busy with clothes, and another woman was fetching a pail of water. Except for them the streets of tents were deserted. Even the American flag by the entrance hadn't been run up yet.

How good the air felt, like cold water, as she breathed it in, the sun warm and friendly as a hand laid on her shoulders.

"Why, hello, sis!" Old Man Blodgett hailed Ora from the row of corrugated tin houses by the gates. "Up kind of early for Saturday morning." Under his scraggly mustache he smiled, and Ora smiled back.

"I'm invited to a party," she told him, "this afternoon from four to six. Over to the Burt ranch," she added.

"Well, now, you don't say." He looked as surprised as she had expected him to. "Going to a party. My, I sure wish't I'd get me an invite. Going to have root beer and cake and ice cream maybe?"

"Maybe." Ora nodded. "You see I've got a friend—"

She left Old Man Blodgett to his patch of garden and crossed the road. The graveled edges felt gritty to her bare feet, but she was glad she hadn't taken a chance wearing her shoes. Jason had helped her clean them with an oily rag last night till they looked almost good as new. He'd also promised her the loan of his Mexican jumping beans to take to the party.

She found the hole in the barbed wire and crawled through without damage to her dress or hair. Looking back across the road, she could see the camp better than when she had been in the midst of it. There was the big silver-gray water tank on its scaffold keeping guard over the familiar buildings—the long, shedlike washrooms and recreation hall, the white clapboard clinic, the coöperative store with the gas pump in front, the office and house where the manager lived. There were the rows of tin houses with their tiny gardens, and the tents stretching out behind, all shades of gray and khaki canvas.

How small they looked from a little way off, like the paper cones Ora had seen set over young melon plants to protect them from the sun. Maybe from up in an airplane the tents looked like that and you wouldn't guess folks were living inside them. Maybe that was how the government camp looked to God, except that He saw everything. God must know about the party, but she would thank Him anyway; only, she'd wait for a prettier spot, not so near the road.

All about her, new green was pushing up between the brittle, ghostlike stalks of last year's grass. They scratched her feet and legs as she crossed to the field beyond, a wide expanse, blue as an inland lake with wild lupin. There was another fence to climb through before she stood knee-high in thickset bloom. All about her the lupin moved softly, lightly under the mountain sun.

"Thank you, God," Ora whispered. "Thanks a million."

Then she flung herself down with her face on her folded arms.

For a whole week now she had known about Hester Burt's party, yet she had to seem not to know. In the schoolroom, she must not show that it mattered if she was left out. Ora had come to be rather good at that in the last year. She wouldn't have minded much, except that it was going to be Hester Burt's party and Hester had never looked at her as if she were a curiosity. Right from the first day of school she'd smiled across the aisle and been friendly.

But all that past week it had been different. Hester had acted, not mean or mad, just stiff and quiet. She went out of her way to be busy if Ora came by, and when she did look up, Ora had seen that her eyes were big and worried, the way they got if she didn't know the answers when the teacher called her name. It had made a kind of chill between them, and every day from Monday on it had grown worse.

"What's come over you, Ora?" Ma had asked by the middle of the week. "You don't act right and you look peaked. Better tell me if you need the nurse over to the clinic to dose you up."

"No, Ma, no," Ora had protested. "I don't need no dosing up. I'm fine."

"You sure don't look it," Ma had sighed.

Miss Jocelyn, the third-grade teacher, had also noticed Ora's behavior. She asked no questions, but she must have had her own suspicions, for she hadn't scolded when Ora lost her place in reading or failed the easiest arithmetic problems. At recess time on Thursday she had kept her in after the rest left the schoolroom.

"I'm afraid I can't give you a gold star this week," she had told Ora regretfully. "I'm sorry, because you haven't missed one for any week this term. Well, never mind, you'll probably make it up next month. You may decorate the blackboard now if you want to. But be careful with the red chalk. You know, it always gets used up so fast."

Ora felt grateful to Miss Jocelyn for letting her stay in with the chalk box. She loved to be chosen to decorate the blackboard. But that day her heart wasn't behind her fingers. Always, when Ora had her choice of subject, she drew the same thing—a house set among trees and flowers.

There was nothing flimsy about Ora's blackboard houses. They were ample, two-storied affairs with green blinds and the biggest chimneys the supply of red chalk would allow. Smoke curled up in thick, blue rings, and her roofs were solidly filled in. Sometimes she made picket fences with hollyhocks behind, and sometimes it was a green lawn sprinkled with yellow dots for dandelions. Her trees were always generously loaded with oranges and lemons. As she worked, Ora would feel herself a part of the house. With her back to the schoolroom she could shut out everything except what her mind and hand created.

But the spell didn't take her that day. Her eyes would keep wandering out to the play yard. She couldn't make the blackboard house seem real.

"A peanut hunt—" Ora heard the magic words in excited whispers as the girls trooped in and took their seats. "Four kinds of cake." "Prizes—"

On Friday she moved doggedly through the hours, waiting for the closing bell to sound. She had given up acting as if she didn't know what all the whisperings were about; she had given up counting on a miracle. Across the aisle Hester Burt was exchanging secret nods and looks with this one and that. Her brown curls lay soft about her warm cheeks and her eyes still avoided Ora, all except once, when Ora saw that they were still puzzled and unhappy.

"You wouldn't ever do it, Hester—" Ora caught the words as Ruth Norton said them on the way to the play yard. "Your mother'd give you Hail Columbia. You know we're not supposed to speak to them out of school."

"I don't care; it's my party—"

"I dare you to!" That had been Florence Dennis, her giggle rising shrill.

"Well, my grandma wouldn't mind, and she's giving me the party . . . Don't forget to come the way I said. There's going to be a prize for the best one— I mean, the funniest—" Hester's voice was swallowed up in more whispers and giggles.

The round-faced schoolroom clock had never moved its metal hands so slowly on any Friday afternoon. But three o'clock came, and the third-graders tumbled out into the sunshine. It was then that the unbelievable thing had happened. Ora saw Hester Burt turn back and make straight for her.

"You come," she had breathed quickly into Ora's ear. "You come, too."

"To the party—?" Ora's throat had gone tight and dry.

"From four to six—" She had heard that much before an onrush of older girls and boys had swept her and Hester apart. Hester had been trying to tell her something else, but no matter, the miracle had happened.

But when she reached their tent, she had found words. They had tumbled out of her like popcorn exploding in one of those glass boxes on little carts. Ma hadn't been so pleased over anything since they'd left Oklahoma. She stood holding the baby, smiling at Pa across the tent.

"The Burt Ranch," he had repeated slowly. "Sure, I know where that is. Been by it plenty of times. They raise apricots and walnuts. I got gas enough to get you there and back."

Only Vida May had been skeptical. "I wouldn't go if'n I was Ora," she had said knowingly. "Sounds funny to me."

"Vida May Larrabie, you hush up!" Ma had turned indignant eyes upon her oldest daughter. "What's wrong about Ora getting asked to a party?"

"I didn't say there was anything wrong, Ma; I just said I wouldn't take a chance. There's bound to be a string to it somewhere."

Ma had silenced Vida May's doubts with another withering glance. "Ora's going to that party and, what's more, she's going in the best we can contrive."

Ma rose to emergencies like yeast. The length of turkey-red cotton she was saving to line a quilt could be pressed into service for a dress, and there was the tatting collar and plaid sash the three girls all took turns borrowing. Jason offered the bluejay wings to spruce up Loretta's brown felt hat, and down at the workrooms[2] they had contributed thread and buttons and plenty of advice. The very last thing Ora had seen the night before had been Ma sewing away for dear life under the tent light . . .

Ora was late for breakfast. But there was mush left in the kettle and Ma had saved some of the canned milk. "Eat all you can," she advised. "You'll need something to hold you together till the party."

In spite of the warning Ora couldn't seem to set her mind on food. By after-

---

[2]**workrooms.** Buildings were provided in government camps for washing clothes, sewing, recreation, etc.

noon her body tingled from a vigorous session in the washrooms under Vida May's supervision; the roots of her hair ached from being tugged into curls. But the family viewed her with awed silence, as if she were about to be initiated into some secret order.

"Come on, now; time to get along."

Pa had the old car started. It stood before the tent, the engine throbbing, while all the Larrabies gathered to watch the departure.

"Now then," Ma tweaked the freshly ironed plaid sash into a more spirited bow.

The turkey-red dress had been made plenty long and full, so it could do double duty for Loretta on occasion. The tatting collar was a little on the ample side, too, but the gold-washed brooch that Vida May had found in a filling station restroom held it firmly in place. The pin part was broken, but Ma had sewed it on, and the green glass stone that looked almost exactly like an emerald showed up well.

"Here—" Loretta handed over her brown felt hat, resplendent with the bluejay wings. "Don't put it on till you get there."

Ora held it tenderly on her lap and smiled her thanks at Jason who had found the dead bluejay and cured the feathers. The wings felt softer than silk to her fingers and they shone bluer than anything under the sun.

"Don't she look a picture, Pa?" Ma had beamed. "You got the handkerchief I ironed out for you?"

"Yes, Ma." Ora smiled solemnly and produced it, with Jason's jumping beans knotted fast in one corner.

"Well," Pa said again, "let's go."

Other eyes were watching, and hands waved all along the way.

Pa maneuvered the car into the open space by the store and gas pump, past the office and gate, before he relaxed in the seat. Once they swung out into the highway and joined the stream of traffic, he pulled down his hat and began to chew his tobacco.

"She's doing all right for her age," he told Ora as they chugged along at twenty-five. "Ed's always kicking 'bout how her valves need grinding. I tell him I wouldn't wonder but mine do, too. Costs money to get 'em fixed, like everything does in this world."

"Yes, Pa," Ora answered.

"Well, it's something to keep going, times being what they are and all. Trouble is it don't get you nowhere to keep going if somone else beats you to the jobs."

"Yes, Pa," Ora said.

Three, four, five cars went by in shining succession. Pa squinted at their disappearing brightness.

"Slow down, Pa." Ora touched his arm and pointed. "We're most there."

A mile or so farther on a dirt road there were big gates, and a painted sign that read: "Rancho Eldora. Private Road. Trespassers will be legally prosecuted by order of G. N. Burt, owner."

Pa brought the car to a stop, but he didn't turn in. "Guess I'd better leave you off here," he decided. "Might not be any good place to turn round when we get inside. It don't look to be very much of a walk. I'll be here round six. Take your time."

It was farther than it looked from the main road to the house, but the way was shaded from the glare by eucalyptus trees that edged the acres of apricots and walnuts on either side.

She must be the first guest, Ora decided, because there were no cars parked in the driveway. She had hoped Hester would be about, but there wasn't a sign of her. The house stood white and ample before her. She hesitated at the steps that led to the vine-covered porch, and she heard the voices.

"Mamma look!" Ora recognized the one that belonged to Hester's mother. "Do you see what I see coming up the path?"

"Yes, daughter," another voice answered. "Maybe it's the rig she's got on, but I don't seem to recognize the child."

"Of course you don't! She's one of them, from the migratory camp. If Hester's asked her here after what I said—"

"Now, now, don't get excited, Emmy. What's one child more at a party?"

"It's not that, Mamma; it's her deliberately disobeying me. I've told Hester, and her father's told her, she mustn't have anything to do with them outside of school. I might have known she was up to something like this, the way she acted when I tried to talk her out of this 'tacky party' idea. I'm going right out and send that child back where she came from—"

"Wait," the other voice broke in. "You're not going to do anything of the kind. Punish Hester afterward, but anyone she asked is going to stay."

"But, Mamma, you know how George and all of us feel about these migratories. It's bad enough having them swarm all over, dirty and shiftless and God knows what else, raising the taxes and overrunning the schools, without Hester taking up with them."

"You can't put a barbed-wire fence round Hester's heart—just remember that, Emmy."

The voices were going on behind the windows, but Ora heard nothing more.

Her ears were ringing dully and she could hardly see where her feet were taking her as she stumbled away from the house. Her throat felt tight, and way down inside of her something pressed chill and hard like an ice cube. Now she knew why Hester had looked worried. Of course, she knew how people who lived in houses felt about people who didn't; people who came looking for work in old cars. They kept different looks and voices for you and always found out if you lived in a tent and had too many brothers and sisters.

She found a bench under a pepper tree and hid as far back in the shade as she could, trying to think what to do. Pa wouldn't be back for two hours. She could wait down by the sign, only all the cars coming to the party would have to turn in there and everyone would see her. She could never face school on Monday and all the jokes and questions. Maybe if she went out on the main road and started walking toward the camp she might thumb a ride back. But Pa would wait and wait, and Ma and the rest would have to know it had all been a mistake. They had been so proud and pleased about her going, especially Ma. And then there was Hester.

She knew for certain now that Hester Burt was her friend. She'd proved it going against her mother to ask her, and she'd be punished afterward, sure as fate. If Ora stayed away, then Hester would think she hadn't wanted to come and that would be worst of all.

Cars were thick in the driveway now. The air was full of honkings and voices. She waited till the lawn was full of moving figures before she came slowly out of hiding.

She found herself suddenly the center

of a noisy group. For a moment she felt confused, as if she were part of a circus parade or a motion-picture show. She recognized the voices and features of her schoolmates, yet each of them had been transformed into a stranger. Dilapidated sweaters and jeans; torn lace and faded ginghams of outlandish pattern, hats minus crowns or weighed down with hideous flowers, were all milling dizzily about her as she stared.

"Hi, Nan!" Millie Robbins was shrilling. "Come here and see Ora! She's got everything but the kitchen stove on her."

"Gee, I'll say!"

Hands were poking her with curious and admiring interest. She stood stiff and uncomfortable in their midst, not knowing whether to be embarrassed or pleased by the unaccustomed cordiality.

"Feathers, too! Oh, boy!" Billy Whitcomb came toward her like a rusty crow, in black, with a crushed-in high hat tilted sideways over his freckles. He poked a cane at her hat and let out one of his best two-finger-in-the-mouth whistles. "Some tacky party, all right."

Ora caught at the words as they went by. A "tacky party." Hester's mother had called it that, too. That must have been what Hester had tried to tell her yesterday on the way out of school. She ought to have listened better, but all she had thought of then had been the wonder of being asked. A party had always meant the best you had, on your back and on your plate.

"Didn't I tell you so?" Hester was coming toward her in a dress of her mother's with obviously new and unnecessary patches plastered all over it. "Didn't I say Ora'd be a good sport if I asked her?"

Ora met Hester's eyes. They shone

with approval as she took in every detail of the costume. Ora put her hand to her throat to try to ease the tightness just above the sewed-on brooch. She tried to smile back as if she'd dressed that way on purpose. But all she really wanted was to run and run and never stop till she got back to the camp. It had been bad enough before, hearing what Hester's mother had said behind the window, but this was worse, because every time they laughed and praised her for looking tacky she was betraying Ma and the rest.

"Some hat!" Jo and Jerry Black snatched it from her head as they dashed by. They chased it all over the lawn as if it were a football. Ora rescued it at last, but not before a lot of the soft small feathers had been scattered and the wing tips broken.

"I mustn't let on," Ora told herself between clenched teeth. "Not to Hester here and not to the folks when I get back."

They were all especially nice to her that afternoon. No one passed remarks about living in a tent, or eating mush three times a day, or any of the jokes she'd come to expect. She found the most peanuts in the hunt without half trying, and the potato race would have been easy to win if she'd wanted to. When it came to pinning the donkey's tail on blindfolded she made no effort, though she'd thought it would be fun.

"Now it's time to vote on the prizes for the tackiest costume," Hester announced importantly. "Grandma's going to sit over there behind the screen, and everybody has to go up, one at a time, and whisper the name. She'll mark it down on paper and count up who gets the most votes. You mustn't say me, because people don't get prizes at their own parties."

Ora took her place at the end of the long, wriggling line that moved forward in single file. "Please, God," she prayed desperately, "please, God, make it a tie if You can."

It was her turn to go behind the screen, but before she could say the name she had chosen, Hester's grandmother reached out, all smiles, and took her by the hand. "Makes no difference who you choose, child"—she spoke up loud enough for them all to hear— "you've got twice as many votes as anyone else. You win the prize all right, and here it is."

They were all clapping and shouting about her, looking on enviously. Then there was a hush while Hester put the package into her hands. Her fingers went numb so she could hardly feel the softness of the white tissue paper and the pink ribbon bow that tied it.

"Open it, open it!" they clamored.

"I picked it out all myself," Hester was saying. "I sure wish I had one just like it for my room."

"Now, don't tease her," the old lady was saying. "Let her open it when she's a mind to. You want to show your folks how it looks all wrapped up, don't you?"

Ora nodded without looking up. She dared not raise her eyes in gratefulness or trust herself to make a sound.

"Well, come on; refreshments are ready!" The summons came not a moment too soon, and Ora was mercifully forgotten in the rush for places about the decorated table.

"*Pop. Pop. Pop.*" The fringed crackers began to crackle and paper caps appeared, to perch at crazy angles.

"Now everybody keep still while Hester makes a wish and blows out the candles. There's eight and one to grow on!"

For a long moment the clear points of orange flame scarcely stirred above the smooth white frosting with its pink sugar roses. Little reflected sparks of brightness caught in all the watching eyes and then were snuffed out. Hester fell back in her chair triumphant, and an answering breath of relief went round the table. She would have her wish.

Ora's piece held a pink sugar rose and citron leaf that had escaped mutilation. She nibbled round the edges and managed to tie it in another corner of the handkerchief with the jumping beans.

"Well, good-by, I've got to be going." Ora slipped over to Hester as they left the table. "Thanks a lot for asking me to your party. I—"

She was glad that someone turned on the radio just then and spared her having to say she'd had a lovely time. But Hester didn't seem to notice the omission.

"Good-by," she said. "I'm glad you won the prize." She gave a quick look to make sure her mother was in the kitchen before she put her arm around Ora and followed her to the door.

"Wait, child, wait!" The old lady was hurrying down the driveway after her, waving something. "Here's some leftover cookies and candy. I expect you've got brothers and sisters who could make use of a few? How many of you are there?"

Ora hesitated. It wouldn't do to act too eager. But she couldn't very well hurt Hester's grandmother.

"Thank you, ma'am," she said. Then, remembering a favorite phrase of Pa's,

she added, "There's quite a snarl of us young ones."

Once the house was out of sight she breathed more easily. She could see the flashing of cars through the tree trunks as she came nearer the road, but no sign of Pa by the gates. There would be time to do what she had made up her mind must be done.

A ditch lay between the road and the fenced-in acres of fruit and walnut trees. It had been deepened by the rains. Mud and dank grass and debris filled it in matted confusion. Ora marked a great ball of tumbleweed and began to climb down toward it, bracing her feet as well as she could in the drying clay. She kept the prize package in the crook of her arm till she was safely down. Then she took it in both hands and turned it round and round. The paper was smooth and white without a wrinkle on it anywhere, and the pink ribbon stood up stiff and beautiful, the way it never did after a second or third tying.

Vida May wouldn't have hesitated. She'd have hunched up one shoulder and grinned and said, "Well, I put one over on those stiff-necks, all right!" After all, a prize was a prize, even if the joke was on you. Hester had picked it out herself. She had been glad Ora had won it, and that made it not quite fair to Hester if she didn't even look inside the box.

"You could say you won the peanut hunt or the donkey pinning—" The words came dry and scratchy, as if the very weeds were tempting her.

"But the folks would be sure to find out," Ora stood up to herself in the bottom of the ditch. "I couldn't ever fool them if I fetched it back, and if Ma thought I looked funny she'd feel bad, real bad. I couldn't hurt Ma's feelings like that. But I guess there's no harm if I take one look."

The ribbon yielded to her fingers with voluptuous softness; the whispering tissue paper parted to show a china vase like no other she had ever seen. The white, tapering fingers of a lady's hand clasped the part meant to hold flowers, and as if it were not enough, little gold-flecked sprigs had been scattered over the smooth surface. Ora half expected to feel them growing, so real they seemed in their painted bloom—the roses so pink, the forget-me-nots so blue. She made sure she had not missed a single leaf or bud. She clasped her own square fingers over the delicate china ones to fix the position in her mind forever.

"It won't hurt if I keep the ribbon," she decided, as she fitted the cover on the box.

When she scrambled up the bank again there was no sign of white paper. Already it was turning the color of the clay that would keep her secret, of the tumbleweed that would hide her shame.

Even with the sun in her eyes she made out the high-bodied car a long way off. Pa drew up and helped her in.

"Well," he said, "have a good time? What's in the bag?"

"Cookies and candy. Want some, Pa? Or a peanut—I found most a whole pocketful in the peanut hunt."

"No, thanks; I'll stick to my quid. Guess the kids and Ma'll be able to help you out, though."

It felt good to settle back beside him and not have to make up things to say for a while. The wild-flower fields were coming in sight, with the highway cutting between. On either side they stretched, clear to the mountains, which were purple now and mottled with cloud shadows. The lupin was turning purple, too, in the late light. It was a pure wonder any way you looked at it.

"Pretty, all right." Pa slowed down. "Sight for sore eyes."

Ora drew a long breath before she answered. "My but there's a lot," she said. "Lots more'n a vase could hold, isn't there, Pa?"

She stayed quiet after that for such a long time that even Pa noticed it.

"You act all in," he said. "Well, sociability can be awful hard work sometimes."

"Yes, Pa," Ora agreed, and edged closer to him on the seat.

THE END

she learns that she is not welcome at the party. Why does she go to the party anyway?

4. *a.* No one at the party is unkind to Ora on purpose. How are the other guests unkind without knowing it?

b. How does Ora react to their thoughtless cruelty?

c. How is Ora's behavior related to the title of the story?

5. Ora feels that "every time they laughed and praised her for looking tacky she was betraying Ma and the rest."

a. What does she do that seems to make up for betraying her family?

b. How does this part of the story fit in with the title?

c. What do Ora's words about lupin—"My, but there's a lot. Lots more'n a vase could hold, isn't there, Pa?"—tell you about the way she feels regarding her decision?

Talking it over

1. *a.* Why does an invitation to Hester's party mean so much to Ora?

b. What tells you that Hester was unhappy about not being able to invite Ora?

2. *a.* What kind of experiences do you infer that Vida May has probably had with people like Hester's family?

b. Why does Vida May help Ora get ready for the party in spite of the way she feels?

c. Why doesn't Ora's family know more about what is suitable for normal party wear?

3. When Ora overhears Hester's mother talking to Hester's grandmother,

Words in action

When Ora overhears Mrs. Burt talking about her, the author writes, "way down inside of her something pressed chill and hard like an ice cube." How else would you describe Ora's feelings or emotions at this point?

Physical reactions are often set off by emotions. When might you feel "butterflies" in your stomach? What might make your hands feel clammy? What emotion is suggested by the expression "My hair stood on end" or "It sent shivers up and down my spine"?

In "Beginning of Wisdom" the author often describes Ora's physical reactions to help you understand her feelings. What are Ora's feelings in each of the following situations?

1. "Ora put her hand to her throat to try to ease the tightness just above the sewed-on brooch." (p. 195)

2. ". . . Ora told herself between clenched teeth." (p. 195)

3. "Her fingers went numb . . . ." (p. 196)

4. "Once the house was out of sight she breathed more easily." (p. 198)

Me: Views and viewpoints

1. Turn to the first page of this unit and reread the questions about growing up. How do they apply to selections in this unit?

2. Which of these stories seem to be saying, "As you grow older, you will change, and so will the attitude of people around you. TIME will solve many of the problems that bother you now"?

3. We can learn from our experiences, and even from the mistakes we make. In these selections, which persons either do learn or have an opportunity to learn from experience?

4. *a.* In which selections does a young person disobey an adult?

   b. What is the reason for this behavior in each case?

   c. Are any of the young people justified in disobeying an adult? Why or why not?

5. Which of the parents show understanding for their children's problems?

6. Which person in this unit would you most like to have as a friend? Why?

6

Central Idea

LESSON ONE: Why does the writer break it up?

The article below, like almost everything you read, is divided into parts called paragraphs.

PEOPLE TALK about a dog being man's best friend, but as often as not it's really the other way around. My Great Dane, Max, for example, seems to think of me as *his* pet. At least he has taken over the house almost as completely as if that were the case.

2 To begin with, he is bigger than I am. Max stands seven and a half feet on his hind legs and weighs 280 pounds. There is something about a dog as big as a Shetland pony that keeps you from ordering him around quite as you would, say, a poodle. But Max has gotten the idea that he was really meant to be a lap dog. He will come when I am asleep and lie across my legs, which makes it quite impossible for me to move until he wants me to. And if he decides to sleep in a spot where I will stumble over him constantly—well, there is no moving him, of course.

3 He is tremendously strong. There is no hope of getting something away from him if he doesn't want to give it up. When he disapproves of me he crawls under the dining table, but he often forgets where he is and will upset the whole table by just getting to his feet. He can knock me flat by putting his paws on my shoulder to show he wants to play. When he is happy, and wags his tail, it almost always means a broken vase or an overturned lamp.

4 Feeding him is also a problem, as you might expect. Max eats much more than I do—about four pounds of food a day. Even so, he is always hungry, and to him anything may be food. He has eaten a pair of my good slippers— not just chewed them up, as puppies will do—but eaten them. He ate the teddy bear I gave him to play with. He ate half of the pad from under the rug (although I think he did this to let me know he doesn't like being left alone). He even eats the mail if he gets to it before I do.

5 Don't bother to ask who is the master in my house. Max is the master, and he won't let me forget it. I'm just thankful he lets me sleep indoors.

1. The title of an article often reveals what the article is about. From the following list, choose the title which would best fit the whole article:

   a. How to Raise Great Danes
   b. The Master of My House
   c. Max's Strange Diet
   d. Undesirable Pets

2. *a.* What three main points did the writer make to prove what he had to say? In what paragraph is each point made?

b. What do you think is the purpose of the other two paragraphs? How are they different from the three paragraphs that gave you detailed information about Max?

c. How are paragraphs 1 and 5 related to the title you chose for the article? How are the other three paragraphs related to the title you chose?

3. What conclusion do you draw about why the writer has divided his material into paragraphs?

The arrangement of a piece of writing into **paragraphs** helps you keep track of what the writer is saying. Most paragraphs begin with a blank space called an **indention,** which sets them apart.

Paragraphs also help a writer make his points stand out more clearly, so that a reader can understand more easily how the material is organized. Each of the three middle paragraphs in the article about Max was about a slightly different part of the writer's problem.

EXERCISE I. Some reasons for paragraphs

Here is some more material about Max. Does it give you general information or specific details?

Max and the Baby Doll
by Donald Abramson

1 Max ate up or chewed to shreds nearly everything I gave him as a plaything. I kept trying, anyway. I hoped that something might hold his interest long enough to keep him away from my slippers (I had bought a new pair) and my other personal possessions.

2 One day I brought him a large baby doll. The doll was made of rubber and was dressed in baby clothes. I knew the clothes wouldn't last more than ten minutes but I hoped the doll would be good for a day, at least.

3 Max pounced on the doll playfully, and not too gently. To him everything was a toy, so he didn't really care that the doll wasn't a slipper or a good sweater. Max's mouth is so huge that when he held the doll in his teeth, almost the whole thing was inside his mouth. A little pink arm stuck out on one side and a foot with a bootee stuck out on the other.

4 I turned him loose in the yard, which is big and is surrounded by a high wire fence, so that I usually don't have to worry that Max will get out unless he really wants to. I left him there and forgot about him for a while.

5 Some time later the doorbell rang. I was startled, when I opened the door, to find two policemen standing there,

carrying shotguns and looking very grim. They were answering a report, they told me, about a mad dog which had gotten hold of one of the neighborhood children and was probably eating him.

6 I dashed to the rear of the house, the policemen following me. Through the window I could see Max frisking about in the yard, tearing up grass and what was left of the bushes. From one side of his mouth still dangled a little pink arm.

7 For some reason, the police did not appreciate my bursting out laughing. Nor did they look any less suspicious when I explained that it was only a plaything I had given Max. They wanted me to get it and show them. This wasn't easy. Max thought I wanted to play. It took twenty minutes of running and bounding and jumping with him before I came back, dirty and out of breath, to show them the wet, half-chewed remains of Max's latest toy.

8 Sometimes I wish Max were just a little bit more like an average dog, the kind who merely chases sticks and butterflies and an occasional car or two. Of course, I shudder to think what might happen if Max ever did take to chasing cars—and caught one!

1. Each of the sentences below states the main action of one of the paragraphs of the article. For each of the eight paragraphs, choose the sentence which tells what happened in that paragraph.

   a. The police come in answer to a report.
   b. The writer has to play with Max to get the doll back.
   c. Max takes the toy and holds it in his mouth.
   d. The writer wishes Max were more like an average dog.
   e. The writer gives Max a baby doll.
   f. Max is left in the yard.
   g. The writer and the policemen see Max playing in the yard.
   h. The writer tries to find playthings for Max.

2. So far in this section you have learned that a new paragraph can signal two different kinds of change: a shift or a change in the action, or a shift to a new point the author wants to make. In which part of the article about Max—the part in Lesson One or the part in this exercise—does a shift to a new paragraph indicate that the author is making a new point?

EXERCISE II. Signaling for other types of change

Below is part of a story. Read it all the way through. Each paragraph indention is a signal that something new and different may be discussed next.

1 Nate drew his horse to a stop at the foot of a bluff that shut out the wind. Two dwarfed trees, one of them lightning-struck and broken, leaned into each other, their mingled branches spreading like the ribs of an umbrella. The damaged tree would offer handy firewood, and a trickle of water hurrying down the eroded cliff met his only other need.

2 Tethering the horse in a grassy spot, he set about making camp. He threw a blanket over the low trees and smiled at the perfect tent he had made. He quickly built a fire and when it was large enough he set a pan of beef stew to warm. In a short time water for coffee was steaming in the small coffee-pot he carried in his gear.

3 While he ate, Nate thought about what was ahead. It was important that all the ranchers in the territory stick together in order to combat the band of outlaws who were said to be moving this way to take over the whole area. In fact, it was more than important—it was vital. And every rancher had to co-operate if their plan for stopping the outlaws was to succeed. That was Nate's mission, to secure their coöperation.

4 Jim Thorne would not be easy to persuade, however. Nate knew him to be a stubborn man who preserved his opinions in vinegar. Thorne had already said he would not go along with the rest. He preferred to handle his own business in his own way. Nate recalled the stubborn set of the man's mouth and the stern refusal in the black eyes —the impatient gesture of a scornful, dismissing hand.

5 The next morning, however, the camper had recovered his courage. Before sunrise he was up and away on his vital journey. Thorne's ranch was about three hours ahead.

1. Look back over the selection. Why did the author write the first paragraph? What did he most want you to get from it?

2. Each new paragraph after the first one signals a shift or change of some sort. For each of these paragraphs (2 through 5) choose one of the following to describe the shift which occurs. (You will not need one of the items.)

   a. A shift in time
   b. A shift to action
   c. A shift to a description of a character
   d. A shift to a different place
   e. A shift to a character's thoughts

EXERCISE III. Signaling for a change of speaker

Here is some conversation from *The Adventures of Tom Sawyer*, by Mark Twain. Tom has just met another boy, a stranger in town, and has challenged him to fight. At this point in the story they are standing shoulder to shoulder, pushing back and forth, and daring each other to make the first move.

The paragraphs will help you keep track of who is speaking. As you read, note what kind of shift is expressed by each new paragraph indention.

After struggling till both were hot and flushed, each relaxed his strain with watchful caution, and Tom said:

"You're a coward and a pup. I'll tell my big brother on you, and he can thrash you with his little finger, and I'll make him do it, too."

"What do I care for your big brother? I've got a brother that's bigger than he is—and what's more, he can throw him over that fence, too." Both brothers were imaginary.

"That's a lie."

"*Your* saying so don't make it so."

Tom drew a line in the dust with his big toe, and said:

"I dare you to step over that, and I'll lick you till you can't stand up. Anybody that'll take a dare will steal sheep."

The new boy stepped over promptly, and said:

"Now you said you'd do it, now let's see you do it."

"Don't you crowd me now; you better look out."

"Well, you *said* you'd do it—why don't you do it?"

"By jingo! for two cents I *will* do it."

1. How can you tell where the speaker changes?
2. Who says, "That's a lie"? How can you tell?

As you have seen, a writer may begin a new paragraph for many different reasons. Although there are no hard-and-fast rules about when a writer *must* begin a new paragraph, most writers use paragraphs to do these things:

1. To talk about a different subject or a different part of the same subject
2. To show a shift in action
3. To describe a new scene or a different part of the same scene
4. To show a change in time
5. To describe a new person or to describe different things about the same person
6. To show shifts from speaker to speaker in a conversation

If a reader knows these possibilities, he will be prepared for something different when he meets a new paragraph.

LESSON TWO: How long should a paragraph be?

Before you read the following article, read the questions which follow it.

The Question

1 Why can't I get along with Miss Marshall, my mother wants to know.

2 So do I.

3 Sometimes I feel I was born only to make my English teacher mad. If she asks for a paragraph about our favorite sport, I eagerly write three pages because I can't explain how I feel about baseball in just one paragraph. Then she writes—in red—that I didn't follow directions. When she wants a two-page paper on the importance of speaking good English, I can think of only three sentences. And I try hard. If somebody is restless and taps a pencil on the desk, it always seems to be me. Or if Miss Marshall thinks her class looks particularly sloppy today, I have to be the one who lost a button off my shirt on the way to school. If Miss Marshall calls me to her desk, I always manage to stumble over somebody's chair, which gets me dirty looks from both the occupant and Miss Marshall. And if I eagerly ask her what the assignment is for tomorrow, she has just given it five minutes before, and where was I? Or she wishes I wouldn't ask until everyone is ready to hear it. Getting along with Miss Marshall seems to be my biggest burden.

4 Why?

5 Some questions, I tell my mother, just don't have any answers.

1. Which paragraph fully states the question referred to in the title?
2. Which paragraph discusses the problem in detail?
3. What connection does the last paragraph have with the first paragraph?
4. Consider the two very short paragraphs, 2 and 4. Following are some possible reasons why the author might have made these paragraphs so short. Choose the reason or reasons which are most likely.

    a. Short paragraphs stand out because they contrast with the longer paragraphs.
    b. There wasn't much space left, or much time.
    c. Paragraphs of different lengths provide variety.
    d. There was nothing more to be said.

EXERCISE IV. Using a short paragraph as a bridge

In the following brief section of a story, a short paragraph has been used in a rather special way:

> 1 I like ghost stories. The eerier the better. But when the story is over and the hair on my head is lying flat again, I invariably laugh and say, "Of course no sensible person believes in ghosts."
>
> 2 Until recently. Now I don't know.
>
> 3 I was in London last January and decided to drive up to Oxford to do some research in one of the libraries there. On the evening of Wednesday the 18th, at the close of a bone-chilling, rainy day, I rented a motorcar and set out on Highway A40. . . .[1]

Consider what paragraph 2 does in this part of the story:

1. What does "until recently" do to what you have read in the first paragraph?
2. When you read "Now I don't know," what do you guess will follow?
3. How does paragraph 2 serve as a "bridge" in the passage you have just read? What other reasons have you seen for short paragraphs?

EXERCISE V. Grouping sentences into paragraphs

Part A

The sentences which follow are the first part of a story.[2] As you read them, think about which ones seem to belong together. At the end, you will find some help in grouping them into paragraphs.

1. One Saturday afternoon I got on my bicycle and started off into the country.

2. I had no particular idea where I was going, but I had decided to explore.

3. Soon I was riding along a path beside a small river which wound through the countryside.

4. I had gone only a mile or two before I noticed something rather curious behind some trees about a quarter of a mile from the stream.

[1]From "I Don't Believe in Ghosts, But . . ." by Jhan Robbins, from *Reader's Digest* (July 1967). Reprinted by permission of The Reader's Digest.

[2]Adaptation of "Mystery on the Hill" from *In the Beginning* by Roger Pilkington. Copyright © 1957 by Roger Pilkington. Reprinted by permission of Independent Press, Ltd.

5. Deciding to look at it more closely, I turned away from the stream and rode down a lane until I found myself at the foot of a little hill which had steep sides and which was a strange bluish-gray in color.

6. I leaned my bike against the fence and crawled through.

7. The hill was about twice as high as a house and very steep, and it was made up of a great pile of grayish powdery stone.

8. I scrambled to the top on all fours, covering my shoes and trousers with the fine dust as I slipped and struggled up the side.

9. When at last I reached the top I could see on the other side a big pit full of water, beyond which were some hills just like the one I was on.

10. Between two of the hills stood the ruins of a small factory building.

11. It was an old cement quarry long unused.

Decide how you would group these eleven sentences into the three paragraphs described below. On your paper, after the number of each paragraph, write the numbers of the sentences which should go into that paragraph.

Paragraph   I. Setting out to explore

Paragraph   II. Discovering an unusual hill

Paragraph III. Exploring the hill

Part B

In the following eleven sentences, the story continues. Proceed as you did in Part A.

12. The whole place seemed dead, a queer kind of relic of days that had passed.

13. Once there had been workmen there, and steam-shovels, and clanking trucks bringing the waste to the heap I was standing on, but now it was deserted.

14. The hinges of a half-rotted door in the ruined building creaked loudly as the wind swung it to and fro.

15. The glass in the skylights was broken in, and here and there the roof itself had collapsed.

16. Work must have been stopped here before I was born.

17. I turned away and walked around on the flat top of the waste heap.

18. It was all very dull and gray and nothing seemed to grow on it apart from a few scraggly weeds.

19. I was just about to go down the slope to my bicycle and return to the river when I noticed a curious object sticking out of the powdery ground.

20. It was long and thin, and looked exactly like a bone, but when I stooped and picked it up I discovered that it was quite heavy, much too heavy for a bone.

21. It was stone.

22. It was a fossil—a fossil bone, in fact.

Indicate how you would group sentences 12-22 into these three paragraphs:

Paragraph IV. Examining the factory from a distance
Paragraph V. Walking around on the hill
Paragraph VI. Discovering the bones

EXERCISE VI. Grouping sentences into paragraphs

The sentences in this exercise continue the story[3] from Exercise V. Read through the sentences quickly to find out what happened. Then go back over them and decide how you would group them to make four paragraphs.

23. I searched the hill very carefully, and by the end of the afternoon I had managed to find about thirty of the fossil bones.

24. Some were whole bones, roundish and flat, about the size of a half-dollar.

25. Others were broken, but a few of them fitted together to make long, thin, and curved pieces, tapering at one end.

26. I gathered them up, ran down the hill, and cycled quickly back.

27. That evening I packed the bones in newspaper and did them up in a package.

28. I also wrote a note which said, "Dear Sir, Please tell me what these are and how old, and send them back."

29. I addressed the package to the Natural History Museum in a nearby city, and next morning I mailed it with my note.

30. A week later the package returned.

31. In great excitement I tore it open.

32. Inside was a letter from the assistant curator of the museum.

33. "Dear Sir," it said, "The specimens which you sent for identification are ribs, vertebrae, and a paddle bone, all of *Ichthyosaurus,* a large marine reptile.

34. They are separately labeled for your convenience and are returned herewith.

35. The date at which the *Ichthyosaurus* lived would be approximately a hundred to a hundred and fifty million years ago."

36. As I put the bones away carefully, I felt the queerest sensation of being somehow in touch with a world that had existed an incredibly long time ago.

37. Just as the ruined cement works had been a relic of workmen who had toiled and steam shovels which had clanked long before I was born, so these remains of a prehistoric creature

[3]From *In the Beginning* by Roger Pilkington.

told of a very different time far further back, so long before the steam shovels I couldn't imagine it.

38. But I felt proud and somehow excited to know that I was part—even a tiny part—of the history which had included creatures such as my *Ichthyosaurus*.

This time you are to decide what each paragraph will be about, and which sentences go into the paragraph.

On your paper, write I, II, III, and IV to indicate four paragraphs. After the paragraph number, write the numbers of the sentences which you would put in that paragraph. Then write for each paragraph a statement of what that paragraph is about. (For a model, you may want to refer to the paragraph descriptions or titles given in Exercise V.)

After you have grouped all the sentences into paragraphs, write your own title for the whole story—Exercise V and Exercise VI together.

LESSON THREE: What's the big idea?

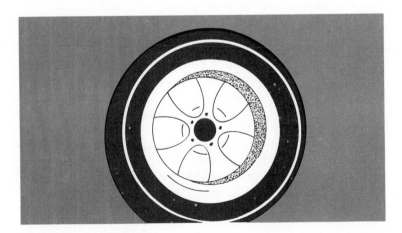

What is this a picture of?

If you say it is a picture of a wheel, you are right. But what does it *mean*? If the picture means nothing to you by itself, look at it again in combination with some other pictures:

1. What is in these pictures that is also in the first picture? What is different in these pictures?
2. Put into one sentence the idea suggested to you by the thing that is the same in all the pictures.

Very often a detail or a piece of information does not mean much until we see that it is meant to be part of a larger picture or a larger idea.

There are several ways you might have worded the idea suggested by the six pictures above. You might have said, "The wheel can be used in many ways," or you might have said, "The wheel is important because it is a part of many things we use." At any rate, you probably got the "big idea," that the wheel is a part of each of the things pictured.

Very often the "big idea," or the **central idea** of a selection, is suggested by the title. You have already identified the central ideas of two of the selections in Lessons One and Two of this unit when you were asked to select a title for the opening article about Max, and to write your own title for the story in Exercises V and VI. In this lesson you will concentrate on finding the central idea.

EXERCISE VII. Finding the central idea of a paragraph

What is the general subject of this paragraph?

> When the weather is fair, inmates of Sing Sing prison may be seen out in the yard playing baseball, softball, lawn bowls, and handball. Groups of men in gray trousers, shirts, and caps gather in a corner to lift weights or pitch horseshoes. Indeed, prisons offer a rich and varied recreational fare that many colleges would find hard to match. At Dannemora, another New York prison, the big yard has a bobsled run in the winter, which is banked against the prison walls. Alongside the start of the bob run is a ski jump—facing inward! At San Quentin in California prisoners can take part in twelve different recreational activities ranging from chess to boxing.[4]

Choose the best ending for each of the following statements:

1. All the sentences in the previous article have to do with
   a. prison security devices.
   b. prisons in New York.
   c. prison recreational programs.

2. Several sentences emphasize
   a. the variety of activities.
   b. how physical activity helps keep prisoners healthy.
   c. how prisoners like their recreation time.

3. Which sentence in the paragraph best states what the entire paragraph is about?

In written material, **details** are the facts, ideas, and bits of information that the author puts into his writing. From these details you get a fuller understanding of what the author wants to tell you. That is, the details all combine to make the central idea.

---

[4]Based on material in "Fight On, Old Sing Sing U" by Robert Boyle, in *Sports Illustrated* for January 23, 1967.

EXERCISE VIII. More practice in finding central idea

What is the central idea in the following paragraph?

> There are more than a half million different kinds of animals on earth today. They range from the tiny water creatures that exist by the billions and are visible only under a microscope, to the mosquitoes that swarm around your head on a summer evening—to man. Many of these animals have vast families. Often there are more worms in a single field than there are people in the whole of New York City. The little red-eyed fruit fly that flits above a pile of apples may produce a family of eight hundred in less than a month. Even the sparrows or starlings that fill our skies outnumber man. Compared to the other forms of life on our planet, we humans are scarce indeed.

1. From the four statements below, select the one which you feel best states the point that the writer of the above paragraph wishes to bring out.

   a. There are more worms than there are people.
   b. Insects multiply rapidly.
   c. Human beings are becoming scarce.
   d. Other types of life outnumber human beings.

2. Copy the statement in the paragraph that says almost the same thing as the central idea you chose.

How can you tell what is the central idea in a piece of writing? In looking for the central ideas of the paragraphs in Exercises VII and VIII, you looked first for some idea that all or most of the details seemed to fit in with. These central ideas turned out to be statements or ideas to which all the details contributed their part. This means that the central idea, or "big idea," will be bigger—that is, more general—than any one of the smaller ideas or details. It also means that the central idea will be a kind of summary of all the smaller ones.

EXERCISE IX. Sorting out ideas

Read the statements below, then decide which one could serve as the central idea for most of the others and which statements do not belong with the others at all.

A. A January vacation would divide the school year more evenly than the Christmas vacation does.

B. The Christmas vacation is not long enough for the Christmas activities and a good rest, too.

C. Last year the weather spoiled our vacation.

D. Most students are tired after four months of school and need time to relax.

E. Schools should close for a full month in January.

F. With a good vacation between semesters, students would return to work with more energy and interest.

G. Our family is planning to buy a travel trailer.

H. Families could take winter vacations instead of always traveling in hot weather.

I. In many parts of the country the weather is uncertain in January, and schools often have to close for some days.

J. Weather prediction is an interesting science.

K. January is a time of many colds and illnesses which cause frequent absences from school.

1. Which sentence best summarizes the idea that most of the rest of the sentences support?
2. Which sentences are not related to the central idea and are out of place among the other supporting ideas?

Do you think this picture is funny? If you do, you have probably understood the central idea already.

1. Which of the following details are important to understanding the picture, and which could be changed or left out without destroying the humor?

   a. The kind of clothes the woman wears
   b. The tree the man wants to plant
   c. The woman's expression
   d. The many holes in the yard
   e. The color of the house
   f. The spade the man has been using
   g. The expression on the man's face

2. What old, familiar idea is the artist poking fun at? Choose from the ideas below the one that you need to be familiar with in order to see the humor in this picture.

    a. Some people seem to have "green thumbs"—anything will grow for them.
    b. Flowers and plants help make a place look more cheerful.
    c. Women change their minds very often.
    d. Certain kinds of plants grow best in certain climates.
    e. Women are said to be more sensitive to beauty than men.

3. Try to describe in one sentence the complete idea in the picture. If you wish, you may use as part of your sentence the idea you chose in question 2, but your sentence should be specific; that is, it should express the idea in this *particular* picture.

Note that not one of the details in the picture expresses the central idea by itself—not the holes in the yard, nor the expression on the woman's face, nor even the expression on the man's face. None of them can tell you *by itself* that the housewife has changed her mind so often that now she has a yard full of holes and the tree still is not planted. This is an *understanding* that you get from the whole picture, with all its details.

EXERCISE X. Finding the central idea of a short article

The details in this brief article will help you understand the central idea.

How Do They Do It?
by Bill Hazelton

1 My parents do not own a crystal ball. No gypsies—no palm readers or tea-leaf fortune tellers—brighten the history of our ancestors. There is not among my relatives even a weather forecaster. And yet my father and mother can tell when I am headed for stormy weather even before the clouds begin to gather.

2 For instance, last Friday my father said I had better get around to repairing my bike before I was sorry I hadn't. But I shrugged it off again that night because I wanted to go to a movie. The next morning, the kids I run around with cooked up a weekend ride with a sleepout at a farm. I scurried around, trying to repair the bike, but the shop didn't have a part I needed and couldn't get it until Monday. Was I sorry!

3 The weekend before that, I came home from school one afternoon in a black temper. I was mad at Jimmy Thompson because he lost us a baseball game. Jimmy is only eight, but he always wants to play with us older guys; and is he shortsighted and clumsy! While I gulped down two fresh doughnuts in our kitchen, I was telling Mom about how I got sore this time and really told him off. Mom said the Thompsons had been very nice to me and that I ought to be more patient with Jimmy. "I suspect you will be sorry you lost your temper," she predicted.

4 Well, the next day, Mr. Thompson took Jimmy to a Big League game, but this time they didn't take me along! See what I mean? It happens all the time.

5 Will I have to study witchcraft or astrology to find out how my parents do it? Or is it just that being a parent can give you certain powers that other —younger—people don't have?

1. What example does Bill give in paragraph 2? What similar example does he give in paragraphs 3 and 4?
2. What details in paragraphs 1 and 5 are similar?
3. What strange ability does Bill accuse his parents of having?
4. How serious do you think Bill is when he suggests that his parents possess a strange ability? Why does he make this suggestion?
5. What is the central idea of the entire article? Does it have to do with many parents, or just Bill's parents?

LESSON FIVE: Central idea in a narrative

You are probably familiar with the brief story which follows. It is very old, and was told originally to express a clear and simple central idea.

The Fox and the Crow
Adapted from the fable by Aesop

A CROW once sat on a branch of a high tree, holding in her beak a piece of cheese that she had stolen. A fox who was passing by smelled the cheese and looked about, trying to locate it. When he saw the crow perched high above him, he immediately set about figuring how he might get the cheese for himself. Finally he called out to the crow, "Hello, my friend! I must say you're looking well today. Your feathers are glossy and beautiful and your eyes are very bright. Dear Crow, if you could only sing as well as you look, I'd have to call you the loveliest bird in all the world!"

As she listened to the flattering words of the fox, the crow held herself more and more proudly. At last she opened her mouth and began to caw her best. But the moment she did so she also let go of the piece of cheese, which fell through the branches to the ground. The fox snatched up the cheese and ate it, then trotted away, laughing back over his shoulder at the poor crow, who remained on her branch, feeling very foolish.

A fable is an animal story which expresses its central idea in the form of a *moral* at the end. Choose, from the possible morals below, the one which best expresses the central idea of this fable:

1. Never try to sing when you have a bad voice.
2. It's best to get your own food.
3. Don't trust the words of a flatterer.
4. In ancient times, animals used to speak.

Most stories are not as simple as this fable, of course, and few of them tell you right out—in the form of a moral or any other statement—what the central idea is. But it is important to realize that usually a writer has more in mind than just telling what happened to particular characters. A story may have the additional purpose of illustrating or explaining something about people in general. It may be making a point about the way things often work out in this world—for example, that a person who commits a crime is usually punished in one way or another.

EXERCISE XI. Finding the central idea in a narrative

The following story is based upon a fable told in India long ago. Read it and then answer the questions which follow it.

The Blind Men and the Elephant
Adapted from a poem by John Godfrey Saxe

THERE WERE six men of Hindoostan who were blind, but each man thought he could see as well with his hands as any one else could with his eyes. Whenever they touched anything they thought they knew all about it, though they had felt only a small part.

Now, these six blind men had never seen an elephant. They did not know what an elephant was like because nobody could describe an elephant so that they could know what it was like. Besides that, these blind men never believed what anybody told them.

One day an elephant came to their town and they decided to pay him a visit. The first blind man approached the elephant and stumbled against his big broad side. He felt along the rough hide up and down and as far as he could reach.

"Why, bless me! the elephant is just like a wall or the side of my house. I had no idea an elephant was like that!" said the first blind man.

Then the second blind man approached the elephant and caught hold of his hard tusks with the sharp points. He felt along the smooth tusks as far as he could reach.

"Why, bless me! the elephant is very like a spear. I had no idea an elephant looked like that!" said the second blind man.

Then the third blind man approached the elephant and caught hold of his trunk. The old elephant moved his trunk from side to side, and squirmed, while the third blind man felt of it as far as he could.

"I see the elephant is very like a snake. I had no idea an elephant was like that!" said the third blind man.

The fourth blind man now came up and took hold of the elephant's leg. He felt how big and solid it was and he felt along the leg as far as he could reach.

"It is very clear to me that an elephant is very like a tree. I had no idea an elephant was like that!" said the fourth blind man.

The fifth blind man came and put his hand on the elephant's ear. He felt along the big ear as far as he could.

"Well, this elephant is very like a fan. I had no idea an elephant looked like that!" said the fifth blind man.

The sixth blind man came up and caught the elephant by the tail. He pulled and twisted as hard as he could.

"I see, the elephant is very like a rope. I had no idea an elephant was like that!" said the sixth blind man.

And they quarreled all one day and late into the night, and they never did know what the elephant was like.

From *Worth While Stories for Every Day,* compiled by Lawton B. Evans. Copyright 1917 by Milton Bradley Company. Used by permission of McGraw-Hill Book Company.

Consider the details in the fable of "The Blind Men and the Elephant" before you determine its central idea:

1. If there had been a seventh blind man who happened to sit upon the elephant's back, would he have been likely to agree or disagree with the statements of the others? Why?

2. All the following statements are true, but some of them are about details which could be changed without changing the central idea of the fable. Which of the following statements are necessary to make the point of the story?

   a. There was more than one man.

   b. Most of the men compared the elephant to a *thing,* rather than to another animal.

> *c.* Each of the men experienced only a part of the elephant.
>
> *d.* The men were from Hindoostan.
>
> *e.* The men never believed what anybody told them.
>
> *f.* Each man felt that he alone understood what an elephant really was.
>
> *g.* The men were all blind.
>
> *h.* The animal they were trying to understand was an elephant, instead of a camel or a giraffe or any other animal.

3. Now think about what the details you have chosen all add up to. Then complete the following comment on the behavior of the blind men: "None of the blind men would ever really know what an elephant is like because_____."

4. Try to state your central idea again, but this time make it a more general statement.

What you should know about paragraphs and central idea

Paragraphs mark divisions in a piece of writing. Whenever a new paragraph begins, there is a shift or change of some kind. The shift may be to a different

—idea or part of an idea
—speaker
—character
—place
—time
—action.

The **central idea** of a paragraph or a longer piece of writing is an understanding the reader gets from the whole piece with all its details. The central idea may be stated outright in one or more sentences, or it may be a general understanding that the reader must piece together for himself.

Narrative, as well as factual, writing can have a central idea, although in a narrative the central idea is usually not stated as clearly as it is in a factual article.

7

If you want to be able to

. . . hold your head high,

. . . keep up your courage

when it would be easy

to give in to fear,

. . . endure hardship and

danger,

. . . survive mainly by

your wits—

then you must learn

to live with

PRESSURE.

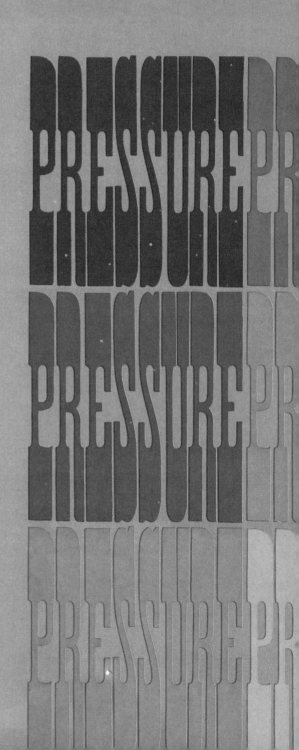

PRESSURE PRESSURE PRESSURE PR

PRESSURE PRESSURE PRESSURE PR

PRESSURE

PRESSURE

FOUL SHOT

by Edwin A. Hoey

With two 60's stuck on the scoreboard
And two seconds hanging on the clock,
The solemn boy in the center of eyes,
Squeezed by silence,
5 Seeks out the line with his feet,
Soothes his hands along his uniform,
Gently drums the ball against the floor,
Then measures the waiting net,
Raises the ball on his right hand,
10 Balances it with his left,
Calms it with fingertips,
Breathes,
Crouches,
Waits,
15 And then through a stretching of stillness,
Nudges it upward.

The ball
Slides up and out,
Lands,
20 Leans,
Wobbles,
Wavers,
Hesitates,
Exasperates,
25 Plays it coy
Until every face begs with unsounding screams—
And then

And then

And then,

30 Right before ROAR-UP,
Dives down and through.

Reprinted by permission of *Read* Magazine, junior high school publication for English and the language arts, published by American Education Publications, Columbus, Ohio.

Talking it over

1. Why is this foul shot so important?

2. *a*. What persons feel pressure in this poem? How can you tell?

b. How do they behave under pressure?

Words in action

1. *ROAR-UP* is a compound word made up by the poet. What is the meaning of the phrase "right before ROAR-UP"? What do all-capital letters add to the meaning?

2. *a*. How does the basketball "play it coy"?

b. What words in the second stanza lead up to this idea?

Millie felt a strange terror.
With a word or a nod she could strike
a final staggering blow.

Millie

by Leah T. Turets

WHEN Millie told her about the gym shoes being gone, Miss Jennings seemed pretty angry. "I'm really sick and tired of this business," she said. "Are you sure you didn't absent-

From *Seventeen* Magazine, March 1948.

mindedly wander off without them or something?"

"I just this minute put them down, Miss Jennings. I went to put my geometry book away and when I got back . . ." Millie couldn't say another word. It was the second pair of gym shoes that semester. She'd left the first pair on the streetcar and her mother had had a right to scold. But she'd written her name in ink inside this pair: "Millie Kane, Soph FAHS." Now Mrs. Kane would have to be told that Millie had lost the new pair too. She began to feel awful. It was as though somebody was tying a bunch of knots in her stomach.

Miss Jennings blew the whistle that hung on a red silk cord under the collar of her gym blouse. It was shrill and she gave it a long, hard blow. You could always tell what kind of a mood Miss Jennings was in by the way she blew that whistle.

The girls hurried into line. They shoved for their places and got into position, feet together, hands clasped behind. But their eyes shifted to Millie. She stood a little apart, wondering if she should take her place beside Hilda with the matted hair that always made Millie feel like scratching. It was a rule that you couldn't get into line without your whole gym outfit being on. But if you weren't in line when the whistle blew, you got a gym demerit.

Millie shifted from one stockinged foot to another. The warm blood rose and she felt it glowing in her face. She put her moist fingers to her brow and smoothed the neat triangle of brown hair already tight in a plaited vise.

Miss Jennings cleared her throat. The girls gave her their undivided attention. "Class," she said, very distinctly, "there's been an unfortunate occurrence." Miss Jennings drew her lips in as though to keep any tell-tale expression from showing on her face, and then she looked up and down the long line of girls. When she spoke, her words clicked off her tongue separately, like so many electric-light buttons snapping.

"Something has disappeared again," she said.

A shocked murmur rippled along the line.

Miss Jennings shook her head and spread her hands in a helpless gesture. "Girls," she said, "this is the limit. Last week it was Sally Jordan's change purse and the week before that someone else's gloves. And now Millie's gym shoes were taken the moment she turned her back." Miss Jennings turned to Millie. "Is that the way it was, Millie?"

Millie nodded. She didn't see what else she could do. But she hadn't said they were *taken*. It scared her even to think of accusing somebody of that.

The girls looked at Millie with quick sympathy. They sighed and clucked their tongues and Arline Thomas said out loud, "It's a darn shame." Arline always said exactly what was on her mind—she wasn't afraid of anyone. Millie often felt that Arline must have been born not caring a hoot what anyone thought. It was probably easy to feel that way when you had hundreds of curls on your head instead of hundreds of freckles on your nose. This was the first time Arline had ever noticed Millie. But the look she gave her now made Millie feel they had clasped hands. She smiled at Arline. It was a gentle smile of fortitude. It was a smile to dedicate the handclasp of friendship.

"We simply can't allow this sort of thing to go on," Miss Jennings was saying. "It isn't fair to the girls who have been properly brought up to abhor common stealing, and it certainly isn't fair to Millie and to the others whose honestly paid-for possessions should be as safe in our school gym as in their own homes."

A rising wave of concern flowed

along the line of girls to engulf Millie. It warmed her, and a good feeling inside pushed against her ribs and made her breathe deep. She lifted her head and let her gaze float over the top curl on Arline's head, through the window beyond and out to the yellow-green and clear blue spring day. There was a robin on the fire escape by the window and the pale pink bud of an oleander tree fluttered against the iron rail.

"Millie," Miss Jennings said in her crisp, athletics-teacher voice, "you're absolutely sure you can identify your gym shoes?" The words jerked Millie back into the room.

"Oh, yes, Miss Jennings." Her voice sounded thin and unimpressive in her ears. A queer lump of apprehension was wedging into her throat. Her eyes flew down the line of rubber-soled feet before her and flew right back, staring fixedly at the mole on Miss Jennings' chin as though in fervent denial that they had ever wavered from that spot.

"All right." Miss Jennings spoke in flat, judicial tones. "Walk down the line, look at the shoes on each girl's feet, and pick out your own pair."

A unified gasp greeted this announcement. Sarah Tilford, the tall girl at the end of the line, holding the basketball, tossed the ball aside with a quick jerk and it thumped the length of the room like a beating tom-tom.

A terror such as she had never known gripped Millie. It had a strange, new shape. It clutched her with sharp piercing stabs down to the icy tips of her fingers, into the numbed ends of her toes. It played an unknown, crazy tune on a whirling disk in her head. She was used to the soft, well-patched fear of scoldings; she lived compatibly with the familiar fear of being overlooked.

She spent long hours in bemused wonderment at the curious character of many small, flighty kinds of fears. She enjoyed poking at them occasionally, seeing if they tingled or just blew away like feathers when she spoke up bravely or ran fast down a big hill.

But now this walking down the long, long line, this looking and looking and judging and judging. This horrible stopping and saying, "*This* one . . . ."

"Class!" Miss Jennings commanded, and a charged quiet settled precariously over the room.

"Atten-*tion!*" Miss Jennings snapped her own heels together, toes pointed at forty-five-degree angles, and almost simultaneously thirty-three pairs of canvas-clad heels clicked in echo and thirty-three pairs of toes spread to the angle of honest inspection.

"P-please." Millie started to say the word, but it came out a funny squeak. Miss Jennings nodded toward the far end of the line. Millie felt the bright eyes of the girls spotlighting her as she padded softly down the room toward Sarah Tilford at the very end.

Sarah Tilford was lanky and had big feet. She had on her brother's old brown gym shoes. Millie smiled wan gratitude at Sarah as she started her search for new white ones with rubber soles still clean, five-and-a-half medium. It was awful, wondering what to do with her eyes. She couldn't look at the girls' faces. She avoided a direct glance at the pointed toes as though they were blazing white spears. Her head bowed, she concentrated on knees—thin knocked ones, broad bowed ones, slender Arline ones. The corner of her eye took in the canvas evidence. Too high, too broad, too old, too scuffed, too little, too, too, too . . . She shuffled along, leaving a trail of acquitted virtue where she had passed.

It was almost the end of the line—there were only a few more. Joan Billings at the very end. Probably a size four. White with black soles, anyway. She pushed ahead. Black with black soles, big old ones, funny written-on ones, little brown ones, new white ones with new white soles . . .

New white ones. The rubber soles were clean—new and clean. She knew she was staring at the white shoes with the clean white soles. She had to drag her eyes away from them and she knew before her eyes reached the face of the girl who wore those shoes that the girl was Hilda Foster. Hilda whose thick matted hair made you feel itchy and whose dirty petticoat always stuck out. Hilda whose grey-looking handkerchief always had some money knotted in the corner because she never carried a pocketbook. There had been talk about Hilda, she remembered now. No names mentioned, but strong hints . . . "There was only one person around when I put my gloves down and I never saw gloves on her before." "I'd be ashamed to show my face if they arrested *my* parents for fighting." Once when Millie was out walking with her mother they passed the Fosters' house. A pane was out of a front window and the sooty end of a curtain kept billowing through it. "Gives me the creeps," Mrs. Kane said. "It's a disgrace to the neighborhood." That was Hilda's place. Hilda whose big dark eyes seemed filled with a depressing secret she didn't want you to look at.

But those dark eyes were looking at Millie now. It was a wild, burning look of fear and hope. Millie put her hand to her face as though it had been scorched. Blindly, she stumbled along to the end of the line.

She turned and looked at Miss Jennings.

"E-hmm," Miss Jennings cleared her throat. She waited a moment. "Well, Millie?" she said.

Millie shook her head. Miss Jennings stared at her, questioning. She knew the girls were staring, too, but Millie only shook her head again. No. No. A sound stuck in her throat. She didn't dare let it out.

Miss Jennings tapped her foot. "You mean to tell me . . ." Suddenly her face brightened. "Of course," she said, her voice relaxed and reasonable, "you want to be sure. We won't consider it an accusation—I mean, if a pair looks like yours, any girl here will want to take them off to make certain. If you have your name written . . ."

"No," Millie said then, "I guess not, Miss Jennings."

Miss Jennings opened her mouth—and then snapped it shut. She bit her lip and jerked the whistle out of her pocket. She gave the whistle a short, piercing blow, called out, "Choose up sides!" and, picking up two basketballs from the bench behind her, she threw them swiftly into the line.

The feverish choosing of sides for marathon ball began. The nimble-footed athletes were grabbed up quickly, the close friends were taken on loyally, and the others were more slowly, more reluctantly chosen until all the girls were lined up behind either Arline or Sarah. They counted their lines and Sarah yelled, "We've got one extra."

Miss Jennings looked at Millie, jerked her thumb toward Arline's line, and said, "Get in."

Throughout the game Millie tried to

keep her thoughts with the ball flying swiftly through the air, down the tunnel of legs, up the aisle in a runner's arms, through the air to the basket again, up down around, fast, fast, fast, never stopping. When it came her turn she clutched the ball to her stomach and ran like a bedeviled fury to the basket, her mercerized lisles slipping dangerously on the smooth gym floor. She made a couple of wild, luckless throws; then, straining every nerve to the task, she took careful aim, threw the ball, and closed her eyes. When she heard the whoop of relief that went up from her line she grabbed the ball and ran to her place.

The three-thirty bell rang at last. Millie followed the crowd of girls pushing through the door to the locker room. She was glad she had last-period gym. She could get dressed and go home now.

The locker room was filled with the damp smell of sweat and the sweet scent of face powder. The girls laughed and called their plans to stop for a malted on the way home, while they zipped their skirts and dug under benches for their loafers. Millie watched Arline putting on lipstick at the wavy locker-room mirror. Arline stretched her upper lip over her small square teeth and drew a careful vermilion outline. She looked funny and yet beautiful. Her figure flowed in lovely grown-up curves under her sloppy-joe sweater. Arline gave swift attention to the seams of her stockings and her hairdo and was out the door before anyone else, calling over her shoulder, "Okay, kids, I'm going." Joan Billings and the Hensell twins ran to catch up with her.

Millie tied the laces of her brown oxfords slowly. She hated those ox-

fords. They were exactly like the pair she'd had before them and the pair before that. Millie's mother believed in sensible oxfords. She also believed in plaits for young girls. The tenets of her faith were strong and unyielding. Millie sighed and pulled the tough knot of her laces hard, as though she would break the dull brown cords binding her forever to a proper childhood.

She gathered her purse and her geometry book and folded the brown Eton jacket over her arm. No use putting *that* on until she got to the corner of her street.

Outside, the day was wonderfully sweet and fresh after the thick air of the locker room. She decided against taking the streetcar home. It was a long trek to her house but she wanted to get used to the day and the thoughts in her head before she got to her own door.

She walked across High School Street and followed the path of the car tracks, turning the familiar corners without even thinking about it, listening to the pleasant sound of her shoes scraping the cement walk, careful, with the habit of all her years, to avoid stepping on the cracks.

At the top of Graham Street she stopped short and looked down the hill. It was a long, steep hill. The streetcar circled around it but it made a good shortcut to her house when she was walking. She always liked the view from the top of the hill. It wasn't special, just houses and porches, with a row of little trees along the curb, growing in square metal cages. But there was such a long string of them, and from where she stood she felt she could run down and step onto the roof of the house at the bottom.

The idea was, of course, childish and

she laughed a little—out loud. The laughter surprised her. She had been so miserable a short while ago. She remembered the cold-hot fear, the way it had held her in a strange terror, the crazy tune it had whirred through her head.

But it was gone now. She touched the coolness of her forehead and she pressed her fingers together, watching the deep pink fill their tips. *Gone.* And she knew with a wonderful certainty that she need never let the ugly thing come back.

But she could think about it now. She could think of how it had grown big and dark inside her as she walked down the line of girls in the strange, despised role of accuser. A word, a nod were the weapons she had that could strike a final staggering blow. Then she had looked at Hilda and seen a bigger, darker trouble than any she had ever known—one that Hilda would perhaps never get rid of.

She thought about Hilda, how the girl would walk home to the house with the angry voices and the dirty curtains that were a disgrace to the neighborhood. She would take her trouble back to that place which was used to darkness and ugliness, where the anger and the dirt made them grow.

The word or the nod that Millie might have used in gym today could make Hilda's trouble grow, too. Millie shivered a little when she thought of it. She took a deep breath: she wanted to fill her lungs full with the soft spring air. It was clean and it tasted sweet, she thought, running her tongue to the corners of her mouth.

Her glance swung down, then up the pattern of red, green, and slate roofs. Nice and neat . . . pretty, strung out that way. Everything would be in order in the rooms under such roofs. It gave her a nice feeling, picturing those rooms. It helped her thoughts to go neatly, cozily into place as she looked down the roller-coaster street to the bright red roof that made a step at the very bottom.

Suddenly, she began to run. Faster and faster, with her laughter streaming out behind her, she ran down the big steep hill.   THE END

↻ **Talking it over**

1. *a.* During the gym-shoes incident, what pressures does Millie feel
  —from her mother?
  —from the teacher?
  —from her classmates?
  —from Hilda?

  b. Which pressure proves to be the strongest? Why?

2. Why does Millie feel terror when she is asked to examine the girls' shoes and pick out her own? How does this fear differ from the fears she is used to?

3. The author indirectly suggests that Millie does the right thing by not accusing Hilda. Tell whether you agree or disagree with this point of view, and why.

4. *a.* What things in Hilda's home situation might help to explain her stealing?

  b. What pressure at school might help to explain it?

5. At the end of the story, Millie suddenly finds herself running and laughing. What do these actions tell you?

*"You know what my old man told me
about your old man? . . . that he
was a drunken bum!"*

The Old Cardinal Spirit

by Joseph Gies

THE MORNING we moved into the new place in Rose Park I helped Dad unload the pickup before I went to look for the ball field. I put his glove and his cap and the picture of him jumping to spear a line drive on a bookshelf. Dad put the picture of Mother on top of the mantel. That picture was taken down in Florida, where the Cards trained. Mother is sitting on top of the dugout, laughing; she looks pretty good, though I don't remember seeing her except in pictures.

Dad had to go report to the rental agent, and so I was not worried about his getting nervous, and as soon as

we had all the stuff inside, I took off.

It was a good field, in a park, with trees around back of the foul lines, and tennis courts behind the screen, and a playground for little kids in deep center.

A bunch of guys were on the field when I walked up, just choosing up sides for a practice game. I said hey, could I play, and they looked me over the way you do a new kid, and a tall, skinny guy with glasses said sure. He was the pitcher and captain of their regular team and his name was Edgar Harrington. He asked me what position I played, and I said shortstop, and he said they already had a regular shortstop, but I could play on the second team in this practice game.

Well, I don't mean to brag or anything like that, because it's just that I've had advantages, but in the second inning there were two guys on and somebody hit a ball past the mound on one hop and I charged it and tagged the runner and threw the batter out at first.

Afterward Edgar Harrington said, "Hey, you're pretty good for a kid your size, Gale," and I told them about Dad. I just said it sort of matter-of-factly, about his being with the Cardinals in 1942 and being named Rookie of the Year,[1] and about his hitting .313 and driving in 102 runs.

A couple of them said they remembered the name Dan Gale, but you could see they didn't remember it too well, because of course they were too young and he didn't last too long, because of his nervousness. Edgar told me they had a workout scheduled the next morning and the first game of their season in the afternoon.

I went on home and started supper going, and pretty soon Dad came in and asked me if I got in a game, and I told him about it, and he said, this is a very nice neighborhood and I expect you will find these are nice kids.

I wasn't worried about Dad getting nervous that evening, even though we had just moved in and he had had the trouble on the previous job, because tonight the Cardinals were on TV.

Of course these aren't the same Cards as in 1942. They are a pretty good team this year, but that 1942 team was the greatest that ever played ball. You don't have to believe me. Go look it up in the record books. Musial, Slaughter,

Walker and Mort Cooper, Whitey Kurowski, Terry Moore, Marty Marion— they're all in Dad's scrapbook. They beat the Yanks in the Series, five games. Dad says that it wasn't just hitting and running that did it, but the team had something more.

"We had that 'we-can-do-it' bug," he told me once. "It was funny, because the Cards hadn't won a pennant in several years then, and we were a pretty young bunch, but we got that 'we-can-do-it' feeling, and we did it."

We finished dinner and the dishes and made out score cards and settled down in front of the TV. The Cards were behind 2-1 in the ninth and Dark got a single and Musial came up and I think the count was two and two when he hit one up on the pavilion roof. I let out a yell, and Dad smiled, and I went out in the kitchen and got a couple of Cokes.

When I came back, Dad had turned off the set, but he was still looking at the screen with a faraway look, and I knew he was thinking about 1942. In the scrapbook there were a couple of stories comparing him with Musial, and now, looking back, he was thinking of what Musial is now and what he is. I don't mean exactly that he's jealous of Stan Musial, because Dad would never be jealous of anybody, but he just thinks of how it might have been different for himself. See what I mean?

After the workout next morning Edgar Harrington put me at shortstop in the game instead of Junior Ransome, the guy he had been going to give the job to. Honestly, this was fair, because Junior did not charge the ball at all; he just waited and let the ball play him, and that is no way to play shortstop.

This Junior Ransome was a kid with blond curly hair, and a baby sort of

[1]**Rookie of the Year.** During a player's first year in the major leagues he is referred to as a rookie. The Baseball Writers Association gives an award each year for the best performance by a rookie in each league.

face, though he had a pretty good build, and he said it wasn't right for me to be playing for the Rose Park Eagles, which was the name of their team. He said I had just moved into the neighborhood, and besides, he said the park was supposed to be for residents of the Rose Park Apartments, and my old man was just a building super.

Edgar Harrington said still, I was a resident, and I got kind of sore and said maybe my old man was a building super but he used to play for the Cardinals, and Junior said what, the South Peoria Cardinals, and a couple of guys laughed. I said the 1942 Cardinals, they won the pennant and beat the Yanks, five games, my old man won the third game with a triple. Junior said aw bull, and I said how would he like a punch in the nose? He said he would show me who was going to get a punch in the nose, and just then a lady's voice said, "What's going on, fellows?"

The lady who said it was grown up, but not very big, only a head or so taller than me. She was wearing blue jeans and a blue blouse that said "Playground Director" in stitching over the pocket, and she had red hair and a nice, cheerful sort of face.

"Aw, Miss Shaughnessy, he says his old man played for the Cards," Junior said. "And Edgar is going to let him play shortstop. And his old man's a _____"

"Hey!" I yelled. "Here comes my Dad now!"

He was walking toward us in the slow, lazy way he has that covers ground pretty fast. I ran up and told him about the argument, and he just laughed and said he felt like some exercise and if we wanted he would pitch some batting practice for us. Of course

Dad was never a pitcher, but he threw the ball right over the plate, and not a lot of wild ones the way most kids do when they try to pitch batting practice, and so it was a real good session. Once in a while Dad would say something like, "Step into the ball, son," or "Choke up on the bat a little," or, most often, the advice he gives me lots of times, "Don't kill it, just try to hit it straight back at me." And you could see the guys sort of paying attention and hitting it better.

Then Dad let Edgar pitch and went out to second and fielded a few grounders. He would groan when he bent over, as if it was quite an effort, but he would scoop the ball up with one hand nice as anything and shoot it underhand to first, or sometimes flip it to me at second.

Finally Edgar said, "How about you taking a bat, Mr. Gale," and Dad went in and picked up a bat. He bats left. He hit a grounder to the third baseman, a nice, easy hopper, and I could see nobody thought that was much of a hit. But then he hit a grounder down to me at short, and then one to the kid playing second, and then to the guy on first, and then he hit a fly ball to each outfielder in succession. Some hitting, all right! Then he laid down a bunt that crept up the line about a foot fair, and then he picked up his jacket where he had tossed it on the grass and went and sat down on the bench by Miss Shaughnessy.

The two of them were talking when we came off the field, and Edgar Harrington said, "Hey, Mr. Gale, would you give us some coaching this summer?"

Dad turned and looked at Miss Shaughnessy in a questioning way, and

she said, "It would be wonderful if you could, Mr. Gale."

Dad said he would see, and we walked home together.

We won the game that afternoon 7-3. The next week we had some more workouts, and Dad came to the park a couple of times and gave the guys pointers, and we played another game that Wednesday. This one went into extra innings, and we finally won it in the twelfth.

I dogtrotted home and shoved open the door and called, "Hey, we won!" but nobody answered.

I thought maybe he was out in back at the incinerator, but when I went around there he wasn't in sight. I took a quick walk down to the shopping center. I should have known I wouldn't find him in a crowded place like that. When I got back and he still wasn't there, I made supper, but I wasn't hungry.

Of course he had done it before a hundred times, but this seemed different. Over on South Hill, where we had lived till he lost that job, it didn't matter much. But here it was different, and finally I did cry a little.

I woke up the next morning and he wasn't there. I walked all around the development and through the shopping center and down along the highway to the next shopping center, but I never saw a trace.

When I got back home the phone was ringing. It was Mr. Clancy, the rental agent, and he was looking for Dad. I said Dad was up on the roof fixing a broken clothes tree, and Mr. Clancy said he should snap into it and get the garbage detail done, because Mrs. Elgood in 21-E was complaining. I said I would tell Dad, and I went to work on the garbage detail, which is some job in a twenty-four-apartment house.

By the time I finished it, the phone was ringing again, and Mr. Clancy said Mrs. Miller in 12-E had her baby locked up in the bathroom and was having hysterics. So I got a screwdriver and went over and the way you do, you unscrew the outside plate and then shove the screwdriver into a little space they leave there and you can open it right up. Mrs. Miller wanted to give me a dollar, but Dad doesn't take tips so I said no thanks.

I didn't sleep much that night, though I kept saying to myself that he would be back in the morning. But in the morning still no sign.

I handled the garbage detail again and when I came in the phone was ringing and Mr. Clancy said Miss Shaughnessy in 13-E wanted some furniture moved. I walked over to the upper-E section and rang the bell of 13-E and there was the lady from the playground.

"Hello, Danny," she said. "Where's your father?"

All I could think of to say was, "He's planting some flowers."

"In September?" she asked, and gave me a funny look.

I said maybe I misunderstood him, and she kept looking at me funny, and then she said, "Say, don't you kids have a ball game this afternoon?"

Good gosh, I had forgotten, and the Eagles were playing the Rangers, the toughest team in the park league.

"Come on, I'll drive you over," she said. Then when we were in the car she asked me, "Listen, Danny, is there anything wrong with your Dad? Is he sick or anything?"

I said yes, he was a little sick, and

she said did we have the doctor, and I said no, but it was just a kind of nervous sickness, and he would be okay in a day or two. Then she didn't say anything more.

She let me out and went across to the wading pool. "Hey, there's Danny!" one of the guys yelled. Edgar Harrington asked me where I had been, I'd missed practice twice, and Junior Ransome said, "Aw, he wants to be Joe Hero, come charging up at the last minute!"

I said, "I had to help my old man . . . ."

"Your old man!" Junior said. "You know what my old man told me about your old man? He said the reason your old man couldn't stick in the big leagues was that he was a drunken bum!"

Everybody else shut up and there was just a dead silence. I felt tears coming, so I took a step forward and socked Junior right on the jaw. He didn't fall down, but he went back a couple steps, and then he socked me.

The guys all gathered around in a circle and began yelling at the top of their voices, some of them for Junior, some of them for me. I don't know how it would have come out if it had lasted, but suddenly somebody had hold of me and I could hear a woman's voice yelling, and it was Miss Shaughnessy. I had a cut lip and Junior's eye was turning black.

A couple of the kids started telling Miss Shaughnessy how the fight started, when I noticed several of the guys looking over toward the street and I looked over there and saw Dad coming.

He was bad. I could see that right away, the way he walked. He stumbled along, and in fact once he fell right down, but he got up again and came on. His clothes were all dirty and streaked, and looking at him I felt like crying again. Nobody said a word.

He came up and said something, you couldn't figure out what it was, and he gave a kind of foolish smile. Somebody had a ball in his hand, and Dad saw it, and held out his hand for a catch. The kid with the ball looked as if he didn't know what to do, but he tossed it. Dad tried to catch it and it went through his fingers and he grabbed at it with his other hand, but missed it and it fell on the ground and rolled away.

Then Miss Shaughnessy said, "Mr. Gale, you come with me."

She said it in a funny, tense sort of voice, as if she was terribly excited but sort of holding back, and Dad said something again that you couldn't understand. Then she grabbed his arm, steered him toward her car. Just before they got there she called over her shoulder, "One of you boys watch the wading pool!" Then she got Dad into the car and they drove off.

Somebody said, "Hey, let's start the game."

Edgar Harrington turned and looked at me and then at Junior, and I could see what he was thinking, and I said, "I'll go watch the wading pool. See you guys later."

I walked on out to the pool, where there were about a million little kids running around and splashing. I sat down and tried not to think about the game.

Finally Miss Shaughnessy came back. She smiled, but sort of as if somebody was making her, and she said, "Thanks for watching the pool for me, Danny."

"That's all right," I said, and I started to walk away.

"Listen, Danny," she said. "Tell me

about him. Please. I really want to know."

I never talked to anyone before about Dad. But the way she said it, you could tell she wasn't just nosy, and I guess maybe I wanted to talk to somebody. Anyway, I told her everything I could remember, about how he would go a long time, maybe six months even, and then would get on a run and not come home for three days. And I told about his different jobs—super, gas-station man, delivery truck, taxi, night watchman.

And I told about how he had come back from the war and Mother was killed in an accident. At first, after that, he had played ball, but then he started having the drinking trouble, like Junior's old man had said. He had gotten traded around the league and finally was sent down to Syracuse and then to Scranton and then started taking any job he could get.

"I see how it was," she said kind of slowly, and then she looked up and said, "Say aren't they calling you?"

Some of the guys were yelling my name, and I trotted across the outfield. On the way, I saw we had guys on second and third, and it turned out Edgar Harrington wanted me to pinch-hit, because the score was tied, 6-6, and it was the last inning. Well, to make a long story short, I got hold of one pretty good and hit it over the shortstop's head and the winning run scored.

All the kids slapped me on the back, and Edgar Harrington said, that was a great hit, Danny, and we all said we would win the park pennant sure now. I started home, but then Junior Ransome came after me. "Hey, Danny," he said, "I'm sorry about what I said— you know. You want to shake hands?"

I said O.K. and we shook hands and I went on home.

Dad was asleep. I started the dinner, and when I heard him get up I took him a cup of coffee and a cigarette, and I held the coffee cup and the match for him, and then turned on the TV for the sportscast. The Cardinals won 7-6, and I said, "Hey, that's the same score we won by!" I told him about the last inning.

The cup rattled around in the saucer as he set it down, and he said, "That's good, Danny."

He came and sat down in front of the TV, though there wasn't anything on, just some sappy program with a girl singing songs. Finally he said, "Danny, I came over to the park today, didn't I?"

I said, "Yeah, you did, Dad."

He said, "That girl brought me home."

The doorbell rang. I opened the door and there was Miss Shaughnessy. She wasn't wearing her park uniform, and she looked pretty good, but mainly she just looked mad.

"Hello, Danny," she said, and barged right in.

My Dad got up out of his chair. "Hello," he said.

"Danny," Miss Shaughnessy said to me, "suppose you run down to the center and get some ice cream."

I didn't give her any argument. I walked pretty fast, and the fountain wasn't very busy, and I got back quite quick. At the front door I stopped. Inside I could hear Miss Shaughnessy's voice, not loud, exactly, but sort of excited and firm. Then she stopped and I heard Dad's voice. He was talking in a kind of slow, strained way.

"I didn't realize what I was doing,"

he said. "But I guess that kid was right. I'm a drunken bum."

I just stood there outside the door with the ice cream sack in my hands, and I was thinking sort of absently that it was lucky they pack ice cream in those silver foil wrappers, it doesn't melt very quick.

After a long time Dad said, "I always tell myself I'll stop after two or three . . ."

And Miss Shaughnessy said, very sharply, "You have to stop before one! I know all about that—there are some people who can't take a drop. Now I'll tell you what you're going to do. You're going to join Alcoholics Anonymous tomorrow. Their system really works. I know."

I wondered how she knew, and I bet Dad did too, only he was too polite to ask. Only pretty soon she said, "My Dad had the trouble for ten years. Then one night he came home and loaded a shotgun and my mother locked us all up in the bedroom and he shot through the door and it hit me, and I almost died but I didn't. And he never touched a drop after that."

Nobody said anything for quite a little while. Then Dad said, "I will try it, for the boy."

She said, "You have to more than try it; you have to do it. And you should think of the boy, but you should think of your own life, too." And then she said, in a little different, quieter voice, "You need the right kind of job. They've authorized a boys' recreation director for the park. It would be a job for a man who liked boys and could teach them baseball and so on."

And Dad said, "You don't mean I would stand a chance at a job like that?"

"You would if I thought you could make good at it," she said.

Dad finally said, "Miss Shaughnessy, I will make good at it."

And then he said, "I will make good at it. Believe me, I *know* I can do it."

Then I figured everything would be okay, because that, as Dad says, is the way the 1942 Cardinals felt, and you know what they did.

THE END

↻ **Talking it over**

1. *a.* How has Mr. Gale's drinking problem affected his life?

b. How has it affected his son's life?

2. What good qualities does Danny have? For each quality you name, cite evidence from the story.

3. *a.* Why does Dan Gale drink?

b. Does his drinking solve anything? Explain.

c. How can you tell that he must be a very likeable person when he is sober?

4. *a.* How is the story title related to the end of the story?

b. Do you find the ending of the story believable? Explain.

5. Which of the following four sentences best expresses the central idea of this story? Remember that the central idea is broader than any of the details in the story.

a. Overcoming a problem depends on facing the problem and believing you can lick it.

b. Forgetting your problems for a while helps you overcome them in the long run. (*cont.*)

c. For a boy, being a good baseball player is a sure way to make friends.

d. Children who have an alcoholic parent must learn to accept responsibility earlier than other children.

⇄ Words in action

Baseball has a colorful language of its own. Many of the nouns mean exactly what they say. For example, a *shortstop* is a player whose job is to stop the ball short in the infield. The *dugout*, the small shelter at the side of the infield, may be partly dug out of the ground. And there are *home run, mound, outfield,* etc.

Sports writers also use colorful verbs to describe the action at a game. Terms like *popped out* or *driving in* originally were more at home in other contexts, but frequent use has made them familiar as baseball terms.

The following sentences or sentence parts are taken from the story, except that general words have been used in place of the author's colorful verbs. Without looking at the story, see if you can substitute more vivid terms for the words in italics. Then look up the sentence to see whether your terms are as vivid as the author's. Perhaps you used the same terms.

1. ". . . the picture of him jumping to *catch* a line drive."

2. "Somebody hit a ball past the mound on one hop and I *ran toward* it and tagged the runner."

3. "Dad would say something like, 'Step into the ball, son,' or '*shorten your grip* on the bat a little.' "

4. "Don't try to *hit* it *too hard*, just try to hit it straight back at me."

It grew out of a true story

A native of Michigan, Joseph Gies says he learned how to read by studying the Tiger box score in the Detroit *News.* Along with his eighty-six-year-old mother-in-law, he is a red-hot Detroit Tiger fan. He is also a St. Louis Cardinal fan, having lived as a boy in Rochester, N.Y., where there is a Cardinal "farm." His two sons are New York Met fans.

"The Old Cardinal Spirit," he says, grew out of "a true story I came across long ago which involved not a baseball player but a former Minnesota football star.

"I connected it up with the 1942 Cardinals because there happened to be several players on that team who somehow or other lost their skill in the war. To the best of my knowledge, none of them had a liquor problem—just knee and shoulder injuries."

Mr. Gies is coauthor of *Stars of the Series,* a book in which the 1942 Cardinals come in for a chapter. Enos Slaughter is the hero of that chapter but Mr. Gies says that Slaughter, "who never drank a drop of anything except milk," is not the model for Dan Gale.

JOSEPH GIES

They didn't know what was out there waiting for them. But sooner or later things would come to a head.

NOT TOO HARD

by Howard Fast

ALL IN the cabin had a sense of being imprisoned, even the four-month-old baby who lay on her back and whimpered. It was hot in the cabin —mid-summer heat—and six persons filled it to overflowing. It wasn't a very large cabin.

The boy was eight years old, tall for his age and skinny; he had a round freckled face, with hair like burnt straw.

The boy said: "Maw, can't I go out? Maw, can't a body go out and play?"

The woman ignored him; she was studying a book that was yellow with age. A girl stood looking over her shoulder at the book. The girl might have been a little older than the boy— or perhaps his twin; she was the same height.

The boy tried again: "Maw, lemme out."

A child of two years, toddling on the cabin floor, glanced at the boy with interest. He spoke the boy's name: "Josh."

A man lay on one of the beds that were built out from the cabin wall. He lay with a quilt drawn up to his chin, and in spite of the heat he seemed to be cold. Sometimes he moved a little, restlessly, but most of the time he lay still, only his eyes moving, watching the other people in the cabin.

Now he said: "Josh, you shut yore mouth! You leave yore mom alone!"

The woman glanced up quickly from the book; her eyes met the man's, and she forced her face to smile.

"Don't excite yourself," she said gently.

The man muttered something, lay back with his eyes closed. The boy crossed the cabin to the one window that had an open shutter. He stood there in a broad beam of sunlight.

"You get from there!" his mother said. She reached out a hand, but he dodged nimbly. He went over to the crib and began to play with the baby.

Drawing up her legs, the baby only whimpered louder. The boy snorted with disgust, and his eyes turned eagerly to the open window. Beyond the window there showed a piece of cultivated ground, a cornfield and waves of ripe wheat, beyond that a stretch of forest. The boy could hear a brook gurgling, and he was thirsty.

The woman sighed and closed the book. On its cover was printed: SELDE'S ANATOMY AND HOUSEHOLD REMEDIES: BOSTON, 1770.

The girl, deprived of the book's fascination, wandered listlessly about the cabin.

When she stopped at the window, the mother snapped: "Get from that window!" But wearily, as if she had said it too many times.

The baby clamored for attention and milk.

"She makes me sick," Josh muttered.

The woman's eyes fixed on him, and he slipped into a corner, alongside the fireplace that dominated a whole wall of the cabin. He sulked there, reaching out curious fingers toward a large clean-bore musket that leaned against the stone.

The woman rose, went to the bed, and leaned over the man. He opened his eyes.

She said: "I thought you were sleeping, Jemmy."

"No—I'm hot, hot like fire. You reckon I need stay covered?"

The boy and the girl were staring at him now, with some curiosity and a little fear. The woman rested her hand on the man's forehead.

"Fever, Sarah?"

"No fever," she smiled, then sat down on the bed beside him. But his eyes told her that he didn't believe, and she felt a strange, wilting fear. She glanced around the cabin. Josh was fooling with the musket. She said: "Josh, you leave that musket alone! You'll be the death of me yet."

"Was there anything in the book to lead you on?" the man asked hesitantly. He twisted himself to face her, and then groaned with pain. He was a big, strong man, suffering doubly, the way a strong man does when strength suddenly leaves him. He had dark hair, but the same light blue eyes as the boy; his face was brown from the sun, but bloodless.

"There ain't a lot about gunshot wounds," the woman told him.

"It said nothing about the bullet being inside?"

She shook her head.

"My pa, he fought in the French war,[1] in Canada. He said a man could take his death, leaving the lead inside of him."

"That ain't so!" she said.

At the word "death," the girl began to cry.

The mother said: "You, Susie—stop that!"

"She ain't much," Josh remarked. "She's plenty scared, all right."

The man whispered: "I don't want to be a load, Sarah, but I'm dreadful hot and thirsty. There's water?"

"Plenty of water." She went to the water jug, and his eyes followed her. She held a pewter cup to the opening, but the water stopped flowing before the cup was full.

The girl screamed: "Maw—maw, gimme a drink of water!"

---

[1] **French war,** war between France and England for control of the North American continent, ending in 1763.

She had left the spigot open. A few drops trickled out, fell on the floor and were absorbed immediately by the packed dirt.

The man had seen; holding himself up on one elbow, he stared at the water keg with wide blue eyes. Then he dropped back on the bed.

Her face impassive, the woman brought the cup of water over to him. He shook his head.

"Please," she begged, "drink it down, Jemmy. There's plenty more water. There's a pot of water I put away for boiling, and a pailful I was thinking to wash the children with."

She lied well; she lied the way only a woman can, when the lie will save, but he knew that she was lying.

Susie began: "Maw, please—" and then saw her mother's face and shrank back. The two-year-old balanced himself over the crib, and the baby stopped her whimpering for a moment to stare into her brother's eyes.

Then, for that moment, it was very still, the only sound being the gurgling of the brook just within the shade of the forest.

The mother's voice had dropped to a hoarse whisper: "For God's sake, Jemmy, drink this."

He didn't answer, only lay there with his eyes closed. The two-year-old had tired watching the baby, and was now poking gingerly at her ribs. The baby began to scream.

"Leave her alone!"

Susie's eyes were on the cup of water. It was late in the afternoon now, and she had had nothing to drink since the morning. She was very, very thirsty. She took a step toward her mother. Josh had stood up and was staring at the window. Now the gurgling of the brook seemed louder than ever.

The mother bent over her husband and touched his face. It was very hot, and there were little beads of sweat all over it. It was a face which she knew and had known for twelve years, every line upon it, every hard fold of the skin. The cheeks were high and the jaw was large and gentle at the same time. A stubble of beard over it. Yet the face was different, and for a moment she imagined that he was dead.

"Jemmy, Jemmy," she pleaded.

Then he opened his eyes.

She held the water toward him, and even though he shook his head, she was relieved. With a few drops of the water she wet his face, and then she gave the rest to Susie.

At first, the girl stared at it and wouldn't drink; but the expression on her mother's face had changed. The woman was not beautiful, or even fair. Her face was too hard and too worn. But now the face was gentle with thankfulness.

The girl gulped down the water.

Josh said: "You let her drink—I don't get no water, but you let her drink."

"Yer a boy. I reckon you can stand a few hours without makin' a pig of yourself over water."

She went to the window, stood just to one side of it and peered out. There was no living thing out there, nothing but the wheat and the corn and the green wall of forest. That was what made it so hard, not knowing. Yet she knew what might be out there, and of the cunning and the patience of what might be there.

The sun had dropped low, and now it was just over the forest's edge, throwing a shadow onto the wheat. A wind had come up with the evening, stirring the wheat. But no life. She knew the way a wind stirred the wheat.

She stood there for a while, glancing back into the cabin every now and then and wondering how it would be. Sooner or later it would come to a head. They would leave the cabin—or what waited out there in the forest would come and investigate the still cabin. The musket would be fired once, and then it would be over.

The water didn't make too much difference. It aggravated the situation, but in the end it would be the same.

Her husband said: "There wouldn't be no sign of them, Sarah."

"I know," she shrugged.

She went over to the bed, lifted the cover and looked at his wound. She held herself so that the children wouldn't see.

Living this way, all in one room, it was a strange life. Not that she complained; she was only thinking that this was a way of transition, that some day this land would be like the land she had left behind in the East, on the other side of the mountains. Yet it was a strange life, all of them in one room, morning, noon, and night.

The wound was in his side, toward the front. He had not coughed any blood, so there was a good chance that his lungs were untouched. Yet the large, gaping hole was red and inflamed. She had treated it the only way she knew, stuffed it full of wet tobacco leaf.

He said: "I hardly felt it at first, like being hit in the side with a bit of rock."

Then, when he would have looked at it, she put back the dressing and covered him.

"It ain't no wound for a man to fret on," he said. "I'll be up outa bed maybe

tomorrow, maybe come another sunset."

Then their eyes met. They trusted each other. She realized that trust was what had drawn them westward, where no sane persons would go.

He whispered: "Boone's stockade[2] is west by north—sixty, seventy miles." Then he closed his eyes, and she sat by his bed, wondering. West by north—sixty or seventy miles.

Josh and his sister had crept to the open window; they stood there, peering out and trembling with excitement.

His mother's hand caught him over the ear.

"I don't see no Injuns, maw."

"You stay from that window!"

She began to set out things for supper. Some salted meat—that would make them thirsty. There was corn on the cob, which she had boiled the day before. She wondered whether to give them the meat. If the cow were only in the house, they could have milk for a day at least. But the cow had wandered away.

She gave them the corn and held back the meat. Some of the corn she mashed up for her husband, but he was asleep when she went to him. She didn't want to wake him.

Josh complained about the food.

"Eat it," she said.

"Why can't we have meat, maw?"

"Time the school was getting out here," she said. "It's a waste of a body's strength to live in a land without a school. You all need a taste of a schoolmaster's rod."

The two-year-old ate with difficulty. He needed water, but he didn't complain. There was something solid about

---

[2]**Boone's stockade.** Daniel Boone established a fort in east central Kentucky in 1775. Boonesboro, Kentucky, is located on the site of the original fort.

him, something that reminded her of his father. He had his father's name. Josh's mouth was swollen and dry.

Sarah realized that she too was dry, all dry, inside and outside. Her mouth was like bad-tasting leather. If it was that way with her, how was it with the children? Before morning came, Jemmy would die. More than anything else, he had to have water.

She put the child back in his crib. Then she went to the window and stared out at the forest. All in the shade now; the sun was setting. A wide band of shadow bordered the forest.

She took down a wooden water pail, stared at it a moment, and set it on the table. She could go herself—Josh was looking at her.

If I don't come back—she thought.

She said to Josh: "If I sent you down to the brook for water, you'd come right back?"

He nodded eagerly.

"You know how with pa? Pa was shot. They're out there, waitin'. You know that?"

He nodded again.

She couldn't say any more. Her throat was tight inside and her heart was a heavy lump in her breast. She gave Josh the pail, all the while wondering what impelled her to do it. And then, at the last moment, she would have kept him back.

"Walk," she said. "Don't run—walk."

He nodded soberly. She opened the door, reached to touch him, and then held herself back. Now it seemed to her that this was the culmination of her life, and that more than this she could not be called upon to do.

A waving track in the corn marked his path. In the wheat, he showed again,

head and shoulders, and then he was lost in the shadow of the forest.

Sarah felt the girl, close to her, ordered her back into the house. Then it seemed to her that she had been standing there for hours, in the doorway—waiting.

There were sounds from the forest now, where there had been no sound before. Or else it was her mind, making sounds for her to be afraid of.

The baby was whimpering again. Her feet were like lead when she went inside, soothed her. If Jemmy woke up and saw that Josh had gone—Josh was his first man-child, a thing to be proud of and called after Jemmy's own father.

She went back to the door. The shadow of the forest had crept out further; it was twilight now.

She saw him in the wheat, head and shoulders. Then she wanted to run forward and meet him; and somehow she held back. When he came out of the corn, he wasn't running—walking as she had said and bearing the pail of water carefully.

The shot from the forest was like the snapping of a dry piece of wood, not terribly loud, but ringing afterward, as if someone had fired again and again. The pail of water in the boy's hand shattered to pieces, splashing him. He ran forward to the house, and she bolted the door behind him. Then she was down on her knees, feeling all over him with her rough hands, which she tried so desperately to make gentle.

He was crying a little. There was a splinter in his arm, and he winced when she drew it out. His arm was bruised, but otherwise he wasn't hurt.

Jemmy was awake, staring at them. She couldn't be sure, because now the cabin was almost dark, but she imagined that there was no reason in his eyes.

Josh said: "I didn't drink, I swear, maw—I didn't drink at the crick."

"I know, I know, child."

"You want me to go back, maw?"

"No—no." She was thinking of what Jemmy would say, knowing that she had sent Josh down there alone.

She went to the single window that was open, closed it, and bolted the shutter. Then she scraped flint and steel until a candle was lit. The baby was sleeping, and she was thankful for that. It was a wonder that she could sleep through it. The two-year-old sat on the floor, playing with a piece of wood. Susie was close to Josh, hardly knowing whether to cry or not.

Jemmy was awake. She saw his eyes as soon as she lit the candle, and she saw that he didn't know. Staring straight at her, he didn't see her. He was repeating what he had told her that morning, when he had come back to the cabin, all wet with blood and barely able to walk:

"I was breaking open that land down the crick bottom. I didn't hear a sound, only the first thing I knew there's a pain in my side, like someone threw a rock at me. Funny about not hearing a shot, just a pain in my side, and then the red devil running at me. I split him with the ax, but there's more. Reckon you kin count on there being plenty more of them holed up here. I got a mortal hurt, Sarah."

The boy and the girl were listening, their eyes wide with horror. Susie crept up to Josh, and he put his arm around her.

She was crying a little, and Josh said: "That ain't no way to carry on."

"Come to bed," Sarah told them, just as if she had heard nothing, and when Jemmy moaned again and again, she made out that it was nothing for the children to be worried over.

The two-year-old slept thankfully and quickly, but it hurt Sarah to see how swollen his mouth was. Josh and his sister slept together in the same bed. There, in the shadow, they became disembodied whispers. Sarah hoped they would sleep soon.

"It's a long way north and west," Jemmy mumbled. "Boone's a fine man and easy to take in strangers. But long walking—for sixty miles. The canebrake ain't easy in summer heat."

Sarah took up the candle and walked around the cabin, from window to window, making sure that the shutters on each were bolted. At the fireplace, she stopped, poking at the ashes. She had heard of a cabin on the River Licking, where they had dropped down the chimney to invade the place. It might be wise for her to start a fire, only in this heat it would make a furnace of the cabin. They wouldn't sleep with a fire in the cabin.

She took the candle in her hand and stood by Jemmy's bed. He had thrown off his covers, and when she drew them back he opened his eyes and looked straight at her without seeing her.

She wiped the beads of sweat from his face.

"The road to the west is a way of darkness," he whispered. "God help me for going where no man stepped before."

"Sleep, Jemmy," she begged him.

He grasped for her hand. "There's no way out of this. I'm awful hot!" He had hesitated, closed his eyes for a while. She still stood by the bed.

"Where's Josh?" he asked her.

"Sleeping."

"I had a dream that he went. I heard a shot fired. Let me up!" He struggled erect, clawed his way from the bed and sprawled on the floor. She had a time getting him back into the bed. His body had relaxed, and he was whimpering like a child.

After that, she sat by the table for a long time, just sat and stared straight in front of her.

She was very, very tired, and she was priming herself for an effort that would keep her awake through the night. Somehow, she had to manage to remain awake.

When she went to Jemmy's bed again, he was sleeping. She took the candle and looked at the children. Josh was sprawled the way a child sleeps in hot weather, arms and legs flung out, his face buried in the pillow. She bent over Josh, made as if to touch him, and then drew back her hand. Susie lay on her back, her soft hair like silk over her face. Sarah put the hair away, strand by strand.

Back at the table, she might have dozed for a moment or an hour. She didn't know, started awake in the dark. The candle had burnt out, and something was scratching at the door.

At first, the darkness frightened and stifled her. She had a sensation of being alone in a world of mystery, in a black world that stretched north and south and east and west for more miles than a man could count. Then, in that moment—fearfully—she lived over the great distance they had come from the east, the mountain passes, the gorges, the mysterious forest that stretched on and on, the sense of going into the wild, where man's law and man's mercy stopped.

She had somehow stumbled across the room and found the musket. She stood in the corner, holding it before her, feeling for the trigger. She felt that when she pulled the trigger, the crash of the gun would mark the end of all that had been for them. That way she waited, her eyes fixed on the place where the door was.

The scratching continued, and once she imagined that she heard steps outside. And then she felt that someone out there was listening.

It required all her courage to clink the gun metal against the stone of the fireplace. That was what they were listening for, and she'd let them hear it. Then she raised the lock of the gun.

In the night, the noise was magnified—unmistakably the sound of a musket being cocked.

And after that, for a long time, silence.

She was wet all over; drops of water running down her face splashed onto her hands. When she put the musket away, it was with a distinct effort that she unclasped her hands from the moist stock and barrel.

At the table, she found a candle, flint, and steel, and tried to make a light. Her hands trembled, and again and again she dropped the flint or the steel. Finally, she had the tinder glowing, the candlewick flickered into life. The light was a benediction and a caress.

The baby was crying. Sarah took her up in her arms and soothed her. A wind had raised itself outside, and the sound of it reminded Sarah of a lullaby her own mother had sung. That was in another world. Perhaps this child would go on that way, westward, as she had gone.

She sat there with the child in her arms. Jemmy awakened; she didn't notice at first, until she saw him sitting up in bed, looking at her.

He said: "Sarah, it's morning?"

"Soon, Jemmy."

"Why don't you get some sleep?"

"I slept a spell before. I'm all right, Jemmy." She knew that he wanted her to come to him and she put the child back in her crib. Next to Jemmy, she passed her hand over his face; it was cooler now.

"I woke up before," he whispered. "It was dark. I thought—"

"No, the candle went out, Jemmy."

"I been thinkin'," he said.

"Rest, Jemmy."

He said: "I been thinkin' for you to slip out—find Boone. They won't leave the cabin, an' tomorrow they'll close in. Take the kids."

"Leave you here?"

"I'm a man shot through; I ain't no good. You're a strong woman an' you need a strong man. Find Boone, an' find a man to marry an' fetch you food—"

"You'll be better, Jemmy."

He turned over with his face to the wall. She felt under the blanket, found his hand and held it. He had large hands, hard and broken with callus. She tried to understand how the hand could be shorn of strength; everything had come with his hands, even the house they lived in.

She left the bed, sat down at the table again, staring at the candle and wondering idly whether it would burn until morning. She watched it until it had flickered out. Through the crevices in the windows, a gray harbinger of dawn filtered in.

She was filled with an almost childish amazement at the fact that another day had come. It was not yet light enough in the cabin to see anything else than vague shapes.

From bed to bed she looked at each of her children. She bent low over Jemmy, the two-year-old, saw that there was a sort of smile on his face; she kissed him and said to herself:

"He'll have schoolin' anyhow. Seems there's bound to be a day when the school'll come away out here. I'd like a school and a church and a preacher. It don't seem right a boy should grow to man's age without listening to a preacher."

Then she sat herself in a chair and prayed, silently. Even with the others sleeping, her reserve was too much for her to pray aloud.

After that, when the noise came at the door again, she didn't care so much, nor was she frightened, the way she had been before. With the dawn, a strange peace had come over her.

She took up the baby in her arms and stood waiting. Someone was pounding at the door.

A white man's voice cried: "Halloo in there!"

She was sobbing, not tears but a heaving inside of her which she felt would rack her apart. She had only enough strength to unbolt the door; and then she dropped into a chair and watched them flood into the room with the gray light of dawn, many tall men in long homespun shirts, carrying rifles.

They filled the cabin, full and overflowing. They were big men and the cabin was small. They spoke in full, throaty voices, grinned at her and petted the baby.

Josh and Susie woke, frightened at first; but in a little while Josh was telling them how the water bucket had been shot out of his hand.

The man they called Dan'l spoke to her, a stocky man who was not very tall, yet gave an impression of great size and easy strength.

He said: "My name's Boone, ma'am —I'm mighty proud to meet you." He took up the baby, fondled it with hands that were wonderfully gentle. "It's a fine girl," he said.

She was holding Susie, touching her hair and explaining: "My man was shot —down in the creek bottom, an Indian. There's a doctor with you?"

"I have a way in healing—a small way."

Jemmy was awake, staring at them.

Sarah was thinking, "He's like them, tall and strong. He will be."

They gave her water, while Boone bent over Jemmy. She let the children drink first, slapped Josh for gulping. The taste of water on her own lips was like a dream.

Then she went to Boone, stood by his side while he dressed her husband's wound.

"He's hurt bad?" she whispered.

Boone held the bullet between his fingers. "He'll mend soon enough. He'll be a strong man, walking and providing."

She dropped down on the bed, put her face in her hands. Jemmy's hand went out, found her arm and caressed it, the callus rough on her skin.

Boone said: "We'll bide here for a spell, until he's up and around. It's a hard task for a woman, minding a family and a sick man. Some of us will bide with you for a spell."

She looked at him, wide eyes in a hard face, but eyes that were soft with knowing.

"Not too hard—" she said. "Forgive me, I'll sleep a little. I'm fair tired now." Then she lay down by her husband and closed her eyes.

THE END

◔ **Talking it over**

1. The woman lies when she tells her husband he has no fever and again when she tells him there is plenty of water. Why does she do this?

2. Is sending Josh for water a brave or a cowardly thing for the mother to do? Why? (cont.)

3. *a.* What pressures do the older children, the father, and the mother feel?

b. How does each of them behave under pressure?

4. *a.* The gurgling of a nearby brook is mentioned several times. What does this detail add to the story?

b. What does the size of the cabin tell you about the life these people live?

c. What seems to be of most concern to the mother about the place where she lives? What does this fact tell you about her?

5. What broad general idea do you think the author wants you to get from this story? Try to use the words of the title in your statement.

⇄ **Words in action**

Find the following six words in the story and arrange them in three columns, according to the strength of the clues to their meaning you find in the surrounding context. Two of the words are surrounded by strong context clues. Write these two in Column 1 and write a definition of each word.

In Column 2 write the two words for which there are clues but not very strong ones. Try writing a definition for each; then turn to the Glossary to check your definition.

In Column 3 write the two words for which there are very few or no clues. Check these in the Glossary and write definitions.

dominated	(242a, middle)
winced	(247b, bottom)
listlessly	(242a, middle)
benediction	(250a, middle)
spigot	(244a, top)
transition	(245a, middle)

A city boy who loves the wilds

Howard Fast learned a lot about America during the Depression years, when he hitchhiked all over the country, working at everything from tailoring to construction work.

Born in New York City in 1914, this city boy developed a love for the wilderness while spending summers at the home of an uncle in the country. "This was before suburbs, shopping centers, and the population explosion," he says.

"I never had enough of the woods, the wide vistas of endless forest country. I remember waking to look out of a window and seeing several hundred deer drinking in the creek. The last mountain lion was killed in Green County when I was seventeen." Out of his boyhood experiences in the forest and things he gathered in reading, he wrote stories like "Not Too Hard" about pioneers in earlier days.

Fast was seventeen when he wrote his first novel, and he published his first short story a year later. He is well known for his historical novels about America, several of which have to do with the Revolutionary War. His books for young people include *Haym Salomon, Goethals and the Panama Canal, Departure,* and *Tall Hunter.*

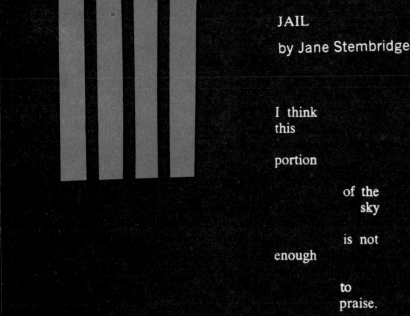

JAIL

by Jane Stembridge

I think
this

portion

         of the
            sky

          is not
enough

      to
      praise.

Talking it over

1. Where is the person who is speaking? Why can't he "praise" the part of the sky he sees?

2. What does "sky" mean to him that it might not mean, for instance, to someone riding along in a convertible on a sunny day?

3. Suggest other suitable titles.

She gives poems to her friends

Jane Stembridge is a young Southerner who since 1960 has been working for civil rights in the South.

Miss Stembridge says she does not want to be a writer. One reason she wrote poems, she says, was to give them to her friends who "were getting smashed down all the time" for their civil rights efforts. "I wanted to say: 'Hey, here's a poem for you.'"

About this particular poem, she says:

" 'Jail' is about anger. Because you're locked up. Instead of the whole big total October Delta blue sky, you got a little square of it. And that square's got black lines across it. That's what you got one day when you wanted everything, the whole sky, and everybody out dancing together a new kind of dance under that whole sky . . . .

"One day you wanted life and freedom for yourself and for everybody walking around. You broke the law. . . .

"So, there you are. It's October. The Delta sky is blue. You want it. You want to see *all of it*. But, no, you just got this square and this square's got those big ugly black lines across it."

BEWARE OF THE DOG

*Slowly the grain of doubt began to grow
. . . and with it came fear.*

by Roald Dahl

doing all right. I'm doing nicely. I know my way home. I'll be there in half an hour. When I land I shall taxi in and switch off my engine and I shall say, help me to get out, will you. I shall make my voice sound ordinary and natural and none of them will take any notice. Then I shall say, someone help me to get out. I can't do it alone because I've lost one of my legs. They'll all laugh and think that I'm joking, and I shall say, all right, come and have a look, you unbelieving idiots. Then Yorky will climb up onto the wing and look inside. He'll probably be sick because of all the blood and the mess. I shall laugh and say, come on now, help me out.

He glanced down again at his right leg. There was not much of it left. The cannon shell had taken him on the thigh, just above the knee, and now there was nothing but a great mess and a lot of blood. But there was no pain. When he looked down, he felt as though he were seeing something that did not belong to him. It had nothing to do with him. It was just a mess which happened to be there in the cockpit; something strange and unusual and rather interesting. It was like finding a dead cat on the sofa.

He really felt fine, and because he still felt fine, he felt excited and unafraid.

I won't even bother to call up on the radio for the blood wagon,[2] he thought. It isn't necessary. And when I land I'll sit there quite normally and say, some of you fellows come and help me out, will you, because I've lost one of my legs. That will be funny. I'll laugh a little while I'm saying it; I'll say it

DOWN below there was only a vast white undulating sea of cloud. Above there was the sun, and the sun was white like the clouds, because it is never yellow when one looks at it from high in the air.

He was still flying the Spitfire.[1] His right hand was on the stick, and he was working the rudder bar with his left leg alone. It was quite easy. The machine was flying well, and he knew what he was doing.

Everything is fine, he thought. I'm

---

[1]**Spitfire,** England's most famous World War II fighter plane.

[2]**blood wagon,** a Red Cross vehicle equipped to give blood transfusions to the badly wounded.

calmly and slowly, and they'll think I'm joking. When Yorky comes up onto the wing and gets sick, I'll say, Yorky, you old so-and-so, have you fixed my car yet? Then when I get out I'll make my report. . . . It doesn't even hurt. And I don't mind about the leg. I'll go everywhere in cars. I always hated walking, except when I walked down the street of the coppersmiths in Bagdad,[3] but I could go in a rickshaw. I could go home and chop wood, but the head always flies off the ax. Hot water, that's what it needs; put it in the bath and make the handle swell. I chopped lots of wood last time I went home, and I put the ax in the bath . . .

Then he saw the sun shining on the engine cowling of his machine. He saw the rivets in the metal, and he remembered where he was. He realized that he was no longer feeling good; that he was sick and giddy. His head kept falling forward onto his chest because his neck seemed no longer to have any strength. But he knew that he was flying the Spitfire, and he could feel the handle of the stick between the fingers of his right hand.

I'm going to pass out, he thought. Any moment now I'm going to pass out.

He looked at his altimeter. Twenty-one thousand. To test himself he tried to read the hundreds as well as the thousands. Twenty-one thousand and what? As he looked the dial became blurred, and he could not even see the needle. He knew then that he must bail out; that there was not a second to lose, otherwise he would become unconscious. Quickly, frantically, he tried to slide back the hood with his left hand, but he had not the strength. For a

second he took his right hand off the stick, and with both hands he managed to push the hood back. The rush of cold air on his face seemed to help. He had a moment of great clearness, and his actions became orderly and precise. That is what happens with a good pilot. He took some quick deep breaths from his oxygen mask, and as he did so, he looked out over the side of the cockpit. Down below there was only a vast white sea of cloud, and he realized that he did not know where he was.

It'll be the Channel,[4] he thought. I'm sure to fall in the drink.

He throttled back, pulled off his helmet, undid his straps, and pushed the stick hard over to the left. The Spitfire turned smoothly over onto its back. The pilot fell out.

As he fell he opened his eyes, because he knew that he must not pass out before he had pulled the cord. On one side he saw the sun; on the other he saw the whiteness of the clouds, and as he fell, as he somersaulted in the air, the white clouds chased the sun and the sun chased the clouds. They chased each other in a small circle; they ran faster and faster, and there was the sun and the clouds and the clouds and the sun, and the clouds came nearer until suddenly there was no longer any sun, but only a great whiteness. The whole world was white, and there was nothing in it. It was so white that sometimes it looked black, and after a time it was either white or black, but mostly it was white. He watched it as it turned from white to black, and then back to white again, and the white stayed for a long time, but the black lasted only for a few seconds. He got into the habit of going

[3]**street of the coppersmiths in Bagdad,** famous copper market in Iraq's capital.

[4]**Channel,** the English Channel, narrow body of water between England and France.

to sleep during the white periods, and of waking up just in time to see the world when it was black. But the black was very quick. Sometimes it was only a flash, like someone switching off the light, and switching it on again at once, and so whenever it was white, he dozed off.

One day, when it was white, he put out a hand and he touched something. He took it between his fingers and crumpled it. For a time he lay there, idly letting the tips of his fingers play with the thing which they had touched. Then slowly he opened his eyes, looked down at his hand, and saw that he was holding something which was white. It was the edge of a sheet. He knew it was a sheet because he could see the texture of the material and the stitching on the hem. He screwed up his eyes, and opened them again quickly. This time he saw the room. He saw the bed in which he was lying; he saw the gray walls and the door and the green curtains over the window. There were some roses on the table by his bed.

Then he saw the basin on the table near the roses. It was a white enamel basin, and beside it there was a small medicine glass.

This is a hospital, he thought. I am in a hospital. But he could remember nothing. He lay back on his pillow, looking at the ceiling and wondering what had happened. He was gazing at the smooth grayness of the ceiling which was so clean and gray, and then suddenly he saw a fly walking upon it. The sight of this fly, the suddenness of seeing this small black speck on a sea of gray, brushed the surface of his brain, and quickly, in that second, he remembered everything. He remembered the Spitfire and he remembered the altime-ter showing twenty-one thousand feet. He remembered the pushing back of the hood with both hands, and he remembered the bailing out. He remembered his leg.

It seemed all right now. He looked down at the end of the bed, but he could not tell. He put one hand underneath the bedclothes and felt for his knees. He found one of them, but when he felt for the other, his hand touched something which was soft and covered in bandages.

Just then the door opened and a nurse came in.

"Hello," she said. "So you've waked up at last."

She was not good-looking, but she was large and clean. She was between thirty and forty and she had fair hair. More than that he did not notice.

"Where am I?"

"You're a lucky fellow. You landed in a wood near the beach. You're in Brighton.[5] They brought you in two days ago, and now you're all fixed up. You look fine."

"I've lost a leg," he said.

"That's nothing. We'll get you another one. Now you must go to sleep. The doctor will be coming to see you in about an hour." She picked up the basin and the medicine glass and went out.

But he did not sleep. He wanted to keep his eyes open because he was frightened that if he shut them again everything would go away. He lay looking at the ceiling. The fly was still there. It was very energetic. It would run forward very fast for a few inches, then it would stop. Then it would run forward again, stop, run forward, stop, and

---

[5]**Brighton,** English town located on the English Channel.

every now and then it would take off and buzz around viciously in small circles. It always landed back in the same place on the ceiling and started running and stopping all over again. He watched it for so long that after a while it was no longer a fly, but only a black speck upon a sea of gray, and he was still watching it when the nurse opened the door, and stood aside while the doctor came in. He was an Army doctor, a major, and he had some last war ribbons on his chest. He was bald and small, but he had a cheerful face and kind eyes.

"Well, well," he said. "So you've decided to wake up at last. How are you feeling?"

"I feel all right."

"That's the stuff. You'll be up and about in no time."

The doctor took his wrist to feel his pulse.

"By the way," he said, "some of the lads from your squadron were ringing up and asking about you. They wanted to come along and see you, but I said that they'd better wait a day or two. Told them you were all right, and that they could come and see you a little later on. Just lie quiet and take it easy for a bit. Got something to read?" He glanced at the table with the roses. "No. Well, nurse will look after you. She'll get you anything you want." With that he waved his hand and went out, followed by the large clean nurse.

When they had gone, he lay back and looked at the ceiling again. The fly was still there and as he lay watching it he heard the noise of an airplane in the distance. He lay listening to the sound of its engines. It was a long way away. I wonder what it is, he thought. Let me see if I can place it. Suddenly he jerked his head sharply to one side. Anyone who has been bombed can tell the noise of a Junkers 88.[6] They can tell most other German bombers for that matter, but especially a Junkers 88. The engines seem to sing a duet. There is a deep vibrating bass voice and with it there is a high pitched tenor. It is the singing of the tenor which makes the sound of a JU-88 something which one cannot mistake.

He lay listening to the noise, and he felt quite certain about what it was. But where were the sirens, and where the guns? That German pilot certainly had a nerve coming near Brighton in daylight.

The aircraft was always far away, and soon the noise faded away into the distance. Later on there was another. This one, too, was far away, but there was the same deep undulating bass and the high singing tenor, and there was no mistaking it. He had heard that noise every day during the battle.

He was puzzled. There was a bell on the table by the bed. He reached out his hand and rang it. He heard the footsteps down the corridor, and the nurse came in.

"Nurse, what were those airplanes?"

"I'm sure I don't know. I didn't hear them. Probably fighters or bombers. I expect they were returning from France. Why, what's the matter?"

"They were JU-88's. I'm sure they were JU-88's. I know the sound of the engines. There were two of them. What were they doing over here?"

The nurse came up to the side of his bed and began to straighten out the sheets and tuck them in under the mattress.

---

[6]**Junkers 88,** German World War II bomber.

"Gracious me, what things you imagine. You mustn't worry about a thing like that. Would you like me to get you something to read?"

"No, thank you."

She patted his pillow and brushed back the hair from his forehead with her hand.

"They never come over in daylight any longer. You know that. They were probably Lancasters[7] or Flying Fortresses."[8]

"Nurse."

"Yes."

"Could I have a cigarette?"

"Why certainly you can."

She went out and came back almost at once with a packet of Players[9] and some matches. She handed one to him and when he had put it in his mouth, she struck a match and lit it.

"If you want me again," she said, "just ring the bell," and she went out.

Once toward evening he heard the noise of another aircraft. It was far away, but even so he knew it was a single-engined machine. But he could not place it. It was going fast; he could tell that. But it wasn't a Spit and it wasn't a Hurricane.[10] It did not sound like an American engine, either. They make more noise. He did not know what it was and it worried him greatly. Perhaps I am very ill, he thought. Perhaps I am imagining things. Perhaps I am a little delirious. I simply do not know what to think.

That evening the nurse came in with a basin of hot water and began to wash him.

"Well," she said, "I hope you don't still think that we're being bombed."

She had taken off his pajama top and was soaping his right arm with a flannel. He did not answer.

She rinsed the flannel in the water, rubbed more soap on it, and began to wash his chest.

"You're looking fine this evening," she said. "They operated on you as soon as you came in. They did a marvelous job. You'll be all right. I've got a brother in the RAF," she added. "Flying bombers."

He said, "I went to school in Brighton."

She looked up quickly. "Well, that's fine," she said. "I expect you'll know some people in the town."

"Yes," he said, "I know quite a few."

She had finished washing his chest and arms, and now she turned back the bedclothes, so that his left leg was uncovered. She did it in such a way that his bandaged stump remained under the sheets. She undid the cord of his pajama trousers and took them off. There was no trouble because they had cut off the right trouser leg, so that it could not interfere with the bandages. She began to wash his left leg and the rest of his body. This was the first time he had had a bed bath, and he was embarrassed. She laid a towel under his leg, and she was washing his foot with the flannel. She said, "This wretched soap won't lather at all. It's the water. It's as hard as nails."

He said, "None of the soap is very good now and, of course, with hard water it's hopeless." As he said it he remembered something. He remembered the baths which he used to take at school in Brighton, in the long stone-floored bathroom which had four baths

---

[7]**Lancaster,** English World War II heavy bomber.

[8]**Flying Fortress,** American World War II heavy bomber.

[9]**Players,** popular brand of cigarettes in England.

[10]**Hurricane,** British World War II fighter plane.

in a room. He remembered how the water was so soft that you had to take a shower afterwards to get all the soap off your body, and he remembered how the foam used to float on the surface of the water, so that you could not see your legs underneath. He remembered that sometimes they were given calcium tablets because the school doctor used to say that soft water was bad for the teeth.

"In Brighton," he said, "the water isn't. . . ."

He did not finish the sentence. Something had occurred to him; something so fantastic and absurd that for a moment he felt like telling the nurse about it and having a good laugh.

She looked up. "The water isn't what?" she said.

"Nothing," he answered. "I was dreaming."

She rinsed the flannel in the basin, wiped the soap off his leg, and dried him with a towel.

"It's nice to be washed," he said. "I feel better." He was feeling his face with his hands. "I need a shave."

"We'll do that tomorrow," she said. "Perhaps you can do it yourself then."

That night he could not sleep. He lay awake thinking of the Junkers 88's and of the hardness of the water. He could think of nothing else. They were JU-88's, he said to himself. I know they were. And yet it is not possible, because they would not be flying around so low over here in broad daylight. I know that it is true, and yet I know that it is impossible. Perhaps I am ill. Perhaps I am behaving like a fool and do not know what I am doing or saying. Perhaps I am delirious. For a long time he lay awake thinking these things, and once he sat up in bed and said aloud,

"I will prove that I am not crazy. I will make a little speech about something complicated and intellectual. I will talk about what to do with Germany after the war." But before he had time to begin, he was asleep.

He woke just as the first light of day was showing through the slit in the curtains over the window. The room was still dark, but he could tell that it was already beginning to get light outside. He lay looking at the gray light which was showing through the slit in the curtain, and as he lay there he remembered the day before. He remembered the Junkers 88's and the hardness of the water; he remembered the large pleasant nurse and the kind doctor, and now the small grain of doubt took root in his mind and it began to grow.

He looked around the room. The nurse had taken the roses out the night before, and there was nothing except the table with a packet of cigarettes, a box of matches, and an ash tray. Otherwise, it was bare. It was no longer warm or friendly. It was not even comfortable. It was cold and empty and very quiet.

Slowly the grain of doubt grew, and with it came fear, a light, dancing fear that warned but did not frighten; the kind of fear that one gets not because one is afraid, but because one feels that there is something wrong. Quickly the doubt and the fear grew so that he became restless and angry, and when he touched his forehead with his hand, he found that it was damp with sweat. He knew then that he must do something; that he must find some way of proving to himself that he was either right or wrong, and he looked up and saw again the window and the green curtains. From where he lay, that window was right in front of him, but it was fully ten yards away. Somehow he must reach it and look out. The idea became an obsession with him, and soon he could think of nothing except the window. But what about his leg? He put his hand underneath the bedclothes and felt the thick bandaged stump which was all that was left on the right-hand side. It seemed all right. It didn't hurt. But it would not be easy.

He sat up. Then he pushed the bedclothes aside and put his left leg on the floor. Slowly, carefully, he swung his body over until he had both hands on the floor as well; and then he was out of bed, kneeling on the carpet. He looked at the stump. It was very short and thick, covered with bandages. It was beginning to hurt and he could feel it throbbing. He wanted to collapse, lie down on the carpet and do nothing, but he knew that he must go on.

With two arms and one leg, he crawled over towards the window. He would reach forward as far as he could with his arms, then he would give a little jump and slide his left leg along after them. Each time he did, it jarred his wound so that he gave a soft grunt of pain, but he continued to crawl across the floor on two hands and one knee. When he got to the window he reached up, and one at a time he placed both hands on the sill. Slowly he raised himself up until he was standing on his left leg. Then quickly he pushed aside the curtains and looked out.

He saw a small house with a gray tiled roof standing alone beside a narrow lane, and immediately behind it there was a plowed field. In front of the house there was an untidy garden, and there was a green hedge separating the garden from the lane. He was looking at the hedge when he saw the sign. It was just a piece of board nailed to the top of a short pole, and because the hedge had not been trimmed for a long time, the branches had grown out around the sign so that it seemed almost as though it had been placed in the middle of the hedge. There was something written on the board with white paint, and he pressed his head against the glass of the window, trying to read what it said. The first letter was a G, he could see that. The second was an A, and the third was an R. One after another he managed to see what the letters were. There were three words, and slowly he spelled the letters out aloud to himself as he managed to read them. G-A-R-D-E A-U C-H-I-E-N. *Garde au chien.*[11] That is what it said.

He stood there balancing on one leg and holding tightly to the edges of the window sill with his hands, staring at the sign and at the white-washed lettering of the words. For a moment he could think of nothing at all. He stood there looking at the sign, repeating the words over and over to himself, and then slowly he began to realize the full meaning of the thing. He looked up at the cottage and at the plowed field. He looked at the small orchard on the left of the cottage and he looked at the green countryside beyond. "So this is France," he said. "I am in France."

Now the throbbing in his right thigh was very great. It felt as though someone was pounding the end of his stump with a hammer, and suddenly the pain became so intense that it affected his head and for a moment he thought he was going to fall. Quickly he knelt down again, crawled back to the bed,

[11]**Garde au chien** (gärd ō shyeɴ), French for "beware of the dog."

and hoisted himself in. He pulled the bedclothes over himself and lay back on the pillow, exhausted. He could still think of nothing at all except the small sign by the hedge, and the plowed field and the orchard. It was the words on the sign that he could not forget.

It was some time before the nurse came in. She came carrying a basin of hot water and she said, "Good morning, how are you today?"

He said, "Good morning, nurse."

The pain was still great under the bandages, but he did not wish to tell this woman anything. He looked at her as she busied herself with getting the washing things ready. He looked at her more carefully now. Her hair was very fair. She was tall and big-boned, and her face seemed pleasant. But there was something a little uneasy about her eyes. They were never still. They never looked at anything for more than a moment and they moved too quickly from one place to another in the room. There was something about her movements also. They were too sharp and nervous to go well with the casual manner in which she spoke.

She set down the basin, took off his pajama top and began to wash him.

"Did you sleep well?"

"Yes."

"Good," she said. She was washing his arms and his chest.

"I believe there's someone coming down to see you from the Air Ministry[12] after breakfast," she went on. "They want a report or something. I expect you know all about it. How you got shot down and all that. I won't let him stay long, so don't worry."

He did not answer. She finished washing him, and gave him a toothbrush and some tooth powder. He brushed his teeth, rinsed his mouth, and spat the water out into the basin.

Later she brought him his breakfast on a tray, but he did not want to eat. He was still feeling weak and sick, and he wished only to lie still and think about what had happened. And there was a sentence running through his head. It was a sentence which Johnny, the Intelligence Officer of his squadron, always repeated to the pilots every day before they went out. He could see Johnny now, leaning against the wall of the dispersal hut with his pipe in his hand, saying, "And if they get you, don't forget, just your name, rank, and number. Nothing else. No matter what they do, say nothing else."

"There you are," she said as she put the tray on his lap. "I've got you an egg. Can you manage all right?"

"Yes."

She stood beside the bed. "Are you feeling all right?"

"Yes."

"Good. If you want another egg I might be able to get you one."

"This is all right."

"Well, just ring the bell if you want any more." And she went out.

He had just finished eating, when the nurse came in again.

She said, "Wing Commander Roberts is here. I've told him that he can only stay for a few minutes."

She beckoned with her hand and the Wing Commander came in.

"Sorry to bother you like this," he said.

He was an ordinary RAF[13] officer, dressed in a uniform which was a little

---

[12] **Air Ministry**, department of the British government which controls the British air force.

[13] **RAF**, Royal Air Force, the British air force.

shabby, and he wore wings and a DFC.[14] He was fairly tall and thin with plenty of black hair. His teeth, which were irregular and widely spaced, stuck out a little even when he closed his mouth. As he spoke he took a printed form and a pencil from his pocket, and he pulled up a chair and sat down.

"How are you feeling?"

There was no answer.

"Tough luck about your leg. I know how you feel. I hear you put up a fine show before they got you."

The man in the bed was lying quite still, watching the man in the chair.

The man in the chair said, "Well, let's get this stuff over. I'm afraid you'll have to answer a few questions so that I can fill in this combat report. Let me see now, first of all, what was your squadron?"

The man in the bed did not move. He looked straight at the Wing Commander and he said, "My name is Peter Williamson. My rank is Squadron Leader and my number is nine seven two four five seven."

THE END

⟳ **Talking it over**

1. After reading the first few paragraphs of this story, how do you know the pilot is not his normal self?

2. In the hospital, the pilot struggles with two kinds of pressure—mental and physical.

   a. What are the two problems he is struggling with?

---
[14]**DFC,** Distinguished Flying Cross, awarded for heroism in an air battle.

   b. How does he settle each one?

3. Why is the sign the pilot sees so important to him?

4. You, like the pilot, need to make certain inferences. What do you infer

   a. from the fact that he isn't told the truth about where he is?

   b. from his new observations about the nurse?

   c. from the Wing Commander's conversation and question?

   d. from the pilot's reply to the Commander's question?

5. The **plot** of a story means the plan of the story—the pattern of incidents or happenings that make up the story. The plot of "Beware of the Dog" is made up of about eight major incidents. They are listed here but their order is scrambled.

Arrange the incidents in the same order that the author did.

   a. A man who calls himself a Wing Commander comes to see the pilot and asks him a question.

   b. An injured British pilot bails out of his plane over what he thinks is British territory.

   c. He discovers that the water is hard; this fact makes him even more suspicious.

   d. He wakes up in a hospital, which he is told is in Brighton, England.

   e. The pilot gives an unexpected answer.

   f. He drags himself to the window of his hospital room and looks out.

   g. He sees a sign with French words.

   h. He hears sounds of enemy bombers (but no sounds of air-raid sirens); these sounds puzzle him and he becomes suspicious.

6. The order of these major incidents is important to the plot. The ar-

rangement should be logical; that is, an incident should grow out of the one before it and should lead into the incident that comes after it. For example:

   a. Because he has been made suspicious by the bomber sounds and the water, what does the pilot do?

   b. Because of the words he sees on the sign, what does the pilot do when the Wing Commander comes to see him?

7. In mystery or suspense stories like this one, the major incidents will build in suspense—in making you care what happens next—up to a peak of excitement.

   Where is the peak of excitement—the point where you felt the most suspense?

There has to be a plot

British novelist and short-story writer Roald Dahl says that "Beware of the Dog" started as "simply an idea that came to me during the war. . . ."

Mr. Dahl is known for his witty stories with unusual plots. He says modestly that "Beware of the Dog" was a very early story of his, "and I hope I have written a few better ones since. But anyway it has the merit of possessing a sound straightforward plot, a beginning, a middle, and an end, and a certain amount of suspense."

Mr. Dahl was born in Wales and now lives with his wife, actress Patricia Neal, and their children in a home called Gipsy House in Buckinghamshire, England.

THE ROALD DAHL FAMILY. MRS. DAHL IS ACTRESS PATRICIA NEAL.

CHARLEY LEE

by Henry Herbert Knibbs

A low moon shone on the desert land and the sage was silver white,
As Lee—a thong round hand and hand—stood straight in the lantern light.
    "You have strung up Red and Burke," said he,
    "And you say that the next will be Charley Lee,
    But there's never a rope was made for me."   5
And he laughed in the quiet night.

They shaped the noose and they flicked the rope and over the limb it fell,
And Charley Lee saw the ghost of hope go glimmering down to hell.
    Two shadows swung from the cottonwood tree,
    And the wind went whispering, "Charley Lee,"   10
    For the turning shadows would soon be three,
And never a stone to tell.

"Have ye more to say for yourself?" said Gray, "a message the like, or prayer?
If ye have, then hasten and have your say. We trailed and we trapped ye fair,
    With fire and iron at Hidden Sink,   15
    Where none but the stolen horses drink.
    And the chain but wanted a final link.
Ye were riding my red roan mare."

"But prove your property first," said Lee. "Would you call the mare your own,
With never a brand or mark to see, or name to the big red roan?   20
    But strip the saddle and turn her loose,
    And I'll show that the mare is my own cayuse.
    And I don't—then take it a fair excuse,
To tighten the rope you've thrown."

Gaunt, grim faces and steady eyes were touched with a somber look,   25
And hands slipped slowly to belted thighs and held on a finger-crook,
    For Gray of Mesa who claimed the mare,
    Had talked too much as he led them there,
    Nor other among them knew the lair,
So a grip on their haste they took.   30

From *Songs of the Last Frontier* by H. H. Knibbs. Reprinted by permission of the publisher, Houghton Mifflin Company.

"Give him a chance," said Monty Wade, and, "What is the use?" said Blake.
"He's done," said Harney; "his string is played. But we'll give him an even break."
    So they led the mare to the cottonwood tree,
    Nor saddle nor bridle nor rope had she.
    "Bonnie, come here!" said Charley Lee,   35
And soft was the word he spake.

The roan mare came and she nosed his side and nuzzled him friendly-wise;
"Kneel!" cried Lee, and he leaped astride and fled as the swallow flies.
    Flashes followed his flight in vain,
    Bullets spattered the ground like rain,   40
    Hoofs drummed far on the midnight plain,
And a low moon rode the skies.

Dawn broke red on the desert land where the turning shadows fell,
And the wind drove over the rolling sand with a whimpering ebb and swell,
    Whimpering, whispering, "Charley Lee,"   45
    As south on the red roan mare rode he,
    Yet the turning shadows they were three,
And never a stone to tell.

Talking it over

1. *a.* At the beginning of the poem, what has happened to Charley Lee?

   b. How does he seem to feel about the prospect of being hanged?

   c. How does this feeling change after the rope with a noose is attached to a tree limb?

   d. What are the two "turning shadows" that are referred to in lines 9 and 11?

2. *a.* What are the circumstances that make Charley Lee look guilty?

   b. What is the meaning of line 17?

3. *a.* How does Charley Lee argue that the evidence against him is only circumstantial?   (*cont.*)

b. What challenge does Charley Lee then make to the men who have captured him?

c. How do the men respond to this challenge?

4. *a.* How does Charley Lee prove his innocence?

b. What does he do that shows he doesn't trust his captors?

5. *a.* What is meant by the line "Yet the turning shadows they were three"?

b. Who is the third "turning shadow"?

c. On what hints or information in the poem do you base your answer?

⇄ **Words in action**

When one of his captors says of Charley Lee, "He's done; his string is played," does the captor mean that

(*a*) Charley's guitar is broken?

(*b*) Charley is tied so securely that he'll never get loose?

(*c*) Charley's arguments that he is innocent have been used up and there is nothing more he can say in his defense?

In western slang, "string" means the group of saddle horses that each cowhand has for his exclusive use. Each rider might have a string of from two to six horses. When one horse gets tired, the cowboy rides another. If his string is "played," then his saddle horses are "played out" or "worn out." A cowboy in this position would have to stop riding; he would be helpless to continue.

If Charley Lee's string of arguments as to his innocence are played out or used up, then he, too, is helpless and at the mercy of his captors. One might also say that he is "at the end of his rope"—comparing his captive situation with that of a roped or tethered animal whose freedom is cut short.

The words *string* and *rope* appear frequently in our language as slang terms. Probably most of these expressions are already familiar to you. Several can be traced to the origins just discussed.

I

For each italicized word or phrase in the sentences below, select the appropriate meaning from the following list. Match the letter of the meaning with the sentence number. One meaning will not be needed.

a. ins and outs, details
b. freedom of action
c. conditions, qualifications
d. follow the lead of
e. deceive a person
f. use his influence
g. dangling at one's pleasure

1. There were no *strings* attached to his offer.

2. Oh, I'll just *string along* with Andy for a while and see what happens.

3. It looks as though Edith has Bob *on a string.*

4. Maybe his father will *pull some strings* to get Gene a job.

5. Give him enough *rope* and he'll hang himself.

6. Charlie said if I drop around to his photo lab he'll teach me the *ropes.*

II

Which of the expressions involving string and rope in the sentences above can you trace to the "western" origins described earlier in this exercise?

He was probably the only man in the history of Texas who deserved hanging more <u>after</u> he was hung than before.

NECKTIE PARTY

by Henry Gregor Felsen

DOWN here in Texas we've got a book that is supposed to show every world's record held by Texas, only it don't. There is one Texas record that ain't in the book and is unknown about even to Texas. As the last living survivor of the posse that helped set that record, I feel it's my duty to claim it for Texas—even if Texas won't want it.

The record I claim is for the longest informal hanging of a cattle rustler. It was set on a August night in 1886 near Spanish Fort, Texas, when we strung up the notorious rustler Shawnee Sam.

The funny part of it is, we didn't know until later it was him. At the time we thought he was just a rustler who needed hanging. He had a fast horse and a head start, and we never would have caught him except that his horse fell and throwed him.

There didn't seem to be anything

special about the feller at the time. He dusted himself off and looked around at us and nodded, and said he sure was glad to see us, and it certainly was funny what had happened to him. What had happened, he said, was that he had been riding at night to escape the heat of the day, and he'd fallen asleep in the saddle until our shooting had woke him up.

To his great surprise, he said, he discovered that his horse had fallen in behind a herd of stray cattle, and was following them at a dead run toward the Oklahoma border. Then his horse stepped in a gopher hole and throwed him, and the fall had somehow pushed his bandanna up over his face.

When the stranger had said his piece, the sheriff said, "All right, boys. The trial is over."

A couple of us rode to a nearby cottonwood tree and throwed a rope over a limb. We got the stranger mounted, tied his hands behind his back, and positioned him under the limb where the noose was. The sheriff slipped the noose over the feller's head. Then he said to me, "Hank, you stand by. When I lift my hat, you lay a quirt to his horse."

"Sheriff," the stranger said in a mild voice, "I think you're forgetting some of my rights and privileges in this hanging. I'd hate for it to get around how slipshod the hangings are in East Texas."

"If you're so stuck on getting hung West Texas style," the sheriff said, "why didn't you stay to home and rustle West Texas cattle?"

"To tell you the truth, Sheriff," the stranger said, "there ain't better stealing beef in the whole world than in East Texas. But we ain't arguing cattle, we're arguing hangings, and when we have a hanging in West Texas, we extend the condemned man the common courtesies of the occasion."

Well, the sheriff just sat there for a minute scratching his chin and thinking. A quick hanging would have been like admitting that East Texas was satisfied with hangings that didn't come up to West Texas standards. On the other hand, it wouldn't look good if it got out that a West Texas outlaw had to instruct an East Texas sheriff on how to hang.

"Stranger," the sheriff said, "you made a kind remark about our East Texas cattle. I guess we can return the kindness. We'll be happy to hang you West Texas style." He thought a moment. "Who might we be having the pleasure to hang here?" he said grandly.

"The name is Tex," the stranger said. "Tex Tyler."

"Tex Tyler," the sheriff said in a loud official voice, "do you have any last words to say before you swing?"

The outlaw bowed his head. "I would like at this time," he said in a soft voice, "to say a few words about Texas." He cleared his throat, and all of us in the posse uncovered.

"Friends and captors," the outlaw said, lifting his face to the sky, "let us consider togetl er how Texas was born. Two billion years ago a wandering star passed too near the sun and tore off a giant chunk of flaming gas. Once it was off by itself in the sky, the gas cooled and got solid, and that bright fragment of the sun became Texas. . . ."

The stranger spoke on, and we sat on our horses and listened. It got late and cold, but the man was talking about Texas, and we listened.

He told how Texas got all covered over with water a thousand feet deep, and how there was fish swimming over Texas that was a hundred times bigger than the biggest whale. And he told how the water drained off Texas to make the oceans that we have now. He went on to tell how grass began to grow in Texas, and animals to appear—critters with tails as long as trees. If he hadn't been talking about Texas, we wouldn't have believed a word he said.

He talked about them things all night, and the sun was coming up before he took a deep breath and was quiet for a minute. The sheriff came awake with a start, but before he could order the hanging, the stranger said: "So much for the birth of Texas. I would now like to say a few words about Texas history." And he started in with the story of mankind in Texas, beginning about fifteen minutes this side of the ape.

Along about seven o'clock in the morning the horses was getting restless, and it was pretty hard for us to think of Texas instead of coffee.

"Tex," the sheriff said, "the boys and myself appreciate your feelings about Texas, but we've got business elsewhere. I know you don't want your hanging to stand in the way of Texas progress."

"Sheriff," Tex answered, "if this was an ordinary hanging, I'd be glad to oblige your request to speed things up. But this is a momentous occasion. How long have I been talking?"

"Nearly six hours, Tex," the sheriff told him.

The prisoner sighed. "Well, Sheriff, I'll never make it. I'm already getting hoarse."

"You'll never make what?" the sheriff asked.

"That was my little secret," Tex said. "I happen to know that the world's record for long hangings is held by Arizona. It was set about eight years ago. The feller talked for nine hours." Tex shook his head in a sad, tired way. "I ain't going to make it. I don't mind for myself so much, but I hate to see Texas in second place. Just tell the world I done my best. I'm ready, Sheriff."

He was, but we wasn't. The sheriff called us all aside. "It ain't that we're after any glory for ourselves," he said, "but we've got to think about Texas. I think our duty is clear."

Naturally we agreed with the sheriff, and we went back to the prisoner. "Tex," the sheriff said, "me and the boys has decided to help you try for that record. It's only three more hours. You've gotta try!"

And the stranger did. He talked for another hour, but we could tell his voice was getting weaker and weaker. Another half hour and he was barely able to whisper. And in two hours, an hour shy of the record, his voice was quite gone.

"There must be some kind of a noise he can make," Ted Brock said, and then he whispered something into the prisoner's ear. The prisoner straightened up with a look of new confidence, and two seconds later he was whistling "Yellow Rose of Texas." We couldn't help but cheer.

He whistled for twenty minutes, and we began to hope. But at thirty minutes his whistle sounded thin, and at forty minutes we had to stand real close to hear.

At fifty minutes two of us was holding him up in the saddle. At fifty-nine minutes he fell back against me, but I put my ear to his lips and I could still hear that Texas song.

Then a gun went off. The sheriff stood before us with his watch in one hand and his pistol in the other. "Nine hours," he said. "We've tied the Arizona record!"

At those words the rustler pulled himself up straight. He took a big breath and found the strength to *sing* the Texas song and break the record!

Well, you never heard such whooping and hollering in your life. We took the rustler down from his horse and gave him water and shook his hand. It was Ted Brock who brung us back to reality.

"Now that we've got the record," Ted said, "we can finish the hanging and go home."

"Finish the hanging!" one of the boys shouted. "After what this feller done for Texas!"

"We have to," said Ted. "Otherwise it won't be no record. You can't claim a record for the longest hanging unless you hang somebody, can you?"

That sobered us up in a hurry. It was a problem, all right, and it took the sheriff to solve it.

"Men," the sheriff said, "we have to hang this man. But no court of law has passed sentence that he be hung by the neck until dead. This is an informal hanging, and as sheriff, I order that this man be hung until we *think* he's dead."

So we dropped the noose down under the rustler's arms. Then we eased his horse forward until the rustler was hanging from the tree. "All right, boys," the sheriff called. "I think this man has been hung until dead. Cut him down."

We helped the rustler down and let him go, and Texas held the record.

We rode back to town at top speed and trooped into the saloon to celebrate—all except the sheriff, who had to ride over to the jail first and make his report.

There was the biggest noise and jollity you ever heard in that saloon, until the sheriff came back. He laid a paper on the bar. "Look at this," he said in a shaking voice. "It just came to me by mail."

I looked with the others and saw a WANTED poster with a picture of Tex Tyler, our recent prisoner, on it. But according to this poster it wasn't Tex Tyler at all. It was Shawnee Sam!

"Men," the sheriff said when we had quieted down, "we can't report this record. We can't ever mention it to anybody. What if the world found out that a Texas posse sat around with its hat off while the world's record for talking Texas at a hanging was set by a Oklahoma boy?"

The bitter part of it was that Shawnee Sam was probably the only man in the history of Texas who deserved hanging more *after* he was hung than before.

THE END

↻ **Talking it over**

1. *a.* When the sheriff says, "The trial is over," what trial does he mean?

b. How does this hanging, which the sheriff calls "informal," differ from what a formal one would be?

2. *a.* What idea about Texas is this story based on?

b. How does Tex Tyler make use of this idea to help himself?

3. Find three passages in the story that describe the men's almost reverent attitude when Tex talks of Texas.

4. Why couldn't the story of the hanging be told before this?

Straight-faced authentic lies

"Unfortunately, most western fiction and history ignore the place of humor in frontier life," says Henry Gregor Felsen. "We get all kinds of grim shoot-'em-up fiction and noble-suffering history, but very little that shows pioneers and frontiersmen as ordinary human beings who liked to laugh as well as plow or be scalped."

About "Necktie Party," he explains: "Both the tall story and the practical joke were a part of western development, and a major source of entertainment. I have tried, in a few stories, to capture this spirit with some straight-faced authentic lies.

"There is a classic western joke about a dentist who was being hanged, and was asked if he had anything to say before the trap was sprung. 'Not at this time,' was his reply. I just reversed that for 'Necktie Party,' and imagined what would happen if the 'last words' went on and on."

Mr. Felsen has traveled widely,—as a runaway during his junior year in high school; as a messboy on a steamship line a couple of years later; and as a U.S. Marine during World War II. He is the author of popular books for young people, among them *Hot Rod, Street Rod, Crash Club, Road Rocket, To My Son, the Teen-age Driver*, and *A Teen-ager's First Car*.

THE MONSTERS ARE DUE ON MAPLE STREET

by Rod Serling

CHARACTERS

Narrator
Figure One
Figure Two

Residents of Maple Street:

Don Martin
Steve Brand
Myra Brand, *Steve's wife*
Pete Van Horn

Charlie
Charlie's Wife
Tommy
Sally, *Tommy's mother*
Les Goodman
Ethel Goodman, *Les's wife*
Man One
Woman One
Woman Two

Adapted from a television play which appeared on *The Twilight Zone*. Used by permission of Rod Serling.

THE MONSTERS ARE DUE ON MAPLE STREET

ACT ONE

SCENE 1. (FADE IN ON SHOT OF THE NIGHT SKY. *The various heavenly bodies stand out in sharp, sparkling relief. As the* CAMERA *begins a* SLOW PAN *across the Heavens, we hear the narrator.*)

Narrator (*off stage*): There is a fifth dimension beyond that which is known to man. It is a dimension as vast as space, and as timeless as infinity. It is the middle ground between light and shadow—between science and superstition. And it lies between the pit of man's fears and the summit of his knowledge. This is the dimension of imagination. It is an area which we call the Twilight Zone.

SCENE 2. (THE CAMERA BEGINS TO PAN DOWN *until it passes the horizon and stops on a sign which reads "Maple Street." It is daytime. Then we see the street below. It is a quiet, tree-lined, small-town American street. The houses have front porches on which people sit and swing on gliders, talking across from house to house. Steve Brand is polishing his car, which is parked in front of his house. His neigh-*

bor, Don Martin, leans against the fender watching him. A Good Humor man riding a bicycle is just in the process of stopping to sell some ice cream to a couple of kids. Two women gossip on the front lawn. Another man is watering his lawn with a garden hose.

At this moment Tommy, one of the two boys buying ice cream from the vendor, looks up to listen to a tremendous screeching roar from overhead. A flash of light plays on the faces of both boys and then moves down the street and disappears.

Various people leave their porches or stop what they are doing to stare up at the sky.

Steve Brand, the man who has been polishing his car, stands there transfixed, staring upwards. He looks at Don Martin, his neighbor from across the street.)

Steve: What was that? A meteor?

Don: That's what it looked like. I didn't hear any crash though, did you?

Steve: Nope. I didn't hear anything except a roar.

Mrs. Brand (*from her porch*): Steve? What was that?

Steve (*raising his voice and looking toward the porch*): Guess it was a meteor, honey. Came awful close, didn't it?

Mrs. Brand: Too close for my money! Much too close.

(THE CAMERA PANS ACROSS THE VARIOUS PORCHES *to people who stand there watching and talking in low conversing tones.*)

Narrator: Maple Street. Six-forty-four P.M. on a late September evening. (*A pause*) Maple Street in the last calm and reflective moment . . . before the monsters came!

(THE CAMERA TAKES US ACROSS THE

PORCHES AGAIN. *A man is screwing a light bulb on a front porch. He gets down off his stool to flick the switch and finds that nothing happens.*

Another man is working on an electric power mower. He plugs in the plug, flicks the switch of the mower off and on, but nothing happens.

Through a window we see a woman pushing her finger back and forth on the dial hook of a telephone. Her voice sounds far away.)

Woman One: Operator, operator, something's wrong on the phone, operator!

(Mrs. Brand comes out on the porch and calls to Steve.)

Mrs. Brand (*calling*): Steve, the power's off. I had the soup on the stove and the stove just stopped working.

Woman One: Same thing over here. I can't get anybody on the phone either. The phone seems to be dead.

(We look down again on the street. Small, mildly disturbed voices creep up from below.)

Voice One: Electricity's off.

Voice Two: Phone won't work.

Voice Three: Can't get a thing on the radio.

Voice Four: My power mower won't move, won't work at all.

Voice Five: Radio's gone dead!

(Pete Van Horn, a tall, thin man, is seen standing in front of his house.)

Van Horn: I'll cut through the back yard . . . see if the power's still on on Floral Street. I'll be right back!

(He walks past the side of his house and disappears into the back yard.

THE CAMERA PANS DOWN SLOWLY *until we are looking at ten or eleven people standing around the street and overflowing to the curb and sidewalk. In the background is Steve Brand's car.)*

Steve: Doesn't make sense. Why should the power go off all of a sudden *and* the phone line?

Don: Maybe some kind of an electrical storm or something.

Charlie: That don't seem likely. Sky's just as blue as anything. Not a cloud. No lightning. No thunder. No nothing. How could it be a storm?

Woman One: I can't get a thing on the radio. Not even the portable.

(The people again murmur softly in wonderment.)

Charlie: Well, why don't you go downtown and check with the police, though they'll probably think we're crazy or something. A little power failure and right away we get all flustered and everything—

Steve: It isn't just the power failure, Charlie. If it was, we'd still be able to get a broadcast on the portable.

(There is a murmur of reaction to this. Steve looks from face to face and then over to his car.)

Steve: I'll run downtown. We'll get this all straightened out.

(He walks over to the car, gets in, and turns the key.

Looking through the open car door, we see the crowd watching Steve from the other side. He starts the engine. It turns over sluggishly and then stops dead. He tries it again, and this time he can't get it to turn over. Then very slowly he turns the key back to "off" and gets out of the car.

The people stare at Steve. He stands for a moment by the car and then walks toward them.)

Steve: I don't understand it. It was working fine before—

Don: Out of gas?

Steve (*shakes his head*): I just had it filled up.

Woman One: What's it mean?

Charlie: It's just as if . . . as if everything had stopped. (*Then he turns toward Steve.*) We'd better *walk* downtown.

(*Another murmur of assent to this.*)

Steve: The two of us can go, Charlie. (*He turns to look back at the car.*) It couldn't be the meteor. A meteor couldn't do *this*.

(*He and Charlie exchange a look. Then they start to walk away from the group.*

Tommy comes into view. He is a serious-faced young boy in spectacles. He stands halfway between the group and the two men who start to walk down the sidewalk.)

Tommy: Mr. Brand . . . you'd better not!

Steve: Why not?

Tommy: They don't want you to.

(*Steve and Charlie exchange a grin and Steve looks back toward the boy.*)

Steve: *Who* doesn't want us to?

Tommy (*jerks his head in the general direction of the distant horizon*): Them!

Steve: Them?

Charlie: Who are them?

Tommy (*intently*): Whoever was in that thing that came by overhead.

(*Steve knits his brows for a moment, cocking his head questioningly. His voice is intense.*)

Steve: What?

Tommy: Whoever was in that thing that came over. I don't think they want us to leave here.

(*Steve leaves Charlie, walks over to the boy, and puts his hand on the boy's shoulder. He forces his voice to remain gentle.*)

Steve: What do you mean? What are you talking about?

Tommy: They don't want us to leave. That's why they shut everything off.

Steve: What makes you say that? Whatever gave you *that* idea?

Woman One (*from the crowd*): Now isn't that the craziest thing you ever heard?

Tommy (*persistent but a little frightened*): It's always that way, in every story I ever read about a ship landing from outer space.

Woman One (*to the boy's mother, Sally, who stands on the fringe of the crowd*): From outer space yet! Sally, you better get that boy of yours up to bed. He's been reading too many comic books or seeing too many movies or something!

Sally: Tommy, come over here and stop that kind of talk.

Steve: Go ahead, Tommy. We'll be right back. And you'll see. That wasn't any ship or anything like it. That was just a . . . a meteor or something. Likely as not—(*He turns to the group, now trying very hard to sound more optimistic than he feels.*) No doubt it did have something to do with all this power failure and the rest of it. Meteors can do some crazy things. Like sun spots.

Don (*picking up the cue*): Sure. That's the kind of thing—like sun spots. They raise Cain with radio reception all over the world. And this thing being so close—why, there's no telling the sort of stuff it can do. (*He wets his lips, smiles nervously.*) Go ahead, Charlie. You and Steve go into town and see if that isn't what's causing it all.

(*Steve and Charlie walk away from the group down the sidewalk as the people watch silently.*

Tommy stares at them, biting his lips, and finally calls out again.)

Tommy: Mr. Brand!

(The two men stop. Tommy takes a step toward them.)

Tommy: Mr. Brand . . . please don't leave here.

(Steve and Charlie stop once again and turn toward the boy. In the crowd there is a murmur of irritation and concern, as if the boy's words—even though they didn't make sense—were bringing up fears that shouldn't be brought up.

Tommy is partly frightened and partly defiant.)

Tommy: You might not even be able to get to town. It was that way in the story. *Nobody* could leave. Nobody except—

Steve: Except who?

Tommy: Except the people they'd sent down ahead of them. They looked just like humans. And it wasn't until the ship landed that—*(The boy suddenly stops, conscious of the people staring at him and his mother and of the sudden hush of the crowd.)*

Sally *(in a whisper, sensing the antagonism of the crowd)*: Tommy, please son . . . honey, don't talk that way—

Man One: That kid shouldn't talk that way . . . and we shouldn't stand here listening to him. Why, this is the craziest thing I ever heard of. The kid tells us a comic book plot and here we stand listening—

(Steve walks toward the camera, and stops beside the boy.)

Steve: Go ahead, Tommy. What kind of story was this? What about the people they sent out ahead?

Tommy: That was the way they prepared things for the landing. They sent four people. A mother and a father and two kids who looked just like humans . . . but they weren't.

(There is another silence as Steve looks toward the crowd and then toward Tommy. He wears a tight grin.)

Steve: Well, I guess what we'd better do then is to run a check on the neighborhood and see which ones of us are really human.

(There is laughter at this, but it's a laughter that comes from a desperate attempt to lighten the atmosphere. The people look at one another in the middle of their laughter.)

Charlie *(rubs his jaw nervously)*: I wonder if Floral Street's got the same deal we got. *(He looks past the houses.)* Where is Pete Van Horn anyway? Didn't he get back yet?

(Suddenly there is the sound of a car's engine starting to turn over.

WE LOOK ACROSS THE STREET TOWARD THE DRIVEWAY OF LES GOODMAN'S HOUSE. *He is at the wheel trying to start the car.)*

Sally: Can you get started, Les?

(Les Goodman gets out of the car, shaking his head.)

Goodman: No dice.

(He walks toward the group. He stops suddenly as, behind him, the car engine starts up all by itself. Goodman whirls around to stare at it.

The car idles roughly, smoke coming from the exhaust, the frame shaking gently.

Goodman's eyes go wide, and he runs over to his car.

The people stare at the car.)

Man One: He got the car started somehow. He got *his* car started!

(The people continue to stare, caught up by this revelation and wildly frightened.)

Woman One: How come his car just up and started like that?

Sally: All by itself. He wasn't anywheres near it. It started all by itself.

(Don Martin approaches the group,

stops a few feet away to look toward Goodman's car and then back toward the group.)

Don: And he never did come out to look at that thing that flew overhead. He wasn't even interested. (*He turns to the group, his face taut and serious.*) Why? Why didn't he come out with the rest of us to look?

Charlie: He always was an odd ball. Him and his whole family. Real odd ball.

Don: What do you say we ask him? (*The group start toward the house. In this brief fraction of a moment they take the first step toward a metamorphosis that changes people from a group into a mob. They begin to head purposefully across the street toward the house. Steve stands in front of them. For a moment their fear almost turns their walk into a wild stampede, but Steve's voice, loud, incisive, and commanding, makes them stop.*)

Steve: Wait a minute . . . wait a minute! Let's not be a mob!

(*The people stop, pause for a moment, and then much more quietly and slowly start to walk across the street.*

Goodman stands alone facing the people.)

Goodman: I just don't understand it. I tried to start it and it wouldn't start. You saw me. All of you saw me.

(*And now, just as suddenly as the engine started, it stops, and there is a long silence that is gradually intruded upon by the frightened murmuring of the people.*)

Goodman: I don't understand. I swear . . . I don't understand. What's happening?

Don: Maybe you better tell us. Nothing's working on this street. Nothing. No lights, no power, no radio. (*Then*

meaningfully) Nothing except one car—yours!

(*The people's murmuring becomes a loud chant filling the air with accusations and demands for action. Two of the men pass Don and head toward Goodman who backs away from them against his car. He is cornered.*)

Goodman: Wait a minute now. You keep your distance—all of you. So I've got a car that starts by itself— well, that's a freak thing—I admit it. But does that make me some kind of a criminal or something? I don't know why the car works—it just does!

(*This stops the crowd momentarily and Goodman, still backing away, goes toward his front porch. He goes up the steps and then stops, facing the mob.*)

Goodman: What's it all about, Steve?

Steve (*quietly*): We're all on a monster kick, Les. Seems that the general impression holds that maybe one family isn't what we think they are. Monsters from outer space or something. Different from us. Fifth columnists from the vast beyond. (*He chuckles.*) You know anybody that might fit that description around here on Maple Street?

Goodman: What is this, a gag? (*He looks around the group again.*) This a practical joke or something?

(*Suddenly the car engine starts all by itself, runs for a moment, and stops. One woman begins to cry. The eyes of the crowd are cold and accusing.*)

Goodman: Now that's supposed to incriminate me, huh? The car engine goes on and off and that really does it, doesn't it? (*He looks around the faces of the people.*) I just don't understand it . . . any more than any of you do! (*He wets his lips, looking* *from face to face.*) Look, you all know me. We've lived here five years. Right in this house. We're no different from any of the rest of you! We're no different at all . . . Really . . . this whole thing is just . . . just weird—

Woman One: Well, if that's the case, Les Goodman, explain why—(*She stops suddenly, clamping her mouth shut.*)

Goodman (*softly*): Explain what?

Steve (*interjecting*): Look, let's forget this—

Charlie (*overlapping him*): Go ahead, let her talk. What about it? Explain what?

Woman One (*a little reluctantly*): Well . . . sometimes I go to bed late at night. A couple of times . . . a couple of times I'd come out here on the porch and I'd see Mr. Goodman here in the wee hours of the morning standing out in front of his house . . . looking up at the sky. (*She looks around the circle of faces.*) That's right, looking up at the sky as if . . . as if he were waiting for something. (*A pause*) As if he were looking for something.

(*There's a murmur of reaction from the crowd again as Goodman backs away.*)

Goodman: She's crazy. Look, I can explain that. Please . . . I can really explain that . . . she's making it up anyway. (*Then he shouts.*) I tell you she's making it up!

(*He takes a step toward the crowd and they back away from him. He walks down the steps after them and they continue to back away. Suddenly he is left completely alone, and he looks like a man caught in the middle of a menacing circle as the scene* SLOWLY FADES TO BLACK.)

Talking it over

1. *a.* At first the neighbors doubt Tommy's people-from-outer-space story, but later they tend to accept it. What causes them to change?

b. What suspicion is planted in their minds?

2. Suspicion turns toward Les Goodman when the engine of his car starts by itself. (Charlie observes that Les "always was an odd ball"; Don says that Les "never did come out to look at the thing that flew overhead," and another neighbor recalls that she has seen Les looking up at the sky during the wee hours.)

a. What inferences or conclusions are the neighbors making from this information?

b. How sound are these inferences?

3. As the group of neighbors start across the street to confront Les Goodman, the stage directions tell you: "In this brief fraction of a moment they [the neighbors] take the first step toward a metamorphosis that changes people from a group into a mob. . . . For a moment their fear almost turns their walk into a wild stampede. . . ."

a. What is the difference between a group and a mob?

b. The word *stampede* is often used in connection with what besides human beings?

c. Why is *stampede* a fitting word to use in this instance?

ACT TWO

SCENE 1. (FADE IN ON MAPLE STREET AT NIGHT. *On the sidewalk, little knots of people stand around talking in low voices. At the end of each conversation they look toward Les Goodman's house. From the various houses we can see candlelight but no electricity. The quiet which blankets the whole area is disturbed only by the almost whispered voices of the people standing around. In one group Charlie stands staring across at Goodman's house. Two men stand across the street from it in almost sentry-like poses.*)

Sally (*in a small, hesitant voice*): It just doesn't seem right, though, keeping watch on them. Why . . . he was right when he said he was one of our neighbors. Why, I've known Ethel Goodman ever since they moved in. We've been good friends—

Charlie: That don't prove a thing. Any guy who'd spend his time lookin' up at the sky early in the morning— well, there's something wrong with that kind of person. There's something that ain't legitimate. Maybe under normal circumstances we could let it go by, but these aren't normal circumstances. Why, look at this street! Nothin' but candles. Why, it's like goin' back into the dark ages or somethin'!

(*Steve walks down the steps of his porch, down the street to Les Goodman's house, and then stops at the foot of the steps. Goodman is standing there; Mrs. Goodman behind him is very frightened.*)

Goodman: Just stay right where you are, Steve. We don't want any trouble, but this time if anybody sets foot on my porch—that's what they're going to get—trouble!

Steve: Look, Les—

Goodman: I've already explained to you people. I don't sleep very well at night sometimes. I get up and I take a walk and I look up at the sky. I look at the stars!

Mrs. Goodman: That's exactly what he does. Why, this whole thing, it's . . . it's some kind of madness or something.

Steve (*nods grimly*): That's exactly what it is—some kind of madness.

Charlie's Voice (*shrill, from across the street*): You best watch who you're seen with, Steve! Until we get this all straightened out, you ain't exactly above suspicion yourself.

Steve (*whirling around toward him*): Or you, Charlie. Or any of us, it seems. From age eight on up!

Woman One: What I'd like to know is —what are we gonna do? Just stand around here all night?

Charlie: There's nothin' else we *can* do! (*He turns back, looking toward Steve and Goodman again.*) One of 'em'll tip their hand. They *got* to.

Steve (*raising his voice*): There's something you can do, Charlie. You can go home and keep your mouth shut. You can quit strutting around like a self-appointed hanging judge and just climb into bed and forget it.

Charlie: You sound real anxious to have that happen, Steve. I think we better keep our eye on you, too!

Don (*as if he were taking the bit in his teeth, takes a hesitant step to the front*): I think everything might as well come out now. (*He turns toward Steve.*) Your wife's done plenty of talking, Steve, about how *odd* you are!

Charlie (*picking this up, his eyes widening*): Go ahead, tell us what she's said.

(*Steve walks toward them from across the street.*)

Steve: Go ahead, what's my wife said? Let's get it *all* out. Let's pick out every idiosyncrasy of every single man, woman, and child on the street. And then we might as well set up some kind of kangaroo court. How about a firing squad at dawn, Charlie, so we can get rid of all the suspects. Narrow them down. Make it easier for you.

Don: There's no need gettin' so upset, Steve. It's just that . . . well . . . Myra's talked about how there's been plenty of nights you spent hours down in your basement workin' on some kind of radio or something. Well, none of us have ever *seen* that radio—

(*By this time Steve has reached the group. He stands there defiantly.*)

Charlie: Go ahead, Steve. What kind of "radio set" you workin' on? I never seen it. Neither has anyone else. Who you talk to on that radio set? And who talks to you?

Steve: I'm surprised at you, Charlie. How come you're so dense all of a sudden? (*A pause*) Who do I talk to? I talk to monsters from outer space. I talk to three-headed green men who fly over here in what look like meteors.

(*Mrs. Brand steps down from the porch, bites her lip, calls out.*)

Mrs. Brand: Steve! Steve, please. (*Then looking around, frightened, she walks toward the group.*) It's just a ham radio set, that's all. I bought him a book on it myself. It's just a ham radio set. A lot of people have them. I can show it to you. It's right down in the basement.

Steve (*whirls around toward her*): Show them nothing! If they want to look inside our house—let them get a search warrant.

Charlie: Look, buddy, you can't afford to—

Steve (*interrupting him*): Charlie, don't start telling me who's dangerous and who isn't and who's safe and who's a menace. (*He turns to the group and shouts.*) And you're with him, too—all of you! You're standing here all set to crucify—all set to find a scapegoat—all desperate to point some kind of a finger at a neighbor! Well now, look, friends, the only thing that's gonna happen is that we'll eat each other up alive—

(*He stops abruptly as Charlie suddenly grabs his arm.*)

Charlie (*in a hushed voice*): That's not the *only* thing that can happen to us.

(*Down the street, a figure has suddenly materialized in the gloom, and in the silence we hear the clickety-clack of slow, measured footsteps on concrete as the figure walks slowly toward them. One of the women lets out a stifled cry. Sally grabs her boy, as do a couple of other mothers.*)

Tommy (*shouting, frightened*): It's the monster! It's the monster!

(*Another woman lets out a wail and the people fall back in a group staring toward the darkness and the approaching figure.*

The people stand in the shadows watching. Don Martin joins them, carrying a shotgun. He holds it up.)

Don: We may need this.

Steve: A shotgun? (*He pulls it out of Don's hand.*) Good Lord—will anybody think a thought around here?

Will you people wise up? What good would a shotgun do against—

(*The dark figure continues to walk toward them as the people stand there, fearful, mothers clutching children, men standing in front of their wives.*)

Charlie (*pulling the gun from Steve's hands*): No more talk, Steve. You're going to talk us into a grave! You'd let whatever's out there walk right over us, wouldn't yuh? Well, some of us won't!

(*Charlie swings around, raises the gun, and suddenly pulls the trigger. The sound of the shot explodes in the stillness.*

The figure suddenly lets out a small cry, stumbles forward onto his knees, and then falls forward on his face. Don, Charlie, and Steve race forward to him. Steve is there first and turns the man over. The crowd gathers around them.)

Steve (*slowly looks up*): It's Pete Van Horn.

Don (*in a hushed voice*): Pete Van Horn! He was just gonna go over to the next block to see if the power was on—

Woman One: You killed him, Charlie. You shot him dead!

Charlie (*looks around at the circle of faces, his eyes frightened, his face contorted*): But . . . but I didn't know who he was. I certainly didn't know who he was. He comes walkin' out of the darkness—how am I supposed to know who he was? (*He grabs Steve.*) Steve—you know why I shot! How was I supposed to know he wasn't a monster or something? (*He grabs Don.*) We're all scared of the same thing. I was just tryin' to . . . tryin' to protect my home, that's all! Look, all of you, that's all I was tryin' to do. (*He looks down wildly*

at the body.) I didn't know it was somebody we knew! I didn't know—

(*There's a sudden hush and then an intake of breath in the group. Across the street all the lights go on in one of the houses.*)

Woman One (*in a hushed voice*): Charlie . . . Charlie . . . the lights just went on in your house. Why did the lights just go on?

Don: What about it, Charlie? How come you're the only one with lights now?

Goodman: That's what I'd like to know.

(*A pause as they all stare toward Charlie.*)

Goodman: You were so quick to kill, Charlie, and you were so quick to tell us who we had to be careful of. Well, maybe you *had* to kill. Maybe Pete there was trying to tell us something. Maybe he'd found out something and came back to tell us who there was amongst us we should watch out for—

(*Charlie backs away from the group, his eyes wide with fright.*)

Charlie: No . . . no . . . it's nothing of the sort! I don't know why the lights are on. I swear I don't. Somebody's pulling a gag or something.

(*He bumps against Steve who grabs him and whirls him around.*)

Steve: *A gag?* A gag? Charlie, there's a dead man on the sidewalk and you killed him! Does this thing look like a gag to you?

(*Charlie breaks away and screams as he runs toward his house.*)

Charlie: No! No! Please!

(*A man breaks away from the crowd to chase Charlie.*

As the man tackles him and lands on top of him, the other people start to run toward them. Charlie gets up, breaks away from the other man's grasp, lands a couple of desperate punches that push the man aside. Then he forces his way, fighting, through the crowd and jumps up on his front porch.

Charlie is on his porch as a rock thrown from the group smashes a window beside him, the broken glass flying past him. A couple of pieces cut him. He stands there perspiring, rumpled, blood running down from a cut on the cheek. His wife breaks away from the group to throw herself into his arms. He buries his face against her. We can see the crowd converging on the porch.*)

Voice One: It must have been him.

Voice Two: He's the one.

Voice Three: We got to get Charlie.

(*Another rock lands on the porch. Charlie pushes his wife behind him, facing the group.*)

Charlie: Look, look I swear to you . . . it isn't me . . . but I do know who it is . . . I swear to you, I do know who it is. I know who the monster is here. I know who it is that doesn't belong. I swear to you I know.

Don (*pushing his way to the front of the crowd*): All right, Charlie, let's hear it!

(*Charlie's eyes dart around wildly.*)

Charlie: It's . . . it's . . .

Man Two (*screaming*): Go ahead, Charlie, tell us.

Charlie: It's . . . it's the kid. It's Tommy. He's the one!

(*There's a gasp from the crowd as we see Sally holding the boy. Tommy at first doesn't understand and then, realizing the eyes are all on him, buries his face against his mother.*)

Sally (*backs away*): That's crazy! He's only a boy.

Woman One: But he knew! He was the

only one who knew! He told us all about it. Well, how did he know? How *could* he have known?

(*Various people take this up and repeat the question.*)

Voice One: How could he know?

Voice Two: Who told him?

Voice Three: Make the kid answer.

(*The crowd starts to converge around the mother who grabs Tommy and starts to run with him. The crowd starts to follow, at first walking fast, and then running after him.*

Suddenly Charlie's lights go off and the lights in other houses go on, then off.)

Man One (*shouting*): It isn't the kid . . . it's Bob Weaver's house.

Woman One: It isn't Bob Weaver's house, it's Don Martin's place.

Charlie: I tell you it's the kid.

Don: It's Charlie. He's the one.

(*People shout, accuse, and scream as the lights go on and off. Then, slowly, in the middle of this nightmarish confusion of sight and sound the* CAMERA STARTS TO PULL AWAY *until once again we have reached the opening shot looking at the Maple Street sign from high above.*)

SCENE 2: (THE CAMERA CONTINUES TO MOVE AWAY WHILE GRADUALLY BRINGING INTO FOCUS *a field. We see the metal side of a space craft which sits shrouded in darkness. An open door throws out a beam of light from the illuminated interior. Two figures appear, silhouetted against the bright lights. We get only a vague feeling of form.*)

Figure One: Understand the procedure now? Just stop a few of their machines and radios and telephones and lawn mowers . . . throw them into darkness for a few hours, and then just sit back and watch the pattern.

Figure Two: And this pattern is always the same?

Figure One: With few variations. They pick the most dangerous enemy they can find . . . and it's themselves. And all we need do is sit back . . . and watch.

Figure Two: Then I take it this place . . . this Maple Street . . . is not unique.

Figure One (*shaking his head*): By no means. Their world is full of Maple Streets. And we'll go from one to the other and let them destroy themselves. One to the other . . . one to the other . . . one to the other—

SCENE 3. (THE CAMERA PANS UP *for a shot of the starry sky, and over this we hear the Narrator's voice.*)

Narrator: The tools of conquest do not necessarily come with bombs and explosions and fall-out. There are weapons that are simply thoughts, attitudes, prejudices—to be found only in the minds of men. For the record, prejudices can kill and suspicion can destroy and a thoughtless, frightened search for a scapegoat has a fall-out all its own for the children . . . and the children yet unborn. (*A pause*) And the pity of it is . . . that these things cannot be confined to . . . The Twilight Zone!

(FADE TO BLACK)

THE END

1. *a.* How does Charlie feel about what he has done to Pete Van Horn? How do you feel about it?

b. What do you think about Charlie's explanation for his act?

2. *a.* Suspicion turns toward Charlie when the lights go on in his house. What other reason makes the neighbors suspect Charlie?

b. Why does Charlie turn the suspicion toward Tommy?

c. What is the difference in the ways Steve and Charlie react to the pressures of their neighbors' accusations?

3. Steve accuses his neighbors of trying to find a scapegoat.

a. What does the word *scapegoat* mean?

b. Is Steve correct about his neighbors? Why do people seem to find it necessary to find scapegoats?

4. *a.* In the overall plan to take over the earth, what was all that the space creatures had to do?

b. What were the space creatures depending on to make their plan successful?

c. Which person in the play could have upset the entire plan? Why?

5. Rod Serling had a purpose in mind when he wrote this television play. (See the article about him at right.) Of course he wanted to provide entertainment, but he also wanted to tell you something by showing how people act in certain situations. Which of the following bits of advice fit in with what you think is the central idea or "message" of the play?

a. Don't jump to conclusions.

b. Don't ever believe a child.

c. Don't refuse to believe a child simply because he is a child.

d. When you're in a group having differing ideas, follow the strongest leader.

e. Let your heart tell you how to act, rather than your head.

f. Don't be prejudiced against someone because he is different from you.

g. Don't listen to gossip.

h. Don't let fear rule the way you act.

i. Use your ability to reason, especially in a crisis.

j. Don't try to find an answer for everything.

Rod Serling: Storyteller and Critic

A writer must be several things, says Rod Serling.

"All writers are storytellers. All writers take a position of morality—at least a position which they assume to be a moral one. And all writers are social critics. Some writers champion certain areas in excess of others.

"I think you'll find that I have an awareness of human conflict—people fighting other people on many levels other than physical. I'm constantly aware of the combat that human beings enter into with themselves and others.

"I suppose I've tried to attack prejudice more than any other social evil. I've always felt that prejudice is probably the most damaging, most fruitless, and most inhuman of human frailties. I think prejudice is a waste—and that it normally leads to violence.

"Needless to say," says Mr. Serling, "I want to entertain. But I have no awareness of whether or not I'm entertaining—I'm only writing a story as honestly and as effectively as I know how. And, if in the process I do entertain, or make laugh, or make weep, or make think, I've done my job."

Pressure: Views and viewpoints

Everyone is under pressure at times. Sometimes it is physical pressure. People who are starving or in physical danger know this kind of pressure. So do athletes, and many kinds of workers.

Pressure may be mental, as when a tough problem has to be solved in a limited time. A student taking an exam is under this kind of pressure. A lawyer faces it in court. A surgeon feels it when a patient's life hangs on his split-second action.

Pressure may also be social or moral, as when a decision of right or wrong must be made.

1. Which of these three kinds of pressure has each of the following experienced? Some of them may have been under more than one kind of pressure.

> Millie in "Millie"
> Sarah in "Not So Hard"
> Steve Brand in "The Monsters Are Due . . ."
> The basketball player in "Foul Shot"
> Shawnee Sam in "Necktie Party"
> The pilot in "Beware of the Dog"

2. *a.* To escape being hanged, Charley Lee depended on his wits and his horsemanship. What did each person below depend on to get him through a situation of extreme pressure?

> The pilot   Shawnee Sam
> Steve Brand   Sarah

b. Why doesn't Dan Gale fit into this list?

3. Tell about some experience you have known—either your own or that of someone else—which grew out of pressure like that experienced by one of the characters named in question 1. The experience itself may have been different (for example, probably no one you know has been threatened by Indians), but the kind of pressure may have been the same.

8

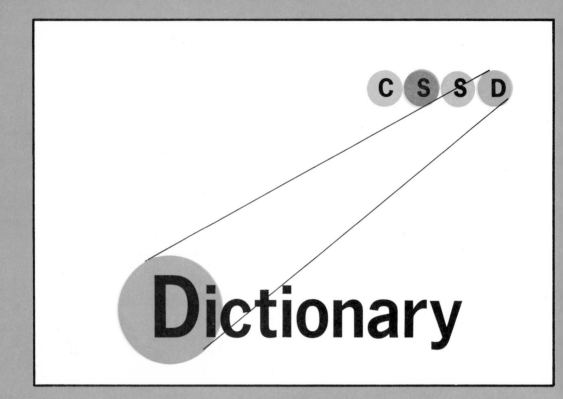

Dictionary

LESSON ONE: Using a dictionary

Suppose you are told to study the paragraph below so that you can read it aloud to the class. Which words will you need to look up in a dictionary to be sure you can pronounce them correctly?

> I decided that before sending a callow young fellow like Forrest on such a crucial mission, I ought to give him some avuncular advice. "Watch your step when you deal with Tompkins," I warned him. "He's as mendacious as they come, and I advise you to be skeptical of anything he tells you. But you can trust our other contacts in Tanganyika. They are some of the most reliable people in Africa."

Now suppose this same paragraph appears in a story which you have been assigned to read and tell in your own words. Which words will you look up? Why?

If you were reading this story just because you enjoyed it, which words, if any, would you look up?

Why would your lists of words probably be different in these three situations?

Some people, of course, never look up words in a dictionary because they really don't know how. The first exercise below will show you how much you already know about using a dictionary. In the rest of this section you will practice some of the skills needed in order to find information quickly and easily in a dictionary. (NOTE: The Glossary in this book is set up like a dictionary and may be used in doing the exercises.)

EXERCISE I.   A check test on using the dictionary

All the questions in this check test have to do with the word *miscreant* as used in this sentence: "Thugs, thieves, and other miscreants of every kind waited in the lawyer's shabby outer office."

1. **miscreant, miscreants**

   Which of these spellings would you expect to find entered in a dictionary? Why wouldn't you expect to find the other one?

2. On the next page are the top parts of four different pages in a dictionary. (a) What is the correct name for the words

that appear at the top of each column? (b) What do these
words tell you? (c) How can you use them to save yourself
time? (d) Why must you be sure of the alphabet in order
to use the words efficiently?

minute	519	misconduct
mi nute¹ (mĭ nüt′ or mĭ nūt′). **1.** very small. **2.** go-		**mis an thro py** (mis an′thrə pē), hatred, dislike, or

misconstruction	520	misquote
mis con struc tion (mis′kən struk′shən), mistaken	**mis guid ance** (mis gĭd′ns), bad or wrong guid-	
meaning; misunderstanding: *What you said was open to*	ance. *n.*	

misread	521	mistral
mis read¹ (mis rēd′), **1.** read wrongly. **2.** misunder-	States. 2,178,000 pop.; 47,716 sq. mi. *Capital:* Jackson.	

mistranslate	522	moa
mis trans late (mis′trans lāt′ or mis trans′lāt), trans-	**miter joint**, a right-angled joint made by cutting the
late incorrectly. *v.*, **mis trans lat ed, mis trans lat ing.**	ends of two pieces of wood on equal slants.
mis trans la tion (mis′trans lā′shən), an incorrect	**Mith ri da tes** (mith′rə dā′tēz), 131?
translation. *n.*	63 B.C., king of Pontus from 120? t~
~**~ treat** (mis trēt′), treat badly. *v.*	and enemy of Rome. H~ ˙
~~**~** (mis trēt′mənt), ill treatment. *n.*	come immune t~

3. On which of these pages would you expect to find *miscreant?*

4. Between which two of the entries below would you expect to
find *miscreant?*

> **mis con strue** (mis′kən strü′), take in a wrong sense;
> misunderstand: *Ethyl's shyness was sometimes miscon-
> strued as rudeness. v.,* **mis con strued, mis con stru ing.**

> **mis count** (mis kount′ for 1; mis′kount for 2), **1.** count
> wrongly. **2.** a wrong count. 1 *v.,*   2 *n.*

> **mis cue** (mis kyü′), **1.** a bad stroke in billiards that
> does not hit the ball squarely. **2.** make a miscue.
> **3.** miss one's cue; respond to a wrong cue. 1 *n.,*   2,3 *v.,*
> **mis cued, mis cu ing.**

> **mis date** (mis dāt′), **1.** date wrongly; assign or affix
> a wrong date to. **2.** a wrong date. 1 *v.,*   **mis dat ed,
> mis dat ing;** 2 *n.*

5. Below is the dictionary entry for *miscreant.* How many syllables are in *miscreant?* What tells you?

> **mis cre ant** (mis′krē ənt), **1.** having very bad morals;
> base. **2.** villain. **3.** *Archaic.* unbeliever; heretic. **4.** *Ar-
> chaic.* unbelieving; heretical. 1,4 *adj.,*   2,3 *n.*

6. Below is a key that is used in reading dictionary pronunciations. Where is this pronunciation key located in a dictionary?

> hat, āge, fär; let, bē, tėrm; it, īce; hot, gō, ôrder; oil, out; cup, pùt, rüle;
> ch, child; ng, long; th, thin; ᴛʜ, then; zh, measure; ə represents *a* in about,
> *e* in taken, *i* in April, *o* in lemon, *u* in circus.

7. Which word in the pronunciation key has the same vowel
sound as the first syllable of *miscreant?*

8. Which key word has the same vowel sound as the second syllable of *miscreant?*

9. Which key word or words have the same vowel sound as the third syllable?

10. Which syllable is accented?

11. Are there any words in the definitions that you don't know? What should you do about such words?

12. What does *Archaic* mean? What does this word tell you about definitions 3 and 4?

13. Which definition of *miscreant* fits best in the sentence "Thugs, thieves, and other miscreants of every kind waited in the lawyer's shabby outer office"?

14. Reword the sentence, using the correct definition in place of *miscreant.*

15. What does (1,4 *adj.,* 2,3 *n.*) at the end of the entry tell you?

LESSON TWO: Understanding dictionary entries

bri dle (brī′dəl), **1.** the head part of a horse's harness, used to hold back or control a horse. **2.** put a bridle on. **3.** anything that holds back or controls. **4.** hold back; check; control: *Bridle your temper.* **5.** hold the head up high with the chin drawn back to express pride, vanity, scorn, or anger: *Jean bridled when we made fun of her new hat.* 1,3 *n.*, 2,4,5 *v.*, **bri dled, bri dling. —bri′dler,** *n.*

Bridle (def. 1)

Do you realize how much information this dictionary entry gives you, in very little space? If the dictionary maker had been able to use all the space he wished, he might have written something like this:

The word *bridle* has two syllables. If you need to divide it at the end of a line when you are writing, you can break it like this: *bri dle.* The first syllable is accented, and the *i* is pronounced with the long sound as in *ice.*

Bridle is used with five different meanings. The first and most common meaning is "the head part of a horse's harness, used to hold back or control a horse." Here is a picture of a horse wearing this kind of bridle. When *bridle* is used to name this object, it is a noun. The same word can also be used as a verb meaning "put a bridle on." A third meaning is related to the other two, but is broader: "anything that holds back or controls." When *bridle* is used in this way, it is a noun. There is also a verb meaning related to this third meaning: "hold back; check; control," as in the sentence *Bridle your temper.* There is still another meaning for *bridle* when it is used as a verb: "hold the head up high with the chin drawn back to express pride, vanity, scorn, or anger." An example of the word used in this sense is: *Jean bridled when we made fun of her new hat.*

The past tense form of the verb *bridle* is *bridled*, and the present participle is *bridling*. These words can be divided like this: *bri dled,* and *bri dling.* By adding the suffix *-er* to *bridle*, the noun *bridler* is formed.

To save space, a dictionary entry is set up according to a definite plan which a dictionary user must understand. For example, you know that the word first appears as it is actually spelled, but divided into syllables. What comes next?

If a word has more than one meaning, each different meaning is numbered. (In many dictionaries, the most common meaning is given first.) The numbers, then, are used to indicate which meanings are for nouns, which for verbs, and so on.

EXERCISE II.   Choosing the right meaning

The right definition is the one that makes the best sense in context. When an entry includes several meanings, you must read them all to decide which is best.

Read sentence A below. Look up the boldface word in the Glossary. Then follow the numbered directions. Do the same with the other sentences.

> A. Egbert was the **scourge** of the playground.

1. Write the number of the definition of *scourge* that fits in this sentence.
2. Which of these statements is true?
   a. Egbert bothered the other children.
   b. Egbert usually carried a whip.
   c. Egbert kept others from bothering the younger children.

> B. Classes continued during the war in a **dismal** bomb shelter.

3. Write the number of the definition of *dismal* that fits in sentence B.

4. Which of these descriptions fits the bomb shelter?

   a. About the size of an average schoolroom, with the usual desks, chalkboard, and books.
   b. A large, bright room, but poorly furnished and too warm.
   c. A dimly lighted, damp room with little fresh air.

> C. The meat was so **corrupt** that even the dogs wouldn't go near it.
>
> D. Because the folk songs were not written down, they became **corrupt** over the years.
>
> E. Mrs. Langford was afraid that working on the docks would **corrupt** her son.

5. Write the number of the definition of *corrupt* which contains the word *inaccurate*. Write after it the letter of the sentence in which this definition fits.

6. Write the number of the definition of *corrupt* that contains the word *rotten*. Write after it the letter of the sentence in which this definition fits.

7. Write the number of the definition of *corrupt* which contains the words *make evil*. Write after it the letter of the sentence in which this definition fits.

> F. After the Japanese children got over their shyness, they were very **inquisitive** about their teacher's home in America.
>
> G. The boys were silent as Mr. Klein walked by. They never said much in front of **inquisitive** adults.

8. Write the number of the definition that applies to *inquisitive* in sentence F.

9. Write the number of the definition that applies to *inquisitive* in sentence G.

LESSON THREE: Using a pronunciation key

In the Glossary of this book you will find a pronunciation key handy wherever you open the pages. Where is it?

At the front of the Glossary, on page 549, is a longer key, with an explanation that will help you understand how to use it.

You will probably be able to get along most of the time by using only the short key. What symbols are not included in the short key? Why are these symbols left out? In what other way is space saved in the short key?

Don't try to memorize either of these pronunciation keys, but learn how to use them. In the next few exercises you will practice using the pronunciation key.

EXERCISE III. Pronouncing one-syllable words

Part A

In this part of the exercise you are to complete five steps for each word in bold type in the numbered sentences below:

   A. Write the sentence number and the boldface word. Leave at least two lines of space between items on your paper to use in doing the second part of the exercise.

   B. Look up the boldface word in the Glossary.

   C. Copy the pronunciation of the word just as it appears in the Glossary entry.

   D. From the short pronunciation key, copy the key word that gives the sound of the vowel. Number 1 will look like this on your paper: 1. feud (fyüd) rule

   E. Practice saying the word to yourself until you can pronounce it easily. Then practice saying the whole sentence.

1. Olga is the cause of the **feud** between Mark and Tom.
2. The wallpaper was covered with big **mauve** flowers.
3. The music was so sweet it began to **cloy**.
4. There was a big red **weal** on his back.
5. What a **suave** gentleman!
6. She wore a **beige** hat with a green veil.

Part B

Read the definitions of each boldface word and decide what the word means in the sentence. Rewrite the sentence on your paper, substituting the correct definition for the boldface word.

EXERCISE IV. Reviewing syllables and accent

> **som er sault** (sum′ər sôlt), **1.** a roll or jump, turning the heels over the head. **2.** roll or jump, turning the heels over the head. 1 *n.*, 2 *v.* Also, **summersault.** **turn a somersault,** somersault.

1. How many syllables are in *somersault*? How can you tell?
2. Which of the following words rhymes with the accented syllable? **hum sir halt**
3. Which of the following words is accented on the same syllable as *somersault*? **elephant decision**

If you could not answer these questions quickly and easily, review pages 102-103, Word Attack/Sound, Lessons Five and Six.

EXERCISE V. Pronouncing two-syllable words

Write the word *hunger* and its pronunciation (hung′gər) at the left-hand side of your paper. Write *support* and its pronunciation (sə pôrt′) at the right-hand side. In *hunger,* which syllable is accented? Which syllable is accented in *support?*

In this exercise you are to do four things with the boldface words in the seven numbered sentences on the next page:

A. Look up the word in the Glossary.

B. If the word has the same accent pattern as *hunger,* write it, with its pronunciation, under *hunger* on your paper. If it has the same accent pattern as *support,* write it under *support.* The first two will look like this:

hunger (hung′gər)   **support** (sə pôrt′)

1. converge (kən vėrj′)

2. clamber (klam′bər)

C. Practice pronouncing the boldface words. Check the pronunciation key for any symbol you are not sure of. Make sure each word is in the column where it belongs. Then practice saying the whole sentence.

D. Read the definitions and decide what the boldface word means in the numbered sentence. Be prepared to reword the sentence using the definition in place of the word.

1. The pigeons began to **converge** on the tower.
2. You'd better wear old clothes when you **clamber** up the tree.
3. Paula is a **genial** hostess.
4. Stop that awful **fracas**!
5. Betty was feeling **morose**.
6. Your pet deserves **humane** treatment.
7. Let's pick up all the **debris** on the playground.

EXERCISE VI. Pronouncing three-syllable words

This exercise is like Exercise V, except that you will work with words of three syllables.

Write *memory* (mem' ə rē) at the left-hand side of your paper. Write *volcano* (vol kā'nō) at the right-hand side. Do the following for each boldface word in the numbered sentences:

A. Look up the word in the Glossary.

B. Write the word and its pronunciation in the column on your paper that is headed by the word which has the same accent pattern. The first two should look like this:

memory (mem' ə rē)   **volcano** (vol kā'nō)

1. plausible (plô' zə bəl)

                    2. reluctant (ri luk'tənt)

C. Check the pronunciation of the word and practice saying the complete sentence.

D. Decide what the word means in the sentence. Be prepared to restate the sentence using the right definition instead of the word.

1. Grace couldn't think of a **plausible** excuse for being late.
2. John was **reluctant** to dive into the cold water.
3. Do you think parents should punish **defiant** children?
4. His staring eyes would **hypnotize** anyone.
5. Many Indians have an **aquiline** nose.
6. We were too far from the **arena** to see the performing dogs.
7. Miss Bell was disgusted with Nick's **fatuous** remarks.

What you should know about using a dictionary

1. A dictionary gives information about how words may be divided into syllables, how words are pronounced, what they mean, and what part of speech they are.

2. Most dictionary entries include more than one meaning. Read all the meanings, then choose the one that makes the best sense in the context.

3. The pronunciation key tells what sound each pronunciation symbol stands for. You should not try to memorize the key, but use it for reference as needed.

9

Relationships

LESSON ONE: Why you need to recognize how ideas are connected

Can you tell what these pictures represent?

Perhaps when you first looked at them, all you saw was a jumble of black-and-white patches. Then you began to see connections or **relationships** among the patches. They began to fit together in a way that suggested something familiar, and suddenly everything made sense. You saw a dog on the left, and a man on horseback at the right.

When you read, you must deal with words in relationship to one another. A word by itself may not be very meaningful. Take *rose,* for example. You probably think you know what *rose* means. But would the meaning you are thinking of fit in the sentence "Sylvia lost her rose sweater" or in "The sun rose at five"? What a word means almost always depends on the way it is **related** to its context.

The relationship between facts and ideas in sentences and paragraphs also determines meaning. You wouldn't get much sense out of just a string of facts or ideas like this: "books fell . . . shelf . . . explosion . . . house shook." You need to know how the facts or ideas are related: "A dozen books fell OFF the shelf AFTER the explosion BECAUSE the whole house shook."

LESSON TWO: Recognizing time order and cause-effect

Part A

1a. After I finished washing the dishes, I settled down to watch "Get Smart."

1b. Before doing the dishes, I settled down to watch "Get Smart."

In which sentence — 1a or 1b — were the dishes washed first? What tells you?

2a. Jane and Nora window-shopped on State Street, and then stopped in a drugstore for a coke.

2b. Jane and Nora had a coke in the drugstore and later walked up State Street window-shopping.

In which sentence — 2a or 2b — did Jane and Nora have a coke first? What tells you?

In 1a and 1b and in 2a and 2b the events are the same. What has changed is their relationship. The difference is in the time order in which the two events took place.

When a series of events are told in the order in which they happened, they are told in **time order.** Most stories or narratives are told in time order. Directions for doing or making something are also likely to be given in time order: first you do this, next you do that, then you do so-and-so.

In the next two pairs, the relationship is not time order. Can you tell what it is?

3a. Bob couldn't listen to his sister tell about the Halloween party, because he didn't have his homework done.

3b. Because Bob's sister kept talking to him about the Halloween party, he couldn't get his homework done.

What word in sentences 3a and 3b alerts you to the fact that a reason or cause is being given?

In which sentence is a reason given to explain why Bob didn't finish his homework?

4a. Since I don't know much about checkers, I don't play very often.

    4b. I don't know much about checkers because I don't play very often.

In which sentence does the speaker's lack of knowledge about checkers cause something else to happen? What is the effect of his not knowing much about the game?

    In 3 and 4, the important difference is not a matter of time, as in 1 and 2. The point is that something makes something else happen: a **cause** or a **reason** ("I don't know much about checkers") leads to an **effect** or a **result** ("I don't play very often"). In *4b,* what is the cause? What is the result?

    Time order and cause-effect are two of the most common and most important thought relationships you will find in written material.

Part B

Divide a sheet of paper into two columns. Head one column TIME ORDER and the other CAUSE-EFFECT. Under the time-order heading, list the signal words or clue words in sentences 1*a* through 2*b* that tell you in what order the actions took place. *After* will be the first word on this list. Under the cause-effect heading, list the clue words that signal the cause-effect relationship in sentences 3*a* through 4*b*.

    What additional clue words or phrases from the sentences below can you add to each of your lists?

5. Lisa eats four or five candy bars every day; **as a result,** she gained ten pounds in one month.

6. **First of all,** take everything out of the box. **Next,** check to see if all items on the list were sent.

7. I broke my arm **not long after** we moved to Chicago.

8. Alvin is six feet tall; **for this reason** everyone thinks he's at least sixteen.

9. Seventh-grade boys eat lunch at 11:30. **Afterward,** they can play baseball for fifteen minutes.

10. Jennie has lost five library books, and **consequently** her library card is being cancelled.

11. People in the front rows should sit down **so that** people in back can see.

12. It poured rain last night; **therefore** the streets are sure to be wet this morning.

Without using the word *and,* make up a sentence explaining what happens in each cartoon strip below. The heading tells you what relationship to use. When you have finished, find the word or words in your sentences that indicate the way in which you are showing the connection between the two pictures in the strip.

A. CAUSE-EFFECT

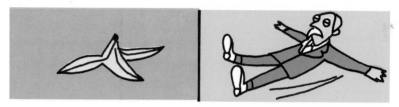

B. TIME ORDER

EXERCISE I.   Recognizing and expressing relationships

On your paper, after the number of each cartoon strip, write either *time order* or *cause-effect,* to indicate which of these relationships you think the artist had in mind. Then write a sentence which explains what happens in the cartoon strip. Refer to your list of clue words if you need help in writing the sentences.

1

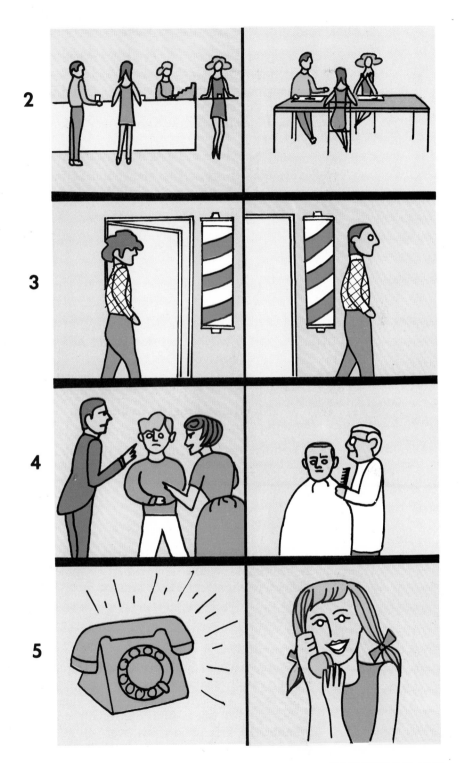

EXERCISE II.   More practice in using relationships

Part A

Put the events below in the order you would use them in writing a story. After the number of each list, write the letters of the events in the order in which you think they belong.

LIST 1   *a.* The school bus gets stuck in the snow.
            b. Sally misses a film shown during first period.
            c. Heavy snow begins to fall before daybreak.
            d. Sally arrives at school late.

LIST 2   *a.* Sandy's father takes a photograph of Sandy and a big fish.
            b. Sandy and his father decide to go fishing at Fox Lake.
            c. Sandy and his father row out from shore in a boat.
            d. Sandy catches a seven-pound fish a hundred feet offshore.

LIST 3   *a.* Mr. Burke is pulled into the lifeboat.
            b. Mr. Burke struggles in the water.
            c. Mr. Burke swims out beyond the breakers.
            d. The lifeguard runs to get the lifeboat.

Part B

Depending on the way you wish to write about these events, a summary of each set could show either a simple time-order or a cause-effect relationship. For example, note the differences between the following paragraphs, both of which tell about the events in List 1.

A

Before daybreak, a heavy snow began to fall. At eight-thirty Sally's school bus got hopelessly stuck in the snow. It was still stuck at 9:00, when her class was supposed to see a film. She finally arrived at school after the first period was over.

Things went wrong for Sally from the time she got up. A heavy snow had been falling since before daybreak, making the streets almost impassable. Her bus got stuck in a snowdrift, and as a result Sally was so late getting to school that she missed the film her class was scheduled to see during first period.

Which paragraph—A or B—mainly tells what happened, in time order? What relationship is emphasized in the other paragraph?

Write two short paragraphs to summarize the action of Lists 2 and 3. Use a time relationship in writing about one set of events, and cause-effect with the other.

NOTE: The rest of the exercises in this section are based on a book by Joan Murray called *The News*, in which she tells about her work as co-host of a TV show, "Two at One," telecast from WCBS-TV in New York City. (A Young Pioneer Book. Copyright © 1968 by McGraw-Hill, Inc. Used with permission of McGraw-Hill Book Company.)

EXERCISE III.   Recognizing relationships in short passages

Joan Murray had been interested in journalism for a long time before she actually had an opportunity to get a job in TV broadcasting. Here are some sentences which tell about her early years. Decide which kind of thought relationship—time order or cause-effect—is emphasized in each passage. On your paper, write the name of the relationship after the number of the item.

1. Joan and her twin sister June were born in Ithaca, New York. Throughout their early childhood they were close companions. In high school, they took part in many activities. After graduation, both girls went to New York City to look for jobs.

2. Joan's mother baked such wonderful pies that the kids in the neighborhood always wanted to eat at the Murray house.

3. When Joan arrived in New York, she got a room at the Y.W.C.A. and took a job with a small manufacturing company. She then worked for a while in a theatrical agency that found jobs for recording and stage artists. After a few months, she had a chance to become a secretary in the CBS-TV press and publicity department, and changed jobs again.

4. Because Joan was such a good worker, her bosses at CBS gave her more and more responsibility beyond her secretarial

duties. As she became more capable, her self-confidence improved, too.

5. In the meantime, Joan was given some experience in front of the camera, as well as behind the scenes. Therefore when she heard that NBC was looking for someone for the job of co-hostess for a show called "Women on the Move," she had courage enough to audition for it. She got the job.

6. When "Women on the Move" went off the air, Joan gathered together her savings, went to Europe, spent the next four months touring many countries, and finally returned to New York—flat broke.

7. When she returned to work at CBS, this time as a news correspondent, she discovered that a few people found it difficult to accept her because she was young, because she was a woman in a man's field, and because she was a Negro as well.

8. Joan says, ". . . there were plenty of things that made my first real reporting jobs exciting—meeting and chatting with Presidents Kennedy, Truman, and Eisenhower, for example."

LESSON THREE: Using time-order relationships

Which of the two kinds of thought relationship (cause-effect or time order) do you think might be especially useful in each of the following situations? Why?

1. You have seen a movie and are trying to tell the story to your family.

2. Your science teacher asks you to describe the growth stages of a frog.

3. You are telling a friend in another school your daily schedule of classes.

What other situations can you think of in which you would need to describe or remember something in time order?

EXERCISE IV.   Using time order to help you remember

Here is Joan Murray's description of a typical working day. As you read it, think not only of what she does but also of WHEN she does these things and WHY she does them at a particular time or in a particular order.

MY ALARM CLOCK rings at 6:30 A.M. Once I'm really awake, the first thing I do is turn on the radio and the television set for the early morning news. I want to be aware of what is happening all the time—because I must keep informed and because a major event may affect my day's schedule.

The next thing I do is check my schedule for the day. It will tell me what filmed stories in which I appear will be shown on this day's show. Then I can plan my wardrobe so that the clothes worn "live" will not clash with the outfit I was wearing when the filmed portion was shot.

When I've decided what to wear, I read aloud for a while to clear my voice and to catch up on current magazines and books.

Then I have a leisurely bath and a light breakfast. During this time I usually plan the rest of my day. There is the show, of course, but in fact this is only a small part of what I have to do. All my other workday activities are preparations, in one way or another, for the live air time, and they cover a wide range. If I don't plan carefully, precious time is lost.

Now I am ready to do my make-up. It takes me about an hour, since I do all my make-up for the show at home. This saves time at the studio—all I need is a little retouching before air time.

When I'm satisfied with my make-up, I dress, make a few phone calls, and pack my bag for a day which often keeps me away from home for as long as twelve or fifteen hours.

During the last fifteen minutes at home, I turn off the TV and radio and just listen to music on the phonograph —mostly classical. It's all part of making a pleasant and relaxing morning. The rest of the day may be filled with tension and unexpected problems, so I want to be as happy and serene as I can before I go to work.

2

When I arrive at the CBS studios, I go directly to the news room—a large room filled with desks for the correspondents and reporters, television sets showing what's on the three major networks, maps of the New York area, and scads of telephones. I pick up any messages that may have come in during the early morning, check in with my producer and the film editors, and catch up on the latest news. I may discuss covering an event with the assignment editor and then find out if I can get a crew for the time needed. I may have to go to the research library in the building to get background material for a story I'll be covering or on a guest I'm scheduled to interview on today's show. I might even have to prepare for a weekend trip to cover a story away from the city.   (*cont.*)

(above) The monitors show what the competition is doing and what we've shot during the day. I'm catching up on paperwork.

(top right) With cameraman Louie Tumola, getting ready for an outdoor assignment.

(right) One of my early days at the studio. Never mind the smile; I was just plain scared.

310 / RELATIONSHIPS

I go over the lineup for the show with the producer, because there may have been last-minute changes. Some days I have to write copy—a script to be read on the air—for a film without sound.

By noon I know it's time to touch up my make-up. Then I gather together my script for the broadcast and go to the studio. On the way, I round up all the guests for this day's program.

Once in the studio, I say "Hello" to everyone, stick my head into the control room to see what's happening there, and take my place at the double desk where my co-host and I sit. It's time to "tense up" (studio slang for "try to relax") for the show.

At the conclusion of the broadcast, I feel pretty good if it was a smooth show. When I return to the news room, I feel as though I were unwinding, but this is only temporary. Momentum soon starts building up for the following show.

After I have checked for phone messages, my next problem is to get a crew for any filming I may want to do that afternoon.

When I've completed the crew arrangements, I have a quick, light lunch. Then I get my crew together, check out with the assignment desk, and take off.

If my assignment is an interview with some noted person, or a visit to a place like the United Nations or a local hospital, I'm pretty much on my own as far as film content goes.

When I feel that I've filmed what I need, I tell my crew to "wrap it up." Then we mark the cans of film, pack up our equipment, and head back to the office, where I give the film to the traffic desk. It's then either processed immediately for airing, or "canned" for use at some later time.

After I supervise the editing of the film, the editor finishes cutting it. The next step is to write the script to go along with the film. Then it's time to "screen" (show) the film to the producer and director of the program. They need to know what I've got and how it will fit into the broadcast.

3

When I've finished my day's work at the studio, I watch the evening news broadcasts, read the late papers and news magazines, and make my plans for the rest of the evening. I also go over my mail and future story ideas at this time, catch up on phone calls, and try to get a few letters out.

Normally, I can't meet all the demands of my job unless I get enough sleep, so to some extent my social life is inhibited by my work. I don't really mind, though. A great part of my life *is* my work. I still find time to be with friends and other interesting people not connected with my job. It's a demanding life, but I love it.

(*cont.*)

Part A

In doing this exercise, refer to the article you have just read.

Here are four pairs of activities from Miss Murray's day. On your paper, after the number of each pair, write the letter of the activity which comes first. Remember that usually there is a good reason why one activity comes before the other.

1. A. Miss Murray decides what outfit she will wear this day.
   B. Miss Murray checks her schedule to see what filmed stories will be shown this day.

2. C. She gathers together her script and heads for the studio.
   D. She rounds up the guests for the day's program.

3. E. She gets a crew for the afternoon's filming.
   F. She checks for phone messages on her return from the broadcast.

4. G. She supervises the editing of the film.
   H. She writes the film script.

Part B

Refer to the article to answer these questions:

1. What clue word tells you when Miss Murray plans her wardrobe for the day? What does it refer back to?

2. What phrase tells you when she rounds up the day's guests? Where is she going?

3. What phrase tells you what she does before getting together a camera crew?

4. When does she write the script to go along with a film?

Part C

Reread the article about Joan Murray and try to remember the sequence of events—what comes first, what second, and so on. Then do the following exercise without looking back.

Copy the letters of the following items on your paper. Decide which of these activities comes first in her day, and write 1 after its letter. After the letter of the thing she does next, write 2; and so on.

A. She listens to music on the phonograph.

B. She gathers a camera crew for a story to be filmed.

C. She plans her evening.

D. She turns on the radio and TV for the early morning news.

E. She goes over the lineup for the day's show.

F. She plans her wardrobe for the day.

G. She writes a script for the film made that afternoon.

H. She puts on her make-up for the day.

I. She "tenses up" for the show.

LESSON FOUR: Using cause-effect relationships

If someone said to you, "'Hank jumped into the pool with all his clothes on," you might automatically ask "How come?" If the person went on to say "Because Ruthie dared him to" or "To save the little girl who couldn't swim," you would feel that the information was complete.

A cause and an effect go together; each helps you understand and remember the other.

EXERCISE V. Using cause-effect to understand and remember

In this exercise are some statements in which Miss Murray expresses cause-effect relationships, but without using the word *because*. Reword each of the items in a sentence of your own, using *because*. Then write the cause and the effect. The first one is done for you.

1. "Until I leave my apartment (usually at about 9:30), I have the television and radio playing—generally both at the same time. I want to be aware of what is happening all the time."

SENTENCE: Because I want to be aware of what is happening all the time, I have the television and radio playing until I leave the apartment.

CAUSE: I want to be aware of what is happening all the time.

EFFECT: I play both the television and the radio.

2. "I read aloud for a while to clear my voice and to catch up on current magazines and books." (*cont.*)

3. "There are often last-minute changes in the show's lineup. Just before air-time I go over the final lineup with my producer."

4. "Almost all film is shot in color these days, now that the processing procedure for color film has been perfected."

5. "Normally, I can't meet all the demands of my job unless I get enough sleep, so to some extent my social life is inhibited by my work."

EXERCISE VI.   More practice in using cause-effect

In addition to being a TV correspondent, Joan Murray is an airplane pilot. She decided to learn to fly so that she could make a documentary film about someone learning to fly a small plane. As you read the following episode, look especially for cause-effect relationships—the *why* of what happened.

WE MADE a second documentary about flying about a year after the first one, when I entered the twentieth annual Women's Transcontinental Air Race, better known as the Powder Puff Derby. Women pilots from all over the world compete in this coast-to-coast air derby. I'm told that I was the first "woman of color" ever to enter the race. It's for private, light aircraft, and you get a handicap according to the strict entrance and mechanical qualifications. (Both the pilots and the planes are carefully checked out.)

My copilot and I had the fastest plane in the race (201 mph), and so we were given the highest handicap— which meant that we were the last to take off. But we were the first to land at practically every stop. We couldn't believe it! The final landing point was Clearwater, Florida, and our $38,000 Aero Commander was the first plane in. Naturally, we got all the publicity, but even though our plane was the last to leave the starting point in Seattle, Washington, and the first to cross the finish line, we were not declared the winner—we didn't beat our handicap by a large enough margin. (Since we were filming for CBS, we planned to decline any winnings anyway.)

(left) An instructor explains some new equipment in the cockpit.

If you thought about cause-effect relationships as you read, you may be able to answer these questions without looking back. If not, reread. Begin each of your answers with *because*.

1. Why were pilots and planes carefully checked before the race?
2. Why were Joan and her copilot given the highest handicap?
3. Why were they the last to take off?
4. Why did they receive all the publicity at the finish line?
5. Why weren't they declared the winner?
6. Why had they decided earlier not to accept any winnings?

LESSON FIVE: Combined time-order and cause-effect relationships

Generally we can see an overall plan in a piece of writing, whether it is a sentence, a paragraph, or even a whole book. Most narratives or accounts of events are written in time order. For example, in the selection you have read from *The News*, Miss Murray tells what her life is like mainly by taking us through an ordinary day. But within such an overall plan there are other relationships. Consider the following paragraph:

> After graduating from high school, I stayed in Ithaca, worked, and continued my education at the Cascadilla School and, briefly, at Ithaca College. My sister June meanwhile decided to come to New York, and got a job with Johnson Publishing—the company that publishes *Ebony* and *Jet* magazines. I was pretty lonely and at loose ends. Six months after June left for New York, I followed her.

1. Mention something Joan did *before* June went to New York.
2. State something she did *after* June went to New York.
3. Which thought relationship (time order or cause-effect) did you use to answer questions 1 and 2?
4. What happened to Joan *because* June went to New York?
5. Which thought relationship did you use to answer question 4?
6. Which of the two relationships do you think is more important to the meaning of the paragraph? State the central idea of the paragraph, using this relationship in your statement.

EXERCISE VII. Using combined relationships

This article telling what happened to Joan while she was covering a visit to New York by the singing group the Beatles will give you further practice in using relationships.

PART OF the fun of being a correspondent comes from meeting interesting people. In doing interviews and covering special events, I've had an opportunity to talk with famous people in the entertainment industry and the arts, and outstanding figures in government. I've met many celebrities—but I've only asked for autographs twice that I can remember: once from Maurice Chevalier,[1] a very impressive and vital man; the second time from the Beatles.

I was assigned to cover the Beatles' second trip to New York in 1965, from the press conference at their hotel, to the taping for the Ed Sullivan show, to the concert at Shea Stadium. I was fantastically lucky at the press conference—for about three minutes. The entire press corps was there: newspaper, magazine, and television reporters from New York and other cities. The choice locations for camera setups in the room were mostly taken by the big, strong men who could elbow through to the front and get a spot for themselves. Somehow, I was pulled into the crush and I wound up on the platform with the Beatles and my microphone! Well, the male reporters pitched a fit. Finally, the Beatles' manager, Brian Epstein, said "All right, Joan, get down," and I returned to the floor. Later I was invited to the boys' suite,

but I couldn't go because my camera crew and I were on a deadline.

Still later, I was in the street outside the studio where the Beatles were taping numbers for the Ed Sullivan show that would be presented the following Sunday, after they'd left New York. Barricades had been set up to hold off the thousands of fans. There were so many policemen trying to keep order that you could hardly see the teen-agers for the police. Somehow, the kids got onto my name, and I could hear wails of "Jo-o-oan, Jo-o-oan, please come over here!"

Finally with my camera crew I went over to interview some of them. As I approached the barricades, the kids dragged me through, into the middle of a group of two hundred or so, and made me promise to get autographs for them. We always carry press credentials, and they enabled me to go backstage. The kids loaded me up with stuffed animals and love notes destined for John, Paul, George, and Ringo. After we finished two or three quick interviews with the teen-agers, I crossed the barricades again, and went into the theater and up to the Beatles' dressing room. By this time it was fun, and besides, we had some time to kill before the next setup.

I gave the toys to the Beatles, and each of them signed about five autographs for me to pass out to the kids. When I returned downstairs, the security guards suggested it was dangerous

---

[1] **Maurice Chevalier** (shə väl′ yā), French actor and singer born in 1888 and still a popular idol in the 1960's.

to cross the barricades because the crowd was becoming unruly. So to this day I still have about twenty autographs from the Beatles.

At Shea Stadium, where the Beatles did a concert before a screaming audience of 55,000, I was down on the grassy field with a camera crew. The guys in the crew had to form a barrier so that I wouldn't get trampled when the boys finished singing and the fans began pouring over the fences to get at them. We went to the far end of the field, where the security officers had a Wells Fargo armored truck waiting. The location was excellent, and we got a good camera angle. When the concert ended, the Beatles shot into the armored truck so fast that you could hardly see them. If they hadn't, they might have been seriously hurt that night.

Covering the Beatles' visit was fascinating, but we were nervous wrecks at the end. Imagine what it's like for them!

1. What three things did the Beatles do on their visit to New York? In what order did they do them?
2. Why couldn't Joan go to the Beatles' hotel suite after the press conference?
3. Why did the teen-agers outside the theater in which the Beatles were taping a show want Joan to come over to them?
4. When did Joan get into the Beatles' dressing room?
5. Why does Joan still have about twenty autographs from the Beatles?
6. What did the Beatles do after their live concert at Shea Stadium? Why did they do this?
7. Which of the two thought relationships (time order or cause-effect) do you consider the more important one in this account? Explain.
8. Reread the account. Then, without looking back at it, write a 150-word summary of what it says. In your summary, emphasize the relationship you think is the more important one.

What you should know about the relationship of ideas

In all written material that makes sense, ideas are connected according to certain **relationships.** Two of the most common and useful relationships are **time order** and **cause-effect.** Recognizing the way ideas are connected or related helps you understand and remember.

10

What is the price of

. . . an error in judgment?

. . . an intentional trick?

. . . and an honest act?

What happens to

. . . a man who ruins his friend?

. . . a boy who steals?

. . . and one who reforms?

What are the results of

. . . ignoring good advice?

. . . capturing a wild creature?

. . . and proving a man's worth?

You may find some

surprising answers in

CONSEQUENCES.

Brad was glad he could still shoot to kill.
He wouldn't want to bungle the job.

The Old Dog

by Donald Vining

FROM TIME to time, when the road was straight away, Brad Turner glanced at the old red dog beside him on the front seat of the car. Benny had thrust his nose out the window into the breeze, and his silky ears blew back along his head and neck. It was just like all the other times, the other years. But no, it wasn't. Benny was as thrilled as ever at the wild flame color of the autumn hills, at the hunting jacket his master wore, at the presence of the gun in the back seat; but somehow he seemed too weary to express all the joy he felt. The wind in his face made Benny's eyes water more than usual; that stiff and paralyzed rear left leg made it harder than ever for him to balance himself around curves; and while there were occasional joyous barks as of old, they were interspersed with an almost steady flow of those half-whine, half-growl noises that Benny made of late, as though he were holding protracted conversations with invisible tormentors. It was these senile mumblings which had disturbed Brad's wife and had forced Brad to exile Benny from the house nights and make a reluctant kennel dog of him after all those years. No, there was nothing for it but to admit that Benny was an old dog. After all, he was going on fifteen.

Fifteen years. That was a long time for a man and a dog to be together. This was the first hunting season in Brad's memory to which he had not looked forward.

For the past year Lucille had been at him. "Brad, I don't see why, when you claim you love the dog so much, you don't put him out of his misery at once. He's almost blind, he's partly paralyzed, he imagines he sees and hears things, and makes a lot of noise over nothing—"

"I know, I know," Brad would protest. "But he gets a lot of fun out of life yet. You don't dispose of people when they get broken down and fanciful."

"People and dogs are different. We're more humane towards animals," Lucille would answer in disgust.

The argument went on and on. Brad came to dread every indication Benny gave of his failing faculties, for it always brought up the subject of getting rid of him. The old dog, in the midst of perfect silence, would dart up from his rug and rush barking to the door to chase some imaginary intruder from the deserted front porch. Or he'd suddenly yelp and cower as though someone were beating him. It was a painful sight for Brad in any case, remembering as he did the days when Benny won annual ribbons in the Blairtown Dog Show; but it was all the more painful because of the unpleasant discussions it brought up.

"A veterinarian could do it so quick-ly and easily, and it wouldn't cost much," Lucille would say for the fiftieth time.

"Hang the cost, if I thought it were the thing to do. But I won't have it that way," Brad said stubbornly.

Benny had always been such an active, vital dog, especially in the hunting field, that death by needle seemed completely inappropriate. Then one day Brad had remembered an incident of one of his early hunting trips. He, Jerry, Doug, and some others had had their dogs in the field and one badly trained dog failed to hold for the scent, leaping just as Jerry shot. He had fallen among the browning field grasses without a cry. Jerry had been upset, of course, but somehow it had always struck Brad as the right kind of death for a dog, death in action. When that memory came back to Brad, he had a good answer ready for Lucille the next time the question came up.

"Next fall," he said, "I'll do it myself. In the fields, where Benny's happiest."

Now autumn was here and today was the day. Brad turned the car off the highway into the dirt road that led up and over the hills to where rabbits, pheasants, and quail were unfailingly to be found. In the sensuous pleasure of breathing in the woody air, Brad's mind strayed for a while from its preoccupation with Benny. Benny, too, gave up his half-articulate noises and devoted himself to delight at homecoming.

Brad found a stretch of fields and woods which he knew of old and which he seemed to have to himself so far. Only as he opened the door of the car for Benny to get out did the business of the day flash back into his mind. Benny forgetfully jumped with abandon, but yelped as he landed painfully. He quickly recovered and ran about sniffing the ground and the withering weeds. Brad got his gun from the back seat and loaded it sadly.

There would be no real hunting today. Benny could not really do his job any more. The devils in his old mind and body were riding him too hard for him to be able to concentrate. No, no hunting today. Today was for Benny. They would roam the fields together as they had done for so many years, and then when the moment came — Brad would have no stomach for hunting after that. He locked the car and with the pathetically eager dog he waded knee-deep into the fields.

In his first joy Benny bobbed here and there, his plumy tail sometimes the only indication of his whereabouts, while at other times his head and floppy ears bobbed up on a leap over a run of brambled creeper or a fallen tree or fence post. Brad tried to let the autumn scene and smell flow over and drown his mind so that he should not think of Benny. But the trees lost their color, the air its snap, as he thought of what he must do. He watched Benny's rheumatic cavorting and thought back to the days when he was the supplest, quickest, most sensitive and best coördinated dog in the field. He remembered Benny's actual look of disdain at the body of the dog which had leapt in the way of Jerry's shot. And this poor wretch was also Benny. Brad remembered how in his childhood he had shed many secret tears over the sudden and early death of various pets; he knew now that that was much easier to bear than standing by and seeing the processes of age and decay.

Benny came running back to him, looking up with those nearly useless eyes. He wagged his tail and whined impatiently in a way that sounded to his master very much as though he himself were angry that his old body was not as it used to be. Brad felt the stock of his gun. It was good that he had kept his marksmanship up to scratch between seasons by shooting clay pigeons. He'd not want to bungle the job. But no, he knew that he could make it clean and quick.

Across the fields rang the yelp of dogs. Brad stopped in the act of climbing a zigzag fence under which Benny was squeezing. Yes, there on the far side of the field plaid coats and gleaming barrels told of the approach of other hunters. The spots of their hounds showed now and then as they galloped through the fields. The dogs' vigor made a heartbreaking contrast with Benny's already weary gait. If anything, they were a little too energetic and uncontrolled. Not fully trained, perhaps.

"Hello there," came the call from the approaching hunters. "Any luck?"

"Just out," Brad replied.

"Same with us."

The young dogs barked loudly at meeting Benny. They all sniffed each other and Benny stuck his neck out as though he were straining to see the newcomers with his dim eyes. The younger dogs seemed to toss their muzzles in the air patronizingly as they completed their inspection of Benny.

"Sort of old dog you've got there, isn't it?" one of the hunters asked Brad.

"Yes, I'm afraid his hunting days are done. But I wanted him to die in the fields," Brad said, rather sharply lest the tightness in his throat betray his feelings.

"Oh," the others said, in chorus, and they looked at Benny in silence. He wagged his tail.

"Well—" the men said, somehow embarrassed, and gesturing their farewells, they moved on, their dogs doing a whirling dervish[1] all over the fields, circling about and about. Benny started to amble lamely after them. Suddenly he stiffened and stopped. His tail stood motionless, only the plumes of soft fur moving in the breeze, and one front paw was held off the ground.

So ghosts were bedeviling Benny again. The younger dogs had romped right by the spot where Benny was now pointing and had picked up no scent. But now Benny thought. . . . This was the moment. Benny had almost some of his old beauty as he stood there, tense and ready. His old body was in ecstasy with the fantasy that he was pointing game for Brad. Swallowing hard, Brad took off the safety catch and put the gun to his shoulder.

Under his breath he murmured, "Good-by, Benny. I love you, old boy."

The shot sounded to Brad like the cracking of the world. Benny fell without a whimper. Up from the grass before him flew a covey of quail.

THE END

◯ **Talking it over**

1. *a.* What makes Brad realize that Benny should be killed?

[1]**whirling dervish,** a wild dance. Named for dervishes, Mohammedan monks, whose rituals include violent dances.

b. Why does he think that death by needle would not be suitable for Benny?

c. What kind of death does Brad think Benny should have? Why?

2. Reread the last three paragraphs of the story before answering the following questions.

a. What inference can you make from the last sentence in the story?

b. What error in judgment did Brad and Lucille make?

c. In your opinion, will Brad feel bad about what he has done? Why might he feel very good about it?

3. The following actions are listed in the order in which they are told in the story.

(1) Brad looks at Benny beside him in the car.
(2) Brad and Lucille argue about having Benny put away.
(3) Brad decides that Benny should die in the field.
(4) Benny jumps painfully out of the car.
(5) Benny enjoys running through the field.

a. Rearrange these five actions into the order in which they actually happened.

b. Find on page 321 the paragraph which begins the flashback and the one in which the flashback ends. What happens during the flashback?

c. Compare the beginning of the story with the beginning of the flashback. Which one makes the more interesting opening for a story? Why?

4. Examine the details in the first paragraph of the story. Which sentence best expresses the central idea? What relationship has the author used to develop this idea?

What would you do if a large sum of money came into your possession by mistake? Would you try to find the owner? Or would you keep the money?

THE $43,000 MISTAKE

by Jean Sharda

I N THESE days of machine-processed information, the possibilities for error are greatly reduced, but not done away with. Human beings must still feed information into the machines and, as we all know, human beings sometimes

Based partly on "Boo-boo at the Bank" by David Nevin, *Life*, June 28, 1963. With permission.

make mistakes. This is the story of one such mistake in the big, impersonal world of banking.

The time was March 1963, the place was Montgomery, Alabama, and the man to whom it happened was Thomas "Cotton" Thaggard.

Thaggard was thirty-seven at the

time, a small man with pale blue eyes, a Southern drawl, and a large, fluffy toupee. He had been fairly successful making money in such ventures as jukeboxes, high-stakes gambling, and a used-car business which he had conducted from an open lot. He had sold the used-car business the year before, keeping for possible future use its name: Alabama Motor Company.

He kept a small bank account in the name of the Alabama Motor Company at the Union Bank and Trust Company in Montgomery, where he also had his personal account.

Around the first of March, Thaggard received through the mail the usual monthly statements for the two accounts. His personal account, as usual, was lower than expected. The other, that of the Alabama Motor Company, was higher—so much higher that he gasped. The Alabama Motor Company showed a balance of $43,498—more than $43,000 over what it should have been!

About a week later, early on the morning of March 6, Thaggard went to the statements window at the rear of the bank. He asked for a reading on his two accounts. The figures were the same as those on the mailed statements. His personal account was lower than expected, while the used-car business account was $43,156 more than he thought it should be.

For the next hour and a half Thaggard strolled about town, thinking. At eleven o'clock he returned to the bank and went straight to the window of Mrs. Edith Owen, one of the tellers. He asked Mrs. Owen for the balance in his used-car account. Mrs. Owen phoned the accounting department. Then she wrote a figure on a slip of pink paper and handed it to Thaggard. There it was again: $43,498. The inflated bank account was confirmed a third time.

What to do? Thaggard had made up his mind. He produced a check payable to himself in the convenient amount of $43,000.

"I'd like to make a withdrawal," he told Mrs. Owen.

Thaggard's request provoked a bustle of activity, because normally the bank did not keep this much money on hand. Mrs. Owen first tried to get cash from her fellow tellers. Then she went to the big safe where the money was kept. Slowly a pile of small bills began to form on the counter.

"If this will run you short," offered Thaggard, "I could take part of it in a cashier's check."

"No, indeed," insisted Mrs. Owen. "We have plenty of money."

Thirty minutes later the money was all there on the counter—a huge pile of small bills.

Bank officials expressed a friendly interest in what was going on. One of them even found a brown paper grocery bag to hold the money. When the bag was stuffed with bills, Thaggard thanked everyone for going to so much trouble. Then he tucked the paper bag under his arm and started for the door.

Watching him go, the assistant cashier turned to the bank auditor with a wink. "You know," he said, "I believe old Cotton Thaggard is up to something."

When Thaggard was questioned later, he was hazy about what he did that afternoon. He did leave town, he recalled, and when he returned late in the afternoon, he learned from a friend that the police had been asking for him. Thaggard went directly to the bank.

Waiting for him there were all the bank's officers. Their faces were flushed and their hands trembled. Immediately they announced that the $43,000 he had withdrawn was not his.

How was he supposed to know that, Thaggard asked. Only that morning the bank had told him the money *was* his.

But, asked the officers, wouldn't any reasonable person suspect that something was wrong when his account jumped suddenly from $342 to $43,498? Thaggard answered that he had supposed some of his less talented gambling partners had dropped in at the bank to deposit what they owed him.

No, nothing like that had happened, retorted the bank auditor. Using deposit slips and other bank records, he soon proved that the $43,156 had been intended, not for the Alabama Motor Company, but for the Alabama Power Company. A clerk had simply entered the deposits on the wrong ledger sheet. Then the bookkeeping machines had taken over. And how could a mere machine know that a large sum of money had been credited to the wrong account?

Faced with all the proof, Thaggard had to agree that a mistake had been made. It certainly did look, he admitted, as though he owed the bank $43,000.

"Well?" asked the bank officers.

"Well," said Thaggard, "at this moment I don't have the necessary $43,000 on hand. However, I always pay my debts and I would be glad to work out some system of repayment—perhaps a few dollars every week?"

A bank officer cut him off. "You have until nine tomorrow morning to get that money back here."

"I don't believe I can quite make it by then," Thaggard said.

"You don't, and you'll land in jail," said the bank officer.

Next day Thaggard was arrested and charged with "false pretenses." His attorneys immediately asked the court to release him on the ground that he was being held illegally. They claimed that no crime had been committed.

The question of Thaggard's guilt or innocence eventually reached the Alabama Court of Appeals. Much to nearly everyone's surprise, this Court set Thaggard free. The judges reasoned that before a man can be convicted of a crime, it must first be shown that he intended to commit the crime.

The decision of the Appeals Court was later upheld by the Alabama Supreme Court.

Meanwhile Thaggard became a sort of folk hero in Montgomery. People of all sorts would stop him on the street, pat his shoulder, and wink. Some of them suggested slyly that if he needed a place to hide the $43,000 he could use their backyards—and they would even lend him a shovel.

Otherwise, his life changed very little. He still visited his old haunts. Resplendent in alligator shoes and a fancy sport coat, he radiated confidence. If anyone mentioned the missing money, Thaggard would merely smile, adjust his toupee, and say, "What $43,000?"

But the story didn't end there. Bank authorities pressed the case until, the following year, it reached a federal court. On November 13, 1964, this court found Thaggard guilty of violating a federal bank larceny statute. A week later he was sentenced to five years in a federal prison. He began serving his term in April 1966.

The Union Bank and Trust Company also filed a civil action to regain the missing $43,000, but when Thaggard's assets were sold at public auction they brought only $10,575. In 1967 the bank was still out $32,425.

A sidelight to the story is that the Alabama legislature passed a bill to prevent a recurrence of the Thaggard action. It is known in the area as the "Cotton Thaggard Bill."

Since the federal court decision, Thaggard has not seemed so popular around Montgomery as he once was. A local newspaperman expressed the feeling of the people he knew by saying, "A lot of us figured Cotton finally got what was coming to him."

THE END

⟳ Talking it over

1. *a.* What kind of man was Cotton Thaggard? Give details which tell you both what he looked like and what kind of person he was.

  b. How did he seem to feel about what he did? What tells you?

2. *a.* How did the townspeople respond when they first heard about the case?

  b. Why do you suppose they acted differently later on?

3. State the effect of each of the following causes:

  a. A clerk's mistake in recording some deposits

  b. The failure of the state courts to convict Thaggard

  c. The sale of Thaggard's possessions

  d. The federal court decision against Thaggard

4. The author never says directly what she thinks of Thaggard, but you can guess her attitude from the details she gives in describing him. What are some of the details she uses?

⇄ Words in action

Many of the boldface words in the following story are used in ways that may be unfamiliar to you, but you should be able to figure out their special meanings here by paying close attention to context clues.

ALL YEAR Dan worked hard and saved his money so that he could go to camp out West the next summer. He wanted to earn interest on the money he saved, so he decided to **deposit** his earnings in a savings **account.** Every Saturday he counted the money he earned cutting lawns, shoveling snow, running errands, washing cars, or doing other odd jobs. Then he went to the bank where he made out a **deposit** slip to show how much he wanted to add to his **account.** The bank **teller** took the **deposit** slip and the money (which was always in change and in bills of small **denominations**) and **credited** the sum to Dan's **account.**

Every month the bank sent Dan a

statement of his **account,** on which were listed his **deposits,** his **withdrawals,** and the **balance** remaining in his savings **account.** Dan was careful with his arithmetic, so the **balance** on the bank's **statement** always checked with the one he had figured. Dan found that he enjoyed the job of keeping track of money, and thought that perhaps he would someday become an **auditor** or other bank official.

By June, Dan's **assets,** including the money he had saved, were sufficient to pay for two weeks at camp. As he made out the **withdrawal** slip, Dan thought back on all his hard work, and he felt quite proud of the amount he could take out. Since the money had to be sent through the mail and he was afraid that cash might be lost or stolen, Dan decided to get either a **cashier's check** or a **money order** instead. Then only the person whose name appeared on the paper could get the money.

Match the terms in the first column below with the definitions in the second column. You will use one definition more than once. You may look back and reread the story about Dan as often as you wish.

1. a bank account
2. to deposit money
3. a bank teller
4. denominations
5. to credit an account
6. a bank statement
7. to withdraw money
8. a bank balance
9. an auditor
10. assets
11. a cashier's check
12. a money order

a. an officer of a bank who examines bank records
b. a monthly report sent by the bank which shows how much money a person has put into and taken out of the bank during that month
c. to take money out of a bank account
d. to put money into a bank account
e. the money a person has in the bank
f. to make a record of money put into a bank account
g. the names of each kind of paper money: ones, fives, tens, etc.
h. a bank clerk who takes in, gives out, and counts money
i. the difference between what a person has put into the bank and what he has drawn out
j. an official substitute for cash
k. total value of all money and property a person owns

Now read about another man
who also came across a "fortune" . . .

UNEXPECTED REWARDS OF VIRTUE

by Fred J. Cook

240,000 IN
10'S + 20'S

O N MARCH 10, 1961, Douglas William Johnson, a fifty-year-old Negro janitor in Los Angeles, a man who had felt the pinch of poverty, drove to an apartment house under construction to see if he could get the job of cleaning up the debris. With him was his wife, Helen. The superintendent whom he had to see about the debris-cleaning chore wasn't at the site, and so Johnson climbed back into his station wagon and started home. He had driven only a short distance when he happened to see, lying in the street in front of his car, a bulky canvas bag. Thinking it might contain something useful, Johnson stopped, picked it up, and tossed it into the back of the station wagon.

As he got behind the wheel and drove off, his wife, possessed by curiosity, turned around and began to examine the bag. It was sealed, but it bore a tag. The tag said that the bag contained $240,000 in $10 and $20 bills.

"Do you know what you've picked up?" Mrs. Johnson asked her husband. "There's $240,000 in that bag!"

"No!" he said—and started to shake all over.

Explaining his reaction later, Johnson told reporters: "I was knocked off my feet. I never dreamed I'd have my hands on anything like that."

Here certainly was king-sized temptation. Bills of relatively small denominations are not easily traced, and Johnson—the part-time maintenance man, father of three sons—had $240,000 worth of those bills at his finger tips. What to do?

"I thought if I kept that money I'd never be able to look my three kids in the face again," Johnson explained, using the simplistic imagery of a bygone age when man had stature and was supposed to be responsible for his acts.

So Johnson acted according to the dictates of pure and simple honesty. As soon as he reached home, he telephoned a friend, a former Chicago policeman, to find out whom he should notify about the money. The friend advised him to call the FBI. He did. In minutes, four FBI agents were at his

door, recovering the money bag that had fallen from the rear of a passing Brink's truck.[1] The truck had traveled for some distance before the $240,000 loss was discovered, and scores of police and FBI agents had begun to search along the truck's route when Johnson telephoned that he had the missing money.

Brink's paid Johnson a $10,000 reward for his honesty, but this wasn't the end of the story. A little more than a month later, on April 21, 1961, the press of the nation recorded the sad and revealing sequel. Johnson's life had been made utterly miserable; the strictly honest deed that should have made him the most admired of men had made him instead the most despised, ridiculed, and harassed.

Crackpots wrote obscene letters to him, neighbors ridiculed him, fellow workers needled him, schoolmates taunted his sons. The universal theme was that Johnson had proven himself to be the world's greatest boob by returning that $240,000 once he had it in his hands. The taunts became too much for his oldest son, Richard, sixteen, who finally ran away from home, returning after a few days, hungry and disillusioned. "The kids kept saying things to me," he explained. "All the time, they were saying my father was dumb, and a fool, and stupid. . . . I just couldn't stand it."

Johnson himself said it was "nice" that Brink's had given him a $10,000 reward, but he added:

"I can't leave the house to get work without someone throws it all up to me and calls me a fool. Can't be on the

_____
[1]**Brink's truck,** an insured truck equipped with armed guards and used for transporting large amounts of money.

job without someone says, 'Why you need work? You had $240,000.' And now it's hurting my boys.

"I wish I'd never seen any of it. I wish we'd let that money sit in the street and rot. I wish we'd thrown it down a sewer or burned it.

"That money? It's not worth anything. It has made me a poor man."

. . . In a moneyed society, Douglas Johnson had committed the cardinal sin; acting on honest impulse, he had returned a fortune that he might have kept.

The following "postscript" to "Unexpected Rewards of Virtue" appeared in an article in the April 27, 1963, *Saturday Review,* entitled "Sweet, Spontaneous Humanity" by Hallowell Bowser.

. . . Eventually, news of the Johnsons' plight got out, and suddenly public sentiment changed. Now encouraging letters poured in, some of them addressed simply to "Honest Man, Los Angeles, California." Both neighbors and strangers began dropping in to say sheepishly that they had at first thought Johnson was a fool, but that the force of his example had made them change their minds.

When President Kennedy heard of the family's ordeal, he wrote to Johnson: "I want to extend my personal commendation for your unflinching honesty. . . . I have read news reports of the incident, and regret the unfortunate few who have since harassed you and your family."

But what if lightning should strike twice? After his ordeal, would Johnson take a more "realistic" view of things? The question was answered recently when a firm sent Mr. Johnson a money order for $90,036, instead of the $36 he had arranged for. He promptly returned the order, saying, "I could sure use that money, but not enough to get it the wrong way."   THE END

Talking it over

1. *a.* How were Johnson and his family treated immediately after they returned the money?

b. Why do you think people reacted as they did?

c. What seemed to change the public response?

2. *a.* Contrast Johnson and Thaggard, especially the circumstances of each one's life.

b. What does each man have to look forward to?

c. How do you suppose each one feels about himself and about the kind of world we live in?

3. *a.* Thaggard winds up in prison; Johnson is honored for his honest actions. What idea about justice do these facts suggest to you?

b. Suppose the story of Cotton Thaggard had ended on page 326 with "What $43,000?" and that "Unexpected Rewards of Virtue" had ended just before the "postscript" in the adjacent column. What would have been left out of each selection?

4. How would your impression of justice have been different if the stories had been shortened as suggested in 3*b*?

*When you die of thirst, you always die just
one way. . . . Before you die of thirst,
you go mad.*

WINE ON
THE DESERT

by Max Brand

THERE WAS no hurry, except for the
thirst, like clotted salt, in the back
of his throat, and Durante rode on
slowly, rather enjoying the last moments of dryness before he reached the
cold water in Tony's house. There was
really no hurry at all. He had almost
twenty-four hours' head start, for they
would not find his dead man until this
morning. After that, there would be

perhaps several hours of delay before
the sheriff gathered a sufficient posse
and started on his trail. Or perhaps the
sheriff would be fool enough to come
alone.

Durante had been able to see the
wheel and fan of Tony's windmill for
more than an hour, but he could not
make out the ten acres of the vineyard
until he had topped the last rise, for the
vines had been planted in a hollow.
The lowness of the ground, Tony used
to say, accounted for the water that
gathered in the well during the wet sea-

son. The rains sank through the desert sand, through the gravels beneath, and gathered in a bowl of clay hardpan far below.

In the middle of the rainless season the well ran dry but, long before that, Tony had every drop of the water pumped up into a score of tanks made of cheap corrugated iron. Slender pipe lines carried the water from the tanks to the vines and from time to time let them sip enough life to keep them until the winter darkened overhead suddenly, one November day, and the rain came down and all the earth made a great hushing sound as it drank. Durante had heard that whisper of drinking when he was here before; but he never had seen the place in the middle of the long drought.

The windmill looked like a sacred emblem to Durante, and the twenty stodgy, tar-painted tanks blessed his eyes; but a heavy sweat broke out at once from his body. For the air of the hollow, unstirred by wind, was hot and still as a bowl of soup. A reddish soup. The vines were powdered with thin red dust, also. They were wretched, dying things to look at, for the grapes had been gathered, the new wine had been made, and now the leaves hung in ragged tatters.

Durante rode up to the squat adobe house and right through the entrance into the patio. A flowering vine clothed three sides of the little court. Durante did not know the name of the plant, but it had large white blossoms with golden hearts that poured sweetness on the air. Durante hated the sweetness. It made him more thirsty.

He threw the reins of his mule and strode into the house. The water cooler stood in the hall outside the kitchen.

There were two jars made of a porous stone, very ancient things, and the liquid which distilled through the pores kept the contents cool. The jar on the left held water; that on the right contained wine. There was a big tin dipper hanging on a peg beside each jar. Durante tossed off the cover of the vase on the left and plunged it in until the delicious coolness closed well above his wrist.

"Hey, Tony," he called. Out of his dusty throat the cry was a mere groaning. He drank and called again, clearly. "Tony!"

A voice pealed from the distance.

Durante, pouring down the second dipper of water, smelled the alkali dust which had shaken off his own clothes. It seemed to him that heat was radiating like light from his clothes, from his body, and the cool dimness of the house was soaking it up. He heard the wooden leg of Tony bumping on the ground, and Durante grinned; then Tony came in with that hitch and side-swing with which he accommodated the stiffness of his artificial leg. His brown face shone with sweat as though a special ray of light were focused on it.

"Ah, Dick!" he said. "Good old Dick! . . . How long since you came last! . . . Wouldn't Julia be glad! Wouldn't she be glad!"

"Ain't she here?" asked Durante, jerking his head suddenly away from the dripping dipper.

"She's away at Nogales,"[1] said Tony. "It gets so hot. I said, 'You go up to Nogales, Julia, where the wind don't forget to blow.' She cried, but I made her go."

Durante put the dipper quickly to his

---

[1]**Nogales** (nō gal'əs), a town on the southern border of Arizona, adjacent to Nogales, Mexico.

lips but did not swallow for a moment. Then he said: "Throw some water into that mule of mine, would you, Tony?"

Tony went out with his wooden leg clumping loud on the wooden floor, softly in the patio dust. Durante found the hammock in the corner of the patio. He lay down in it and watched the sunset flush the mists of desert dust that rose to the zenith. The water was soaking through his body; hunger began, and then the rattling of pans in the kitchen and the cheerful cry of Tony's voice:

"What you want, Dick? I got some pork. You don't want pork. I'll make you some good Mexican beans. Hot. Ah ha, I know that old Dick. I have plenty of good wine for you, Dick. Tortillas. Even Julia can't make tortillas like me. . . . And what about a nice young rabbit?"

"All blowed full of buckshot?" growled Durante.

"No, no. I kill them with the rifle."

"You kill rabbits with a rifle?" repeated Durante, with a quick interest.

"It's the only gun I have," said Tony. "If I catch them in the sights, they are dead. A wooden leg cannot walk very far . . . I must kill them quick. You see? They come close to the house about sunrise and flop their ears. I shoot through the head."

"Yeah? Yeah?" muttered Durante. "Through the head?" He relaxed, scowling. He passed his hand over his face, over his head.

Then Tony began to bring the food out into the patio and lay it on a small wooden table; a lantern hanging against the wall of the house included the table in a dim half circle of light. They sat there and ate. Tony had scrubbed himself for the meal. His hair was soaked

in water and sleeked back over his round skull. A man in the desert might be willing to pay five dollars for as much water as went to the soaking of that hair.

Everything was good. Tony knew how to cook, and he knew how to keep the glasses filled with his wine.

"This is old wine. This is my father's wine. Eleven years old," said Tony. "You look at the light through it. You see that brown in the red? That's the soft that time puts in a good wine, my father always said."

"What killed your father?" asked Durante.

Tony lifted his hand as though he were listening or as though he were pointing out a thought.

"The desert killed him. I found his mule. It was dead, too. There was a leak in the canteen. My father was only five miles away when the buzzards showed him to me."

"Five miles? Just an hour. . . . Good Lord!" said Durante. He stared with big eyes. "Just dropped down and died?" he asked.

"No," said Tony. "When you die of thirst, you always die just one way. First you tear off your shirt, then your undershirt. That's to be cooler. And the sun comes and cooks your bare skin. . . . And then you think . . . there is water everywhere, if you dig down far enough. You begin to dig. The dust comes up your nose. You start screaming. You break your nails in the sand. You wear the flesh off the tips of your fingers, to the bone." He took a quick swallow of wine.

"Without you seen a man die of thirst, how d'you know they start to screaming?" asked Durante.

"They got a screaming look when

you find them," said Tony. "Take some more wine. The desert never can get to you here. My father showed me the way to keep the desert away from the hollow. We live pretty good here? No?"

"Yeah," said Durante, loosening his shirt collar. "Yeah, pretty good."

Afterward he slept well in the hammock until the report of a rifle waked him and he saw the color of dawn in the sky. It was such a great, round bowl that for a moment he felt as though he were above, looking down into it.

He got up and saw Tony coming in holding a rabbit by the ears, the rifle in his other hand.

"You see?" said Tony. "Breakfast came and called on us!" He laughed.

Durante examined the rabbit with care. It was nice and fat and it had been shot through the head. Through the middle of the head. Such a shudder went down the back of Durante that he washed gingerly before breakfast; he felt that his blood was cooled for the entire day.

It was a good breakfast, too, with flapjacks and stewed rabbit with green peppers, and a quart of strong coffee. Before they had finished, the sun struck through the east window and started them sweating.

"Gimme a look at that rifle of yours, Tony, will you?" Durante asked.

"You take a look at my rifle, but don't you steal the luck that's in it," laughed Tony. He brought the fifteen-shot Winchester.[2]

"Loaded right to the brim?" asked Durante.

<hr />

[2] **Winchester,** a kind of repeating rifle first manufactured about 1866. In the West after 1870, all rifles were referred to as Winchesters, no matter what their make.

They went out from the house. The sun turned the sweat of Durante to hot water and then dried his skin so that his clothes felt transparent.

"Tony, I gotta be damn mean," said Durante. "Stand right there where I can see you. Don't try to get close. Now listen. . . . The sheriff's gonna be along this trail some time today, looking for me. He'll load up himself and all his gang with water out of your tanks. Then he'll follow my sign across the desert. Get me? He'll follow if he finds water on the place. But he's not gunna find water."

"What you done, poor Dick?" said Tony. "Now look . . . I could hide you in the old wine cellar where nobody . . ."

"The sheriff's not gunna find any water," said Durante. "It's gunna be like this."

He put the rifle to his shoulder, aimed, fired. The shot struck the base of the nearest tank, ranging down through the bottom. A semicircle of darkness began to stain the soil near the edge of the iron wall.

Tony fell on his knees. "No, no, Dick! Good Dick!" he said. "Look! All the vineyard. It will die. It will turn into old, dead wood, Dick. . . ."

"Shut your face," said Durante. "Now I've started, I kinda like the job."

Tony fell on his face and put his hands over his ears. Durante drilled a bullet hole through the tanks, one after another. Afterward, he leaned on the rifle.

"Take my canteen and go in and fill it with water out of the cooling jar," he said. "Snap into it, Tony!"

Tony got up. He raised the canteen and looked around him, not at the tanks from which the water was pouring so that the noise of the earth drinking was audible, but at the rows of his vineyard. Then he went into the house.

Durante mounted his mule. He shifted the rifle to his left hand and drew out the heavy Colt from its holster. Tony came dragging back to him, his head down. Durante watched Tony with a careful revolver but he gave up the canteen without lifting his eyes.

"The trouble with you, Tony," said Durante, "is you're yellow. I'd of fought a tribe of wildcats with my bare hands, before I'd let 'em do what I'm doin' to you. But you sit back and take it."

Tony did not seem to hear. He stretched his hands to the vines.

"Ah, my God," said Tony. "Will you let them all die?"

Durante shrugged his shoulders. He shook the canteen to make sure that it was full. It was so brimming that there was hardly room for the liquid to make a sloshing sound. Then he turned the mule and kicked it into a dogtrot.

Half a mile from the house of Tony, he threw the empty rifle to the ground. There was no sense packing that useless weight, and Tony with his peg leg would hardly come this far.

Durante looked back, a mile or so later, and saw the little image of Tony picking up the rifle from the dust, then staring earnestly after his guest. Durante remembered the neat little hole clipped through the head of the rabbit. Wherever he went, his trail never could return again to the vineyard in the desert. But then, commencing to picture to himself the arrival of the sweating sheriff and his posse at the house of Tony, Durante laughed heartily.

The sheriff's posse could get plenty of wine, of course, but without water a man could not hope to make the desert

voyage, even with a mule or a horse to help him on the way. Durante patted the full, rounding side of his canteen. He might even now begin with the first sip but it was a luxury to postpone pleasure until desire became greater.

He raised his eyes along the trail. Close by, it was merely dotted with occasional bones, but distance joined the dots into an unbroken chalk line which wavered with a strange leisure across the Apache Desert, pointing to the cool blue promise of the mountains. The next morning he would be among them.

A coyote whisked out of a gully and ran like a gray puff of dust on the wind. His tongue hung out like a little red rag from the side of his mouth; and suddenly Durante was dry to the marrow. He uncorked and lifted his canteen. It had a slightly sour smell; perhaps the sacking which covered it had grown a trifle old. And then he poured a great mouthful of lukewarm liquid. He swallowed it before his senses could give him warning.

It was wine!

He looked first of all toward the mountains. They were as calmly blue, as distant as when he had started that morning. Twenty-four hours not on water, but on wine!

"I deserve it," said Durante. "I trusted him to fill the canteen. . . . I deserve it. Curse him!" With a mighty resolution, he quieted the panic in his soul. He would not touch the stuff until noon. Then he would take one discreet sip. He would win through.

Hours went by. He looked at his watch and found it was only ten o'clock. And he had thought that it was on the verge of noon! He uncorked the wine and drank freely and, corking the canteen, felt almost as though he needed a drink of water more than before. He sloshed the contents of the canteen. Already it was horribly light.

Once, he turned the mule and considered the return trip; but he could remember the head of the rabbit too clearly, drilled right through the center. The vineyard, the rows of old twisted, gnarled little trunks with the bark peeling off . . . every vine was to Tony like a human life. And Durante had condemned them all to death!

He faced the blue of the mountains again. His heart raced in his breast with terror. Perhaps it was fear and not the suction of that dry and deadly air that made his tongue cleave to the roof of his mouth.

The day grew old. Nausea began to work in his stomach, nausea alternating with sharp pains. When he looked down, he saw that there was blood on his boots. He had been spurring the mule until the red ran down from its flanks. It went with a curious stagger, like a rocking horse with a broken rocker; and Durante grew aware that he had been keeping the mule at a gallop for a long time. He pulled it to a halt. It stood with wide-braced legs. Its head was down. When he leaned from the saddle, he saw that its mouth was open.

"It's gunna die," said Durante. "It's gunna die . . . what a fool I been. . . ."

The mule did not die until after sunset. Durante left everything except his revolver. He packed the weight of that for an hour and discarded it, in turn. His knees were growing weak. When he looked up at the stars they shone white and clear for a moment only, and then whirled into little racing circles and scrawls of red.

He lay down. He kept his eyes closed

and waited for the shaking to go out of his body, but it would not stop. And every breath of darkness was like an inhalation of black dust.

He got up and went on, staggering. Sometimes he found himself running.

Before you die of thirst, you go mad. He kept remembering that his tongue had swollen big. Before it choked him, if he lanced it with his knife the blood would help him; he would be able to swallow. Then he remembered that the taste of blood is salty.

Once, in his boyhood, he had ridden through a pass with his father and they had looked down on the sapphire of a mountain lake, a hundred thousand million tons of water as cold as snow. . . .

When he looked up, now, there were no stars; and this frightened him terribly. He never had seen a desert night so dark. His eyes were failing, he was being blinded. When the morning came, he would not be able to see the mountains, and he would walk around and around in a circle until he dropped and died.

No stars, no wind; the air was still as the waters of a stale pool, and he in the dregs at the bottom. . . .

He seized his shirt at the throat and tore it away so that it hung in two rags from his hips.

He could see the earth only well enough to stumble on the rocks. But there were no stars in the heavens. He was blind: he had no more hope than a rat in a well. Ah, but Italian devils know how to put poison in wine that will steal all the senses or any one of them: and Tony had chosen to blind Durante.

He heard a sound like water. It was the swishing of the soft deep sand through which he was treading; sand so soft that a man could dig it away with his bare hands. . . .

Afterward, after many hours, out of the blind face of that sky the rain began to fall. It made first a whispering and then a delicate murmur like voices conversing, but after that, just at the dawn, it roared like the hoofs of ten thousand charging horses. Even through that thundering confusion the big birds with naked heads and red, raw necks found their way down to one place in the Apache Desert.   THE END

Talking it over

1. Tony tries to persuade Durante to hide in the wine cellar. Why does Durante choose to destroy Tony's water supply instead?

2. *a.* What does Durante mean when he says that he deserves the wine? Does he feel guilty for what he has done to Tony?

b. Why can't he go back for water?

3. *a.* How do you explain the fact that Tony doesn't fight back at Durante before the man can damage the water containers?

b. Is Tony a murderer? Explain.

4. A person who meets exactly the fate he deserves is said to receive

poetic justice: for example, a TV villain who sets a trap for someone and is caught in it himself. He is the kind of person about whom we say "He asked for it!" In what way is what happens to Durante an example of poetic justice?

5. *a.* What details throughout the story made you feel the heat and dryness of the desert?

b. For what reasons might the author emphasize these ideas so much?

He wrote thousands of stories

Recognizing cause-effect relationships

In the first group below are some details from the story. Each of these things causes something else to happen. Match each numbered cause with its effect or result. You will not use one of the effects.

CAUSES

1. Tony keeps water stored in tanks.
2. Durante has killed a man.
3. Tony fills Durante's canteen with wine instead of water.
4. Durante sees that Tony is a good enough shot to put a rifle bullet through the head of a rabbit.

EFFECTS

a. Durante dies of thirst in the desert.

b. In spite of the risk that he will die of thirst in the desert, Durante does not return to Tony's place.

c. Tony can keep his vineyard alive during the dry season.

d. Tony tells Durante how his father was killed by the desert.

e. Durante has to prevent the sheriff from catching up with him.

Max Brand wrote an average of 20,000 words a day—probably an all-time record for a writer of fiction. He used a variety of pen names (his real name was Frederick Faust) and sometimes had several stories in the same issue of a magazine. He wrote westerns, detective and spy stories, science fiction, adventure tales, stories about doctors, flyers, and soldiers, and about just ordinary people. Among the characters he created was young Dr. Kildare, who became the hero of a long-popular television series. Three dozen movies have been made from his works. The cowboy picture "Destry Rides Again" was filmed three different times.

Max Brand grew up in California. His family was poor, but he managed to attend the University of California, where he began to write. Later he gathered material for his stories from a variety of jobs—as a ditch digger, sailor, soldier, and reporter. He was a war correspondent in World War II, and was killed in Italy while accompanying an infantry attack.

THE BUILDERS

by Sara Henderson Hay

I told them a thousand times if I told them once:
Stop fooling around, I said, with straw and sticks;
They won't hold up; you're taking an awful chance.
Brick is the stuff to build with, solid bricks.
5 You want to be impractical, go ahead.
But just remember, I told them; wait and see.
You're making a big mistake. Awright, I said,
But when the wolf comes, don't come running to me.

The funny thing is, they didn't. There they sat,
10 One in his crummy yellow shack, and one
Under his roof of twigs, and the wolf ate
Them, hair and hide. Well, what is done is done.
But I'd been willing to help them, all along,
If only they'd once admitted they were wrong.

Talking it over

1. *a.* On what well-known nursery story is this poem based?

b. What clues tell you?

c. Who is telling the story? What does he think of those who build with straw and sticks?

2. *a.* Reread the last two lines. Under what condition would the speaker have helped the other builders?

b. What does the speaker really care about?

3. *a.* How is the story in the poem different from the original?

b. What is the poet suggesting about people like the speaker?

ANGUS McGREGOR

by Lew Sarett

Angus McGregor lies brittle as ice,
With snow tucked up to his jaws,
Somewhere tonight where the hemlocks moan
And crack in the wind like straws.

5 Angus went cruising the woods last month,
With a blanket-roll on his back,
With never an ax, a dirk, a gun,
Or a compass in his pack.

"The hills at thirty below have teeth;
10 McGregor," I said, "you're daft
To tackle the woods like a simple child."
But he looked at me and laughed.

He flashed his teeth in a grin and said:
"The earth is an open book;
15 I've followed the woods for forty years,
I know each cranny and crook.

"I've battled her weather, her winds, her brutes,
I've stood with them toe to toe;
I can beat them back with my naked fist
20 And answer them blow for blow."

Angus McGregor sleeps under the stars,
With an icicle gripped in his hand,
Somewhere tonight where the grim-lipped peaks
Brood on a haggard land.

25 Oh, the face of the moon is dark tonight,
And dark the gaunt wind's sigh;
And the hollow laughter troubles me
In the wild wolves' cry.

From *Covenant with Earth*, by Lew Sarett. Edited and copyrighted, 1956, by Alma Johnson Sarett. Gainesville: University of Florida Press, 1956. Reprinted by permission of Mrs. Sarett.

ea

Talking it over

1. *a.* Who was Angus McGregor?
   b. What did he do?
   c. What happened to him?
2. *a.* Who is telling the story of Angus McGregor?
   b. Why does the "hollow laughter" trouble him?
3. In your opinion, was Angus McGregor brave, or was he foolish? Was his fate an example of poetic justice?

4. In both this poem and "The Builders" the speaker had given good advice which was ignored. How does each speaker feel about being right?

5. Pick out words and phrases that you think are particularly good in helping you see the scene and feel the cold.

"I guess it's like you come into class for a test,
not thinking of cheating at all,
and then some girl, one of the smart ones,
goes for a drink and you see her paper
right there in front of you."

JOEY'S BALL

by Norman Katkov

PA CAME UP the driveway in the truck, a load of bananas in the back looking like a field of dandelions. He pulled alongside the garage and put his arm around me when he got out.

"How's for taking a ride, Joey?" Pa asked. He wanted me to help sell the bananas. That would mean missing practice.

"Pa, I can't. We got to practice, and besides we got to buy a ball. Pa, will you give me two-fifty for it, Pa?"

"No," Ma said. I turned. She was standing behind us, holding Bobby, my baby brother, in her arms.

"I got to have it, Pa." I was talking to him. *She* would never give it to me. "I'll pay it back. Honest I will." He shook his head, smiling at me, and went into the house.

While he was eating breakfast, I wondered what I was going to tell the guys. I pitch for the Riverview Midgets in the St. Paul city softball league. We had a game coming up the next day, and we had to have a new ball. Most

of the kids, I guess, were even poorer than we were, and it was tough for us getting balls. I'd told the guys yesterday not to worry; Pa would give it to me.

When he came out, Ma was with him, carrying his lunch. "Joey, you go with your father," Ma said. "He can't work alone today." That's the way she was all the time.

"You'll be late for practice, Joey," Pa said, talking to the bananas. That did it for me. I'd been helping him on the truck since I was ten, and he'd never once asked me. He'd just say something so that I'd have to be a rat not to go with him.

"Please, Pa, I need the money." He was getting ready to go.

"So do we, boy. Your mother and Bobby and you." He got into the truck. I let him get almost down the drive before I went after him. There wasn't any use in trying to pitch when he made me feel *this* way.

He didn't stop when I got on the running board. He turned out on Concord and headed for George Street up on the Heights. He slowed up for the traffic light on State, figuring it would show green when he got there, but the light fooled him. I saw him roll a cigarette, and then, talking like I was sitting on the radiator cap, he said, "Come up front with your old man, kid."

"Pa."

"I haven't got it to spare, kid." He was leaning over the wheel, laying on it from his hands to his elbows. All during the summer Pa peddles. Every morning he goes down to the market down on Eleventh Street and buys stuff: bananas, or strawberries, peaches and grapes and tomatoes. He's smart; he buys a lot of just one thing. That way he gets it cheaper.

We stopped up on West George near the library. "What side of the street you want, Joey?" Pa asked. The way we work it: I take a hand of bananas in each arm, he tells me the price, and then I try the doors. I always go to the back door. If it's one thing Pa doesn't like, it's me stepping on the grass. That really sets him off, boy.

"Left side," I said. "For luck." I'm a southpaw myself. He gave me a half dollar's worth of change and two bunches of bananas.

"Thirty-five cents a dozen, four bits[1] for each bunch," he said.

I went up the sidewalk. When I first started helping, I didn't like it. It was like begging, I thought, and besides, lots of the houses I went to, the kids who lived there were in school with me at Roosevelt Junior. I used to duck low in the truck when I saw a gang of them. But then one day, when I bent down next to the emergency brake, Pa stopped right in the middle of a bunch of them.

---

[1]**four bits,** fifty cents. American slang.

"Hey, gang!" he yelled. They came around, and he told them to get up on the fenders and on the hood. Then he pointed at me, but I'd straightened up and was sitting on the seat.

"What do you think of this guy?" he asked.

" 'Stead of playing ball with you fellows, he asks if he can help me. And he's ashamed of it. Some dope, eh? Ashamed 'cause he helps his dad." That was the last time I ducked.

A real young woman opened the door of the first house. "Yes?" she said. She looked like she'd been cooking for fifty kids since five o'clock that morning.

"Nice bananas, lady. Thirty-five cents a dozen, or fifty cents for the bunch."

"Yeh?" She pawed over them like she was kneading dough. "Too much," she decided.

"They're fifty cents a dozen at the store."

"I'll give you fifty cents for that bunch." She pointed at the biggest one.

"All right, lady." She told me to wait while she got the money, and she closed the door on me. I laid the smallest bunch down, got a good grip on the one she'd chosen and ripped three bananas off the back row. I shoved two in one pocket and one in the other and then picked both bunches up and stood there waiting.

She opened the door and took the bunch off my arm. Then she handed me the money—nickels and dimes— and slammed the door.

I sold a dozen next door. I had six left from that hand, and with the three I'd shoved in my pockets, I sold them upstairs for thirty-five cents because they were so big. When I came out

front again, Pa was up the street a ways, clanking his bell and hollering: "Bananas! Nice, big bananas!"

I was walking up the street, thinking of what he'd say when I told him I'd gotten a buck-twenty instead of just a buck, when all of a sudden I stopped like I'd been hit by a pitched ball. I don't know what made me think of it right then; I guess it's like you come into class for a test, not thinking of cheating at all, and then some girl, one of the smart ones, goes for a drink and you see her paper right there in front of you. Counting the half-buck in change Pa had handed me, I had a buck-seventy on me. All he expected back was a buck and a half. It was like we were ten runs ahead going into the ninth inning.

Women were flocking out to the truck now. For a while I didn't have a chance to give Pa the money, but I got twenty cents from the rest of the dough and put it in my back pocket—and I had a grip on our new ball.

I was a little scared. It was just like walking down to the West Side and just thinking of the guys there, always wanting to start a fight.

But after that it wasn't so hard. I got some of it from Pa, when he was too busy to notice, and some of it over-charging. I even got seventy-five cents for one hand from a woman. It had big bananas, and I dropped the quarter in my back pocket with the rest of the dough. I could almost feel every dime and nickel in there, like somebody was poking me with a stick every time I moved. I walked like I had a limp, taking it easy on that side.

Around one o'clock we drove up Stryker Avenue and then cut over into the alley between Isable and Congress.

Pa parked the truck in the middle of the block. "If we sell these, your ma is going to take you to the Orpheum. How's that?" I didn't want movies. I couldn't see nothing but the game the next day. Maybe you don't know how it is, waiting all week to play ball. Maybe you never stayed up late the night before a game, just watching to see it didn't rain, like you could keep it away. Maybe you never laid in bed figuring how you were going to pitch.

It was banana day all right. We stayed for about an hour, then drove to a drugstore on George and Stryker. We got malted milks and had those with the lunch sandwiches, and the malted was as good as being in a lake.

There was another hour's work after that, and then all there was left of those bananas was three or four dozen half-black ones that I knew were going to the lady who runs a boarding house up on Hall and Isable.

Pa sat on the running board and figured up. I could see him moving his lips, and pretty soon he was up to twenty-six dollars. Then he counted the bills, and laughed. "A good day! Ma'll be happy, huh, Joe?"

We drove over toward the boarding-house lady's. Pa pulled into the drive-way, and I turned the ignition key. He looked over at me, flicked the ashes from his cigarette on my jeans, and climbed out of the truck. Then he stuck his head back in. "I'll sell her the rest of that stuff. You drive home. Deal?"

"A deal." I didn't want him to be nice to me now. I wasn't mad any more, because I had the dough for the ball, but I felt like I had to stay mad, so he wouldn't catch on.

I watched him knock on the door. When the boarding-house lady opened it and he walked in, I quick grabbed all the money out of my back pocket. There was two dollars and eighty-five cents there. I stuffed all but thirty-five cents back in my pocket. I couldn't take that. The dough for the ball was one thing: like it was over on one side of my head; then there was a foul line, and then, on the other side of my head was all I felt about stealing and what Pa felt about it. A wrong count, he always called it.

Pa and the woman came out. She was a little woman, always wore a black shawl, and Pa liked her, gave her lots of stuff. He told me to take the bananas in.

When I came out, he had all the bushel baskets stacked up by her garage. He gets them for nothing down at the commission houses,[2] and lots of times he sells them.

He got in beside me, grinning. "Two bucks gravy, Joe."

"How come?"

"The baskets. She gave me a dime apiece for them." He took four halves out of his pocket and dropped them in his shirt pocket. "When we get down to Concord," he said, "you drive."

"Here." I handed him the thirty-five cents.

"What's that?"

"Found it in my pocket. Here." I held out my hand. He closed my fingers on it, making a fist. "Keep it, Joey. We won't tell Ma."

"Take it. It's yours."

"All right, kid. Don't get excited." He dropped the money in his shirt pocket with the halves and started the motor.

Down on Concord he stopped and we switched seats. I started out kind of jerky, real slow, and all I could see through the windshield was the gray softball, coming at the glass. He put his hand on my shoulder and, when we got clear of the traffic light on Robert Street, he rubbed my arm. "How's the wing?" he asked.

"Okay, I guess."

"Gonna win tomorrow?"

"What do you care?" I was really mad at him. Why didn't he just forget about it, instead of always talking about the game? He didn't care enough about it to buy me a ball.

"I'll set you on your ear, champ," he warned me. I didn't say anything. I just wanted to get that money out of my pockets and change clothes and buy the ball. I guess nothing ever went as slow as that truck. When I stopped in front of the house, he told me to go in. "Tell Ma I'm going to grease the truck," he said. "I want to see you home when I get back, kid. Take a bath and lay around."

I walked up the driveway and into the front door, trying to get upstairs without Ma seeing me. But she spotted me, and I had to explain Pa's leaving to her.

In my bedroom I looked for a place to hide the dough till after supper. Finally I got me a chair and stood on it, laying all the money on the ledge over the door.

Then I took a bath and changed clothes and came downstairs. I got the paper off the steps and sat on the swing inside the porch, reading about the Saints and the other Association teams. When I heard the truck, Pa was coming up the driveway. After a minute he was in the house, and I heard him and Ma

---

[2]**commission houses,** wholesale dealers who provide peddlers like Joey's father with produce and collect a share of the sales.

talking in whispers in the kitchen, and I knew he had found out about the dough.

I laid the paper down real easy and, holding the swing with both hands so it wouldn't creak, I slipped off. I was almost out the door when Pa said, "Joey."

They were both in the hallway, Ma standing next to him, poking him in the ribs. Then he pulled his arm from behind and hollered, "Catch!" and the ball was sailing at me, the tissue paper falling off it.

He laughed. "You better win tomorrow, kid. Them bushel baskets were velvet."

I watched him go upstairs for his bath, and I held onto the ball, squeezing it to keep my hands from shaking; and I could almost feel it give, I was pushing against it so hard. Ma walked back in the kitchen, and I went out on the porch. The swing was rocking, but I couldn't stop it; and the toes of my shoes were scuffing the floor and I couldn't stop them. I felt the same as when I was vaccinated, just all shaky and waiting to faint. This time I wouldn't faint. I knew what I was going to have to do, all right.

I heard Pa coming down the stairs. Then he stuck his head out the door of the porch and said, "Supper." I waited a minute before I got up. Then I went upstairs.

When I came down, they were all at the table, Bobby yelling about the milk, Pa sitting in his chair wearing a white sports shirt and bedroom slippers, but no socks. I had the money in one fist and the ball in my other hand. I guess he knew something was fishy. Instead of eating he watched me, and so did Ma. Bobby stopped hollering. I walked around to Pa's chair and laid the ball on the table and the money next to it.

"Where'd you get it, boy?" he asked, and he sounded softer than our coach after we've lost.

"From you," I said, "and some from the customers."

"How?" he asked, and Ma yelled, "Crook! He's a little crook!" Pa put his left hand on her wrist, quieting her. "How, kid?" he asked me.

"Overcharging," I said. I knew he wouldn't hit me. I guess that's what had me scared, wondering what he was going to do. He picked up the dough, one coin at a time, and then he took the ball and got up from the table.

"Come on, kid," he said. He held out the hand with the money in it for me to take, but I just watched him, looking at him from his forehead to his eyebrows, like I was hypnotized.

"Take it," he said.

"No."

He kept his hand out, and I took it. It weighed a hundred pounds.

"Come on," he ordered. Ma said, "Pa, your supper. You haven't started your supper." But he shoved me out ahead of him through the back door.

We got in the truck, and he headed for the Heights. I could see the veins running down into his ankles, and I could see the emergency brake and the clutch and wires underneath the dashboard.

"You'll have to give it back, Joey," he said. "Whatever you took, even if it's a penny. It all goes back."

"Will you go with me?" I should have known better than to ask. He just kept driving until he got to the library and then he stopped. "Who's first, Joey?" I told him about taking three bananas off the first bunch and charging thirty-five cents for nine next door.

"That's a dime apiece," he said. He drove over in front of the house. Out in the street some of the guys I go to school with were playing ball. He turned off the ignition and sat there, rolling himself a cigarette and waiting.

I went into the first house. The woman opened the back door to my knock. I handed her the dime, "I overcharged you, ma'am." She grabbed the dime and slammed the door.

The woman next door was nice. She thanked me and wanted to give me a glass of milk, but I told her I had to eat supper. Back at the truck the kids had collected around Pa and he was telling them stories about when he was a fighter. He stopped smiling when he saw me and told the kids we had to get going.

We went to several more houses.

"Anybody else, boy?" Pa asked.

"Most of it is yours and what women gave me extra."

"The truth?"

I nodded.

"Nobody else?"

"I charged one woman, that lady whose husband is a fireman, seventy-five cents." He turned the truck for her house.

She and her husband were sitting on the porch. Pa waved at them just to be friendly, but he didn't get out. I gave her a quarter and said I'd overcharged her and was sorry.

She turned to her husband. "Isn't that nice, Phil?" She held out her hand. "You keep it, son. A boy as honest as you are has earned it."

"No!" I yelled. "No! I can't. No!" I jumped over the three steps and ran across their lawn. Their dog came after me, but I was running so fast I could have stole home from first base. I got

in the truck and I couldn't hold the tears any more; they just came down. Pa gave me his handkerchief, and I ducked my head, crying against his knee. He started the truck and drove back down to Smith Avenue.

"Any more, Joey?"

I was trying to stop crying now and I was hiccoughing, but I couldn't say anything or I would have started again. I shook my head and handed him the rest of the money.

He put the dough in his shirt pocket. When he stopped for the traffic light, he rolled himself a cigarette, and I got a match out of his pocket and almost burned my thumb off lighting it on my fingernail the way he does. He blew the smoke in my face and shook his head back and forth through the blue haze.

"You can't get away with that stuff, kid. Never."

The light changed and we got going. He stopped at Baker and Smith in front of the sports store and took the ball inside with him. He was right, I guess. Even if he couldn't get all his money back, he was right. I waited about ten minutes, trying to spot him inside the store, but it was getting dark and I couldn't make him out through the windows. Then I heard him whistling.

He had the ball in one hand, tossing it up and catching it, and over his shoulder was the biggest, yellowest, most beautiful baseball bat I ever saw. He climbed in on the driver's side and stuck it between my knees. He was tough-looking and not smiling.

"No kid of mine is going to play ball with a bum bat," he said. He turned the key and I could feel the tears coming up again in my eyes and I couldn't stop them.

THE END

Talking it over

1. *a.* How do Joey and his father get along with each other? Explain how their actions tell you this.

   b. How does the father's reaction to Joey's stealing differ from the reaction of his mother? Which parent understands Joey better?

2. How does Joey feel

   a. the first time he cheats a customer?

   b. after he has cheated a few customers?

   c. when he has enough money for a ball?

   d. when he hears his parents whispering?

   e. as he returns the money?

   f. when he sees his father with a ball and bat?

3. Discuss whether Joey's father was right in making him return the money, or whether the boy's confession would have been punishment enough.

Words in action

Joey sometimes explains his feelings by referring to baseball. Explain what Joey means when he uses the expressions in italic type below.

1. "I was walking up the street, thinking of what he'd say when I told him I'd gotten a buck-twenty instead of just a buck, when all of a sudden I stopped *like I'd been hit by a pitched ball.*" (top of page 347)

2. *"It was like we were ten runs ahead and going into the ninth inning."* (end of same paragraph)

3. "The dough for the ball was one thing: like it was over on one side of my head; then there was a *foul line,* and then, on the other side of my head was all I felt about stealing and what Pa felt about it. A *wrong count,* he always called it." (top of page 348)

4. "Their dog came after me, but I was running so fast *I could have stole home from first base.*" (page 350)

Son of an extraordinary man

Joey's father might well have been modeled after Norman Katkov's own father, a man he once described as "an extraordinary man, the most devoted to his children I've ever seen. He had the most humility, the most generosity, the most fear, and the most bravery of any human being I ever knew."

Katkov's parents brought their family from Russia to St. Paul, Minnesota, where Norman grew up and worked for a time in his father's grocery store. Before becoming a full-time fiction writer, Norman Katkov also wrote articles and stories for newspapers and magazines, at one time spending his nights haunting police stations for interesting stories for the St. Paul *Pioneer Press.*

JOEY'S BALL / 351

Spike lived in the shadow of a great danger, but we couldn't help him.

Death of a Tsotsi[1]

by Alan Paton

ABRAHAM MOLETISANE[2] was his name, but no one ever called him anything but Spike. He was a true child of the city, gay, careless, plausible; but for all that he was easy to manage and anxious to please. He was clean though flashy in his private dress. The khaki shirts and shorts of the reformatory were too drab for him, and he had a red scarf and yellow handkerchief which he arranged to peep out of his shirt pocket. He also had a pair of black and white shoes and a small but highly colored feather in his cap. Now the use of private clothes, except after the day's work, was forbidden; but he wore the red scarf on all occasions, saying, with an earnest expression that changed into an enigmatic smile if you looked too long at him, that his throat was sore.

That was a great habit of his, to look away when you talked to him, and to smile at some unseen thing.

He passed through the first stages of the reformatory very successfully. He had two distinct sets of visitors, one his hard-working mother and his younger sister, and the other a group of flashy young men from the city. His mother and the young men never came together, and I think he arranged it so. While we did not welcome his second set of visitors, we did not forbid them so long as they behaved themselves; it was better for us to know about them than otherwise.

One day his mother and sister brought a friend, Elizabeth, who was a quiet and clean-looking person like themselves. Spike told me that his mother wished him to marry this girl, but that the girl was very independent, and refused to hear of it unless he reformed and gave up the company of the *tsotsis*.

[1]**Tsotsi** (tsô′tsē)
[2]**Moletisane** (mō let i sä′nē)

"And what do you say, Spike?"

He would not look at me, but tilted his head up and surveyed the ceiling, smiling hard at it, and dropping his eyes but not his head to take an occasional glance at me. I did not know exactly what was in his mind, but it was clear to me that he was beginning to feel confidence in the reformatory.

"It doesn't help to say to her, just O.K., O.K.," he said. "She wants it done before everybody, as the Principal gives the first freedom."[3]

"What do you mean, before everybody?"

"Before my family and hers."

"And are you willing?"

Spike smiled harder than ever at the ceiling, as though at some secret but delicious joy. Whether it was that he was savoring the delight of deciding his future, I do not know. Or whether he was savoring the delight of keeping guessing two whole families and the reformatory, I do not know either.

He was suddenly serious. "If I promise her, I'll keep it," he said. "But I won't be forced."

"No one's forcing you," I said.

He lowered his head and looked at me, as though I did not understand the ways of women.

Although Spike was regarded as a weak character, he met all the temptations of increasing physical freedom very successfully. He went to the free hostels,[4] and after some months there he received the special privilege of special weekend leave to go home. He swaggered out, and he swaggered back, punctual to the minute. How he timed it I do not know, for he had no watch; but in all the months that he had the privilege, he was never late.

It was just after he had received his first special leave that one of his city friends was sent to the reformatory also. The friend's name was Walter, and within a week of his arrival he and Spike had a fight, and both were sent to me. Walter alleged that Spike had hit him first, and Spike did not deny it.

"Why did you hit him, Spike?"

"He insulted me, *meneer*."[5]

"How?"

At length he came out with it.

"He said I was reformed."

We could not help laughing at that, not much of course, for it was clear to me that Spike did not understand our laughter, and that he accepted it only because he knew we were well-disposed towards him.

"If I said you were reformed, Spike," I said, "would you be insulted?"

"No, meneer."

"Then why did he insult you?"

He thought that it was a difficult question. Then he said, "He did not mean anything good, meneer. He meant I was back to being a child."

"You are not," I said. "You are going forward to being a man."

He was mollified by that, and I warned him not to fight again. He accepted my rebuke, but he said to me, "This fellow is out to make trouble for me. He says I must go back to the tsotsis when I come out."

I said to Walter, "Did you say that?"

---

[3]**first freedom.** At the reformatory where the author was Principal, after boys showed they would obey the rules when closely supervised, they were given more freedom. First, however, they had to promise they would obey the rules when not being watched.

[4]**free hostels,** cottages where twelve boys lived with a teacher and his wife. Boys were moved to a free hostel when they proved trustworthy during their stay in the main building.

[5]**meneer** (mə nir′), a respectful term used in South Africa to address a man. An American would use the word *sir* in its place.

Walter was hurt to the depths and said, "No, meneer."

When they had gone I sent for de Villiers[6] whose job it is to know every home in Johannesburg[7] that has a boy at the reformatory. It was not an uncommon story, of a decent widow left with a son and daughter. She had managed to control the daughter, but not the son, and Spike had got in with a gang of tsotsis; as a result of one of their exploits he had found himself in court, but had not betrayed his friends. Then he had gone to the reformatory, which apart from anything it did itself, had enabled his mother to regain her hold on him, so that he had now decided to forsake the tsotsis, to get a job through de Villiers, and to marry the girl Elizabeth and live with her in his mother's house.

A week later Spike came to see me again.

"The Principal must forbid these friends of Walter to visit the reformatory," he said.

"Why, Spike?"

"They are planning trouble for me, meneer."

The boy was no longer smiling, but looked troubled, and I sat considering his request. I called in de Villiers, and we discussed it in Afrikaans,[8] which Spike understood. But we were talking a rather high Afrikaans for him, and his eyes went from one face to the other, trying to follow what we said. If I forbade these boys to visit the reformatory, what help would that be to Spike? Would their resentment against him be any the less? Would they forget it because they did not see him? Might this not be a further cause for resentment against him? After all, one cannot remake the world; one can do all one can in a reformatory, but when the time comes, one has to take away one's hands. It was true that de Villiers would look after him, but such supervision had its defined limits. As I looked at the boy's troubled face, I also was full of trouble for him; for he had of his choice bound himself with chains, and now, when he wanted of his choice to put them off, he found it was not so easy to do. He looked at us intently, and I could see that he felt excluded, and wished to be brought in again.

"Did you understand what we said, Spike?"

"Not everything, meneer."

"I am worried about one thing," I said. "Which is better for you, to forbid these boys, or not to forbid them?"

"To forbid them," he said.

"They might say," I said, "Now he'll pay for this."

"The Principal does not understand," he said. "My time is almost finished at the reformatory. I don't want trouble before I leave."

"I'm not worried about trouble here," I said. "I'm worried about trouble outside."

He looked at me anxiously, as though I had not fully grasped the matter.

"I'm not worried about here," I said with asperity. "I can look after you here. If someone tries to make trouble, do you think I can't find the truth?"

He did not wish to doubt my ability, but he remained anxious.

"You still want me to forbid them?" I asked.

"Yes, meneer."

---

[6] **de Villiers** (də fil′yāz)
[7] **Johannesburg** (jō han′is bèrg), the largest city in the Union of South Africa.
[8] **Afrikaans** (af rə käns′), a language of South Africa that is very much like Dutch. Dutch people began settling in South Africa more than 300 years ago.

"Mr. de Villiers," I said, "find out all you can about these boys. Then let me know."

"And then," I said to Spike, "I'll talk to you about forbidding them."

"They're a tough lot," de Villiers told me later. "No parental control. In fact they have left home and are living with George, the head of the gang. George's mother is quite without hope for her son, but she's old now and depends on him. He gives her money, and she sees nothing, hears nothing, says nothing. She cooks for them."

"And they won't allow Spike to leave the gang?" I asked.

"I couldn't prove that, but it's a funny business. The reason why they don't want to let Spike go is because he has the brains and the courage. He makes the plans and they all obey him on the job. But off the job he's nobody. Off the job they all listen to George."

"Did you see George?"

"I saw George," he said, "and I reckon he's a bad fellow. He's morose and sullen, and physically bigger than Spike.

"If you got in his way," he added emphatically, "he'd wipe you out—like that."

We both sat there rather gloomy about Spike's future.

"Spike's the best of the lot," he said. "It's tragic that he ever got in with them. Now that he wants to get out . . . well. . . ."

He left his sentence unfinished.

"Let's see him," I said.

"We've seen these friends of Walter's," I said to Spike, "and we don't like them very much. But whether it will help to forbid their visits, I truly do not know. But I am willing to do what you say."

"The Principal must forbid them," he said at once.

So I forbade them. They listened to me in silence, neither humble nor insolent, not affronted nor surprised; they put up no pleas or protests. George said, "Good, sir," and one by one they followed him out.

When a boy finally leaves the reformatory, he is usually elated, and does not hide his high spirits. He comes to the office for a final conversation, and goes off like one who has brought off an extraordinary coup. But Spike was subdued.

"Spike," I said privately, with only de Villiers there, "are you afraid?"

He looked down at the floor and said, "I'm not afraid," as though his fear were private also, and would neither be lessened nor made greater by confession.

He was duly married and de Villiers and I made him a present of a watch so that he could always be on time for his work. He had a good job in a factory in Industria, and worked magnificently; he saved money, and spent surprisingly little on clothes. But he had none of his old gaiety and attractive carelessness. He came home promptly, and once home, never stirred out.

It was summer when he was released, and with the approach of winter he asked if de Villiers would not see the manager of the factory, and arrange for him to leave half an hour earlier, so that he could reach his home before dark. But the manager said it was impossible, as Spike was on the kind of job that would come to a standstill if one man left earlier. De Villiers waited for him after work and he could see that the boy was profoundly depressed.

"Have they said anything to you?" de Villiers asked him.

The boy would not answer for a long time, and at last he said with a finality that was meant to stop further discussion, "They'll get me." He was devoid of hope, and did not wish to talk about it, like a man who has a great pain and does not wish to discuss it, but prefers to suffer it alone and silent. This hopelessness had affected his wife and mother and sister, so that all of them sat darkly and heavily. And de Villiers noted that there were new bars on every door and window. So he left darkly and heavily too, and Spike went with him to the little gate.

And Spike asked him, "Can I carry a knife?"

It was a hard question and the difficulty of it angered de Villiers, so that he said harshly, "How can I say that you can carry a knife?"

"You," said Spike, "my mother, my sister, Elizabeth."

He looked at de Villiers.

"I obey you all," he said, and went back into the house.

So still more darkly and heavily de Villiers went back to the reformatory, and sitting in my office, communicated his mood to me. We decided that he would visit Spike more often than he visited any other boy. This he did, and he even went to the length of calling frequently at the factory at five o'clock, and taking Spike home. He tried to cheer and encourage the boy, but the dark heavy mood could not be shifted.

One day Spike said to him, "I tell you, sir, you all did your best for me."

The next day he was stabbed to death just by the little gate.

In spite of my inside knowledge, Spike's death so shocked me that I could do no work. I sat in my office, hopeless and defeated. Then I sent for the boy Walter.

"I sent for you," I said, "to tell you that Spike is dead."

He had no answer to make. Nothing showed in his face to tell whether he cared whether Spike were alive or dead. He stood there impassively, obedient and respectful, ready to go or ready to stand there forever.

"He's dead," I said angrily. "He was killed. Don't you care?"

"I care," he said.

He would have cared very deeply, had I pressed him. He surveyed me unwinkingly, ready to comply with my slightest request. Between him and me there was an unbridgeable chasm; so far as I know there was nothing in the world, not one hurt or grievance or jest or sorrow, that could have stirred us both together.

Therefore I let him go.

De Villiers and I went to the funeral, and spoke words of sympathy to Spike's mother and wife and sister. But the words fell like dead things to the ground, for something deeper than sorrow was there. We were all of us, white and black, rich and poor, learned and untutored, bowed down by a knowledge that we lived in the shadow of a great danger, and were powerless against it. It was no place for a white person to pose in any mantle of power or authority; for this death gave the lie to both of them.[9]

And this death would go on, too, for nothing less than the reform of a society would bring it to an end. It was the menace of the socially frustrated,

---

[9]**gave the lie to both of them,** showed them to be false.

strangers to mercy, striking like adders[10] for the dark reasons of ancient
minds, at any who crossed their paths.

• THE END

Talking it over

1. *a.* What kind of person is Spike
when you first meet him? Give details
from the story.

b. Why is he in the reformatory?

2. *a.* What decision does Spike have
to make in the reformatory? Why does
he decide as he does?

b. In what ways does he seem
different after he leaves the reformatory? How do you explain the changes?

3. Does Spike make the right decision? What might have happened had
he gone back to the tsotsis?

4. Which of the following statements
expresses a central idea in the story?
(There may be several correct answers.)

a. There is no such thing as "reforming"; it is impossible to change
one's ways.

b. Even when you do the right
thing, you won't necessarily be happy
and secure.

c. There is a lot of injustice in
the world.

d. Once you take a wrong step,
you may suffer for it the rest of your
life.

___
[10]**adders,** large poisonous snakes.

Words in action

Read each excerpt below and decide
which of the three choices following
means most nearly the same thing as
the word or phrase in bold type. Be
prepared to explain whether you could
figure out the meaning through context
or by breaking the word into meaningful parts (structure), or whether you
had to look up the word in the Glossary.

1. "Now the use of private clothes,
except after the day's work, was forbidden; but he wore the red scarf on
all occasions, saying, with an earnest
expression that changed into an **enigmatic** smile if you looked too long at
him, that his throat was sore. That was
a great habit of his, to look away when
you talked to him, and to smile at some
unseen thing." (page 352)

a. happy
b. mysterious
c. toothless

2. "We could not help laughing at
that, not much of course, for it was
clear to me that Spike did not understand our laughter, and that he accepted it only because he knew we were
well-disposed towards him." (page 353)

a. friendly
b. without feeling
c. leaning

3. "He looked at us intently, and I
could see that he felt **excluded,** and
wished to be brought in again." (page
354)

a. ashamed
b. hopeful
c. left out

4. "When a boy finally leaves the
reformatory, he is usually **elated,** *and*

does not hide his high spirits." (page 355)

   a. sad
   b. anxious
   c. joyful

5. "De Villiers waited for him after work and he could see that the boy was **profoundly** depressed." (page 355)

   a. a little
   b. deeply
   c. not at all

6. "This hopelessness had affected his wife and mother and sister, so that all of them sat **darkly and heavily."** (top of page 357)

   a. without light, in warm clothing
   b. blindly and overfed
   c. gloomily and cheerlessly

7. "Nothing showed in his face to tell whether he cared whether Spike were alive or dead. He stood there **impassively** . . . ready to go or ready to stand there forever." (page 357)

   a. without emotion
   b. without smiling
   c. without sadness

8. "Between him and me there was an **unbridgeable chasm;** so far as I know there was nothing in the world . . . that could have stirred us both together." (page 357)

   a. deep valley
   b. never-ending hatred
   c. hopeless difference

He took down the fences

"Death of a Tsotsi," like most of the stories in Alan Paton's book *Tales from a Troubled Land,* is based on his own

experiences as principal of a reformatory in South Africa.

Until he was thirty-two, Mr. Paton was a high-school teacher of white boys. Then, in 1935, the South African Parliament took all its reform schools away from the Department of Prisons and transferred them to the Department of Education. Mr. Paton was appointed Principal of Diepkloof Reformatory for African boys, the largest of its kind in the whole continent of Africa.

It was Mr. Paton's duty to "reform the reformatory itself," as he says, and he changed it in thirteen years from a closed prison to a half-closed, half-open school. The open part of the school consisted of cottages in which small groups of boys lived with an African teacher and his wife. These "free" boys were allowed the freedom of the Diepkloof farm on non-working days, and were allowed to pay weekend visits once a month to their homes. The effect of these and other changes was that only one fourth as many boys ran away as before. Mr. Paton became known and respected as "the man who pulled up barbed wire fences and planted geraniums."

Mr. Paton has written a number of books about South Africa. His novel *Cry, the Beloved Country* is known all over the world.

THE MEADOW MOUSE

by Theodore Roethke

-I-

In a shoe box stuffed in an old nylon stocking
Sleeps the baby mouse I found in the meadow,
Where he trembled and shook beneath a stick
Till I caught him up by the tail and brought him in,
5 Cradled in my hand,
A little quaker, the whole body of him trembling,
His absurd whiskers sticking out like a cartoon-mouse,
His feet like small leaves,
Little lizard-feet,
10 Whitish and spread wide when he tried to struggle away,
Wriggling like a miniscule puppy.

Now he's eaten his three kinds of cheese and drunk from
      his bottle-cap watering-trough—
So much he just lies in one corner,
His tail curled under him, his belly big
15 As his head; his bat-like ears
Twitching, tilting toward the least sound.

Do I imagine he no longer trembles
When I come close to him?
He seems no longer to tremble.

-II-

20 But this morning the shoe-box house on the back porch is empty.
Where has he gone, my meadow mouse,
My thumb of a child that nuzzled in my palm?—
To run under the hawk's wing,
Under the eye of the great owl watching from the elm-tree,
25 To live by the courtesy of the shrike, the snake, the tom-cat.
I think of the nestling fallen into the deep grass,
The turtle gasping in the dusty rubble of the highway,
The paralytic stunned in the tub, and the water rising,—
All things innocent, hapless, forsaken.

Talking it over

1. *a.* What is the situation in Part I of the poem (the first 19 lines)?

b. Why has the speaker brought the mouse home with him?

2. *a.* With what things does the speaker compare parts of the mouse's body? How do these descriptions make you feel about the mouse?

b. How does the speaker make you realize how small the mouse is?

c. Why does the speaker emphasize the smallness of the mouse?

3. *a.* What has happened when Part II begins?

b. What dangers does the mouse now face?

c. Why do you suppose the mouse ran away, in spite of everything the speaker did for it?

4. What other creatures does the mouse make the speaker think of?

5. The central idea of this poem has to do with what feelings of the poet's?

a. Pity for all helpless animals and humans

b. Fear for the safety of a baby mouse which may be killed by a hawk

c. Love for all living things

I felt plain ashamed of being me,
of being a boy with a father who'd made
a fool of himself like he had. . . .

HARVEY KENDALL, A FATHER WHO GREW UP

by Jack Schaefer

M Y FATHER had two pairs of boots. He had a pair of shoes but he wore those only when my mother made him, to church on Sundays and to funerals and the like. The boots were what you'd call his regular footwear.

One pair was plain, just rough-and-ready old-style cowboy boots, nearly knee high, made of stiff cowhide with canvas pulling-straps we used to call "mule ears" that dangled and flapped on the outside when he walked along. He wore those at work on weekdays. He was cattle inspector at the local stockyards, where the ranchers for quite a stretch around brought their stuff to be checked and weighed before being shipped out. He'd pull out of bed in the morning and pad around the house in his socks, or when Mother got after him, in the slippers she'd bought for him, until after breakfast and then he'd squat on the edge of a chair and heave and yank at those boots till they were on and tuck his work pants down inside the tops and stand up and stretch and say, "Another day, another dollar," which was sort of silly because he earned more than a dollar a day, and out the door he'd go with those mule ears flapping.

We lived a short ways out of town and sometimes he'd walk in those boots down to where the stockyards spread out beside and behind the station about a half mile away, and sometimes he'd saddle his old cow pony and ride down and maybe during the day circulate some through the pens helping the handlers move the stuff around, which he didn't need to do because he wasn't paid for that. "Can't let this Mark horse get too lazy and fat," he used to say, but that was only an excuse. The truth was he plain liked the feel of that horse under him now and again and the tickle of dust rising up in a man's nose saddle-high and the fun of shooing a few steers through some tricky gates. It reminded him of the old days when he was a free-roaming cowhand with a saddle roll for a home before my mother herded him into the same corral with a preacher and tied him down to family responsibilities.

Those cowhide boots were just every-day knockabout working boots. The others were something else again. They didn't reach quite as far up the legs but they had high narrow heels that curved under in back with a real swoop, and they were made of soft calfskin that fitted like a glove over the feet and ankles and then opened out some to take care of the pants if those were folded over neat and tucked in careful. The tops were curved up on the sides with little leather pulling-straps that stayed out of sight inside and those tops were made of separate pieces of the calfskin, darker brown in color than the bottoms, and they had a clever design of a rope loop stitched to them. He wore those boots on Sundays after he came home from church and on special occasions like meetings of the stockmen's association and when he was riding old Mark near the front in the annual Fourth of July parade. They reminded him of the best part of the old days, the times he was representing whatever range outfit he was with that season in the early rodeos and showing the other cowhands from the whole country roundabout what a man could do with a good horse and a good rope.

When he wore those calfskin boots my father always wore the belt that went with them. It was made of calfskin too and it was so wide my mother had to fix new belt straps on every pair of new pants she bought for him. It had a big solid slide-through silver buckle that had three lines of printing engraved in the metal. The first line said "First Honors" and the second line said the one word "Roping" and the third line said "Cheyenne 1893." That belt and that buckle, tight around his waist above those calfskin boots, reminded him of the best thing of all about the old days, the time he set a record busting and hog-tying[1] a steer, a record that

---

[1] **busting and hog-tying,** forcing the steer to the ground and tying his hind legs and one front leg together.

stood seven years before anyone beat it, and then it was beat only because they shortened the run some and changed the rules a bit and fast work was really easier to do.

Anyone knows anything about kids knows which pair of boots I liked. Cleaning and polishing both pairs with good saddle soap to keep the leather in right condition was one of my regular chores every Sunday morning before church. I'd get out the soap and a moist rag and if my father wasn't around watching I'd give those old cowskin boots a lick and a promise and then I'd really go to work on those calfskins even though they didn't need much, not being worn often. Sometimes I wouldn't do more than just run the rag quick over the old cowskins and figure my father wouldn't notice. I'd let them go because that old leather was rough and stiff all the time anyway and then like as not I'd be enjoying myself on the calfskins and sudden I'd look up and there my father would be watching me with his eyebrows pulled down till they about met over his nose.

"Gee-rusalem, boy," he'd say. "One of these days you'll rub those boots clean through. It's the others need the limbering so my feet don't ache in them. Get busy on them now afore I sideswipe you one."

Mention of sideswiping points to maybe one reason I didn't like working on those old cowskins. Whenever I'd done something wrong, broke one of the rules my folks made for me or messed up some chore when I should've known better, my father would come after me from behind and hop on his left foot and turn his right foot toe outward and swing his right leg so that the side of his foot swiped me hard and

hurting on my rump. He'd sideswipe me a good one or two or three, according to how bad it was that I'd done, and until I began to get some size there were times he raised me smack off the ground. Just about every time he did that he had those old cowskins on. But likely that didn't have too much to do with my feeling about them. I never was mad after a thumping or went around being sulky. My father sideswiped me only when I had it coming and he'd do it quick and thorough and tell me why, and then to show it was over and done and he was ready to forget about it he'd tell me to stick close around after supper and we'd saddle old Mark and he'd let me sit the saddle and get in some practice throws roping a fence-post before dark.

The truth was I didn't like working on those old cowskins because they were tough and hard to do anything with and old-fashioned and pretty well battered and they didn't mean a thing to me. Working on those others, those fine-looking calfskins, meant plenty. I'd rub away on that soft dark-shining leather and talk proud to myself inside. Not many boys had a father who had been a roping champion and in country where roping was real business and a man had to be good at it just to hold an ordinary ranch job. Not another boy anywhere had a father who had made a roping record that stood seven years and might still be standing if changes hadn't been made. I could work on that leather and see in my mind what I never saw with my eyes because all that was over and finished before I was born, my father on old Mark, young then, firm and straight in the saddle with the rope a living thing in his hands, my father and young Mark, working together, busting the meanest toughest trickiest steer with the hard-and-fast method he always said was the best. I could see every move, as he had told them to me over and over, young Mark reaching eager for speed to overtake the steer and knowing what to do every second without a word or a touch on the reins and my father riding easy and relaxed with the loop forming under his right hand and the loop going forward and opening and dropping over the wide horns and Mark slowing as my father took up the slack and pulled the loop tight and Mark speeding again to give him slack again, enough so he could flip the rope over to the right side of the steer, and then Mark swinging left in a burst of power and speed and the rope tightening along and down the steer's right side and pulling its head around in an outside arc and at the same time yanking its hind legs out from under it and making it flip in a complete side-winding somersault to lie with the wind knocked clean out of it and then all in the same motion, Mark pivoting to face the steer and bracing to keep the rope taut and my father using that pivot-swing to lift and carry him right out of the saddle and land on his feet and run down the taut rope with his pigging string[2] in his hand and wrap it quick around three of the steer's legs and draw it close and tie it and Mark watching and keeping the rope taut, ready to yank and make that steer behave if it started causing trouble, and then easing some slack at the right instant so my father could cast the loop loose and stand up to show the job was done and walk casual back to Mark without even looking at the steer again

---

[2]**pigging string,** string or rope used to hog-tie an animal.

like he was saying in the very set of his head on his shoulders that's that and there's a steer hog-tied for branding or earmarking or anything anybody's a mind to do with it.

Well, what I'm telling about this time had a lot to do with those boots and that belt and my father and old Mark too but mostly my father. It began the night before the sort of combination fair and rodeo at our town that year. The committee running things had some extra money available and they'd telegraphed and persuaded Cal Bennett to agree to come for the price and they'd plastered the town with bills saying the topnotch champion roper of the big-town circuit would be on hand to give some fancy exhibitions and everybody'd been talking about that for days. We were finishing supper, my father and my mother and me, and I notched up nerve enough and finally I said it.

"Father," I said, "can I wear your belt tomorrow? Just a little while anyway?"

My father settled back in his chair and looked at me. "What's on your mind boy? Must be something special."

"I'm sick of it," I said. "I'm sick of all the other kids talking about that Cal Bennett all the time. There's a new kid too and I was trying to tell him about you setting a record once and he won't believe me."

My father kept on looking at me and his eyebrows pulled down together. "Won't believe you, eh?"

"That's it," I said. "If I was to be wearing that belt and let him see it then he'd know all right."

"Expect he would," my father said and he leaned back further in his chair, feeling good the way he usually did with a good meal inside him, and he said in a sort of half-joking voice, "Expect he would even more if I was to get out there tomorrow and swing a rope in the free-style steer busting and show everyone around here a thing or two."

That was when my mother started laughing. She laughed so she near choked on the last bite she was chewing and my father and I stared at her.

"Gee-rusalem," my father said. "What's so blamed funny?"

My mother swallowed down the bite. "You are," she said. "Why it's eleven years since you did anything like that. You sitting there and getting to be middle-aged and getting thick around the middle and talking about going up against young fellows that are doing it all the time and could run circles around you nowadays."

"Oh, they could, could they?" my father said and his eyebrows were really together over his nose.

"That horse of yours too," my mother said and to her it was still just something to chuckle at. "He's the same. Getting old and fat and lazy. He couldn't even do it any more."

"He couldn't, eh?" my father said. "I'll have you know being young and full of sass ain't so all-fired important as you seem to think. It's brains and know-how that count too and that's what that horse's got and that's what I've got and like riding a bicycle it's something you don't ever forget."

He was mighty serious and my mother realized that and was serious too. "Well, anyway," she said, "you're not going to try it and that's final."

"Gee-rusalem," my father said and he thumped a fist on the table so hard the dishes jumped. "Just like a woman. Giving orders. Tie a man down so he has to keep his nose to a grindstone getting the things they want and start giving orders the moment he even thinks a bit about maybe showing he still can do something."

"Harvey Kendall," my mother said, "you listen to me. I saw you near break your neck too many times in those shows before we were married. That's why I made you stop. I don't intend to have anything happen to you."

They were glaring at each other across the table and after a while my father sighed and looked down and began pushing at his coffee cup with one finger the way he always did when they'd been having an argument. "Expect you're right," he said and he sighed again and his voice was soft. "It was just an idea. No sense us flaring at each other over a little idea." He turned to me. "Wear the belt," he said. "All day if you've a mind to. If your feet were big enough you could wear the boots too."

In the morning my father didn't go to work because that day was a local holiday so we had a late breakfast and he sat around quiet like he was thinking things over in his mind the way he'd been all the evening before after supper. Then he pulled on the calfskin boots, looking a bit different in them without the belt on up above, and he went out and saddled old Mark and rode into town to help with the preparations there. I couldn't go along because just before he left he told me to stick close to my mother and watch out for her, which was a backhand style of putting it because she would really be watching out for me and that was just his usual little scheme to tie me to her so I wouldn't be roaming around and getting into any devilment.

Soon as he was gone I got out the belt and put it on and it went around me almost twice but I could fix it so the buckle was in the middle in front as it should be and I stood on a chair to admire that part of myself in the little mirror my father used for shaving. I waited while my mother fussed with her good dress and the trimmings, doing the things women do to make themselves look what they call stylish, and then the two of us, my mother and me, walked the half mile into town and the day's activities.

We stopped at all the exhibits and saw who had won the prizes for jams and jellies and raising vegetables and the like and we spent some time looking over the small pens where the prize-winning stock animals were. I stood on one foot and then the other and chewed molasses candy till my jaws were tired while my mother talked to women and then more women and I didn't get a chance to roam around much and show off that belt because she was watching out for me just about every minute. Three or four times we bumped into my father busy circulating all over the place as the cattle judge and one of the local greeters of out-of-town folks and he'd stop and talk to us some and hurry away. He was enjoying himself the way he always did at these affairs, joshing with all the men and tipping his hat to the women, and he was developing a sort of glow from a drink or two with the other greeters.

He joined us for a quick lunch at the hotel. He was feeling good again and he joked me over being about half hidden inside that belt and as soon as we were through eating he hustled us out and to the temporary grandstand along one side of the main stockyard pen so

we all could have good seats for the rodeo goings. He picked a place in the third row where he always said you could see best and he sat in the middle with my mother on one side of him and me on the other and it wasn't till we had been there a little while and the two of them were talking hearty with other folks around that I had my chance to slip away by sliding through and under the grandstand and go find some of the other kids so I could strut and show off that belt. I went hunting them, proud and happy as I'd ever been, and I found them and in maybe five minutes I was running back under the grandstand as mad and near crying as I'd ever been too. I knew where to crawl up through my father's boots and I did and he felt me squirming through against his legs because the stand was filled now and he took hold of me and pulled me up on the seat beside him.

"Quiet now, boy," he said. "We wouldn't want your mother to know you've been slipping away like that." He swung his head to look at her on the other side and saw she was busy talking to a woman beyond and he swung back to me and saw my face. "Gee-rusalem, boy," he said. "What's eating at you?"

"Father," I said, "he doesn't believe it about you."

"Who doesn't believe it?" he said.

"That new kid," I said.

"Did you show him that belt?" my father said.

"Yes," I said. "But he just laughed. He said it's a fake. He said if it isn't you just found it somewhere or got it from some old pawnshop."

"Found it?" my father said. His eyebrows were starting to draw down together but the people all round were starting to buzz louder and things were beginning out in the big pen that was the arena for the day. "All right, boy," my father said. "We'll do something about that when this shindig's over. Maybe a good sideswipe'd do that kid some good. Be quiet now, the bronc riding's coming up." He didn't pay any more attention to me because he was busy paying attention to what was happening in the arena but not all his attention was out there because he kept fidgeting on the plank seat and every now and then he was muttering to himself and once he did it loud enough so I could hear. "Pawnshop," he said and kept on fidgeting around and didn't seem even to know he was doing that.

Plenty was happening out in the arena, the kind of things I always enjoyed and got excited about, but I wasn't in any mind to enjoy much that day and then sudden there was an extra flurry of activity and the main gates swung open and the people began to shout and cheer. A man came riding through the gateway on a beautiful big buckskin that was jouncing with each step like it had springs in its feet and you could tell right away the man was Cal Bennett. He was slim and tall and straight in the saddle and he was mighty young-looking and mighty capable-looking all at the same time. He had on boots just like my father's calfskins, maybe not exactly the same but so close to it there wasn't much difference, and a wide belt like the one I was wearing, and sitting there so easy on that jouncing saddle like he was glued to it he was about the best-looking figure of a man I ever saw. He had a coiled rope in his hand and he shook out a loop as he came forward and began spinning it and it grew bigger and bigger and sudden he flipped it up and over and it was spinning right around him and that buckskin and sudden he flipped it again and it was spinning big and wide in front of the horse and he gave a quick little wriggle with his heels and the horse jumped forward and he and that horse went right through the loop and it was spinning behind them and the people really went wild. They shouted and clapped and stomped their feet.

Cal Bennett let the loop fall slack on the ground and bowed all around and took off his big hat to the women and put it back on and coiled in his rope and rode over to the side of the arena where he'd wait for time to do his real roping stunts and still the people shouted and stomped. And my father sat there beside me and pulled up straight with his head high, looking around at the shouting people, and his face got tight and red and he shrank down till he was hunched low on the seat and he sat very still. He didn't fidget any more or mutter to himself. He just sat still, staring out at the arena and things happened out there, and then the announcer was shouting through his megaphone that the free-style steer busting for the local championship was next and sudden my father turned and grabbed me by the arm.

"Hey, boy," he said, "take off that belt."

I fumbled with it and got it off and handed it to him and he stood up right there on the grandstand and yanked off the ordinary belt he was wearing and began slipping that big belt through the special pants straps my mother had sewed for him. She saw him looming up there beside her and what he was doing and she was startled.

"Harvey Kendall," she said, "just what do you think you're going to do?"

"You keep out of this," my father said, and the way he said it would have made anybody shy away. He pulled the belt tight through the buckle and started down toward the arena, pushing through the people in the two rows ahead. He stepped to the ground and turned to look back at my mother. "Just keep your eyes on that arena," he said, "and you'll see something."

He squeezed through the fence rails into the arena and went straight to the little bunch of men who were acting as judges for the rodeo events. He was reaching in his money pocket as he went and he took out two dollar bills. "I'm in this one," he said to the men. "Here's my entry fee."

They all turned and stared at him. "Look-a-here, Harve," one of them said. "You want to show us how you used to do it, that's fine. That's wonderful. We'll be proud to have you. But don't you go trying to do it racing against a stopwatch."

"Shut up, Sam," my father said. "I know what I'm doing. You just take this money."

He pushed the bills into the man's hand and swung away, hurrying, and by the time the other entries were lined up he was back leading old Mark and with a good rope he'd borrowed somewheres in his hand. He took a place in the line and the judges put all the names on slips of paper in a hat and pulled them out one by one to get a running order and my father's name was one of the last. He stood there among those younger men and their young horses, quiet and waiting by old Mark, just running the rope through his hands to see it had no kinks and coiling it careful and exact, and all the while the excitement was building up in me, and my mother sat still and silent on the plank seat with her hands tight together in her lap.

One after another the others made their runs, flipping their steers and dashing in to hog-tie them, and they used a lot of different methods, some forefooting[3] the steers and some going straight for the heads and quick pull-arounds, some risking long throws to save time and some playing it safer and chasing till they were close in, and some of them were good and some maybe better than just good but you could tell easy enough none of them were in the real champion class, and then it was my father's turn. He led old Mark out and walked around by old Mark's head and reached up a hand to scratch around the ears and he whispered something to that old horse nobody could hear and he came back around and swung up to the saddle. Seeing him there, straight and sturdy in the saddle, I couldn't hold it in any longer. I jumped standing right up on the seat.

"Father!" I shouted. "Father! You show them! The whole bunch of them!"

My mother pulled me down quick but she was just as excited because her hands trembled and out there in the arena my father didn't pay any attention to anything around him. He sat quiet on old Mark, checking the rope again, and a hush spread over the whole place and off to the side Cal Bennett reined his big buckskin around so he could watch close and sudden my father let out a whoop. "Turn that critter loose!" he yelled and the bars on the chute were yanked away and a big rangy steer rushed out into the arena and as it crossed the starting line the timer slammed down with his hat and old Mark was leaping forward.

Not three jumps and there wasn't a person watching didn't know that old horse knew what he was doing and maybe he was a mite slower than the young cow ponies that'd been performing but he was right up there in the champion class with the know-how. The steer was tricky and started twisting right away and old Mark was after it like a hound on a hot scent, keeping just the right distance to the left of it and closing in steady. My father was riding high in the stirrups and a loop was forming under his right hand and while he was still a ways back the loop whipped forward fast like a snake striking and opened out over the steer's head and the steer twisted and the loop struck on one horn tip and fell over the other horn and pulled off.

"Gee-rusalem!" My father's voice roared out over that whole arena. "Stick with him, Mark!" And old Mark was hard on that steer's tail with every twist and turn and my father yanked in the rope and whipped out another loop and it settled smack over the horns and head and he pulled it tight and flipped the rope over to the steer's right side and old Mark swung left, head low and plowing into the sudden strain coming, and that steer spun like a cartwheel, somersaulting as it spun, and was down flat and old Mark pivoted to face the steer and keep the rope taut and my father tried to use that pivot-swing to lift him out of the saddle and his foot caught on the cantle[4] going over and he went sprawling on his face in the

---

[3] **forefooting,** roping an animal by the front feet.

[4] **cantle,** the hind part of a saddle which curves upward from the seat.

Cheyenne Rodeo

HARVEY KENDALL / 371

dust. He scrambled up and scrabbled in the dust for the pigging string and started down the taut rope trying to run too fast and stumbled and went down again. He came up this time puffing with his face dark red and ran on and just about threw himself on that steer. He grabbed at the legs and got the string around three of them and tied it quick and jumped to the steer's head and old Mark eased some on the rope and he loosened the loop and threw it off and straightened up. He didn't even turn to look at the timekeeper. He didn't turn around at all. He just looked down at the ground and walked slow toward old Mark. And while he was walking there, slow and heavy-footed, the one thing that could rule him out even if he'd made good time and was the worst thing that could happen happened. The steer had some breath back now and was struggling and the knot had been tied in such a hurry that it slipped and the steer got its feet free and pushed up hot and mad and started after my father. Maybe it was the shouts that warned him or maybe it was old Mark shying back and snorting but anyway he turned and saw and dodged quick and began to run and the steer was right after him and sudden a rope came fast and low to the ground and the loop in it whipped up and around the steer's hind legs and tightened and the steer hit the ground again with a thump and at the other end of that rope were Cal Bennett and his big buckskin.

The people went wild again and they had a right to because that was about as fast and tricky a job of roping as they'd ever seen anytime and it wasn't just a show-off stunt, it was serious business, but my father didn't pay any attention to the shouting or even to Cal Bennett. He just stopped running and looked around once and started walking toward old Mark, slow and heavy-footed with those calfskin boots all dusty. He reached and took hold of the reins and went right on walking and old Mark followed him and he remembered the rope dragging from the saddle horn and stopped and unfastened it and coiled it in and went on walking and old Mark followed and together they went to the outside gate and someone opened it enough for them to go through and he left the rope hanging on a gatepost and they went outside and along around the fence toward the road, the two of them alone together, my father walking like an old man and sweaty old Mark tagging with his head low.

I felt plain ashamed of being me, of being a boy with a father who'd made a fool of himself like he had, and I wanted to crawl away somewhere and hide but I couldn't do that because my mother was standing up and telling me to come along and starting down out of the grandstand right in front of all those people. She had her head high and she looked like she was just daring anyone to say anything to her. She marched along in front of the grandstand and around the side toward the road and I had to follow, trying not to look at anybody. She hurried a little and came alongside my father and he kept staring at the ground ahead of him and didn't seem to notice but all the same he knew she was there because he put out a hand and she took hold of it and they walked on along the road toward our house like that, neither of them saying a word.

It was sad-feeling and mournful

around our place the rest of that afternoon. My father was as silent as if he'd forgotten how to speak. After he took care of Mark he came in the house and pulled off those calfskin boots and tossed them in the hall closet with the other pair and put on his slippers and went out and sat on the back steps. My mother was just as silent. She hustled around in the kitchen and it looked like she was baking things but for once I wasn't interested in that. I didn't want to be anywhere close to my father so I took the front steps and I sat there whittling some and chewing on my knuckles and being miserable. I was mad at what he'd done to me, made me feel ashamed and fixed it so the other kids would have something to torment me about and so that new kid never would believe it about him. "He ain't so much," I said to myself. "He's just an old has-been, that's all he is."

Then we had supper and we were all just as silent as before and Mother had fixed the things my father liked best, which was kind of a waste because he only picked at the food and didn't seem to be tasting it. But he perked some and at last he looked up at her and grinned a sick little grin and looked down and began pushing at his coffee cup.

"I told you you'd see something in that arena," he said. "Well, you did."

"Yes," my mother said. "I did." She hesitated a moment and then she found something to say. "And I've been to a lot of those shows and I never saw a steer slapped down as hard and thorough as that one."

"That wasn't me," my father said. "That was Mark." He pushed up and turned away quick and went out again to the back steps.

It was only a while later and I was on the front steps again when I saw something that made me jump up and my heart start to pound and what I saw was a big buckskin coming along the road and turning in at our place and sitting easy in the saddle was Cal Bennett.

"Howdy, bub," he said. "Is your father handy?"

"He's around back," I said. He nudged the buckskin and started around the house and all at once it came rushing up in me and I had to shout it at him. "Don't you dare make fun of him! He was better'n you once! He made a record nobody's ever really beat!"

Cal Bennett reined in his horse and leaned over toward me and his eyes were clear and bright looking down at me. "I know that," he said. "I wasn't much bigger'n you are now when I saw him make it. That's what started me practicing." He straightened in the saddle and went on around the house. I stood still in the surprise of his words and then I had to follow him and when I went around the rear corner of the house there was my father sitting on the steps looking up and there was Cal Bennett on that big buckskin looking down and they were holding a silence there between them for what seemed a long while.

My father shifted a little on the steps. "Nice of you to come around," he said. His voice was taut and careful. "I forgot to thank you for pulling that steer off me this afternoon."

"Shucks," Cal Bennett said. "That wasn't much. You've done it yourself many a time. There ain't a man ever worked cows ain't done it often for another man out on the range."

They kept looking at each other and

the tightness that had been in my father's face all those last hours began to ease away and when he spoke again his voice was steady and friendly the way it usually was.

"I sort of messed it up out there today, didn't I."

"Yes," Cal Bennett said. "You did kind of hooraw it some." He chuckled and sudden my father chuckled too and then they both grinned like a pair of kids.

"From what I hear," my father said, "you're good. You're damn good."

"Yes," Cal Bennett said and his voice was easy and natural and he wasn't boasting at all. "Yes, I am. I'm as good as a man named Harvey Kendall was some years back. Maybe even a mite better."

"Expect you are," my father said. "Yes, I expect you are." He leaned backwards on his elbows on the steps. "But you didn't come here just to chew that kind of fat, pleasant as that can be as I used to know."

"No," Cal Bennett said. "I didn't. I've been figuring. This rodeo business is all right for a young fellow long as he's young but there ain't no future in it. It's getting to be more fancy show for the crowds and less real roping all the time anyway. I've been saving my money. With what I collected in town a while ago I've got the tally I was aiming at. Now I'm figuring to get me a nice little spread somewhere in this territory and put some good stock on it and try raising me some good beef."

"Keep talking," my father said. "There's a lot of sense in what you're saying."

"Well, now," Cal Bennett said. "I figured to ask you to help me some getting started."

My father straightened on the steps and he cocked his head to one side, looking up. "Tell me something, Bennett," he said. "There's a woman mixed up in this somewhere."

"Yes," Cal Bennett said. "There is."

"And she wants you to quit risking your fool young neck showing off with a rope in front of a lot of shouting people."

"Yes," Cal Bennett said. "She does."

"And she's right," my father said. "And now you tell me something else. Why did you come to me?"

"Simple," Cal Bennett said. "I been asking questions round about for some months. Found out a few things. Found out there's one name signed to a checklist on a cattle shipment that'll be accepted without question anywhere the rails run and that name's Harvey Kendall. Heard people say and for quite a ways around these parts that when you want good stock picked out and straight advice on how to handle them right you go find that same man. Heard them say that man never did another man dirt and never will. Heard them say—"

My father put up a hand to stop him. "Whoa, now," my father said. "No need to pile it on too thick. Of course I'll help you best I can. You knew that before you started all that palaver. Stop being so damn formal up there on that horse. Hop down and squat on these boards and tell me just what you have in mind."

And there the two of them were side by side on the steps talking quiet and friendly and the buckskin wandered off far enough to find a few grass tufts by our little pasture fence and whiffle some over the rails at old Mark and I was standing by the house corner with the strangest feeling in me. Somehow I didn't want to disturb them or even let them notice I was there and I stepped back soft and around the house again, wondering what was happening to me, and then I knew what I wanted to do. I went in through the front door and past my mother sitting quiet in the front room with our old photograph album in her lap and I went straight to the hall closet. I hardly even looked at those calfskin boots even though they were mighty dusty and could stand a cleaning. I took out the rough old cowskins and I got the saddle soap and a moist rag and I went over by the back door, where I could sit on a stool and hear them talking, and I really went to work on those old boots. I wanted to make that hard old leather comfortable as I could for his feet. I wanted to make those old boots shine.

THE END

Talking it over

1. The boy's feelings toward his father change several times during the story. Describe how the boy feels toward his dad at each of the following times:
   a. When the story opens
   b. After the roping event
   c. When Cal Bennett comes looking for Harvey Kendall
   d. At the end of the story

2. a. How does Mrs. Kendall react when her husband says that maybe he should enter the roping contest?

   b. How does she act after the contest?

   c. What do her actions tell you about her?

3. a. Give at least two reasons why Harvey Kendall enters the roping contest.

   b. How does he feel after the contest is over?

   c. What makes him feel different by the time the story ends?

   d. Explain the title of the story.

4. a. Describe each pair of boots. For what purpose is each worn?

   b. At the beginning of the story, what does each pair of boots mean to the boy? How does he show which pair he favors?

   c. At the end of the story, why does he go to work on the old boots?

Words in action

A compound word is made up of two or more shorter words. For each compound in bold type below, write the words from which it is made. Then write a definition of the compound. Be ready to discuss in class how the meaning of the compound is related to the meaning of its separate parts. You may use a dictionary if necessary.

1. Put on his regular **footwear**
2. Boots made of **cowhide**
3. An inspector at the **stockyard**
4. A free-roaming **cowhand**
5. Work for a range **outfit**
6. Bust and **hog-tie** a steer
7. A **top-notch** champion roper
8. His **knockabout** working boots
9. Give a **sideswipe** with his foot
10. A **hard-and-fast** rule

He was peeved at rodeos

"At the time I wrote 'Harvey Kendall,'" writes Jack Schaefer, "I was probably peeved at rodeos. Little or no connection for a long time now with any actual cowboying or ranch work. Stunts and show stuff. A man can be a bigwig rodeo star—and a pain-in-the-neck as a cowhand. So I wrote a story about a boy who learned that the important thing about his father was not that he once set a rodeo record but that he was a decent all-around human being and a competent workday cattle inspector. Just like the boy, I wanted to make his old boots shine. . . ."

Consequences: Views and viewpoints

In this unit, many characters make decisions or perform actions which lead to consequences over which they have no control. In some cases the consequences are deserved; in others, they are not. Six of these characters are listed below:

Durante	Spike
Douglas Johnson	Joey
Cotton Thaggard	Harvey Kendall

Discuss these characters, answering the following questions about each one:

1. What decisions does he make or what action does he take?
2. What are the consequences?
3. Does he deserve the consequences? Explain.

11

CSSD REVIEW

Read the following article quickly to get an overall picture of the events described. Do not stop to figure out the words in bold type at this time, even though some are unfamiliar.

THE TIME was 1:15 P.M.; the date was January 7, 1948; the place, the airport control tower at Godman Air Force Base on the **outskirts** of Louisville, Kentucky. A call had just come in from the Kentucky highway patrol. It seemed that several people in Marysville, a small town about eighty miles away, were worried about a strange **phenomenon** they had seen in the sky. The police considered **celestial** problems outside of their **jurisdiction** and therefore turned the matter over to the Air Force. But the men at Godman knew of no aircraft that had not been accounted for.

At 1:35 the highway patrol called again. The strange object in the sky had passed to the west of Louisville, and by this time a number of people had seen it. The spotters were able to report that the mysterious object was circular in shape, about 300 feet in diameter, and moving westward at a good clip.

Ten minutes later the men in the control tower saw the **unidentified** object on their radar screen, but no one would **hazard** a guess as to what it might be.

Adapted from a portion of "Celestial Crockery" in *Rumor, Fear and the Madness of Crowds* by J. P. Chaplin. Copyright © 1959 by J. P. Chaplin, published by Ballantine Books, Inc.

About 2:30 P.M. four planes belonging to the National Guard came within range of the control tower. The tower radioed Captain Thomas F. Mantell, Jr., the leader of the group, and asked him to look into the matter of the **unidentified** object. The captain took two of his **wingmen** (the third was low on gas) after the mysterious visitor. Since none of the pilots could see the object, the tower gave Mantell a bearing, and the planes began to climb in the direction the tower suggested.

By the time they reached an altitude of 10,000 feet, Mantell had taken such a lead on his **wingmen** that they could hardly see him. Shortly afterwards, Captain Mantell called the tower and reported that at last he could see his target. Later there was some **disagreement** as to just how he described the object, but according to the men in the tower he is supposed to have said the object was "**metallic,** and **tremendous** in size." A little later he added, "It's bright and climbing away from me."

By this time Mantell had climbed to 15,000 feet and was without oxygen. When asked for a further report, Mantell replied that he was going to 20,000 feet, and if he failed to close in on the object, he would give up the chase.

This was the last anyone heard from Mantell. Neither the tower nor his

wingmen could see him, and, after flying around for a while, the wingmen landed long enough to **refuel** and take on oxygen. They took off again to look for their leader but were unable to find any trace of him. At 3:53 P.M. the tower lost sight of the mysterious object, and a few minutes later word was received that Mantell had crashed and was dead. An **eyewitness** to the plane's final moments said the pilot acted as if he didn't know where he was going just before the plane went into a dive towards the ground. The plane seemed to explode halfway down.

Since this was one of the first reports of a **hypothetical** flying saucer, wild stories about what had happened soon began to **circulate.** Mantell's plane, according to various reports, was said to have been "**disintegrated**," "shot full of holes," and "**magnetized**" by its **encounter** with the "flying saucer."

The more reasonable explanation of the accident given out by the Air Force was that Mantell had unwisely climbed to a height at which he blacked out from lack of oxygen, and in the resulting dive his out-of-control plane had lost a wing. The Air Force **concluded** the report by suggesting that Mantell had been **pursuing** the planet Venus. This was the first death resulting from an attempted saucer **interception.**

Review the following chart, which describes the way you should apply the C S S D approach to words you do not recognize at first glance.

APPLY C S S D   ⟶   REVIEW YOUR FINDINGS

---

1. CONTEXT

Think of possible meanings of the word which make sense in the passage.

If you have heard this word before, you may recognize it when you begin to think about meaning clues you discover in the context. Even if you don't recognize it, there may be enough information in the context to allow a good guess as to what it means.

---

2. STRUCTURE

Look to see whether the word is a compound (like ear/muff) or made up of a familiar root word plus a prefix or a suffix, or both (like im/pass/able).

Do you recognize any part of the word? Does this part suggest a meaning for the word? Does this meaning make sense in the passage where it is used?

---

3. SOUND

Look to see if the arrangement of vowels and consonants in the word suggests how it is pronounced. Try accenting first one syllable, then another.

In trying different pronunciations, do you produce a word that sounds familiar? If so, is that familiar-sounding word one whose meaning you know? Does this meaning make sense in the passage?

4. DICTIONARY

If you are still not sure of the meaning or pronunciation of the word, look it up in a dictionary. Practice saying the dictionary pronunciation. Read all the definitions and choose the one that fits in the context.

Check to see whether the definition you chose is right by rewording the sentence using the definition instead of the original word.

Did you come close to the right meaning when you guessed from context or structure clues? Did spelling clues suggest the right pronunciation, or one close to it?

Divide your paper into three columns. In the first column, copy the following list of words. Then reread the article. Apply C S S D to the words in bold type. Then, in the second column, write a definition beside each word. In the third column, indicate which method or methods (context, structure, sound, or dictionary) you used to find the meaning and pronunciation of the word. If you already knew the word and recognized it without using C S S D, put an X in the third column.

1. outskirts
2. phenomenon
3. celestial
4. jurisdiction
5. unidentified
6. hazard
7. wingmen
8. disagreement
9. metallic
10. tremendous
11. refuel
12. eyewitness
13. hypothetical
14. circulate
15. disintegrated
16. magnetized
17. encounter
18. concluded
19. pursuing
20. interception

12

Inventory

LESSON ONE: Remembering what you read

Suppose you want a part-time job this summer. This ad catches your eye:

PART-TIME SUMMER EMPLOYMENT

Part-time summer job available for a teen-ager who doesn't mind getting his hands dirty. Owner of large home needs a responsible boy or girl to help caretaker. Duties will include mowing grass, trimming bushes, and weeding flower beds.
Hours: 8 to 12 Mon., Wed., & Fri.
Salary: $1.65 per hour.
Call Mrs. Simpson at 241-2121 to make an appointment for an interview.

Before calling for an appointment you should know if you are qualified for the job and if it is the kind you want. Without rereading the ad, answer the following questions to see if you read carefully enough. Would you apply for the job if—

1. You want to work in a restaurant only?
2. You want to make at least $1.50 an hour?
3. Your parents will let you work no more than three days a week?
4. You are allergic to flowers?
5. You are thirteen years old?

If you answered all five questions correctly, you are already using some good method for remembering and understanding what you read. For example, in order to answer question 1 correctly, you had to grasp the general idea of the advertisement —that it is an ad for a caretaker's assistant. And to answer question 2, you had to remember an important detail—the salary. These are the first two steps in **taking inventory,** a way of reading you will practice in the lessons that follow.

LESSON TWO: What taking inventory means

The expression "taking inventory" usually applies to business. You have probably noticed signs in store windows saying "This store closed for inventory August 15." Instead of doing their regular sales work that day, employees will take stock, or count each piece of merchandise, so that the owner will know exactly how many of each item he has.

You sometimes need to take stock when you read, too. The kind of reading called **taking inventory** is done when you want to be sure you understand and remember what you have read. Here are the four steps usually included when you take inventory:

1. Read enough of the material to find out what it is about in a general way. If it is very short, you might skim all of it. If it is longer, use the survey technique described in the section on Purpose (pages 132-135).

2. Once you have an idea of what the selection is about, go back and read it carefully. Stop often to fix important details in your memory. Also try to figure out the meaning of difficult words or sentences.

3. When you have read a paragraph or two, stop and think back over what you have read. Then try to predict or guess what the author will say next. (The predicting part may be unnecessary if the selection is short.)

4. Summarize the entire selection by telling briefly in your own words what it says.

As you go through this unit you will realize that taking inventory is work. You won't use this complete process, of course, when your only purpose is to get a general idea of what is on the page, or when you are looking for a particular bit of information. However, taking inventory is useful when you want to remember fully what you have read.

LESSON THREE: Taking inventory of a short article

As an assignment in social studies, you are asked to select the news story you find most interesting during the week and write a brief report on it. As you scan the newspaper that evening, you notice an article that might prove interesting. You therefore stop and do the first step in taking inventory.

STEP I—Read enough of the selection to get a general idea of what it is about.

Read the title and the two opening paragraphs below.

Hot Line for Help

"ARE YOU a teen with a hang-up? Call 666-1015. We're here to listen 6 P.M. to 12 P.M. daily, 6 P.M. to 4 A.M. Friday and Saturday."

This message, printed on 2500 small blue cards and passed out among students at four Los Angeles high schools recently, was the initial announcement of Hot Line, the name of a listening project which aids teen-agers with personal problems.

What is the general subject of this article?

After surveying several other articles in the paper, you decide that none is as interesting as the one about Hot Line. You choose to report on it.

STEP II—Read the selection carefully.

Your next step is to read the entire article, but this time your purpose is different. Now you want to understand the article fully and to remember as many important facts as you can so that your report will be accurate as well as interesting.

This step will require a much slower rate of reading. Stop frequently to work out the meanings of difficult words or sentences and to note important details.

Which details *are* the important ones? Deciding this can be difficult, since there is no set rule to follow. However, the most important information in a news article can usually be found by asking these simple questions:

WHO or WHAT did WHAT?
WHEN?
WHERE?
WHY?
HOW?

Not all these questions will apply to everything you read, but they are useful as a start. To the answers, add any other details that you feel are important.

Let's see how this step works. As you read the complete article about Hot Line, stop whenever you see this sign □ and answer the question in the margin which has the same number or letter that is shown in the square. The questions in the right-hand margin refer to the most important points in the article. The question in the left-hand margin refer to other details that are worth noting.

Hot Line for Help

DETAILS

A. At what hours can one call?

B. What does "initial" mean here?

"ARE YOU a teen with a hang-up? Call 666-1015. ☐ We're here to listen 6 P.M. to 12 P.M. daily, 6 P.M. to 4 A.M. Friday and Saturday." Ⓐ

This message, printed on 2500 small blue cards and passed out among students at four Los Angeles ② high schools recently, was the initial announcement of Hot Line Ⓑ, the name of a listening project designed to aid teen-agers with personal problems. ③

When teens have problems, they can call Hot Line and talk with a listener who is interested in helping them. ④ Hot Line was set up because the adolescent unit of Children's Hospital in Los Angeles thought many teen-agers needed someone to listen to their troubles. ⑤

In emergencies, such as a suicide threat, professional help is immediately

MAIN POINTS

1. HOW does one get in touch with Hot Line?

2. WHERE is Hot Line?

3. WHAT is Hot Line?

4. HOW does Hot Line work?

5. WHO set it up? WHY was it set up?

Based on an article in the *National Observer* for May 12, 1968.

C. What kind of people are available to help?

D. What kind of problems do teen-agers want to talk about?

E. Who else may call?

F. What do callers especially like about Hot Line?

G. When did Hot Line begin?

available. ⑥ Doctors, ministers, lawyers, and other specialists are standing by. ⓒ Most of the time, however, the callers have less serious problems. Sometimes a teen-ager just needs someone to confide in. Frequently, teen-agers call to talk about difficulties with parents and boy-girl relationships. ⓓ Even parents sometimes call when they know their teen-ager has a problem. ⓔ

One appealing feature of Hot Line is that callers do not get a lecture when they telephone. The listeners offer opinions only when asked. ⓕ

Since the project started three weeks ago ⓖ, the number of calls has almost tripled. Teen-agers apparently need Hot Line and want it to stay in Los Angeles. ⑦

6. WHEN is professional help called in?

7. HOW successful has Hot Line been?

STEP III—Predict what the author will say next.

With a short selection like the Hot Line article you often will not need to use the third step in taking inventory. How to predict what the author will say next will therefore be discussed separately, in Lesson Four.

STEP IV—Summarize the selection.

The last step in taking inventory is summarizing or briefly stating the main points of the selection. Here is such a summary of the Hot Line article:

> In Los Angeles, the adolescent unit of Children's Hospital has set up a telephone service called Hot Line to help teen-agers with problems. A troubled teen-ager can call Hot Line any evening from 6 P.M. to midnight and on weekends to 4 A.M. and talk to a person interested in listening and willing to offer advice if asked. If teen-agers have serious problems they can get professional help. But most calls are about less serious problems concerning parents or the opposite sex. Three times as many teen-agers now call Hot Line as when it began.

Your own summary would probably be different. But it should contain the information that tells WHO, WHAT, WHEN, WHERE, WHY, and HOW, plus any other information that you want to remember.

LESSON FOUR: Predicting what will come next

You probably were able to take inventory on the Hot Line article fairly quickly. It isn't long, and the questions in the margins helped you focus on important points.

However, when you are dealing with a longer selection which you want to understand and remember in detail—for example, an assignment in your science book—a timesaver can be helpful. The third step in taking inventory—predicting what the author will say next—is such a timesaver. If you think ahead to what will probably come next, you will be better able to recognize which facts or ideas are important for you to remember, and which ones are just interesting details. Then you will need to spend less time reading.

As you are reading carefully, stop occasionally to review what you have just read. Then try to figure out what the author will say next. To be accurate in predicting, you will need to recognize clues that will help you follow the author's train of thought. No one, of course, is expected to predict accurately all the time. But even if your predictions are wrong, you will be more alert to what the writer *does* say.

As you read the following examples, look for key words or sentences that help you determine what the next part probably will be about.

(A) If ski boots fit properly and receive good care, they can be worn for years. Ski shops are responsible for making sure the boots fit well, but it is the skier's job to keep his footgear in working condition. Here's how.

1. What will the next material probably be about?
   a. How to buy a good ski boot
   b. How to take care of ski boots
   c. How the condition of ski boots affects a skier's performance

(B) In the last ten years, the popularity of the guitar has grown very rapidly, with over ten million instruments in American homes. Where did it all begin? To answer this question we must go back in time.

2. In the next paragraph the author will
   a. discuss whether or not the guitar will continue to be popular.
   b. discuss the history of the guitar.

(C) Hockey is one sport in which nice guys really do finish last—and for six out of the past seven years, last place in the National Hockey League has belonged to the Boston Bruins, a team that couldn't have thrown a scare into Goldilocks. This season, however, the Bruins have turned into a tough team to beat.[1]

3. In the next paragraph the writer will explain
   a. why the Bruins lost last year.
   b. why the Bruins are winning this year.

In paragraphs A, B, and C, key sentences prepare you for what you will read next; for example, "Here's how" [to keep footgear in working condition]. The writer knows that if he helps you follow his thinking by announcing (or at least hinting at) what will come next, there is a better chance you will understand and remember what he has to say.

(D) Leaving their car parked at the side of the road, the two men plunged into the thick brush of southern New Jersey's pine barrens. Falling mist failed to dampen their holiday spirit. They expected to return in two hours with holly to decorate their homes for Christmas.

When the snow started to fall, neither became excited. They weren't more than a few miles from their car—and they knew the country well and had a good sense of direction. Worry didn't set in until the mild snowstorm turned into a raging blizzard.[2]

4. What will the next part of this selection be about?

In D, there are no key sentences or words to guide your thinking. However, you could probably predict correctly just by making inferences based on what you know from your own experience or from common sense. As the storm worsens and the men begin to worry, you naturally expect they may get lost in the storm or meet some other kind of danger.

Now that you have worked through four examples, predicting probably doesn't seem too difficult. Remember to look for key sentences like the ones in the first three examples, and for information from which you can make inferences.

---

[1]Abridgement of "Big, Bad Bruins" from *Time* (January 5, 1968). Reprinted by permission of Time, Inc.

[2]Abridged from "Make Your Own Survival Kit" by Jack Jeffers from *Boys' Life* (March 1968). Reprinted by permission of the author and *Boys' Life,* published by the Boy Scouts of America.

LESSON FIVE: Taking inventory of a longer article

Part A

On pages 389-392 is a longer article on which you are to practice taking inventory. To get a general idea of what it is about, look at the illustration and title and read the first paragraph, given below.

Marques Haynes—King of the Court Clowns

by Frank Litsky

IT WAS a night much like all other nights for a touring comedy basketball team. The place was South Plainfield, New Jersey, but it could have been Gallup, New Mexico; Dubuque, Iowa; Midland, Texas, or anywhere else.

QUESTION: What will this article be about?

Now you are ready to read the article as a whole. Start again and read carefully, stopping frequently to figure out unfamiliar expressions and to check yourself on important details. Places where you should stop are marked with this sign: □ The number or letter in the square refers to the question in the margin which you might ask yourself at this point.

Marques Haynes—King of the Court Clowns

by Frank Litsky

DETAILS

A. Where does this team perform?

B. Who is Woods? Will the article be mainly about Woods?

C. What does "baiting the referee" mean?

D. What does "courtesy of" mean here?

E. What is "sleight-of-hand passing"?

MAIN POINTS

1. WHAT kind of team is it?

2. WHAT were some of the tricks performed?

IT WAS a night much like all other nights for a touring comedy basketball team. ① The place was South Plainfield, New Jersey, but it could have been Gallup, New Mexico; Dubuque, Iowa; Midland, Texas, or anywhere else. Ⓐ

The comic, a six-foot-six former football player named Bob (Trick) Woods Ⓑ , was baiting the referee Ⓒ , kidding his opponents and the customers, and shooting a behind-the-back flip shot from mid-court (he made it), a mid-court shot while lying on his back (he made it), and a shot from the top row of the stands (yes, he made it). Someone sneaked into the game a ball that flew ten feet through the air and then returned (courtesy of a heavy rubber band) Ⓓ . When the referee threw out that ball, it was replaced by a ball that bounced as crazily as a Mexican jumping bean. ②

The capacity crowd stopped laughing only long enough to *oooh* and *aaah* at the sleight-of-hand passing Ⓔ . But its appetite wasn't satisfied yet. "Dribble," a boy pleaded from the stands.

Adapted from "Marques Haynes—King of the Court Clowns" by Frank Litsky from *Boys' Life* (February 1968). Reprinted by permission of the author and *Boys' Life*, published by the Boy Scouts of America.

"Yeah, dribble," another shouted. ③

A fragile man ⒡ —six feet tall and barely 160 pounds—heard the call. His basketball shirt, at least two sizes too large, hung from his shoulders, but the team name was easy to read. It said MAGICIANS ④ , and the man was the No. 1 magician of the Magicians⑤ .

He started to dribble. The player guarding him darted for the ball, and presto! the ball and dribbler were gone, both working their magic on another victim across the court. In and out of the pack he moved, dribbling high and low, quickly and slowly, on his knees and sitting. In 22 seconds he dribbled 57 times before driving in and sinking a lay-up.[1] ⒢ ⑥

The crowd screamed and applauded and stamped their feet. Strangers looked at each other, shook their heads, and smiled. They had heard about Marques Oreole Haynes and his dribbling and hadn't believed it. ⑦ Now they had seen it for themselves and they still didn't believe it.

---

[1]**sinking a lay-up,** making a jumping one-hand shot off the backboard from close under the basket.

G. What does "sinking a lay-up" mean?

3. WHAT does the audience want?

4. WHO (what team) is performing?

5. WHO is the "fragile man"?

6. WHAT is so unusual about the player's performance?

7. WHO is the dribbler?

Part B

You have read approximately the first 15 per cent of the article that appeared in *Boys' Life* magazine. Can you predict what will follow?

Checking for key phrases or sentences will lead to a dead end this time. The selection doesn't contain any obvious clues.

However, two clues used in surveying may be helpful—the title and the illustration. The title tells you that the selection will be about Marques Haynes. The picture shows Haynes dribbling. Do these facts give you a clue as to what will probably follow? What would you expect to learn about Haynes?

Continue reading carefully to see if your predictions were correct. Stop frequently to concentrate on important details or to work out the meanings of unfamiliar words. This time no questions will be written in the margin, but some good stopping points are indicated by squares.

When you come to a square, pause to think back over what you have just read. What questions does that part seem to answer? Does it deal with main points or with details? (This time you will have to decide for yourself what is important to remember.) Pause now and then and try to guess what will come next.

Sometimes a square means that you should make sure you understand the meaning of an unusual word or phrase.

1 Marques Oreole Haynes, the world's greatest dribbler, wasn't especially impressed with his performance. "I could have done more against a more experienced team," he said. "If your opponent is aggressive and good, it makes a better show because they fight you for the ball. This was a high-school alumni team, and these boys just weren't in shape." □

2 Against sturdy competition, Marques estimates that, at a rate of three dribbles per second, he could dribble 5400 times in a half hour □ —"If I have the strength to keep it up for a half hour."

3 Marques Haynes is always in shape. He is the founder, president, chief booking agent, road secretary, publicist □, typist, bookkeeper, coach, and star attraction of the Fabulous Magicians. □ From early October to the first week in May, he plays basketball almost seven nights a week (and Sunday afternoons, too) in majestic settings such as New York's Madison Square Garden and the Los Angeles Sports Arena and in high-school gyms and armories and YMCA's and college field houses and almost every other imaginable home of a basketball court. □

4 His record is filled with superlatives. □ In 22 years as a pro—seven with the Harlem Globetrotters and fifteen with the Fabulous Magicians □ —he has played over 4500 games, more than any other player in history. □ His Magicians started the season with a record of more than 3000 victories and nine defeats □, playing against any teams the local promoters chose. His basketball travels have covered 2,100,000 miles □, the equivalent of four round trips to the moon plus seven round-the-world cruises plus five jaunts from New York to Miami and back. He has dribbled more than 850,000 times in his show-stopping routines. □ His act has been seen by 5,000,000 to 6,000,000 people in person □ and by millions of others on television □.

5 Marques Haynes' performance may seem magical, but he had to work hard to develop his talent. □

6 His first exposure to basketball came in his home town of Sand Springs, Oklahoma, when he was six or seven years old. □ His sister was star on the high-school girls' team, and she took Marques to practice every day. While she played, Marques would stand on the sidelines, bouncing a ball. □

7 He was one of eleven neighborhood boys who played all sports together,

and when sides were chosen for basket-ball, he was usually the 11th man. So it was off to the sidelines again, and again he dribbled to amuse himself. When someone got hurt or was called home, Marques played. Even then, instead of shooting, he dribbled. □

8 That was the beginning of his play-ing. By the 11th grade he made the high-school varsity. □ By his senior year he had been chosen for the second-team all-American. □

9 After graduating from high school, Haynes entered college on a half schol-arship. One day after football practice (he played quarterback), the coach allowed his boys to fool around with a basketball. Haynes tried some of his trick dribbling, and thought it strange that no one could get the ball away from him. The more they tried the more he dribbled. The seed had been planted. □ It would grow and lead him to fame first with the Harlem Globetrotters and later with his own team, the Magi-cians. □

Without looking back, answer the following questions to see if you read carefully enough.

1. Marques Haynes is famous as
    a. the basketball player who has traveled farthest on his tours.
    b. the world's greatest dribbler.
    c. the first Negro to break into professional basketball.

2. Why does Haynes prefer to play against good, aggressive players?

3. How many times per second can he bounce the ball?

4. Why did he become such an expert at dribbling?

5. What does the word *seed* refer to in the following sentences? "The seed had been planted. It would grow and lead him to fame." (paragraph 9)
    a. The idea of specializing in dribbling
    b. The desire to have his own basketball team
    c. The idea of making a lot of money

6. Indicate whether each statement below is true or false. Which two statements express the most important ideas?
    a. Marques Haynes was the first man to dribble a million times.
    b. A great many people in a great many places have seen Marques Haynes play basketball.
    c. He decided early in life to become a famous dribbler.
    d. He serves the Magicians in many ways besides being their most famous player.

 e. He developed his talent for dribbling through a great deal of practice, beginning in early childhood.

 f. His sister taught him to play basketball.

 g. He was a successful high-school basketball player.

Part C

Practice the last step of taking inventory by writing a brief summary of the article about Marques Haynes. Your summary should include information about WHO, WHAT, WHERE, WHY, and HOW.

What you should know about taking inventory

When your purpose for reading is complete understanding and recall, you should take inventory. Four steps are involved:

1. Read enough of the selection to get a general idea of what it is about.
2. Read the entire selection slowly and carefully. Stop frequently to fix important details in your memory and to make sure you understand difficult words and sentences.
3. Stop occasionally to review what you have read. Then try to predict what will come next. Look for hints the author gives, and use common sense.
4. Summarize the entire selection by giving briefly its main points.

13

Food, water, shelter . . .

Love, freedom, the feeling

that you belong . . .

Things you cannot do without

are NECESSITIES.

HA'PENNY [1]

If he had had a mother like that, he would not have stolen at all.

by Alan Paton

O F THE six hundred boys at the reformatory, about one hundred were from ten to fourteen years of age. My Department had from time to time expressed the intention of taking them away, and of establishing a special institution for them, more like an industrial school than a reformatory. This would have been a good thing, for their offences were very trivial, and they would have been better by themselves. Had such a school been established, I should have liked to have been Principal of it myself, for it would have been an easier job; small boys turn instinctively towards affection, and one controls them by it, naturally and easily.

Some of them, if I came near them, either on parade or in school or at football, would observe me watchfully, not directly or fully, but obliquely and secretly; sometimes I would surprise them at it, and make some small sign of recognition, which would satisfy them so that they would cease to observe me, and would give their full attention to the event of the moment. But I knew that my authority was thus confirmed and strengthened.

These secret relations with them were a source of continuous pleasure to me. Had they been my own children I would no doubt have given a greater expression to it. But often I would move through the silent and orderly parade, and stand by one of them. He would look straight in front of him with a little frown of concentration that expressed both childish awareness of and manly indifference to my nearness. Sometimes I would tweak his ear, and he would give me a brief smile of acknowledgment, or frown with still greater concentration. It was natural, I suppose, to confine these outward expressions to the very smallest, but they were taken as symbolic, and some older boys would observe them and take themselves to be included. It was a relief when the reformatory was passing through times

Reprinted with the permission of Charles Scribner's Sons and Jonathan Cape, Limited, from *Tales from a Troubled Land* (British title, *Debbie Go Home*) by Alan Paton. Copyright © 1961 Alan Paton.

[1]**Ha'penny** (hā́ pə nē), contraction of *halfpenny* (pronounced the same), a coin of half the value of a penny.

of turbulence and trouble, and when there was danger of estrangement between authority and boys, to make these simple and natural gestures, which were reassurances both to me and them that nothing important had changed.

On Sunday afternoons when I was on duty, I would take my car to the reformatory and watch the free boys being signed out at the gate. This simple operation was also watched by many boys not free, who would tell each other "in so many weeks I'll be signed out myself." Amongst the watchers were always some of the small boys, and these I would take by turns in the car. We would go out to the Potchefstroom[2] Road with its ceaseless stream of traffic, and to the Baragwanath[2] crossroads, and come back by the Van Wyksrus[2] road to the reformatory. I would talk to them about their families, their parents, their sisters and brothers, and I would pretend to know nothing of Durban, Port Elizabeth, Potchefstroom, and Clocolan,[3] and ask them if these places were bigger than Johannesburg.[4]

One of the small boys was Ha'penny, and he was about twelve years old. He came from Bloemfontein[5] and was the biggest talker of them all. His mother worked in a white person's house, and he had two brothers and two sisters. His brothers were Richard and Dickie and his sisters Anna and Mina.

"Richard and Dickie?" I asked.

"Yes, *meneer*.[6]"

"In English," I said, "Richard and Dickie are the same name."

When we returned to the reformatory, I sent for Ha'penny's papers; there it was plainly set down, Ha'penny was a waif, with no relatives at all. He had been taken in from one home to another, but he was naughty and uncontrollable, and eventually had taken to pilfering at the market.

I then sent for the Letter Book, and found that Ha'penny wrote regularly, or rather that others wrote for him till he could write himself, to Mrs. Betty Maarman, of 48 Vlak[7] Street, Bloemfontein. But Mrs. Maarman had never once replied to him. When questioned, he had said, perhaps she is sick. I sat down and wrote at once to the Social Welfare Officer at Bloemfontein, asking him to investigate.

The next time I had Ha'penny out in the car, I questioned him again about his family. And he told me the same as before, his mother, Richard and Dickie, Anna and Mina. But he softened the "D" of "Dickie," so that it sounded now like Tickie.

"I thought you said Dickie," I said.

"I said Tickie," he said.

He watched me with concealed apprehension, and I came to the conclusion that this waif of Bloemfontein was a clever boy, who had told me a story that was all imagination, and had changed one single letter of it to make it safe from any question. And I thought I understood it all, too, that he was ashamed of being without a family, and had invented them all, so that no one might discover that he was fatherless

---

[2]**Potchefstroom** (pôch/ əf strüm) **Road . . . Baragwanath** (bar ə gwä/ nəth) **crossroads . . . Van Wyksrus** (fon väks/ rús) **road,** roads in and around the city of Johannesburg.
[3]**Durban** (dèr/ bən), **Port Elizabeth, Potchefstroom, and Clocolan** (klō kō/ lən), cities in the Union of South Africa.
[4]**Johannesburg** (jō han/ əs bèrg), the largest city in the Union of South Africa.
[5]**Bloemfontein** (blüm fôn/ tān), a city in the Union of South Africa.

---

[6]**meneer** (mə nir/), the South African equivalent of *sir.*
[7]**Vlak** (flok) **Street.**

and motherless, and that no one in the world cared whether he was alive or dead. This gave me a strong feeling for him, and I went out of my way to manifest towards him that fatherly care that the State, though not in those words, had enjoined upon me by giving me this job.

Then the letter came from the Social Welfare Officer in Bloemfontein, saying that Mrs. Betty Maarman of 48 Vlak Street was a real person, and that she had four children, Richard and Dickie, Anna and Mina, but that Ha'penny was no child of hers, and she knew him only as a derelict of the streets. She had never answered his letters, because he wrote to her as *mother*, and she was no mother of his, nor did she wish to play any such role. She was a decent woman, a faithful member of the church, and she had no thought of corrupting her family by letting them have anything to do with such a child.

But Ha'penny seemed to me anything but the usual delinquent, his desire to have a family was so strong, and his reformatory record was so blameless, and his anxiety to please and obey so great, that I began to feel a great duty towards him. Therefore I asked him about his "mother."

He could not speak enough of her, nor with too high praise. She was loving, honest, and strict. Her home was clean. She had affection for all her children. It was clear that the homeless child, even as he had attached himself to me, would have attached himself to her; he had observed her even as he had observed me, but did not know the secret of how to open her heart, so that she would take him in, and save him from the lonely life that he led.

"Why did you steal when you had such a mother?" I asked.

He could not answer that; not all his brains nor his courage could find an answer to such a question, for he knew that with such a mother he would not have stolen at all.

"The boy's name is Dickie," I said, "not Tickie."

And then he knew the deception was revealed. Another boy might have said, "I told you it was Dickie," but he was too intelligent for that; he knew that if I had established that the boy's name was *Dickie*, I must have established other things too. I was shocked by the immediate and visible effect of my action. His whole brave assurance died within him, and he stood there exposed, not as a liar, but as a homeless child who had surrounded himself with mother, brothers, and sisters who did not exist. I had shattered the very foundations of his pride, and his sense of human significance.

He fell sick at once, and the doctor said it was tuberculosis. I wrote at once to Mrs. Maarman, telling her the whole story, of how this small boy had observed her, and had decided that she was the person he desired for his mother. But she wrote back saying that she could take no responsibility for him. For one thing, Ha'penny was a Mosuto,[8] and she was a colored[9] woman; for another, she had never had a child in trouble, and how could she take such a boy?

Tuberculosis is a strange thing; sometimes it manifests itself suddenly

---

[8] **Mosuto** (mô sü′ tü), a member of an African tribe.
[9] **colored**, a person of mixed white and native African ancestry. The government of the Union of South Africa has strict laws regulating race relations. Colored people are considered a different race from whites and natives.

in the most unlikely host, and swiftly sweeps to the end. Ha'penny withdrew himself from the world, from all Principals and mothers, and the doctor said there was little hope. In desperation I sent money for Mrs. Maarman to come.

She was a decent homely woman, and seeing that the situation was serious, she, without fuss or embarrassment, adopted Ha'penny for her own. The whole reformatory accepted her as his mother. She sat the whole day with him, and talked to him of Richard and Dickie, Anna and Mina, and how they were all waiting for him to come home. She poured out her affection on him, and had no fear of his sickness, nor did she allow it to prevent her from satisfying his hunger to be owned. She talked to him of what they would do when he came back, and how he would go to the school, and what they would buy for Guy Fawkes[10] night.

He in his turn gave his whole attention to her, and when I visited him he was grateful, but I had passed out of his world. I felt judged in that I had sensed only the existence and not the measure of his desire. I wished I had

[10] **Guy Fawkes** (gī fôks) **night,** a holiday. Guy Fawkes was one of several men who, in 1605, planned to blow up the British Houses of Parliament and kill the king. The plot was discovered on November 5, and this day is still celebrated with bonfires and festivities in Great Britain and other countries of the British Commonwealth.

done something sooner, more wise, more prodigal.

We buried him on the reformatory farm, and Mrs. Maarman said to me, "When you put up the cross, put he was my son.

"I'm ashamed," she said, "that I wouldn't take him."

"The sickness," I said, "the sickness would have come."

"No," she said, shaking her head with certainty. "It wouldn't have come. And if it had come at home, it would have been different."

She left for Bloemfontein, after her strange visit to a reformatory. And I was left, too, with the resolve to be more prodigal in the task that the State, though not in so many words, had enjoined on me.   THE END

⟳ Talking it over

1. *a.* Why does Ha'penny tell the story he does about his family?

b. Why does Ha'penny choose Mrs. Maarman to be his mother?

2. *a.* Mrs. Maarman refuses to answer Ha'penny's letters, and when he first falls sick she refuses to come to the reformatory. Why does she act this way?

b. Why does she come to the reformatory later on?

3. Reread the last five paragraphs, beginning with "We buried him. . . ."

a. What does Mrs. Maarman think caused Ha'penny's death?

b. What does the narrator *say* to her about why Ha'penny died?

c. What does the narrator really think caused the boy's death?

d. Put the last sentence of the story into words of your own.

4. Ha'penny died either because of tuberculosis or because something was taken from him that he could not live without. Or perhaps both these things were responsible.

a. What was taken from him?

b. How do you explain the fact that Ha'penny died even after Mrs. Maarman "adopted" him?

5. What is the central idea of this story?

⇄ Words in action

home ly (hōm'lē), 1. *U.S.* not good-looking; ugly; plain. 2. suited to home life; simple; everyday: *homely pleasures, homely food.* **3.** of plain manners; unpretending: *a simple, homely man. adj.,* **home li er, home li est.** —**home'li ness,** *n.*

Notice that the definition of *homely* that Americans usually think of, definition 1, is marked *U.S.* The meaning "not good-looking; ugly; plain" is commonly used only in the United States. English-speaking people from other countries probably mean definition 2 or 3 when they use the word *homely.*

Considering that "Ha'penny" takes place in the Union of South Africa, what does the narrator probably mean when he describes Mrs. Maarman as "a decent homely woman"?

I

On page 401, find the dictionary entry for each boldface word in the following sentences. Then answer these questions about each one:

A. By whom is the word commonly used?

B. What word would you use instead?

1. Before criticizing the police officer for using his **truncheon,** consider what you would have done in his place.

2. Carmedy's angry speeches are always accompanied by violent gestures. On this occasion he tore off his tie, coat, and **waistcoat** before he was finished.

3. When Jimmy told the tourist his car was now repaired and ready to go, the man replied, "**Jolly** good."

II

C. Why might people outside the United States be puzzled by the boldface words in sentences 4–6?

D. What more common word or words could be used instead?

4. The Air Force **brass** use computers to sort the different kinds of mail they receive concerning "flying saucers."

5. Miller was so **prissy** it was hard to believe his confession that he had robbed a bank.

6. As she **sashayed** to the witness stand, Kitty batted her false eyelashes at the foreman of the jury.

brass (bras), **1.** a yellow metal that is an alloy of two parts copper and one part zinc. **2.** thing made of brass, such as ornaments, dishes, etc. **3.** made of brass. **4.** *Informal.* money. **5.** *Informal.* shamelessness; impudence. **6.** *U.S. Slang.* high-ranking military officers. 1,2,4-6 *n.*, 3 *adj.*
brasses, musical wind instruments made of brass. The trumpet, trombone, and French horn are brasses.
jol ly (jol′ē), **1.** full of fun; merry. **2.** *Esp. Brit. Informal.* pleasant; agreeable; delightful. **3.** *Esp. Brit. Informal.* extremely; very. **4.** *Informal.* flatter (a person) to make him feel good or agreeable. 1,2 *adj.*, jol li er, jol li est; 3 *adv.*, 4 *v.*, jol lied, jol ly ing. —jol′li ly, *adv.* —jol′li ness, *n.*
pris sy (pris′ē), *U.S. Informal.* **1.** too precise and fussy. **2.** too easily shocked; overnice. *adj.*, pris si er, pris si est.
sa shay (sa shā′), *U.S. Informal.* glide, move, or go about. *v.*
trun cheon (trun′chən), **1.** *Esp. Brit.* stick; club: *a policeman's truncheon.* **2.** staff of office or authority: *a herald's truncheon.* **3.** beat with a club. 1,2 *n.*, 3 *v.*
waist coat (wāst′kōt′ or wes′kət), *Esp. Brit.* a man's vest. *n.*

Ha'penny really existed

Although the story "Ha'penny" comes mostly from the author's imagination, the little boy really existed and Alan Paton knew him well. He was one of Mr. Paton's six hundred pupils in Diepkloof Reformatory in Johannesburg, South Africa, the largest reformatory in Africa.

At that time, says Mr. Paton, there weren't many welfare agencies for African boys, "so that Diepkloof contained a number of boys who were not real delinquents, but were waifs, strays, orphans, or neglected children. Ha'penny was one of the waifs.

"He had never known his father and had been abandoned by his mother. He lived in the markets and among the refuse bins, and was finally sent to Diepkloof for theft—of food, of course —at the age of twelve years. If ever a boy was in search of a family, it was he."

The author says that Ha'penny "attached himself to the Principal (Paton) in his own secret unobtrusive way, never thrusting himself forward but waiting always for the sign of recognition that satisfied some hunger. It was during these encounters that he told the whole story of his mother and sisters and brothers."

Hunger

by Jane Stembridge

I
gave
an orange

to
a child
in Spain

and
saw
six
children

fight.

 Talking it over

  1. Why do the children fight?
  2. Could this incident happen in the United States?

HUNGER

*I shook with fright. I was alone upon the
dark, hostile streets, and gangs were after me.*

by Richard Wright

HUNGER stole upon me so slowly
that at first I was not aware of
what hunger really meant. Hunger had
always been more or less at my elbow
when I played, but now I began to
wake up at night to find hunger standing at my bedside, staring at me gauntly.
The hunger I had known before this
had been no grim, hostile stranger; it
had been a normal hunger that had
made me beg constantly for bread, and
when I ate a crust or two I was satisfied.
But this new hunger baffled me, scared
me, made me angry and insistent.
Whenever I begged for food now my
mother would pour me a cup of tea
which would still the clamor in my
stomach for a moment or two; but a
little later I would feel hunger nudging
my ribs, twisting my empty guts until
they ached. I would grow dizzy and my
vision would dim. I became less active
in my play, and for the first time in my
life I had to pause and think of what
was happening to me.

"Mama, I'm hungry," I complained
one afternoon.

"Jump up and catch a kungry," she
said, trying to make me laugh and
forget.

"What's a *kungry?*"

"It's what little boys eat when they
get hungry," she said.

"What does it taste like?"

"I don't know."

"Then why do you tell me to catch
one?"

"Because you said that you were
hungry," she said, smiling.

I sensed that she was teasing me and
it made me angry.

"But I'm hungry. I want to eat."

"You'll have to wait."

"But I want to eat now."

"But there's nothing to eat," she told
me.

"Why?"

"Just because there's none," she explained.

"But I want to eat," I said, beginning to cry.

"You'll just have to wait," she said again.

"But why?"

"For God to send some food."

"When is He going to send it?"

"I don't know."

"But I'm hungry!"

She was ironing and she paused and looked at me with tears in her eyes.

"Where's your father?" she asked me.

I stared in bewilderment. Yes, it was true that my father had not come home to sleep for many days now and I could make as much noise as I wanted. Though I had not known why he was absent, I had been glad that he was not there to shout his restrictions at me. But it had never occurred to me that his absence would mean that there would be no food.

"I don't know," I said.

"Who brings food into the house?" my mother asked me.

"Papa," I said. "He always brought food."

"Well, your father isn't here now," she said.

"Where is he?"

"I don't know," she said.

"But I'm hungry," I whimpered, stomping my feet.

"You'll have to wait until I get a job and buy food," she said.

As the days slid past, the image of my father became associated with my pangs of hunger, and whenever I felt hunger I thought of him with a deep biological bitterness.

My mother finally went to work as a cook and left me and my brother alone in the flat each day with a loaf of bread and a pot of tea. When she returned at evening she would be tired and dispirited and would cry a lot. Sometimes, when she was in despair, she would call us to her and talk to us for hours, telling us that we now had no father, that our lives would be different from those of other children, that we must learn as soon as possible to take care of ourselves, to dress ourselves, to prepare our own food; that we must take upon ourselves the responsibility of the flat while she worked. Half frightened, we would promise solemnly. We did not understand what had happened between our father and our mother and the most that these long talks did to us was to make us feel a vague dread. Whenever we asked why father had left, she would tell us that we were too young to know.

One evening my mother told me that thereafter I would have to do the shopping for food. She took me to the corner store to show me the way. I was proud; I felt like a grown-up. The next afternoon I looped the basket over my arm and went down the pavement toward the store. When I reached the corner, a gang of boys grabbed me, knocked me down, snatched the basket, took the money, and sent me running home in panic. That evening I told my mother what had happened, but she made no comment; she sat down at once, wrote another note, gave me more money, and sent me out to the grocery again. I crept down the steps and saw the same gang of boys playing down the street. I ran back into the house.

"What's the matter?" my mother asked.

"It's those same boys," I said. "They'll beat me."

"You've got to get over that," she said. "Now, go on."

"I'm scared," I said.

"Go on and don't pay any attention to them," she said.

I went out of the door and walked briskly down the sidewalk, praying that the gang would not molest me. But when I came abreast of them someone shouted.

"There he is!"

They came toward me and I broke into a wild run toward home. They overtook me and flung me to the pavement. I yelled, pleaded, kicked, but they wrenched the money out of my hand. They yanked me to my feet, gave me a few slaps, and sent me home sobbing. My mother met me at the door.

"They b-beat m-me," I gasped. "They t-t-took the m-money."

I started up the steps, seeking the shelter of the house.

"Don't you come in here," my mother warned me.

I froze in my tracks and stared at her.

"But they're coming after me," I said.

"You just stay right where you are," she said in a deadly tone. "I'm going to teach you this night to stand up and fight for yourself."

She went into the house and I waited, terrified, wondering what she was about. Presently she returned with more money and another note; she also had a long heavy stick.

"Take this money, this note, and this stick," she said. "Go to the store and buy those groceries. If those boys bother you, then fight."

I was baffled. My mother was telling

me to fight, a thing that she had never done before.

"But I'm scared," I said.

"Don't you come into this house until you've gotten those groceries," she said.

"They'll beat me; they'll beat me," I said.

"Then stay in the streets; don't come back here!"

I ran up the steps and tried to force my way past her into the house. A stinging slap came on my jaw. I stood on the sidewalk, crying.

"Please, let me wait until tomorrow," I begged.

"No," she said. "Go now! If you come back into this house without those groceries, I'll whip you!"

She slammed the door and I heard the key turn in the lock. I shook with fright. I was alone upon the dark, hostile streets and gangs were after me. I had the choice of being beaten at home or away from home. I clutched the stick, crying, trying to reason. If I were beaten at home, there was absolutely nothing that I could do about it; but if I were beaten in the streets, I had a chance to fight and defend myself. I walked slowly down the sidewalk, coming closer to the gang of boys, holding the stick tightly. I was so full of fear that I could scarcely breathe. I was almost upon them now.

"There he is again!" the cry went up.

They surrounded me quickly and began to grab for my hand.

"I'll kill you!" I threatened.

They closed in. In blind fear I let the stick fly, feeling it crack against a boy's skull. I swung again, lamming another skull, then another. Realizing that they would retaliate if I let up for but a second, I fought to lay them low, to knock them cold, to kill them so that they could not strike back at me. I flayed with tears in my eyes, teeth clenched, stark fear making me throw every ounce of my strength behind each blow. I hit again and again, dropping the money and the grocery list. The boys scattered, yelling, nursing their heads, staring at me in utter disbelief. They had never seen such frenzy. I stood panting, egging them on, taunting them to come on and fight. When they refused, I ran after them and they tore out for their homes, screaming. The parents of the boys rushed into the streets and threatened me, and for the first time in my life I shouted at grown-ups, telling them that I would give them the same if they bothered me. I finally found my grocery list and the money and went to the store. On my way back I kept my stick poised for instant use, but there was not a single boy in sight. That night I won the right to the streets of Memphis.   THE END

From unruly boy to noted writer

As a child, Richard Wright lived with unhappiness as well as hunger. His father deserted the family when Richard was five. For the next few years, Mrs. Wright supported herself and her two small sons as best she could, first in Memphis, Tennessee, and later in Arkansas. For a time, she had to put her sons in an orphan asylum. When they refused to stay there, she had to borrow money from relatives to feed and shelter them.

Richard's mother was ill for years and, before he was ten, she became

completely paralyzed. Then the two boys became entirely dependent on relatives. Because he was rude and hard to manage, Richard was shunted from one relative to another. Finally he was sent to a school in Mississippi where his aunt taught, and here he found an outlet for some of his energy in reading.

At fifteen, Richard went back to Memphis, where he worked at various unskilled jobs and made up his mind to become a writer. Later he moved to Chicago and then to New York, where he began to sell stories to magazines. His novel *Native Son* became a best seller, and with the money he earned he bought a house in Chicago for his mother.

In 1939 Richard Wright was chosen one of the most distinguished Negroes of the year. In 1940, in accepting an award for high achievement in the field of Negro interests, he said that in his writing he tried to mirror the Negroes' struggle for freedom.

Black Boy, the autobiography from which "Hunger" is taken, was published in 1945. The next year Wright moved to Paris. He died there in 1960, at the age of fifty-two.

Talking it over

1. This is a true story about Richard Wright, a famous Negro author.

  a. What serious family problems are described early in the story?

  b. Which problem was most urgent at the moment?

  c. How did Mrs. Wright solve this problem?

  d. What problems remained for her to solve?

2. *a.* What was Richard's mother trying to accomplish when she sent him to the store with a big stick?

  b. How well did her method work?

  c. What might have been the consequences if things had turned out differently?

  d. What other solutions might Mrs. Wright have found?

  e. Was her solution a good one or not? Explain.

3. *a.* How do you suppose Richard felt toward his mother when she forced him—in spite of his fear—to go back into the street?

  b. What do you infer that Richard Wright meant when he later wrote, "That night I won the right to the streets of Memphis"?

  c. How do you suppose he felt about his mother at the time he wrote of this incident?

4. *a.* What inference can you make as to what necessity or necessities—besides food—this story is about?

  b. Write your own title for this story.

(cont.)

It is often easier to say what a whole phrase means than to tell what each word in the phrase means. When you read the sentence, "They closed in," you know what "they" did, yet none of the usual meanings of *close* fits this context.

In dictionaries, the meanings of such phrases as "close in" are at the end of the entry for one of the words in the phrase. Look first under the word that seems most important. You may have to look under more than one word before you find such a phrase defined.

Use the dictionary entries on this page to complete the exercise.

I

1. At the end of which word entry —"close" or "in"—is the phrase "close in" defined?

2. *a.* Which of the italicized words in the following sentence are defined as a phrase? "I fought *to lay them low.*"

   b. At the end of what entry do you find the phrase?

   c. What does the phrase mean?

II

3. Show that you understand the meaning of the following phrases by using each one in a sentence.

   a. in for
   b. lay into
   c. lie low
   d. close down
   e. in with

close¹ (klōz), 1. shut: *Close the door. The sleepy child's eyes are closing.* 2. stop up; fill; block: *close a gap.* 3. bring together; come together: *close the ranks of troops.* 4. end; finish: *The meeting closed with a speech by the president* (v.). *He spoke at the close of the meeting* (n.). 5. come to terms; agree: *The labor union closed with the company.* 6. grapple. 1-6 v., closed, clos ing; 4 n. —clos′er, n.
close down, shut completely; stop.
close in, come near and shut in on all sides.
close out, sell to get rid of.
close up, 1. shut completely; stop up; block. 2. bring or come nearer together. 3. of a wound, heal.
in (in), *In* expresses inclusion, situation, presence, existence, position, and action within limits of space, time, state, circumstances, etc. 1. inside; within: *in~~~~~~~~~~~~nto: Go in the house~~~~~~~~~~~~~~~~~~~~~~~~~~~an*

~~~~~~

13. coming or going in. 1-9 *prep.*, 10,11~ 12,13 *adj.*
in for, unable to avoid; sure to get or have.
ins, people in office; political party in power.
ins and outs, 1. turns and twists; nooks and corners. 2. different parts; details.
in that, because.
in with, 1. friendly with. 2. partners with.
lay¹ (lā), 1. bring down; beat down: *A storm laid the crops low.* 2. put down; keep down: *Lay your hat on the table. A shower has laid the ~~ ~~* make quiet or make disappear: *la~* ~~~~h down: lay the~ ~~~n posit~~*

~~~~~~

16. way o~ ~~~~~~~~~~~~~nch a thing is laid or lies: *the lay of the ground.* 1-15 v., laid, lay ing; 16 n.
lay about, hit out on all sides.
lay aside, away, or **by,** put away for future use; save.
lay down, 1. declare; state. 2. give; sacrifice. 3. *Slang.* quit; resign. 4. store away for future use. 5. bet.
lay for, *Informal.* lie in wait for.
lay in, provide; save; put aside for the future.
lay into, 1. beat; thrash. 2. *Slang.* scold.
lay off, 1. put aside. 2. *Slang.* stop for a time; stop; desist. 3. put out of work. 4. mark off.
lay on, 1. apply. 2. supply. 3. strike; inflict.
lay oneself out, *Informal.* make a big effort; take great pains.
lay out, 1. spread out. 2. prepare (a dead body) for burial. 3. arrange; plan. 4. *Slang.* spend.
lay to, 1. blame on; accuse of. 2. head into the wind and stand still.
lay up, 1. put away for future use; save. 2. cause to stay in bed or indoors because of illness or injury. 3. put (a ship) in dock.
low¹ (lō), 1. not high or tall: *low walls.* 2. rising but slightly from a surface: *low relief.* 3. of less than ordinary height, depth, or quantity: *The well is getting low.* 1-6,8,10-12, 14-22 *adj.*, 4,7,9,13,18,19,23 *adv.*, 24-26 n. —low′ness, n.
lay low, 1. knock down. 2. kill
lie low, *Informal.* stay hidden; keep still.

*He didn't think his father liked him very much,
because he couldn't play football or anything.
So he thought if maybe he could just run . . .*

Stainless Steele

by William R. Scott

IT WAS a warm Friday night in early spring, with a big full moon coming over the Steeles' house east of us. I was in the front yard, waiting for Betty Wheatley to show up in her father's car and drive me to the movies. I was thinking about Betty and graduating and what I would do all summer—you know, first one thing and then another—but I wasn't thinking about Stainless Steele.

Then a bike came down the sidewalk, something thudded on the porch next door west of us, and there was Stainless, coming home from his paper route. We were his last customers, but instead of throwing the folded paper at the porch as usual, he stopped, got off his bike, and came through the gate.

"That you, Joe?" he asked. He was seventeen, but he usually squeaked some when he talked.

"Who else would it be?" I retorted. I didn't want to talk to him. I didn't want his squeaky voice interrupting my thoughts.

"Well, I couldn't see you very well in the dark," he said. He couldn't have seen me very well if it had been broad daylight, either. "Here's the paper." He handed it to me and kept standing there.

"Okay," I said. "You want a receipt or something?"

He was fiddling with the earpieces of his spectacles and peering at me in the moonlight. He said, "No, I just—well—I just wanted to ask you something, Joe."

"Shoot," I said.

He sat down by the steps, and the lights from a front window glinted on his glasses. "Joe, I was wondering—

can just anybody go out for track?"

"That's a good question," I replied. "What brings it up, Stainless?"

"Why, I thought I might give it a try myself."

"You're kidding," I said. "You're amusing yourself at my expense again, Stainless." That's how we all talked to him. I wasn't the only one.

He didn't say anything, so I asked, "What do you plan to specialize in? The shot-put? Or maybe you're planning to make me look cheap in the high jump, huh?" He was about five feet five and weighed maybe a hundred and thirty pounds, soaking wet and carrying books.

"No," he replied, squeaking. "I don't expect to be much good at track, but I just thought—well, how's it going to look in the yearbook, Joe, after my name where it says Extracurricular Activities? 'None,' they'll have to put there. So I thought maybe this way— well, they'd put that I went out for track, see."

He was right about the yearbook. His size and the thick-lensed glasses he wore kept him from going out for football or basketball, and I suppose he couldn't even see a baseball. He didn't sing in the glee club, or make the debating society or the drama society, although I knew he'd tried out every year for all three. I suppose the only outstanding thing about him was that he'd never missed a day on his paper route or skipped a customer, and that wasn't yearbook copy.

"What do you care?" I shrugged. "Who reads the yearbook anyhow?"

He didn't say anything for a while. Then he looked up at me and said in a low voice, "I'm not worried about the yearbook, Joe. It's—well, I don't think

my father likes me very much, because I can't play football or anything. I can't do anything, and when he was a kid he could do everything. So I thought if I could maybe just run. You don't have to be big or strong just to run. Maybe you don't even need to have good eyesight. See, Joe?"

I was embarrassed. I knew his father never kidded around the way my father did, but it had never entered my head that he didn't like Stainless. For Pete's sake!

Stainless got up and cleared his throat. "I guess I shouldn't have said that, Joe. But I'd like to show him I can do something. Maybe I'm being silly, though, thinking I could make the track squad."

"I'm no authority on the subject," I said. "There's no law that says you can't talk to the coach about it." A car came down the street and stopped out front. As I started down the walk, I said to Stainless, "They're going to check out gear Monday afternoon."

Betty looked out the car window. "Hi, Stan," she said. "How's my dream man?"

"Aw, okay," he said, and went on down the walk, pushing his bike.

Betty and I drove downtown and saw the movie, and afterwards we got malteds in cartons. Everything should have been great, but I felt gloomy. It wasn't like me. Why should I feel gloomy?

"Something gnawing at your brain?" Betty asked me.

"I was just wondering," I said, "how a fellow feels when he knows his father doesn't like him. You know, just can't see him?"

"You mean Stanley Steele?" she asked. I looked at her, surprised that she'd guessed, and she said, "Nature played a trick on Stan's father—he wanted an All-American end or something, and what he got was just a nice kid."

"Yeah," I nodded. "It makes me gloomy. I can't help trying to imagine how I'd feel if I were Stanley Steele's father. Maybe if I were middle-aged, and all I had were hazy memories and a batch of faded newspaper clippings—"

Later, lying awake in my bed, I thought about Stainless. All I'd ever worried about was whether I'd be good enough to make first string at the university. I never brooded much about people. Maybe I just assumed that people like Stainless didn't mind being that way. My dad liked me, and I guess I just figured all fathers liked their sons.

Monday morning I met Mr. Higby in the hall at school. He's the principal and track coach, and a good fellow.

"Listen, Coach, you know Stainless Steele?" I began.

"Sure," he said.

"Well, he wants to come out for track. Maybe he won't have the nerve to ask you, so I'm asking you for him."

Mr. Higby chuckled. "What does he do, Joe? Pole vault?"

"I don't know whether he can do anything," I replied. "He wants to try."

Mr. Higby shook his head. "His legs are too short. Besides, we're going to be short on spikes."

There it was: Tell the kid to stop dreaming; tell him to stop pretending he's human like other people.

All of a sudden I saw red. But it wasn't just Mr. Higby; I was sore at myself too.

"Okay," I said. "Give him my spikes." Sure—I was six one; I wore size ten shoes, and Stainless probably wore sevens, or smaller. Just hearing myself talk like that made me madder. "Give him my gear, if you're the kind of coach who won't give a kid a break."

"Joe!" People going past were staring at us. "You can't talk to me like that." He didn't seem angry, just surprised. "What's all this about, Joe?"

I looked at his middle vest button, feeling like a fool, and I couldn't tell him. I didn't know myself.

"Forget it, Mr. Higby," I said. "I'm sorry." The buzzer rang, and I looked at him and tried to grin. "I'm sorry I blew my top, Coach."

"Sure, fella." He made a fist and poked my shoulder good-naturedly. "Go on to your class."

I thought that was the end of Stainless and track, but it wasn't. He went to the sporting-goods store and got spikes on his own. Mr. Higby let him come out for track and found him some running pants and a sweat suit.

We didn't run any that day; we just checked our gear and were assigned lockers. When I came out of the gym, there was Stainless, waiting. I felt a little sick, seeing him there. Now he'll start treating me like an equal, I thought. But it wasn't that way at all.

"Joe," he said, "I heard about your talking to Coach Higby for me. I just—well, I'm much obliged, Joe. I'll try not to let you down." Then he got on his bike, acting embarrassed.

"What about your paper route?" I asked. "How are you going to keep from being late?"

He looked solemn. "Birch Rosen has an early-morning route. He's always wanted to swap routes with me because he doesn't like to get up at three o'clock in the morning. So now I'm going to swap."

I stood there watching him ride across the school ground, and I thought: three o'clock in the morning! You certainly have to admire determination like that.

Tuesday afternoon Stainless came to the stadium wearing his new spikes and a sweat shirt that was too big. He looked almost comical, but I kept thinking how much he wanted to look good in track—enough to give up an afternoon paper route for a three-o'clock route in the morning. I saw him every afternoon that week, jogging around the track in his new spikes, but I got so I didn't pay him any attention. I was looking good in the broad jump and high jump, and everything was fine.

On Saturday afternoon I was in the drugstore, hoping Betty would drift in, when Stanley Steele's father came across the street from his insurance office. He walked back to where I was.

"I want to talk with you, Riley," he said.

I was surprised. "What about, Mr. Steele?"

"I understand this practical joke was your idea," he said grimly.

I didn't know what he was talking about. "What joke, Mr. Steele?"

"This business of getting Stanley excited about going out for the track squad. I don't like your making him the butt of your joke, Riley."

"You have it all wrong," I began. "It was his idea. All I did—"

"You know he can't make the track team, Riley. He's no athlete; you know that. With his short legs he couldn't even make the girls' track team." Mr. Steele's face was getting red now. "I suppose you smart alecks think he's comical, don't you? I'll bet you lettermen get a big laugh out of it."

"No, sir—"

He pushed his chin out at me, and his voice shook. "I've ordered Stanley to check in his gear and stop making a ridiculous spectacle of himself—and you'd better leave it at that, Riley."

I thought of telling him why Stainless wanted to make good in track, but all of a sudden he whirled around and went out of there.

I went home. I was boiling inside, and I wanted to take something apart. The way I felt, I didn't even want to see Betty. So I went home and spaded up a couple of flower beds for Mom. Pretty soon Stainless came over.

"Joe," he said. "Listen, my father is sore, and he's looking for you. I told him you helped me go out for track, and he's—"

"He found me," I interrupted.

"Oh." Stainless began leveling off a place in the dirt with his foot, acting as if it was very important to make it smooth. "I'm sorry if he got on you, Joe. He said I had to check in my gear."

"He told me," I said.

Stainless kept looking down at the dirt. "You think I should, Joe?"

"He's your problem," I said. "He buys your clothes, doesn't he?"

"I buy my own clothes," Stainless said. "I buy my own books, too, and I bought my own spikes." He sounded different, somehow. He sounded as if he were angry himself. "I'm not going to do it!" he said suddenly. He kicked dirt over the smooth place and looked at me, squinting through his glasses. "Maybe he won't find out until after next Friday, Joe, and at least I'll— well, maybe I'll have shown him."

Stop dreaming, I thought; you won't show anybody anything, Stainless.

"The coach hasn't said who's going

to run in the relays yet," he went on, "or the half mile. Maybe he'll let me run in something."

Sure, he'll let you run in after some adhesive tape, I thought.

The next day was Sunday, and I went fishing with Dad and had a good time in a depressing sort of way. Then Monday rolled around.

After school Mr. Higby was pulling his hair out by handfuls. There'd been a tentative agreement in the district to drop the cross-country race from all district track meets this spring. But the five schools coming to town for this meet claimed it wasn't a district meet, and they were expecting to enter their cross-country teams. So now in a week's time Mr. Higby had to lay out a course and get a team of his own to enter.

"If we don't enter a team, we'll lose total points," he said. "Nobody can become a distance runner in a week, but we'll have to enter the race. So I'm choosing the team."

He picked a couple of country boys, Simmons and Tate, who were milers but not very good ones. For the third man he picked Herman Deeler, and we all knew that was a kind of punishment, because Herman was always "gold-bricking" at practice—and maybe, too, because Mr. Higby suspected that he smoked cigarettes all the time.

The rest of the week I steered clear of Stainless. Mr. Higby had the cross-country team running every afternoon, but only for a mile, and he wasn't pushing them hard. He said all he asked was that they finish on Friday. "Just cross that finish line," he told them.

Friday came, and it was a hot, airless day for that early in spring—not too bad for the sprints and jumping, but it would be rugged for the distance run-

ners, especially cross-country. Maybe Herman Deeler figured it would be too rugged, because during the noon hour he managed to get caught smoking.

"You're through, Deeler," the coach said. "Check in your gear."

And that's why Stainless Steele was tapped for the cross-country. Mr. Higby had to have three men, and he couldn't spare anybody else.

This meet wasn't really important. The regular official county and district track meets would come later in the spring. This was just a kind of shake-down cruise, a preview of how the district teams would shape up. But since it was at home, Mr. Higby wanted to win if he could. He wanted us to look good in front of the home-town crowd. And it was a pretty good crowd, for a track meet.

Dad was there. He always turned up when I was in anything. School was dismissed for the meet, and most of the kids came out to watch.

I was taking my high-jump warm-ups when someone tapped me on the shoulder. I turned around, and it was Mr. Steele. "Riley," he said. "I guess I went off half cocked the other day. I was upset—but I owe you an apology. I hope you'll forget the whole thing."

"Sure," I said. "It wasn't anything."

Then he gave me a funny look. "Stanley disobeyed my orders, didn't he, Riley?" He looked almost wistful.

"He's entered in the cross-country race," I said.

He looked at me as if he didn't believe me. "Why, Stanley isn't up to the cross-country grind. He won't get half-way around the course in this heat! What's wrong with Higby anyway?"

He turned around and pushed through the people on the infield grass, and I supposed that he was going to make the coach take Stainless out of the race.

I went ahead with my warm-up jumps, and then a little later I cleared the bar at five seven for a second place, behind a long-legged kid from Skedee. Then I was walking around to keep my legs from stiffening up, and the cross-country runners were getting ready to start their race, so I went over to watch. Mr. Higby was talking to Stainless and Simmons and Tate, but I didn't see Mr. Steele anywhere.

"Look, fellows, just do the best you can," the coach said, "but don't hurt yourselves. You haven't had a chance to get ready for this race, and this heat is sickening. If you get tired, drop out and come on in. Don't even try to finish. It doesn't matter."

They nodded, Stainless squinting solemnly through his glasses. Then they lined up on the track, and the race started. Stainless looked out of place with all of those long-legged guys. When they passed through the east gate of the stadium, he was already trailing.

The stadium is at the edge of town, and a course had been laid out through fields and timber and across the creek and back again to the stadium. The course was about a mile long from east to west, and about a quarter of a mile from north to south. Part of it was through a pasture with deep gullies, and a couple of hundred yards crossed a field that had been plowed but not harrowed. The course twisted from side to side, and the turns were marked by colored flags—white for right turns, red for left, and blue for straight ahead. I hoped Stainless wasn't color-blind. I hadn't thought of that before.

While they were running the cross-country, we went on with the other events in the stadium. After the mile relay I had to keep sweating for the 220 hurdles. I didn't expect to win, and I didn't. I was lucky to get third place when the fellow ahead of me tripped on the last hurdle and fell.

I was walking around the infield when Dad came over and put his arm on my shoulder.

"Too bad, Joe. You should have had at least second in the hurdles."

I grinned at him. "I should've had fourth, and you know it."

He grinned too. "Well, too much success might ruin a youngster like you, Joe. You need to be a poor third or worse once in a while, or there'd be no living with you."

He left me, and I saw Simmons walking across the infield toward the coach; so I went over there in time to hear him tell the coach he just couldn't take it and had dropped out. "But I waited until two other fellows quit first," he panted.

"Good boy," Mr. Higby said. "Cool off and get yourself a shower."

"What about Stainless, Simmons?" I asked.

"Why, I don't know," he answered. "He was quite a way behind."

I went back to the infield just as the announcer said, "Clear the track, please. Clear the track."

It was the first six fellows finishing the cross-country. They were scattered and their tongues were hanging out; a two-year-old baby could have beat them in their sprint for the tape. Stainless wasn't one of them. Four more came along through the west gate in the next minute or so, and I wondered if Stainless had dropped out like Simmons. Quite a while after the first fel-

lows came in, Tate came through the west gate, but he wasn't finishing. He was walking, limping onto the infield, holding his side and spitting cotton. I decided Stainless must have dropped out early in the race and come on back, and I hadn't seen him.

It was then that the laughing started. Somebody yelled, and somebody else cheered in a phony voice, and the laughter swept through the crowd like wind through ripe wheat. Everybody was looking toward the west gate.

I couldn't see from the ground, so I climbed up the side of the bleachers and looked. It was Stainless. He'd come in the west gate and was staggering around the cinder track, and the crowd was laughing at him. He looked funny all right—but he looked pitiful, too. He looked forlorn and pathetic, and seeing him like that made my throat feel tight and dry. The cross-country had been over for quite a while, and here he came finishing a bad last, if he finished. He lifted his feet as if they weighed fifty pounds apiece.

Even from the bleachers I could see he wasn't wearing his glasses, and he must have twisted his ankle or gotten a charley horse, the way he was favoring his right leg. I saw Mr. Higby leave a group of men on the infield grass and start off as if he might get in front of Stainless and head him off. But then he turned around and came plowing through the officials and other people on the infield, toward the finish line in front of the bleachers. And Stainless kept coming, his head back and his mouth open. I could see the tendons in his neck.

Where the straightaway ended and the turn started, Stainless wasn't making his cut sharp enough. At the end of

the turn, he veered into the raised concrete edge of the track. He seemed to realize his mistake and tried to turn sharp, but his reactions were slow and he was too close. He slammed into the board fence at the end of the oval, bounced off, and went sprawling on the cinders.

Feeling sick inside, I looked back at the track, where a couple of fellows had run out to Stainless and were trying to help him up, but he pushed them away and got up by himself. Nobody was laughing now. It wasn't funny, and the crowd knew it.

I could see now that Stainless was dirty, from sweat and dust that was streaked into mud. The veins stood out in his forehead, and his stomach was all caved in; his knees were skinned from sliding in the gravel when he fell. In the hush you could hear how he was fighting to get some air into his lungs.

I dropped off the bleachers and headed for the finish line. I had to do something; I couldn't stand it just watching. Mr. Higby was there. "Help me, Joe," he said. "We have to keep him moving."

Stainless made the east turn all right and came toward us. He was wobbling and staggering, but he got across the finish line. We caught him and held him up between us and started walking with him, making him keep moving so he wouldn't get cramps, or worse. He gasped and sobbed and tried to talk, but Mr. Higby told him not to try yet, but just to keep moving.

Then all at once the crowd let go. Nobody told them to; they did it because Stainless had the courage to come in, even when he knew he was the poorest last that ever finished a race. They weren't applauding his ability; they were applauding his courage.

After a while the coach said, "All right, Joe. There's the doctor—we'll let him rest now." We put Stainless on the grass, and the doc felt his pulse and listened to his chest, while Mr. Higby had some guys take off their sweat suits and cover him up.

I didn't see Mr. Steele until he was already kneeling in the grass beside Stainless. The doc said, "Don't worry. He's okay. Just one mighty tired lad, that's all. He's had a hard afternoon."

Stainless looked at the coach, squinting. "Did I finish?"

"You made it," Mr. Higby said. "You finished the race, fellow."

"But did it count?" He was still having trouble with his breathing.

"Of course," Mr. Higby said.

Stainless relaxed and grinned. "I fell down in that plowed field," he said. "I lost my glasses and I couldn't find them. I guess I got a charley horse, too, but it wouldn't have been so bad if I hadn't lost my glasses."

"We'll get you some new glasses, Stan," his father said.

Stainless squinted up at his father. "I'm sorry I disobeyed, Father," he said. "I had to."

"I know, Stan," his father said. "I'm glad you did."

"No, you were right," Stainless said, squeaking a little. "I'm not cut out for an athlete. I'm short-winded, I can't run—"

His father spoke quietly. "It takes time, but you can do it if you want to, Stan." He put his hand on his son's head and shook it gently. "All a fellow needs is courage, son—and you have it." He looked prouder than if Stainless had won the race.

"Joe," the coach said, "it's time for the broad jump. How about winning this one for Stan?"

I looked at Stainless. "All right," I said. "I'll win it for you, Stainless." I didn't break any records, but I won first place. Then I put on my sweat suit and went across the track. Betty was waiting for me by the bleachers. She looked beautiful.

"You did it for me," she said.

I took her hand and we started walking toward the gym. I had so many things to tell her I didn't know where to start: about how Stainless was wrong and his father liked him fine all the time—only maybe he tried too hard to keep him from getting hurt, from being laughed at; about how Stainless just got mixed up in his thinking.

"Not this one," I said. "I won this one for Stainless."

She smiled. "I'm glad you did."

THE END

⟳ Talking it over

1. How does Joe become involved in Stanley's problem? What does Joe say and do that shows a change in his attitude toward Stanley?

2. Before the day of the race, what things had Stanley done that should have made his father admire him?

3. How are Mr. Riley's feelings for his son different from Mr. Steele's feelings for Stanley? How are their feelings alike?

4. What does Stanley hope to accomplish by going out for track? What does he actually accomplish?

5. Authors often contrast their characters to make them stand out more dramatically. What examples are there in this story? *(cont.)*

No one knows if there was a person named Alexander who was such an outrageous show-off that his name was added to our language in the phrase "smart aleck." Although it is likely that *aleck* comes from Alexander, just how the phrase got started is a mystery.

Names have become part of many such phrases, as in the "charley horse" which Stanley suffered in the race. Experts do know how some of these phrases got started.

1. The term "charley horse," which means "stiffness caused by straining a muscle," first showed up in baseball slang. Two possible explanations of the way this expression originated have been suggested. One is that a crippled horse named Charley worked in the Chicago White Sox ball park back in the days before power lawn mowers were used. Other authorities believe that we owe the phrase, not to one horse, but to the hundreds of broken-down horses that were used to pull family carriages. Charley was a favorite name for the family horse.

What possible connection do you see between the phrase and each of the suggested explanations?

2. While President Theodore (Teddy) Roosevelt was on a hunting trip, a friend jokingly brought a tiny cub bear into camp on a chain for the President to "bag." Roosevelt laughed and told the man to set the bear free. When this story circulated, a new toy and a new phrase were invented. What toy is named after Theodore Roosevelt?

3. The characters Punch and Judy were famous in the days when puppet shows were popular. The act was always basically the same: Punch and Judy would quarrel, struggle, and finally strike one another. Judging from the two expressions that have entered our language as a result of these shows, "proud as punch" and "pleased as punch," who do you think won the "argument" each time?

"Stainless" was his best

William R. Scott considers "Stainless Steele" to be "the best story I ever wrote . . . the most moving . . . the most real."

The scene where Stanley appears, long after the race is presumed over, and staggers blindly around the track, was the key scene from which the story grew, although when and where it happened Mr. Scott can't remember. "But I couldn't forget the indelible impression it made—that courage is a greater asset than muscular agility or natural aptitude. More lasting than glory, too."

Mr. Scott says he has known "more than a few instances where an ex-athlete parent has been dismayed by a son's lack of ability or interest regarding a physical accomplishment. I know of a football coach whose brawny son flatly refused even to check out a uniform—but I suspect that was a deep-rooted fear of proving inadequate."

Mr. Scott lives on a small farm in the Ozark foothills, where he raises beef cattle and writes books under the pen name of Weldon Hill. One book, *Onionhead,* has been made into a motion picture.

MONEY

by Richard Armour

Workers earn it,
Spendthrifts burn it,
Bankers lend it,
Women spend it,
5 Forgers fake it,
Taxes take it,
Dying leave it,
Heirs receive it,
Thrifty save it,
10 Misers crave it,
Robbers seize it,
Rich increase it,
Gamblers lose it . . .
I could use it.

 Talking it over

1. What idea about money is expressed in this poem?

2. With what attitude or "tone of voice" does the author treat the idea?

From *Yours for the Asking* by Richard Armour. Reprinted by permission of Bruce Humphries, Publishers, Boston, Mass.

A swing-spiritual based on

the authentic proverb

"God blessed the child that's got his own"

GOD BLESS' THE CHILD

by Arthur Herzog, Jr. and Billie Holiday

Them that's got shall get,
Them that's not shall lose.
So the Bible[1] says,
And it still is news.
5 Mama may have,
Papa may have,
But God bless' the child that's got his own!
That's got his own.

Yes, the strong get more
10 While the weak ones fade.
Empty pockets don't
Ever make the grade.
Mama may have,
Papa may have,
15 But God bless' the child that's got his own!
That's got his own.

Money, you've got lots of friends
Crowdin' round the door.
When you're gone and spending ends,
20 They don't come no more.

Rich relations give
Crusts of bread and such.
You can help yourself,
But don't take too much.
25 Mama may have,
Papa may have,
But God bless' the child that's got his own!
That's got his own.

---

[1]**Bible.** This refers to a verse in the Book of Matthew, chapter 13: "For to him who has will more be given."

Talking it over

1. A well-known saying about rich people and poor people expresses the same idea as the first two lines of the first two stanzas. What is the saying?

2. What is said in the song about strong persons and weak persons? about friends and money? about the generosity of rich relatives?

3. Do you think the speaker in this song is talking only about money? What advantage does she seem to feel that money gives a person?

4. What is another way of saying "God bless' the child"?

She sang the blues

Billie Holiday was a blues singer who greatly influenced American popular singing. She became widely known around 1938, and during the next ten years she sang with some of the most famous jazz and swing bands of the time. Many jazz musicians and critics call her the greatest vocalist in the history of jazz.

Her life was full of tragedy, but Miss Holiday somehow preserved a basic dignity and courage which she managed to express through the songs she sang.

"God Bless' the Child" is the lyric for a song written in 1941. The idea for the song—and its title—came to Miss Holiday following an argument with her mother over money. However, it was actually written in collaboration with Arthur Herzog, Jr., a well-known song-writer, who was a friend of hers. He also wrote several other songs with Miss Holiday.

GOD BLESS' THE CHILD / **421**

The Soup Stone

by Maria Leach

ONE DAY a soldier was walking home from the wars and came to a village. The wind was cold; the sky was gray; and the soldier was hungry. He stopped at a house on the edge of the village and asked for something to eat. "We have nothing for ourselves," the people said, so the soldier went on.

He stopped at the next house and asked for something to eat. "We have nothing ourselves," the people said.

"Have you got a big pot?" said the soldier. Yes, they had a big iron pot.

"Have you got water?" he asked. Yes, they had plenty of water.

"Fill the pot with water and put it on the fire," said the soldier, "for I have a soup stone with me."

"A soup stone?" they said. "What is that?"

"It is a stone that makes soup," the soldier said. And they all gathered round to see this wonder.

The woman of the house filled the big pot with water and hung it over the fire. The soldier took a stone from his pocket (it looked like any stone a man might pick up in a road) and tossed it into the pot.

Reprinted from *The Soup Stone: The Magic of Familiar Things* by Maria Leach. By permission of the publishers, Funk & Wagnalls, New York.

"Now let it boil," he said. So they all sat down to wait for the pot to boil.

"Could you spare a bit of salt for it?" said the soldier.

"Of course," said the woman, and pulled out the salt box. The soldier took a fistful and threw it in, for it was a big pot. Then they all sat back to wait.

"A few carrots would taste good in it," said the soldier, longingly.

"Oh, we have a few carrots," said the woman, and pulled them out from under a bench, where the soldier had been eyeing them. So they threw in the carrots. And while the carrots boiled, the soldier told them stories of his adventures.

"A few potatoes would be good, wouldn't they?" said the soldier. "They'd thicken the soup a bit."

"We have a few potatoes," said the oldest girl. "I'll get them." So they put the potatoes in the pot and waited for the soup to boil.

"An onion does give a good flavor," said the soldier.

"Run next door and ask the neighbor for an onion," said the farmer to the smallest son. The child ran out of the house and came back with three onions. So they put the onions in. While they

waited they were cracking jokes and telling tales.

"—and I haven't tasted cabbage since I left my mother's house," the soldier was saying.

"Run out in the garden and pull a cabbage," said the mother. And a small girl ran out and came back with a cabbage. And they put that in.

"It won't be long now," said the soldier.

"Just a little longer," said the woman, stirring the pot with a long ladle.

Just then the oldest son came in. He had been hunting and brought home two rabbits.

"Just what we need for the finishing touch!" cried the soldier, and it was only a matter of minutes before the rabbits were cut and thrown into the pot.

"Ha!" said the hungry hunter. "The smell of a fine soup."

"The traveler has brought a soup stone," said the farmer to his son, "and he is making soup with it in the pot."

At last the soup was ready, and it was good. There was enough for all: the soldier and the farmer and his wife, the oldest girl and the oldest son, the little girl, and the little son.

"It's a wonderful soup," said the farmer.

"It's a wonderful stone," said the wife.

"It is," said the soldier, "and it will make soup forever if you follow the formula we used today."

So they finished the soup. And when the soldier bade them good-by, he gave the woman the stone to pay back the kindness. She protested politely.

"It is nothing," the soldier said and went on his way without the stone. Luckily he found another one just be-fore he came to the next village.

The soldier with the soup stone has visited nearly every town in northern Europe. He has made soup in many a small New England village, and occasionally one hears of his travels down South or out West.

The magic of the soup stone ALWAYS WORKS if you follow the formula, though some say the magic lies in whose hands it falls into.   THE END

Talking it over

1. *a.* Why do the villagers first claim they have no food, even for themselves?

b. When the soldier stops at the second house, how much of what follows do you think he has planned in advance?

c. Why are the people now willing to bring out their food and contribute it to the soup?

2. Why does the storyteller say that the stone looks like any other (page 422)?

3. *a.* What is the "formula" by which the stone will make soup forever?

b. Why should the magic lie "in whose hands it falls into"?

4. How do you explain the statements in the next-to-last paragraph about how the soldier has turned up in many different places?

5. Richard Wright's "Hunger" is also about satisfying the need for food. How did you feel about each of these stories when you finished reading them? How do you account for the difference in your feelings?

PRAIRIE KID

"You're ready to travel now,"
Elmer told the man softly.
"And this gun says so."

by Dorothy Johnson

WHEN Elmer Merrick was eleven years old, he marched an outlaw off the Ainsworth place at the point of a gun.

They still talk about it in Montana, telling the story with a proud chuckle, implying that in the old days all the boys were men, and all the men were tough as saddle leather. After Elmer grew up, he was as tough as he needed to be, but when he held a gun on Buck Saddler on that summer night in 1888, he was a frightened, desperate child.

Except for size, he didn't look like a child. He walked like a tired old man, with his shoulders drooping; when he rested, he sagged with patient weariness, not fidgeting. He looked sullen and puzzled and hostile, and he felt hostile toward just about everybody except Lute Kimball. Lute was his idol, for two good reasons: Lute treated him like an equal, and Lute could do well everything that Elmer was still learning. But Lute lived up in Miles City in those days, close to two days' ride on a good horse, so they did not meet often.

In one respect only, Elmer doubted Lute's judgment. Lute was courting Charlotte Ainsworth, and Elmer considered her a fool and a tenderfoot. A tenderfoot she certainly was, for she had come out from the East only that summer to keep house for her brother, Steve. She had to be told the most elementary things, such as the rule that all comers had to be offered food, unless they were Indians.

That summer, while Charlotte Ainsworth was enjoying the privileges of being the only single white girl in almost a hundred miles, Elmer Merrick, on his father's ranch three hours' ride to the westward, was learning to live with fear. Waking or sleeping, it stalked him, and sometimes it leaped and took his breath away, and a jeering voice in his own mind demanded, If your pa dies, what are you going to do about Varina?

His sister Varina was six years old, sunny and carefree, unreliable and perverse. She did not know she was lonely, because she had always lived on the prairie. She was of no use to anyone, and she worried about nothing except her chances of getting over to Steve's place fairly often to visit Miss Charlotte.

Miss Charlotte, she said, had a little rosewood melodeon that she had brought out in a trunk; Miss Charlotte was teaching her to play it; Miss Charlotte washed Varina's fair hair and made it hang in curls. Elmer, sick with his own worries, sometimes shouted, "Aw, shut up about Miss Charlotte!" but Varina would answer smugly, "Miss Charlotte likes me."

Once Elmer snapped, "Aw, she pretends she likes everybody," and then was ashamed of himself because Varina cried so hard.

He had enough to worry him. More than half his father's cattle starved in the snow in the terrible winter of 1887; his mother died the following fall; and his father, old Slope Merrick, was crippled with a gnawing pain in his belly. Slope had arranged with three cowboys, who were following the roundups for other outfits, to brand and tally his remaining scattered cattle, and sell them if anyone wanted to buy; but that

meant putting a lot of trust in frail human nature. He and Elmer, between them, had found and branded only twenty head of calves.

If Slope had any plans for the future, he did not confide in his son, and Elmer confided in nobody. He wanted to talk to Lute Kimball, but Lute spent his time shining up to Miss Charlotte.

The fear pounced at Elmer more than once that summer; he sent it slinking back by ignoring it. He could forget about it if he worked hard enough, and there was work enough to do, with Slope lying in his bunk a good share of the time. Even when Slope decided, one morning before dawn, that he had to get a doctor, the boy still did not quite face his problems. He was too busy to think about it for a while, after his father groaned, "Elmer! Elmer, git up! We're going to Steve's."

Elmer woke his sister by giving her tangled blonde hair a jerk. Varina whimpered and slapped at him blindly.

"We're going to Steve's place for a while," he snapped. "You want to go along, you pile out and git ready!" He was wide awake now, and planning.

"You're going over ahead of us, by yourself."

Slope groaned, "No! Not alone."

But Elmer had his first taste of mastery. "She kin do it," he answered, and his father did not argue.

By the time Varina was dressed and had her extra dress rolled up, Elmer had roped and saddled three horses and tied a rope halter on the cow. It did not occur to him to help his sister mount her horse; she scrambled on with what Lute Kimball, smiling, had called a flying clamber. It was the same system Elmer used himself.

"Hurry up!" Elmer barked. "Tell

'em to git the team and wagon ready to take Pa up to town. We'll be coming along directly."

It was midmorning when Steve Ainsworth helped Slope down from the saddle and into the hay-filled wagon bed.

"I'll take good care of the children, Mr. Merrick," Miss Charlotte promised. "Don't you worry about them for a minute." She held Varina by the hand.

Slope lay back on the blankets and the hay. "Elmer!" he said. "Look after the women."

Elmer answered, "Yuh, sure." He stood with his hands in his pockets, his shoulders hunched.

"My old Colt,"[1] Slope said between his teeth. "You can carry it."

Elmer said, "All right," as calmly as if a dream had not suddenly come true. The old cap-and-ball .44[2] was in Pa's saddle bag with its belt and powder flask and leather sacks of lead bullets and caps.

Steve Ainsworth let go the brake on the wagon. "You'll be all right," he told his sister with what he hoped sounded like conviction. "We'll be back as soon as we can make it. Maybe I can send Lute Kimball down ahead."

"Take good care of Mr. Merrick," she cautioned. "Children, don't you want to wave good-bye?"

Varina obediently waved, but Elmer stood with his hands in his pockets, thinking, Children, huh!

The cow lowed, recalling him to duty.

"I gotta milk," he announced, turning his back as the wagon dropped out of sight beyond the first low ridge. "You could cook us some breakfast. We ain't et yet."

Miss Charlotte was off in a flurry of skirts, exclaiming, "Oh, dear, when will I remember that visitors have to be fed! Come, Varina—you may play the melodeon."

Elmer scowled. "Don't you let her fool around with that!" he ordered. "Make her do something useful. She's got a lot of things to learn."

Miss Charlotte turned, looking puzzled and amused. "She's just a little girl, Elmer. What should she be learning at her age?"

"If I knowed," he burst out in exasperation, "I'd learn her myself. Start her off with cooking. She won't pay no attention to me."

As he plodded with the bucket toward the cow, the fear came right up to meet him, and for the first time he faced it. It said, What you going to do about Varina if your pa dies? and he answered, I'm gonna leave Miss Charlotte look after her.

And what for would Miss Charlotte or anybody want to have her around? How you going to fix that, eh?

He answered honestly, I ain't got that quite figured out yet.

Three days up by wagon, a day to see the doctor, and three days back, if all went well. A week before Steve could get back to the cabin. But Lute could make the return trip in less time. If Steve located him, he might get back late on the fifth day.

The first day Elmer kept busy cutting firewood down by the river, annoyed because Miss Charlotte was pampering Varina, letting her waste time playing the melodeon; although when he came

---

[1]**Colt,** (kōlt), American revolver invented by Samuel Colt, who patented the first successful repeating pistol in 1836.

[2]**cap-and-ball .44,** the .44-caliber revolver just mentioned. This early model required a percussion (priming) cap to fire each separately loaded charge, consisting of powder and a lead ball.

in for meals, Varina industriously peeled potatoes and wiped dishes.

The second day, seven Indians came by. Elmer sent them on their way—an old buck, four squaws, a young girl, and a boy about his own age—but he was embarrassed at having let them get clear to the cabin. He did not go back to cutting wood by the river.

After that, when the water buckets needed filling, he made the women go with him down to the river. Miss Charlotte obviously thought he wanted her for protection and made quite a show of being gay to let him know she wasn't scared. Elmer didn't tell her any differ-

ent. He was learning the patience a man has to have with women.

Miss Charlotte was slightly amused about his wearing the Colt. With what Miss Charlotte didn't know about guns, you could win battles. She didn't even suspect the Colt was loaded; the bright copper caps were plain to see, but she didn't notice. Elmer felt a little guilty about having all six chambers charged; Lute played safer than that, and he had a Frontier model—a Peacemaker[3]— that took regular cartridges. Lute kept

---

[3]a **Frontier model—a Peacemaker,** the most famous of the Colt revolvers. This six-shooter was invented in 1873 and used metal cartridges.

the hammer on an empty chamber. But Elmer Merrick preferred to take chances on shooting himself in the foot accidentally, as long as he could convince himself that he was ready for six kinds of trouble. Reloading took a lot of time; many a man had been killed and scalped, in the old days, while he fumbled with powder and ball.

The third day, Elmer chopped the wood into stove lengths, and on the day after that he started to dig post holes for Steve's horse corral.

When Miss Charlotte saw what he was doing, she came flying out, exclaiming, "Elmer, now you stop that! I don't want you working so hard as you've been doing, Elmer Merrick. I want you to settle down. My goodness, don't you ever play?"

He had not played for a long time; his spare time he had usually spent in practicing things he needed to learn, like roping, or pulling his gun fast. But while he was affronted by her insistence that he was a child, he was pleased that she had noticed how hard he worked.

He set out to chink the cracks of the lean-to, built that spring for Miss Charlotte's bedroom. While he worked at it, he solved part of his problem: What he was going to do if his father did not come back. Somewhere there must be an outfit that needed a wrangler on the home place, a helper to bring in the cavy[4] for the cowboys and chore around for the cook. He dreamed about an imaginary boss saying, "That boy ain't very big for what I had in mind," and Miss Charlotte assuring him, "Oh, but he's a very hard worker. Elmer just works all the time."

And what are you going to do about Varina? his conscience nagged.

I'm figuring about that, he answered patiently. I'm figuring how to get Miss Charlotte to keep her.

That was on the fourth day. On the fifth, Lute Kimball might have come, but a fair-haired stranger got there first, a wary man with quick-darting gray eyes. It was Miss Charlotte's fault that he stayed instead of riding on. She convinced Elmer all over again that she was a tenderfoot and a fool. But it was Elmer's fault that the stranger ever had a chance to feel so much at home.

When the man came, Elmer was in sight, but he was down at the edge of the river grove, with Steve's deer rifle, scouting around where he had seen deer signs.

He did not hear the stranger's horse, but a tingling on the back of his neck made him aware that something was going on. When he saw the buckskin horse and the buckskin-shirted rider, he set out for the cabin at a run.

But Miss Charlotte was already making the stranger welcome. And the man was saying, "Well, now, if you're sure it ain't too much trouble, I could eat all right, and that's a fact."

He whirled when he heard Elmer's pounding feet on the hard earth but the steel-spring tension went out of him when he saw only a boy and not a man. He turned back to Miss Charlotte and took off his dusty hat with a flourish.

"Buck Saddler, ma'am, and pleased to make your acquaintance."

"I am Miss Charlotte Ainsworth," she answered, smiling, "and these are the Merrick children, Elmer and Varina. If you'd like to wash up, Mr. Saddler, there's the basin."

The man hesitated for just a mo-

---

[4]cavy (ka′vē) or cavvy, saddle horses.

ment. "Thank you kindly. I'll just look after my horse first." He loosened the saddle cinch and walked around the horse, frowning and shaking his head. "Poor boy!" he murmured, slapping the animal's shoulder. "Plumb beat, ain't you?" Then he turned to Elmer and commented, grinning, "You sure carry a lot of artillery."

Elmer glanced at the man's sagging gunbelt and loaded saddle and answered, "So do you." Buck Saddler carried a rifle and a shotgun on the saddle, and two belts of cartridges slung over the horn—not unreasonable armament for a long journey, but impressive.

The stranger glanced at the hogleg[5] that pulled Elmer's belt down and smiled with unwise condescension. "I gollies, one of them old cap-and-ball Colts! Let's look at it, kid."

Elmer backed off, scowling. "Nobody touches my gun but me."

"If you was to show it to me," the stranger offered, teasing, "I might let you see mine."

"I kin see it," Elmer informed him. "It's a Peacemaker." In the old days before he had so many other things to worry about, he had dreamed of owning a Peacemaker himself, and money enough to buy all the ammunition he wanted, and hands big enough to handle a man-sized gun easily.

Miss Charlotte called, "I've got the griddle heating for pancakes. It's close to suppertime, so we'll all eat."

"You'll be wanting to go on before dark," Elmer told the stranger, hinting strongly. "We better git in there and eat, so's you won't be delayed."

Buck Saddler looked down at him through half-shut eyes. "I might have

to delay anyway," he said deliberately. He walked toward the cabin and left Elmer worrying. Miss Charlotte worried him more. She fussed as if Buck Saddler were a welcome guest. "Now, if you'll sit here, Mr. Saddler! You prefer the other side of the table? Of course, of course. Varina, Elmer, did you wash?"

Buck Saddler, Elmer noted, preferred to sit facing the window. You got some good reason for that, Elmer decided. And there's nothing wrong with that horse you're so cut up about.

Miss Charlotte raised her eyebrows at Elmer. "Young man, you can't come to the table with that gun on." Elmer kept his mouth shut, but it required effort. Never before in his life had he wanted so much to have a gun handy. But Buck Saddler stood up, grinning, unbuckled his own belt and hung it ostentatiously on a peg on the wall. Elmer did the same and sat down at the table without appetite.

Where's Lute? he fretted. It's time you come, Lute Kimball!

Lute Kimball was riding as hard as he dared on a spent horse, but he was also dreaming, as he often did, of being a hero for Miss Charlotte. No one would have suspected so stern-faced a man of dreaming about anything. He was a dark and silent man, thoughtful and practical. He had never stayed very long in any territory or on any job, but he had never quit any job so long as the boss needed him. He had made two trail drives up from Texas, and for most of his life had been looking for greener pastures. When Steve Ainsworth's sister came West, he saw them for the first time—green pastures, full of flowers, wherever Miss Charlotte was. Lute Kimball was twenty-seven

---

[5]hogleg, a large single-action revolver.

years old that summer, and ready to settle down.

He missed his chance to be a hero for Steve's pretty sister, after all. He reached the cabin a few minutes too late.

Elmer had to admit that Miss Charlotte didn't make any more fuss over Buck Saddler than she did over anybody else; she always seemed delighted to see anyone who happened to come. But the stranger, following her quick movements with his darting eyes, assumed that he was a favored guest. He turned courtly and affable.

"That there pretty little organ," he commented, "that's a mighty nice thing to have. I bet you play it mighty pretty, Miss Charlotte."

"Only a few tunes," Miss Charlotte fibbed modestly. "But Varina, my goodness, Varina is learning to play it very nicely." To Elmer's disgust his little sister piped up, "I sure do play it good."

Charlotte beamed and did not reprimand her for boasting.

If Miss Charlotte wanted to bring the little girl into the conversation, the stranger was willing to play along. He said fatuously to Varina, "You're a real smart little girl, ain't you? And all fixed up with your hair in curls, anybody'd think it was your birthday, maybe."

"When is your birthday, dear?" Charlotte inquired.

Varina looked puzzled. Elmer answered, "Fifteenth of August. She don't know nothing."

Miss Charlotte glanced up at the calendar. "I declare," she cried, "that's today! If I'd known, I'd have baked a cake!"

Birthdays had never been of much account in the Merrick cabin; Varina would never have thought of making a fuss if she hadn't been encouraged. But Buck Saddler encouraged her.

"By George, a nice bright little girl like that, and she ain't got no cake or no presents! Now that sure is a shame!"

Varina's eyes flooded with tears. She began to cry, with her face in Miss Charlotte's lap.

Elmer growled, "Shut up, Foolish!" Embarrassed, he explained, "She don't howl like that when she falls off a horse."

Miss Charlotte patted the child's shoulder. "We'll have a present for Varina. I know just the thing—a pretty ribbon I brought in my trunk. Would you like a ribbon for your hair, Varina?"

Varina heard that, in spite of her squalling, and nodded emphatically.

The stranger said, "I can't have a lady beating my time with this here little girl. I'm gonna give her a present, too." He dug in his pocket, fished around a little, and brought out a coin. He opened Varina's hand and closed her fingers over the gift. Tear-stained, she stared at it.

Miss Charlotte cried, "Mr. Saddler, you can't do that! Why, it's a double eagle!"[6]

He said with reproach, "Wouldn't want me to take back what I give her, would you, Miss Charlotte? No sir, that's for the little lady." He looked so smug that Elmer wanted to hit him.

And then he said the thing that scared Elmer: "Plenty more where that came from," said Buck Saddler.

For a few seconds Elmer forgot to breathe. A man might possibly have

---

[6]**double eagle,** a twenty-dollar gold piece.

one gold piece or a couple. But if there's plenty more where that came from, Elmer realized, he never earned it. Was it a bank or a stage?

Miss Charlotte's face had colored, and she looked even a little scared, Elmer thought. Glowering at her, he could suddenly tell what she was thinking: Go away, you man! We don't want you here!

Never before had he been able to see so clearly what was in an adult's mind. The revelation startled him so much that, for a moment, he was dazed by his own cleverness. And then, with desperate cunning, he arrived at the answer to that dismal question: What are you going to do about Varina?

If Miss Charlotte was to owe me a debt, he thought, might be she'd take Foolish and raise her. Might be she'd be that grateful. Well, how can I get rid of this man?

That was how Elmer got on the track of saving Miss Charlotte—for cold, calculating reasons of his own. Lute Kimball, who had another reason for wanting to do the same thing if he ever had a chance—no less selfish a reason, but very different—still had nine miles to ride.

Miss Charlotte was not one to depend on someone else if she could do a thing herself. She started in a business-like way to pick up the dirty dishes. Pointedly she remarked, "It'll be dark in no time. You'll be wanting to go on, Mr. Saddler."

The stranger frowned. "I don't rightly like to leave you all here without no menfolks," he objected. "No telling what might come along."

"How true," Miss Charlotte murmured. "Don't give it a thought, Mr. Saddler. Elmer is our menfolks, and we are entirely confident that he will look after everything."

Elmer stared, for the first time thinking that Charlotte Ainsworth was, though still a tenderfoot, not actually a fool.

He began to figure: If I do this, he'll do that, but maybe he won't. Well, if I do that, what'll he do? Elmer was eleven years old and scared silly. But he was a prairie boy, and if he had not been self-reliant, he would not have lived to be eleven years old.

Buck Saddler gave him time to think. Buck wiped his mustache on his sleeve and strolled over to look at the melodeon. To the entranced Varina, he suggested, "How'd you like to play me a little tune, girlie?"

Miss Charlotte said, "Varina is going to help me with the dishes," but Varina did no such thing. She started to pump the melodeon; she had to stand up to reach the keyboard, and pump the little metal pedal with one foot. Looking very well pleased with herself, she began picking out notes.

In the midst of figuring about Buck, Elmer thought, however would Miss Charlotte or anybody want to raise her, when she don't mind no better than that?

But he got his problem solved. If I do that, he will do this. There were only a few maybe's this time. Almost everything depended on: If I do that.

When he reached up to get his gun belt, Buck Saddler was instantly alert, but he only watched. He was within reaching distance of his Peacemaker. Elmer removed the old .44 from its holster, but left the belt and holster hanging on the peg. He walked over to

Steve's small box of tools on the window sill and began to rummage.

Charlotte, scraping plates, asked tensely, "What are you looking for?"

"Worm," he muttered. "Think Steve's got a worm here. I want to unload my gun."

She looked so sick and helpless Elmer was afraid she would cry out and give everything away.

"This'll do it," Elmer remarked.

Buck watched him, slit-eyed, not moving. Elmer took his own sweet time. Never once did he move quickly; he kept the old Cavalry Colt carefully pointed at the wall while he worked, with the casual carefulness of one who had always handled firearms and had not pointed a gun at anyone since he got his ears boxed for it at the age of four. Delicately, he pried five caps off their nipples and let them lay on the table in plain sight. Painstakingly, he reamed the powder and ball from five chambers, and Buck could count if he chose.

Buck relaxed enough to comment, "Mighty pretty tune you're playing, girlie." Miss Charlotte did not relax at all.

Elmer, on the far side of the table, put the gun down on the bench where he sat, with enough force to make his heart stop, because one chamber was still charged, and the cap was on the nipple. He sat for a little while, yawning, while he slid the long weapon down through his torn pocket and along his leg. The hole in his pocket was just right to catch and hold the hammer. When he stood up, yawning, Buck Saddler demanded, "Where you think you're going?"

"A person can go outside, can't they?" Elmer answered with elaborate dignity. "Maybe I'm gonna hunt rabbits."

Buck grinned. Hunting rabbits was what gentlemen passengers were invited to do when stage coaches with lady passengers made a comfort stop. Ladies "picked flowers."

When Elmer Merrick went outside to start to rescue Miss Charlotte, Lute Kimball was still two miles away.

"You was gone quite a while," Buck commented a little later.

"I come back," Elmer pointed out. "Your horse is down," he announced, as if he didn't care one way or the other. "I'll get the lantern if you'd like to take a look."

Buck scowled. "There wasn't nothing wrong with that horse!"

He was cornered and puzzled. But how could he be cornered by a small boy who had just unloaded his gun in plain sight? Buck Saddler relaxed and grinned.

"We'll be right back," he promised Miss Charlotte. "And the little girl can play me another tune." So complete was his disdain that he did not even reach up to the peg for his gun belt. Elmer came close to choking, because he wanted to draw a deep breath of relief and could not. That had been one of the maybe's.

He lighted the lantern and held it in front of him so that his shadow was in Buck Saddler's path. Buck grunted and snatched the lantern. Beyond the saddle shed he held the lantern high.

"There's nothing wrong with that horse!" he growled.

"Not a thing," agreed Elmer. "He's all cinched up and ready to travel."

Saddler laughed. "I ain't traveling nowhere. Not till I get ready."

"You're ready now," Elmer told him softly. "And this gun says so."

Saddler sneered. "I seen you unload it."

"You seen me unload five chambers. I got one charge left—and that's all it takes. You want to find out for sure, mister?" he demanded with tense urgency. "You ever get hit with a ball from a .44 not ten feet away from you?" Buck glanced toward his saddle. "Your other artillery is on my saddle," Elmer told him. "You'll get it back, but not just yet. Hold the lantern nice and steady, Buck."

Getting on his horse was another of the maybe's, but Saddler was wise enough to make no false moves. Elmer went up to his saddle like a flying bird, and when he got there, he cocked the hammer.

He heard Buck's grunt at the triple click, as the stranger realized that the gun had not been ready for action until that moment. Buck had been a man for too many years; he had forgotten that a boy's hand might not be big enough to cock and fire a single-action revolver with one quick motion.

"Git on your horse, mister," Elmer told him.

They rode away from the cabin. And Lute Kimball, coming over a hill, saw the lantern on the ground.

Half an hour later, several hills away, Elmer said, "You kin stop now. I'm gonna drop your guns and cartridge belts. You can pick 'em up, and I'll be watching, still with my gun in my hand, Buck. Your rifle and shotgun are plumb empty."

The cabin was dark when Elmer got back to it. He could feel the waiting silence. Lute Kimball called, "Elmer, anybody with you?"

Elmer went limp in the saddle as the strength went out of him along with the tension. "Nope," he croaked.

Miss Charlotte called, "Are you all right?"

"Aw, sure," he answered. But when he slid from the saddle, his knees went limber. He landed in a heap.

Lute said, "Come in the cabin. We're not going to have a light any more." He was standing in the doorway with his rifle ready, watching into the darkness.

Miss Charlotte said, "Varina is asleep in the lean-to. She doesn't know anything special happened."

Foolish is the lucky one, Elmer thought. All hell could bust loose and she'd never know it.

He remarked, "I don't think he'll come back."

Lute laughed, one short laugh. "I don't think he will. Getting run off by a runt of a boy with an empty gun."

"It wasn't empty," Elmer explained. "I had one chamber loaded."

"Did you now?" Lute sounded half smothered. "One charge, so you was all ready for bear!" He moved aside as Elmer entered the cabin, but he stayed near the doorway, watching into the night with the rifle over his arm.

Elmer took three deep breaths and asked, "How's Pa?"

Lute cleared his throat, and Miss Charlotte said softly in the darkness, "Elmer, come over here to me. Please?" She put her arm around his shoulders, and he tried to stop shivering. "Lute?" she prompted.

Lute told him then. "Your pa died just before Steve got him to town. Steve stayed to see he got a good funeral. Your pa wanted him to."

Elmer stepped away from the gentle

pressure of Miss Charlotte's arm, and his voice was gruff in his own ears. "I been figuring," he said. "I can make a deal."

"What kind of a deal, Elmer?" Miss Charlotte's voice was like rippling creek water.

"If you was to take her back East with you," he stumbled along, "I'd turn over our stock to your brother, and maybe it would bring enough to pay for raising her." He could not remind her that she owed him anything; he was suddenly a man, burdened with a man's gallantry. He was asking her for a favor. "If it ain't enough," he offered, "I kin earn the rest after I git bigger."

She said, "Oh, Elmer!" as if she might cry any minute. "I—I might not go back East," she said. Lute, standing there black against the night, jerked his head.

"I don't want her raised out here!" Elmer cried out frantically. "Ma always said this ain't no country for women!"

"It will be," Miss Charlotte promised. "It's going to be, before long. Men like you and Mr. Kimball will make it so. This is going to be a good place to live."

He was not a man any more. He was eleven years old and had nothing more to do with problems that were too big for him. He put his hands up to his face and began to sob. He cried for a long time, and neither Lute nor Miss Charlotte said a word or made a move.

When he was through, Lute spoke as if nothing had happened. "Tomorrow," he said, "you can be a kid if you want to. If you haven't forgotten how. You got that coming to you. But tonight I need a partner."

Until dawn, Elmer stood in the doorway with his new gun in his hand—the

Peacemaker that had been Buck Saddler's. Lute prowled around farther away with a rifle, listening and watching. Nobody came.

Twelve years later, Varina Merrick spent her double eagle to buy her wedding clothes. Elmer, stiff and solemn in a new suit—tall and sturdy, a good hand at anything he undertook—gave the bride away. He had almost forgotten how hard he tried to give Varina away once before.   THE END

↻ **Talking it over**

1. *a.* Which of the following needs does Elmer worry about when he first realizes his father may die?
    (1) His and his sister's need for affection
    (2) Varina's need for someone to take care of her
    (3) His own need to be recognized as a person who can handle adult responsibilities
  b. What plans does he make?

2. *a.* Elmer's reasons for saving Miss Charlotte are described as "cold and calculating." In what sense is this true?
  b. How might another person—Lute Kimball, for instance —view Elmer's reasons?

3. When Buck Saddler gives Varina a gold coin and announces, "Plenty more where that came from," Elmer decides that Saddler didn't earn all that money.
    a. Find at least three places in the story before this point where you infer that something about the stranger makes Elmer suspicious.

b. What inferences might Elmer make from the things he notices?

4. Why does Elmer think Miss Charlotte is a fool? Discuss whether or not he is right, using things Miss Charlotte says or does as evidence.

5. *a.* Elmer is a boy who is on the verge of becoming a man. From which of the following can you infer that Elmer is still a child in many ways?

(1) He worries about and plans for Varina's future.

(2) He thinks no one would want Varina because she is so useless.

(3) On Steve's ranch, he milks the cows, cuts firewood, and digs post holes.

(4) When the water buckets need filling, he makes the women go with him to the river.

(5) He wears the Colt with all six chambers loaded.

(6) He is annoyed because Miss Charlotte pampers Varina.

(7) He daydreams about Miss Charlotte complimenting him in front of an imaginary boss.

(8) He takes the blame for letting a stranger get as far as the house.

b. What do the other thoughts and actions show about Elmer?

⇄ **Words in action**

What is the "it" referred to at the top of page 426: "Waking or sleeping it stalked him and sometimes it leaped and took his breath away"?

To say that fear stalks, leaps, and takes, gives one the idea that fear is a person or an animal that is able to think, move, and act on its own.

1. Find the paragraph on page 427 where fear is spoken of as if it were a living creature.

2. How does Richard Wright use the same method of expressing an idea in the first paragraph of "Hunger" on page 403?

3. What things in the following sentences are spoken of as if they were people or animals?

a. If lightning is going to strike me, it will find me in the basement.

b. When asked why his nose was always red, a man replied: "It's so proud of staying out of other people's business that it's blushing."

c. The wind whispered and sighed and was silent.

She's an honorary Blackfoot

Dorothy Johnson is in love with the West, especially with the state of Montana, where she lives. "We have all this wonderful space with practically nobody in it," she explains. Most of her books are about the West. Several television programs and two motion pictures, "The Hanging Tree" and "The Man Who Shot Liberty Valance," have been based on her western stories.

Miss Johnson was born in Iowa but grew up in Whitefish, Montana, in the Rocky Mountains. After working for several years in New York as a magazine editor, she happily returned to Montana. She now teaches journalism at Montana State University.

She is an honorary member of Montana's Blackfoot Indian tribe.

A MEETING WITH STONE AGE ESKIMOS

by Vilhjalmur Stefansson

*In 1910 there were still parts of the world
which had never been visited by white men,
and primitive people who lived the way
Europeans lived ten thousand years ago.
There were rumors that a group of such people
lived in the mysterious arctic region of Canada,
around Coronation Gulf and on Victoria Island.
Finding these people was one of the main objectives
of the polar explorer and anthropologist,
Vilhjalmur Stefansson. With him were three
Eskimos—two men, Natkusiak and Tannaumirk,
who were to drive the dog teams and help with
hunting, and an elderly widow, Pannigabluk,
whose job was to make and repair the men's
fur clothing and to cook their food.*

ON APRIL 21, 1910, we left our expedition camp at Cape Parry and set out eastward into unknown territory with a sledgeload of two weeks' supplies and a brainload of theory about living off the land. Bear and seal had been scarce at Cape Parry, and all the Eskimo insisted that game was sure to be even scarcer farther east. Most of the group also insisted that there were no people living between Cape Parry and Cape Krusenstern, two hundred miles east.

From the start we found game, and it was not long before we found traces of humans as well, remains of whaling villages. Though it was plain that these villages had not been inhabited

Adapted from *Discovery: The Autobiography of Vilhjalmur Stefansson* by Vilhjalmur Stefansson. Copyright 1964 by Evelyn Stefansson. Used by permission of McGraw-Hill Book Company.

recently, I was encouraged to believe that if Eskimo had once found the region livable they might do so still. My Eskimos were not greatly impressed by this reasoning. Each time we shot a caribou they insisted that it was probably only a straggler and that there would be no more. They were gloomy even while they were gorging themselves on huge quantities of seal meat.

Nineteen days after leaving Cape Parry we were still a long way from the place where the nearest humans were supposed to live. But on May 9 we had a surprise. At Point Wise we came upon a beach strewn with driftwood. There was nothing unusual in that, but what I saw when I stopped to examine the first piece *was* unusual. The wood had been hacked at with a dull adz-like tool. This could only mean that men who were unknown to the western Eskimos and to white whalers and explorers had been here looking for sledge-making material.

My Eskimos were immediately alarmed. Tannaumirk had been entertaining us with wild tales of the "People of the Caribou Antler" who captured their brides with a crook of caribou horn, often killing them as they did so, and who supposedly killed all strangers. These must be the people who had been here.

Excitement grew the following day when we found footprints and sled tracks not more than three months old. That evening we found a deserted village of more than fifty snowhouses, an astonishing number. Tannaumirk had never seen a village among his own people of more than twelve or fifteen houses. The occupants of the houses had apparently moved on during the midwinter. Their broad trail led out across the ice in the direction of Victoria Island.

I now decided that I would try to locate the people who had made this trail. I left Pannigabluk in charge of our camp and told Tannaumirk, who had scared himself into a sweat with his own stories, that he might stay with her if he wished. When he realized that the Caribou Antler people might just as easily descend on our base camp as on us while we crossed the ice, he decided that Natkusiak and I would be better protectors than the elderly lady Pannigabluk.

On May 13 the three of us set out across the ice, coming, in a few hours, to another large deserted village. From the roof of one of its snowhouses I could see, a long way off, a scattering of men sitting at seal holes, watching.

Our dogs became suddenly alert. The Eskimos looked at each other somewhat doubtfully. As we drew nearer, apparently unseen, we singled out one still figure and approached cautiously. Tannaumirk, fascinated though terrified, led the way.

The strange Eskimo did not move until Tannaumirk was within five paces of him. Suddenly he jumped to his feet and stood in a threatening position brandishing a long knife. Tannaumirk cringed a little and began talking wildly. The frightened sealer began a monotonous, staccato intonation that seemed to be merely sound without words. I later learned that this was a defense against being struck dumb, since a man confronted by a spirit will never speak again unless he makes a sound with every breath he draws.

Finally, the strange Eskimo recovered himself enough to notice our dogs and their harness, which seemed to convince him that we were no evil spirits. Tannaumirk, too, got hold of himself and began to explain that he was unarmed and meant no harm. The sealer came slowly forward and touched Tannaumirk's arm. Convinced that it was a human arm, he said that he would take us to his village. Tannaumirk followed him, and Natkusiak and I decided to remain a little behind until the villagers had been convinced that they could safely accept us. We soon were left in no doubt about our welcome.

From all about on the white ice, dark figures converged upon us, crowding about and scaring Tannaumirk all over again. Women and children and old men came from their houses in the distance. When convinced that we were men and not spirits, they ran toward us, shouting, "I am So-and-So. I am friendly. See—no knife! Who are you?" We introduced ourselves while the women went back to their houses to cook for us. We had become very important persons.

The men asked where we would like to camp. I pointed out a spot a little way from their village, explaining that I did not want our dogs to have any chance to fight with theirs. Children rushed back into the houses to get their fathers' snow knives and building mittens. We were not allowed to do anything but watch the rapid construction of our snowhouse and its furnishing with skin and lamps. We were told that it was ours to occupy until all the food in the village was used up. The next day was to be a holiday, with no hunting or fishing but with plenty of opportunity for each of us to learn about the others' ways.

I have since looked back to that day with the warmest and most vivid of memories. It marked my introduction to men and women of a bygone age. These Eskimos were much like the hunting tribes of Britain and Gaul during the Ice Age more than ten thousand years ago. They gathered their food with the weapons of the Stone Age.

The dialect that these people spoke differed so little from the speech which I had learned in three years of living with the western Eskimos that we could make ourselves understood from the first. It cannot have happened often in the history of the world that the first explorer to visit a primitive people was one who spoke their language.

Before the house the men were building for us was quite ready, children came running from the village to announce that their mothers had dinner cooked. The houses were so small that it was not convenient to invite all three of us into the same one. Moreover, it was not etiquette to do so, as we learned. Each of us was therefore taken to a different place. My host was the seal hunter whom we had first approached on the ice. His house would, he said, be a fitting one in which to offer me my first meal among them. It happened that his wife had been born farther west on the mainland coast than anyone else in the village. She would therefore like to ask me questions.

It turned out that his wife was not a talkative or inquisitive person. She was motherly, kindly, and hospitable. Her first questions were about my footgear. Were my feet just a little damp? Might she not pull my boots off for me and dry them over the lamp? Would I not put on a pair of her husband's dry socks? Was there no little hole in my mittens or my coat that she could mend for me?

She had boiled some lean seal meat for me, but she had not boiled any fat, for she thought I might prefer it raw. They always cut the fat in small pieces and ate it raw themselves. However, the pot still hung over the lamp, and anything she put into it would be cooked in a moment.

When I told her that my taste in seal fat was the same as theirs she was delighted. People were much alike, then, after all, though they came from a great distance. She would accordingly treat me as if I were one of their own people come to visit them from afar.

When we entered the house the boiled pieces of seal meat had already been taken out of the pot and lay steaming on a wooden side table. My hostess

picked out for me the lower joint of a seal's foreleg, squeezed it firmly with her hands to make sure that nothing would later drip from it, and handed it to me, along with her own copper-bladed knife. The next most desirable piece was similarly squeezed and handed to her husband, and other pieces given in turn to the rest of the family.

When this had been done, one extra piece was set aside in case I should want a second helping. The rest of the boiled meat was divided into four portions, with the explanation that there were four families in the village who had no fresh meat. The little adopted daughter of the house, a girl of seven or eight, took a wooden platter and carried the four pieces of meat to the

families who had none of their own. I learned later that every house in the village in which any cooking was done had likewise sent four portions. During our meal, presents of food were also brought from other houses.

As we ate we sat on the front edge of the bed-platform, each holding his piece of meat in the left hand and a knife in the right. This was my first experience with a knife of native copper. I found it sharp and serviceable.

My hostess sat on my right in front of the cooking lamp, her husband on my left. As the house was an ordinary oval snow dome, about seven by nine feet, there was room only for the three of us on the front edge of the two-foot-high snow platform, over which reindeer, bear, and musk-ox skins had been spread to make the bed. The children, therefore, ate standing in the bit of open floor space to the left of the door. The lamp and cooking gear and frames for drying clothing took up the space to the right.

Our meal consisted of two courses— the first, lean and fat meat; the second, soup. Soup was made by chopping frozen seal blood into the boiling broth immediately after the cooked meat had been taken out of the pot. The pot was then stirred briskly until the whole came nearly, but never quite, to a second boil. This made a soup of a thickness comparable to our pea soup. A few handfuls of snow were stirred into the soup to cool it. With a dipper the housewife then filled large musk-ox-horn drinking cups and gave one to each person.

After I had eaten my fill of fresh seal and drunk two cupfuls of blood soup, my host and I moved farther back on the bed-platform, where we could sit comfortably propped up against bundles of soft caribou skins while we talked. He and his wife said they understood why we had left behind the woman of our party, for it is always safest to assume that strangers are going to prove hostile. Now that we had found them to be harmless and friendly, would we not allow them to send a sledge in the morning to bring her to the village? They would like to see a western woman.

It must be a very long way to the land from which we came, they said. Were we not tired of traveling, and did we not think of spending the summer with them? Of course, all the eastern groups would treat us well, unless we went too far to the east and fell in with the treacherous Netsilik people of

King William Island. Still farther east, they had heard, lived the white men (Kablunat), of whom, no doubt, we had never heard, seeing that we came from the west.

The white men, they told me, live farthest to the east of all people. They were said to have various physical deformities and to be of a strange disposition. Sometimes when they gave valuable things to an Eskimo they would take no pay for them. At other times they wanted huge prices for useless articles. White people would not eat good, ordinary food, but lived on various things that a normal person could not think of forcing himself to swallow except in case of starvation. The strange thing was that the white men could have had better things to eat if they wanted to. Seals, whales, fish, and even caribou abound in their country.

I had only to give a hint of what interested me to be told whatever they knew. In the telling, they differentiated between what they considered certain, merely probable, or possibly unreliable. They showed delicacy in asking questions. Were they not interested, I asked them, to know why I had come and where I was going? Yes, they were interested, but they knew that if I wanted them to know I would tell them. Asking many questions of strangers was not their custom. They considered that I asked many questions because to do so was no doubt good manners among my people. It was to be expected that men coming from so great a distance would have customs different from theirs.

We sat and talked perhaps an hour, until a messenger came (it was always the children who carried messages) to say that my companions had gone to the house that had been built for us and that the people hoped I could come there too.

At the house I found that although several people had already arrived, there was still plenty of room for the four or five who had come along to see me home. The floor of the inner half of the house had been raised into the usual two-foot-high snow sleeping platform, covered with skins, partly ours and partly contributed by various households. A seal-oil lamp for heating and lighting had been installed. It was a cozy place, heated by the lamp to 60° F. Our guests stayed only a few minutes. Someone suggested that we were no doubt tired and sleepy and would like to be left alone. In the morning, they said, we would have plenty of time for talking.

When they were all gone, however, we did not go to sleep, but sat up half the night discussing the strange things we had seen and heard. My companions were quite as excited as I. It was, they said, as if we were living through a story such as old people tell in the assembly house when the sun is away during the winter. What kindly, inoffensive-looking people these were! No doubt, however, they were powerful and dangerous magicians, such as the stories tell about.

Tannaumirk had heard something that seemed to bear this out. He had been guest in the house of a man who last winter had dropped his knife into a seal hole through the ice where the sea was very deep. So powerful was the spell the hunter pronounced that when he reached down into the sea the water came only to his elbow, yet he picked the knife right off the ocean bottom! This, Tannaumirk commented, was where the ice alone was at least six feet thick, and the water beneath the ice so deep that a stone dropped into it would take a long time to sink to the bottom.

I asked my companions if they believed such stories. I knew what the answer would be. Of course they did. Why should I ask? Had they not often told me that their own people were able to do such things until a few years ago, when they gave up their familiar spirits after learning from missionaries that no one can attain salvation who employs spirits to do his bidding?

Next morning, when we woke up and began to stir about, we were aware that someone had been listening outside our snowhouse for a long time, waiting for signs that we were awake. I now know that it was a signal from this watcher that brought us our earliest visitor of the morning, the hunter whom we had first met. He came from the village, walking slowly and singing at the top of his voice so that we might have ample warning of his approach. When he came to the outer door of our twenty-foot alleyway he stopped and announced himself: "I am So-and-So; my intentions are friendly; I have no knife. May I come in?" This was the formula in dealing with us. Among themselves they would merely announce as they were about to enter the house, "I am So-and-So; I am coming in."

The talk that morning turned on various things. They had never seen white men, they told me. Nor had they ever seen the woodland Indians. They had, however, discovered traces of these people on the mainland to the south, and they knew by hearsay from the Coppermine River Eskimos that the Indians were treacherous, blood-thirsty people, wicked and great magicians.

And what did they think of me—to what people did they suppose I belonged? Oh, but they did not have to guess; they knew. Tannaumirk had told them that he belonged to the Kupagmiut, of whom they had heard many stories from their fathers. My accent made it plain that I belonged to the Kupagmiut also.

But, I asked, did they not consider the color of my blue-gray eyes and of my light brown beard unusual? Did not these things incline them to believe that I must belong to a different people? They replied, "We have no reason to think that you belong to a different people. Your speech differs from ours only a little more than does that of some people with whom we trade every year. As for your eyes and beard, they are much like those of some of our neighbors to the north, whom you must visit."[1]

One of the things that interested me was to see some shooting with the strong-looking bows and long copper-tipped arrows owned by every man of the tribe. I therefore said that I would like to have them illustrate to me the manner in which they killed caribou, and I would in turn show them the weapons and methods used by us.

Half a dozen of the men at once sent home for their bows, and a block of snow to serve as a target was set up in front of our house. The range at

which a target a foot square could be hit with fair regularity turned out to be about thirty or thirty-five yards, and the extreme range of the bow was a bit over one hundred yards. The range at which caribou are ordinarily shot was shown to be about seventy-five yards.

When the exhibition was over, I set up a stick at about two hundred yards and fired at it. The people who stood around had no idea as to the character of the thing I was about to do, and when they heard the loud report of my gun all the women and children made a scramble for the houses, while the men ran back about fifteen or twenty yards and stood talking together excitedly behind a snow wall. I asked them to come with me to the stick and see what happened to it. After some persuasion three of them complied, but unfortunately for me it turned out that I had failed to score. At this they seemed much relieved, but when I told them I would try again they protested earnestly, saying that so loud a noise would scare all the seals away from their hunting grounds, and the people would therefore starve.

It seemed to me important, however, to show them I could keep my word and pierce the stick at two hundred yards. So in spite of their protests I got ready to shoot again, telling them that we used these weapons in the west for seal-hunting, and that the noise did not scare seals away. The second shot happened to hit, but on the whole the mark of the bullet on the stick impressed them far less than the noise. In fact, they did not seem to marvel at it at all. When I explained to them that I could kill a polar bear or a caribou at even twice the distance the stick had been from me they showed no surprise, but

[1]Stefansson later visited these Eskimos and found that they had many of the physical traits of Europeans, although they had had no contact with white men for more than a hundred years. He came to the conclusion that ancestors of these people had intermarried with white settlers who disappeared mysteriously from Greenland a thousand years ago.

asked me if I could with my rifle kill a caribou on the other side of a mountain. When I said that I could not, they told me a great shaman in the neighboring tribe had a magic arrow by which he could kill caribou on the other side of no matter how big a mountain. In other words, much to my surprise, they considered the performance of my rifle nothing wonderful.

I understand the point of view better now than I did then. It is simply this: if you were to show an Eskimo a bow that would shoot fifty yards farther than any bow he ever saw, he would never cease marveling, and he would tell of that bow as long as he lived. He would understand exactly the principle on which it works, would judge it by the standards of the natural, and would find it to excel marvelously. But show him the work of the rifle, which he does not in the least understand, and he is face to face with a miracle; he judges it by the standards of the supernatural instead of by the standards of the natural; he compares it with other miraculous things of which he has heard and which he may even think he has himself seen, and he finds it not at all beyond the average of miracles.

It was near noon of our first day when someone asked me if there were not some way in which the western people customarily celebrated the arrival of visitors. We replied that usually all the village gathered in a great dance. That was their way, too, our hosts told us. Seeing that our customs were the same, they immediately planned to make a large dance house. We should see how they danced, and possibly we might dance for them too.

By midafternoon the dance house was finished, a snow dome at least nine feet high. Since a snowhouse is half a sphere, this meant a floor eighteen feet in diameter. It was large enough to hold forty people standing in a circle around a five-foot dancing space in the center.

While the men were putting the finishing touches on the dance house, someone brought the drum and a young woman sang for us to its accompaniment. She handled it like a tambourine and played it in a manner quite different from that of the western Eskimos. The songs were different too. She sang them charmingly. One song had a rhythm that seemed to me to resemble that of the ancient Norse scaldic poems. The girl who sang it was very fair for an Eskimo and had the long-fingered hands I have seen only among half-bloods in Alaska.

The festival continued all through the afternoon. Many of the dances were performed without moving the feet at all, merely by swaying the body and gesticulating with the arms. In some cases the performer sang, recited, or uttered a series of exclamations. In others he was silent.

At this time of year—the middle of May—there was no darkness at midnight. Nevertheless, the people ate three meals a day with fair regularity. When our dance ended, about eight o'clock in the evening, the women announced supper. After supper I sat awhile and talked with my host and hostess and one or two visitors. When I got up to go, all of them walked home with me. Some others were already there, as they had been the evening before. They stayed only a short while. By eleven o'clock the last visitors had said good night and our first whole day among the Stone Age people had come to its end.   THE END

1. *a.* Why were his companions uneasy about meeting the people Stefansson was looking for?

b. Describe what happened when Stefansson's party approached the seal hunter. Why did the hunter behave the way he did?

c. How did the Stone Age Eskimos behave toward the visitors when they understood they were harmless?

2. *a.* What ideas did the Eskimos have about white people to the east, whom they had never seen?

b. What explanation can you offer for the tales they told?

c. Why didn't they realize that Stefansson was a white man?

3. How did these Eskimos explain puzzling things that happened around them? Why weren't they impressed with what Stefansson's gun could do?

4. Compare the way the Eskimos treated Stefansson and his companions with the way visitors from far away would be entertained in homes you know. In what specific ways did the Eskimos try to make their guests feel comfortable and at ease?

5. Stefansson hoped that the primitive Eskimos could be protected from modern "civilization." (See biographical article.) What things about the Eskimos—the way they provided for basic necessities—might have made him feel that their way of life should stay as it was?

6. *a.* Which relationship — cause-effect or time order—did Stefansson mainly use in writing this account?

b. Though the article as a whole is based mainly on one relationship, it also contains many examples of the other. Mention two or three.

⇄ **Words in action**

1. How are the following words alike in structure? *snowhouse, hearsay, bygone, half-blood, footgear*

2. *a.* The dictionary entry below gives seven definitions for *blood.* Which meaning does *blood* have in *half-blood* on page 447?

b. In which of the following sentences does *blood* have the same meaning as in *half-blood?* (1) Blood is thicker than water. (2) He killed him in cold blood.

3. *a.* The dictionary entry gives eight definitions of *gear.* Which meaning does *gear* have in *footgear* on page 441?

b. In which of the following sentences does *gear* have the same meaning as in *footgear?* (1) The driver shifted into third *gear.* (2) Teddy carried extra *gear* in his saddlebag.

blood (blud), **1.** the red liquid in the veins and arteries of vertebrates; the red liquid that flows from a cut. Blood is circulated by the heart, and carries oxygen and digested food to all parts of the body and takes away waste materials. **2.** the corresponding liquid in lower animals. **3.** bloodshed; slaughter. **4.** family; birth; relationship; parentage; descent: *Love of the sea runs in his blood.* **5.** high lineage, especially royal lineage: *a prince of the blood.* **6.** temper; state of mind: *There was bad blood between them.* **7.** man of dash and spirit. *n.*
in cold blood, 1. cruelly. **2.** on purpose.

gear (gir), **1.** wheel having teeth that hit into the teeth of another wheel of the same kind. If the wheels are of different sizes, they will turn at different speeds. See cogwheel for picture. **2.** connect by gears. An automobile moves when the motor is geared to the rear wheels. **3.** fit or work together; mesh: *The cogs gear smoothly.* **4.** arrangement of fixed and moving parts for transmitting or changing motion; mechanism; machinery: *The car ran off the road when the steering gear broke.* **5.** working order; adjustment: *His watch got out of gear and would not run.* **6.** equipment needed for some purpose. Harness, clothes, household goods, tools, tackle, and rigging are various kinds of gear. **7.** provide with gear; equip; harness. **8.** make subordinate to in order to serve: *The steel industry was geared to the needs of war.* 1,4-6 *n.,* 2,3,7,8 *v.*

He wanted to protect the Eskimos

Vilhjalmur Stefansson's career took many unexpected turns.

His parents came to North Dakota from Iceland. At eighteen he was a cowboy. When a scheme to get a cattle ranch of his own failed, he entered the University of North Dakota. He was expelled in his junior year because he was absent so much. Since he could not transfer with credit to another school, he entered the University of Iowa as a freshman. Iowa agreed to give him credit for any courses whose final examination he could pass with a grade of C. He managed to graduate after only one year of study.

Stefansson then went to Harvard to study to be a minister. At the end of a year he decided to change his course and study anthropology. He was preparing for an expedition to Africa when he got a better offer and went on an Arctic expedition instead. From then on, his life centered on the Arctic.

He soon became a headline personality—not only for his daring deeds as an explorer of unknown northern lands, but also because he often disagreed with other noted explorers and scientists. He argued and proved that the Arctic is not a barren wasteland, as most explorers then claimed, but that it is full of natural resources. By adopting the Eskimo way of life, he demon-

strated that man can survive in the far North by living off the land. He also gathered evidence to show that an all-meat diet is the most healthful one for humans.

Stefansson greatly admired the Eskimos who still lived according to primitive ways. He felt that it would be a great mistake for them to give up their own healthful way of life and adopt the ways of "civilization." Unfortunately, he and others who felt the same way did not succeed in protecting these people from change.

He did, however, succeed in another of his goals—convincing people that the Arctic can be useful. Today commercial air lines fly over the polar regions, and stations have been set up there for defense and for gathering weather and other scientific information.

During the later years of his life, Stefansson was recognized as one of the world's greatest authorities on the polar regions. He died in 1962.

SOME BROWN SPARROWS

by Bruce Fearing

Some brown sparrows who live
in the Bronx Zoo visit often
the captive Victoria Crested
Pheasant, visit captive Peacocks,
5 Cockatoos. They fly through bars
to visit also monkeys, jackals,
bears. They delouse themselves in
cage dust, shaking joyously;
they hunt for bread crumbs, seeds
10 or other tidbits. Briefly,
they lead free sparrow lives
and fly free.

↻ **Talking it over**

1. What do the brown sparrows
have that the other animals who live
in the Bronx Zoo do not have?

2. In what way is what the sparrows
have necessary to most living creatures?

Necessities: Views and viewpoints

In answering the questions, think particularly about the following people in this unit:

Ha'penny	Stainless Steele
Richard Wright's mother	The hungry soldier
Young Richard Wright	Elmer Merrick
Billie Holiday	The Stone Age Eskimos

1. What are the absolute necessities for all living creatures? What people in this unit were trying to provide necessities of this kind?

2. What kinds of things may be necessities for some people but not for others? Give at least one example from the unit of something that seemed necessary to one individual, but which other people might get along without.

3. A number of people in this unit did something almost superhuman because they felt they had to. Tell who they were, and the circumstances.

4. Which people got what they needed by fooling others? Discuss whether there was a good enough reason to justify what they did.

5. *a.* Which people seemed to feel that it is best to provide for your needs through your own efforts?

b. Which ones recognized that they had to coöperate with other people to provide the necessities of life?

c. Which, if any, of these people discovered that they could get along without help of any kind from other people?

Herbie's Ride

by Herman Wouk

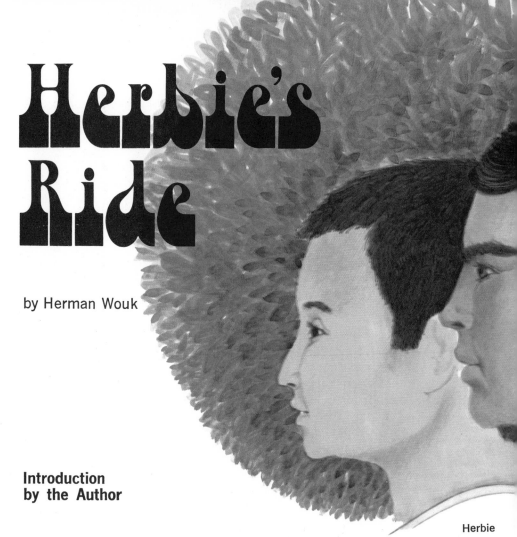

Herbie

Introduction
by the Author

HERBIE'S RIDE, an excerpt from my novel *The City Boy,* makes an adventure story in itself.

My hero is **Herbie Bookbinder,** a short fat unathletic boy of eleven and a half. Not much of a hero for an adventure story, you may think. But Herbie has nerve, brains, and a wild imagination. These qualities often land him in trouble. He lives in the Bronx, the part of New York where I grew up many years ago. I too was a short fat unathletic boy. I too got into trouble through an overheated imagination.

When the adventure of the Ride begins, Herbie is spending the summer at a camp in the mountains called **Camp Manitou.** The owner is **Mr. Julius Gauss,** a villain of the book. Mr. Gauss during the winter is the principal of the public school where Herbie goes. He is also a mean sanctimonious phony.

The other villain is **Lennie Krieger,** almost two years older than Herbie, and rather stupid. Lennie is a strong handsome athlete. On the streets of the Bronx he is a big shot, but in school he has fallen a year behind Herbie. The fathers of these two boys are partners

Lennie

Lucille

Cliff

in business. Naturally they are always comparing their sons. Lennie can't stand Herbie's success in school. He takes it out on the little fat boy by bullying him, beating him up, and seizing every chance to make trouble for him. It was Lennie who long ago stuck Herbie with the nickname "General Garbage."

The cruelest thing Lennie did was to steal Herbie's girl, **Lucille Glass,** a beautiful vain redhead of eleven, with all the arts and wiles of a grown woman. Herbie was crazy about her. He came to Camp Manitou just to be near her. (Mr. Gauss runs a girls' camp on the other side of the hill.) Lucille liked the fat boy at first. But when the athletic star Lennie Krieger started paying attention to her, she dropped Herbie like a worn-out toy. Herbie is ready to die to get her back. That is what leads to Herbie's Ride.

The Ride would be impossible without Herbie's cousin, **Cliff Block.** Cliff is a quiet boy, not a great athlete. But in a pinch, he can show surprising strength and courage. Cliff admires Herbie for his brains and his inventive imagination. They have been through

Mr. Gauss   Uncle Sandy

many tight spots together. Herbie usually gets the ideas, and Cliff supplies the brawn.

Cliff is the only person at Camp Manitou who can ride **Clever Sam,** a cantankerous, smart old horse bought by Mr. Gauss for five dollars. The ancient animal is tired of horseback riding as a sport. He can throw anybody off his back, and usually does. But for some reason he loves Herbie's cousin.

Elmer Bean is the rough-and-ready handy man of the camp, a native of the mountains, very different from the New York people.

Uncle Sandy is the head counselor. (Counselors are young men who watch over the campers. One of them sleeps in each bungalow, or "bunk," with seven or eight boys.) Sandy is not a bad fellow. But he has to carry out Mr. Gauss's orders, to earn his salary.

Uncle Sid is Herbie's counselor. He teaches music at the camp, and has no understanding of boys.

Felicia is Herbie's older sister. Lennie threw her over for Lucille, and she is in a rage at the athlete.

That's about all you have to know about the people at Camp Manitou.

Remember that the fathers of Lennie

Elmer Bean

Clever Sam

Krieger and Herbie Bookbinder are business partners. They own the Bronx River Ice Company, which they call "the Place." At this ice-making plant in the Bronx, there is a safe full of money. Herbie knows the combination. You'll soon see how important *that* is!

One more thing is in that safe besides money: **The Blue Paper.** It is a business document which gives Herbie's father control of the ice plant. There is another partner, Mr. Powers, a bad fellow who is plotting with Lennie's father to sell "the Place." If not for The Blue Paper, Powers and Krieger would have enough stock to force Herbie's father to sell the business, which would break Mr. Bookbinder's heart.

Now you can start the story.

I hope you will enjoy *Herbie's Ride.* I had more fun writing this book than any of my others. You see, there really was once a stupid athlete named Lennie, who made my life miserable in the Bronx. Herbie's ride and Herbie's triumph are my boyhood dreams come true; especially, winning back Lucille!

But that I never did.

Herman Wouk

Herbie's Ride

by Herman Wouk

1. Planning the Crime

BOYS enter upon this planet as free wild animals, and have to be tamed. Respect for the law comes, but slowly. The sweetest molly-coddle will swipe an apple from a fruit stand—if only once; the saintliest choir boy will "borrow" a quarter from his mother's purse—if only once. What makes them all behave at last is partly upbringing, partly what Mr. Gauss calls Character, and partly the invisible barbed wire of Law, which sooner or later gives nearly every boy a nasty raking—if only once.

It was the last week of camp, and everyone was in the doldrums. Uncle Sandy's schedule was exhausted. The giant struggle between the Yellows and the Reds, with one half of the camp pitted against the other for three racking days, had passed into history.

This "camp war," as it was called, had been fought in the early years of Manitou during the last three days of the season, but the arrangement developed weaknesses which caused Mr.

Gauss to change it. First of all, it sent half of the camp home in a mood of embitterment which no amount of talk about a Gaussian victory[1] could heal (the defeated team always won a tremendous Gaussian victory, according to the camp owner). Second, it returned victors and losers alike to their homes worn out, nervous, and often battered. Mr. Gauss had therefore issued another of his unpopular decrees advancing the date of the camp war a week and leaving seven days for the recuperation and fattening of his campers. The price was heavy: a week of anticlimax and boredom. But Mr. Gauss, caught in the old dilemma of expediency versus the children's desires, had gone his usual way.

To assuage the postwar dullness he invented a couple of holidays: Manitou Mardi Gras, which was held two days before the season ended, and Campers'

[1]**Gaussian victory,** a moral victory. This is a reference to a talk Mr. Gauss gave after Camp Manitou's baseball and basketball teams were roundly defeated by those of neighboring Camp Penobscot. Mr. Gauss always tries to make the losers feel better by emphasizing their tremendous camp spirit.

Day, which followed it. The boy who was judged to have invented the best diversion of the Mardi Gras—whether it was a costume, an act, or a display—was acclaimed "Skipper-for-a-Day." He ruled the camp, appointed boys to supplant all the counselors (the counselors became those boys), and all in all won an enviable amount of glory. Uncle Sandy and Mr. Gauss usually managed to give the award to one of the more sober Super-seniors,[2] who could be counted on to keep Campers' Day from becoming an orgy of hazing of the counselors.

It was a good idea. The boys consumed several mornings and afternoons preparing for the Mardi Gras, which usually became a gay sort of carnival. Campers' Day gave them a chance to release the grudges of a whole season in horseplay. The climax of the festivity was always the throwing of Uncle Sandy into the lake by the Seniors, in the presence of the whole camp. This happy event in itself reconciled large numbers of the boys to life at Manitou, and made them look forward to next year when they could see it done again. Every summer there were elaborate conspiracies to throw Mr. Gauss into the water, too, but the plots had never come off. He always seemed to vanish at the critical time.

"What th' heck does Mardigrass mean, anyhow?" said Lennie, addressing a circle of boys sitting on the grass around him. Bunks Twelve and Thirteen were having a period of horseback riding again, which meant, as usual, that Cliff gave Clever Sam a workout

for an hour while the others lolled and gossiped.

"Hey, Lennie, is it Mardigrass or Mardigrah?" said one of the boys. "Uncle Gussie keeps sayin' 'Mardigrah.'"

"Shucks, dincha see the big sign they got stretched across Company Street?[3]" said Lennie. "It says 'Mardigrass Saturday,' don't it? Mardigrass with a *s*."

"Uncle Gussie says it's French."

"Maybe, but I ain't no Frenchman."

This caused a burst of laughter. Lennie had solidified his position as a hero during the camp war by winning a couple of crucial games for the Yellows. Everything about a hero is magnified, and a joke uttered by him is much funnier than if it comes from ordinary flesh and blood. Encouraged by the laugh, Lennie added, "Maybe Uncle Gussie is French. He always sounds like he's been eatin' frogs."

This was considered pricelessly humorous, and several of the boys rolled on the grass in merriment.

"That still don't answer what it means, though," said Lennie.

The boys sobered, and tried to think of an explanation.

"Maybe," said Ted, "it has somethin' to do with grass. This is grass-cuttin' time, for makin' hay, ain't it? O.K., maybe in French Mar-di-grass means 'Cut the grass.'"

The circle all looked to Lennie for his opinion. The hero wrinkled his brow judiciously and said, "Sounds right. I bet that's it."

Everyone else nodded now, except Herbie, and one boy said, "Pretty smart, Ted, figuring it out like that."

"Er—I looked it up in the diction-

[2]**Super-seniors.** The camp is divided according to age and grade level: Midgets, Juniors, Intermediates, Seniors, and Super-seniors. Herbie, Cliff, and Lennie are all Intermediates.

[3]**Company Street,** the path between the two rows of bunks, leading to the dining room.

ary," Herbie put in diffidently. "It means 'Fat Tuesday.'"

"What!" Lennie's tone hovered between amazement and scorn.

Herbie was at low ebb in his own esteem and everyone else's. He had been of no use at all to the Reds in the camp war. His usual good spirits had been lacking since the night of the fateful dance,[4] and Lucille had avoided his presence and even his glance since that time.

"Well, I know it sounds funny," he faltered. "But—but Fat Tuesday is what it says."

Murmurs of resentment were heard.

"General Garbage, the only thing you can do good is lie," said Lennie. "If we'd of had a lying contest, the Reds would of won the camp war."

"Haw! Haw! Haw!" from the chorus.

Then a rapid fire of wit:

"How could they have a Fat Tuesday on a Saturday?"

"You sure it wasn't Skinny Wednesday?"

"Or Pot-Bellied Friday?"

"Or Bowlegged Sunday?"

"Haw! Haw! Haw! Fat Tuesday!"

"I know what he means, guys," exclaimed Lennie. "He means *he's* fat Tuesday and every other day."

The hilarity which followed was so prolonged that Uncle Sid broke away from a conversation with Elmer Bean and inquired what the joke was.

"Herbie says," Lennie gasped between guffaws, "that Mardigrass means 'Fat Tuesday.'"

"You pronounce it 'Mardigrah,' and it does mean 'Fat Tuesday.' It's the name of an ancient religious holiday," answered the counselor, and walked away.

After a short silence conversation was resumed on other topics. No more jokes were made about Fat Tuesday. Herbie was noticeably shouldered out of the talk. He had committed that breach of manners, unforgivable among adults as well as among boys: he had known more than the leader.

When the group started down the hill for the swimming period, Herbie got permission to remain behind with Cliff and Elmer Bean while they unsaddled Clever Sam.

"Say, Elmer," said Herbie, as he watched Cliff and the handy man fussing with the horse's girths, "has a Intermediate got a chance to become Skipper-for-a-Day?"

Elmer paused in his work, and regarded Herbie with a twinkling eye. "Why? You figger on bein' it?"

"Well, no," said Herbie, "course not. But still a guy likes to know if he got a chance."

"Nobody but a Super-senior ain't got it yet, Herb. Mr. Gauss likes to make sure, see, that the thing don't get to be all hog-wild."

"O.K. That's all I wanted to know."

Cliff swung the saddle off Clever Sam's back and stood holding it. "Why, Herbie?" he said. "You got a good idea for the Mardigrass?"

"Pretty fair, I thought. But it don't make no difference."

"What's the idea?" said Elmer Bean.

"Aw, just a ride."

"What kind of ride?"

"It's—it's hard to explain. Anyway, I might as well forget it."

Elmer took the horse's bridle, and led him toward the barn. "Come on,

---

[4] **the night of the fateful dance.** Herbie had made a fool of himself by falling down on the dance floor. Lucille then turned her attention to Lennie.

talk up, Herb," he said. "What's yer big idea? Maybe you might be the first Intermediate to make Skipper."

"Well," Herbie began, following Elmer, "I figure this Mardigrass is kind of like Coney Island,[5] ain't it? Well, my pop took me to Coney Island once. The most fun I had was on a thing they called the Devil's Slide. It was a big boat that slid down into a tank of water. Boy, oh boy, when that thing hit the water—zowie!"

Cliff said, "I been on that. You ain't figuring to build no Devil's Slide out here, are you, Herbie? Heck, that would take a year."

"It's all built, Cliff!" Herbie answered excitedly. "Don't you see? The doggone girls' lawn slants right down to the lake, don't it? All right. All you gotta do is put a rowboat on wheels, see, an' bang! You got the Devil's Slide!"

"How," said Elmer dryly, "do you steer this rowboat on wheels an' keep it from runnin' into a beach or Aunt Tillie?"[6]

Herbie's face fell. "I never thought of that."

Cliff said, "Heck, you could steer it with ropes or somethin'."

"A heavy rowboat fulla people barrelin' down a hill? Son, you need wire cables and Samson pullin' 'em to steer that."

They were in the tumble-down stable now, smelling faintly of straw and strongly of Clever Sam. Elmer backed the horse into his stall and closed the door. Clever Sam leaned against the wall and closed his eyes with a peaceful sigh.

---

[5] **Coney Island,** an amusement park on the Atlantic side of Brooklyn, in New York City.
[6] **Aunt Tillie,** the head counselor at the girls' camp.

"I tell you what," said Herbie. "What's the matter with layin' a couple of rails down the hill just like they had it in Coney? The boat could slide down the rails. All you need's a few boards."

"You mean greased boards," said Elmer.

"Of course greased boards," replied Herbie, although it hadn't occurred to him that the boards would have to be greased.

"Hm. Four hundred feet of two-by-fours and twenty gallons of axle grease wouldn't hardly begin to do it."

"O.K.," said Herbie dejectedly. "I said forget about it."

"An' after the boat gets down in the water once, how do you git it back up the hill?"

"O.K., o.k., Elmer."

"An' anyway, what keeps the boat from flyin' clean off the greased boards halfway down the hill an' roostin' up in a tree?"

"Heck, Elmer, do you have to poke fun at me? It was a crazy idea, that's all. I'll go to the lousy Mardigrass dressed like a old lady or somethin'. You said I couldn't win, anyhow." He sat on a perilous old chair with one leg missing, tilted it against the horse's stall, and slouched.

"For that matter," Cliff remarked slowly, as though talking to himself, "Clever Sam could pull the boat back up the hill easy."

"For cryin' out loud, forget the thing, Cliff," said Herbie.

"Why are you so red-hot for gettin' to be Skipper?" asked Elmer, squatting opposite Herbie and stuffing a grimy pipe from a tobacco pouch.

"Because I'm the camp joke, that's why!" burst out Herbie. "The little fat baby that can't run, can't play ball, can't fight, can't do nothin'! That's me an' everyone knows it. An' they're right. That's just what I am."

"Why, hold on, Herb. A guy shouldn't think that bad of hisself. You're a good kid, an' you got brains. You'll have the laugh on 'em all someday. You know you ain't that terrible."

"Lennie stole his girl," observed Cliff, looking out at the sunny green fields.

"Hm." Elmer smiled for an instant, but when Herbie glanced at him suspiciously his face was serious. "Why, Herb, any girl who likes Lennie I say oughta be welcome to him, an' good riddance to both of 'em."

"An' why does the boat have to fly off the rails, now I think of it?" said Herbie. "Heck, you nail a couple boards under the rowboat, see, so's they fit just inside the rails, an' how's that rotten boat gonna slip off them rotten rails?"

Elmer smiled, and lit his pipe with a thick wooden match. Cliff looked at his cousin admiringly. "Hey, Herb, that's good. I told you"—he turned to Elmer—"he's got a head."

"Say, Herb, which girl is it?" asked the handy man, still grinning.

"Aw, Cliff's crazy."

"I think maybe he ain't."

"O.K., I don't care if you know. It's Lucille, the redheaded one."

"Oh. That one." Elmer nodded with great comprehension. "Yeah. Many's the snake I've known like that one. Bigger, but the same idea."

"Snake!" said Herbie, aghast.

Cliff explained, with a little pride of inside knowledge, "That's what they call girls in the Navy."

"You been in the Navy, Elmer?"

"He had four years," said Cliff.

Herbie looked at the handy man with new admiration.

"Herb, she ain't worth feelin' low about," said Elmer. The boy dropped his eyes. "But I reckon my sayin' so don't make it so."

"She said she was my girl. An' then just 'cause I couldn't dance good—" Herbie choked.

"Where you gonna get fifty dollars?" Elmer asked.

Herbie was startled. "What for?"

"Why, with fifty dollars fer lumber and grease and a little help from me I think maybe you could rig up yer doggone ride at that."

Hope gleamed in the boy's eye. He sputtered, "Why Mr. Gauss—Uncle Sandy—anybody'll give it to me. Shucks, you charge a quarter a ride, an' with everybody takin' a couple rides an' the parents an' the visitors from the village an' all, you'd make easy a hundred an' fifty dollars. I figured all that out."

Elmer shook his head. "I guess possibly you would, but them guys won't lend you no fifty dollars. The whole idea sounds crazy. Maybe it could work, but you ain't gonna get them convinced. Would yer ma er pa give it to you?"

Herbie thought of wrangles with his mother over quarters, and the frequent earnest discussions between his parents over the narrowness of the family income. He shrugged. "I could try, but Mom is pretty tough. An' whenever I want somethin' my pop just says what my mom says."

Cliff remarked, "I got five dollars."

They all fell silent. Some happy horseflies buzzed back and forth between the sunshine outside and the fragrant shade of the stable. Clever

Sam pawed the floor and heaved another long sigh in his sleep.

"It wouldn't be fair anyhow," Herbie spoke up, "if you helped me build it. They'd disqualify me."

Elmer blew a vast cloud of blue smoke, which wreathed in the still air. "Wouldn't nobody get to be Skipper if that was how it worked. I build the whole Mardigrass, more or less. Last year they give Skipper to Yishy Gabelson for the House of Hell. Shucks, all he did was say 'Elmer, less make Bunk Sixteen into a House of Hell.' I thought up th' traps an' all that, an' built 'em, what's more."

"I'd help build it," said Cliff. "I ain't got no idea of my own. This sounds like fun."

"Well, I think I know where I can get the fifty dollars," Herbie said, slowly and reluctantly.

The handy man's eyes opened wide. "Yeah? Where?"

"Never mind. I can get it."

Elmer stood and knocked grey ash and red embers out of his pipe against the heel of his boot. "You git it an' I'll build it," he said. "That's to say, I'll help you build it. You kids'll have to work like stevedores. I have a heap o' other things to build, too." He slipped the pipe into his shirt pocket and walked out.

Cliff whispered excitedly, "Hey Herb, where in the—" and broke off as he saw the handy man's head poke around the doorway again.

"Herb, I still say she ain't worth it. There ain't no snake worth all that work," he said. His head disappeared and the boys heard him shuffling placidly away.

"Cliff," whispered Herbie, though there was no reason to whisper, "re-member the time we sneaked in the Place on a Sunday?"

"Yeah."

"An' that safe in the office, and my pop saying the combination was my birthday?"

Cliff's jaw fell open, and he stared at his cousin.

"I'm gonna get the fifty dollars outta that safe!" Herbie said defiantly.

"Herb, you—you gonna *steal?*"

"Steal your Aunt Sadie! I'm gonna *borrow* fifty bucks. You heard Elmer say we'd make a hundred fifty easy. All right, I get that money tonight, we build the ride, I earn a hundred fifty Saturday night. Sunday I mail fifty bucks back to the Place—no, seventy-five bucks, twenty-five bucks interest. Is that fair or ain't it?"

"Yeah, but Herbie—opening yer own father's safe—"

"I'll stick a note in the safe, see? It'll *say* that the money ain't stole, only borrowed." Herbie was warming up to the project. "If *they* know I ain't stole it, and *I* know I ain't stole it, then who says it's stealing?"

"I say so," answered Cliff.

"Why?"

"'Cause it is."

Herbie considered this a very vexing answer, the more so since it had a ring of truth. But he felt logic all on his side.

"Look, Cliff. Suppose I were to take Clever Sam outta here now, see? An' ride him away, an' never bring him back, but instead bring back a fine race horse and stick him in the stall. Would that be stealing?"

"Takin' Clever Sam sure would be."

"The heck it would! How about the race horse?"

"Where would you get the race horse?"

"What difference does that make? I'd swap Clever Sam for him."

"Oh! Then you wouldn't have the race horse to start with?"

"'Course not, stupid. If I had the race horse, I wouldn't need Clever Sam."

"Guess not."

"All right, then. You see my point."

"Yeah. If you had fifty bucks, you wouldn't hafta steal it."

Herbie grew red in the face and shouted, "All right, all right, all right! Then it's stealing! You'll die before you admit a plain fact. I don't care what you call it, I'm gonna do it!"

"How you gonna get to New York?"

"Hitch-hike."

"How you gonna get outta camp?"

"Sneak out after taps."

"You gonna go to New York an' back in one night an' get back before reveille?"

"Yeah."

"Herbie, it's three miles to the main highway. There ain't no cars go by here after sunset, you know that."

"I'll walk to the main highway." Herbie's answers were getting weaker and more sullen.

"An' back in the morning?"

"An' back in the morning."

"O.K. Taps is at ten o'clock, reveille at seven. That's nine hours. You got two hours of walkin', seven hours of drivin'—that's sayin' you get hitches right away, no waits—an' at least an hour gettin' the money. Ten hours' work to do in nine hours."

Herbie saw his plan in all its outrageous foolishness. He walked up and down the stable and kicked disconsolately at stones and straws. "You win. I go to Mardigrass as an old lady. I wasn't so anxious to steal from my pop's safe, anyway. What are you gonna do?"

"I dunno. I can't ever think of them kinda things."

"Whyncha go as Tarzan? We could fake up a leopard skin—"

"I know how you could save pretty near an hour gettin' to the highway," interrupted Cliff.

Herbie looked at his cousin doubtfully. Cliff seemed serious.

"Well, how?"

"Clever Sam."

"Are you nuts? I can't ride him."

"No. But both of us can, I think."

"Cliff, you wanna get mixed up in this? I thought you said it was bad business."

"I said it was stealin'. I dunno if it's bad or not. If you think it ain't bad, I guess it ain't. Maybe sometime a guy's gotta steal."

"Would Clever Sam stand for it?"

"We can find out easy enough."

Cliff opened the door of the stall and punched Clever Sam in the ribs. The horse opened his eyes and looked around murderously, until he saw who was disturbing him. Then he groaned, yawned, heaved himself away from the wall, and suffered himself to be led out of his stall. Cliff leaped up on his bare back.

"We don't have to saddle him. Get up on this bench here and climb aboard."

Herbie obeyed, not without some trembling. Seated astride the beast in front of Cliff he felt himself seventeen feet in the air and very insecure. The horse's long backbone seemed to sag slightly at the double weight, and he looked around at his burden and snorted indignantly.

"Yeah, I know, Sam," said Cliff,

"but this is an emergency. If you don't like it, we won't do it. Gee-up."

Clever Sam shuffled, backed, pawed the floor, and moaned. Then, at a few coaxing tugs of the reins, he walked out of the stable. Cliff made him trot twenty yards and turned him back. The animal was obedient, but the short trot was enough to jar the bones loose in Herbie's skeleton, or so he felt. Back in the stable he climbed shakily off Clever Sam and sensed a new sweetness in the feeling of a floor under his feet.

"He'll do it," said Cliff, returning the horse to his stall.

"I'm beginning to think that it's just a crazy notion," said Herbie, running his tongue over extremely dry lips.

But Cliff, whose ignition point was higher than Herbie's, was at last taking fire from the flame of adventure. "No, no, Herb. Honest, I think you could get away with it."

"But it *is* stealing. You were right."

"Yeah, sure, but if you give 'em back seventy-five, there ain't anything really wrong with it, is there?"

"Aw, it's impossible. Hitching all the way to the city, alone at night—I musta been outta my head. The heck with Lennie. The heck with Lucille. Who cares about her? That snake!"

"Herbie—*I'll go with you to the city!*"

Herbie was dumfounded.

"I mean it. That'll make it a cinch. I tie up Clever Sam in the woods by the highway, see? He'll just eat grass or sleep till we get back. You know you can't climb in the window of the Place, anyway. You need a boost from me."

Herbie had forgotten this little detail, which would have been enough to wreck his whole enterprise. He wondered frantically what other pitfalls there were, even as he felt tempted. Until now the project had merely been one of the dreams which his imagination produced so easily. But he had made the mistake of sharing this dream with Cliff, so that he could no longer let it die away when it ceased to amuse him. It had become half-substantial in the act of speaking it aloud.

"Gosh, Cliff, suppose we get caught! Why should you take any risks? We could get put in jail!"

"Heck, Herbie, if you wanna do the thing, I wanna help you, that's all. Do you wanna do it or doncha?"

"Why, I—sure, I wanna do it. Why d'you suppose I thought it all up?"

"O.K. When do we go?"

And just as daydreams sometimes seemed as vivid as reality to Herbie, this reality now began to seem to him as far off and tenuous as a dream. Still not quite believing it was all happening, he heard himself say with the coolness of a general, "First off we gotta get our city clothes outta the camphor locker. They'd pick us up sure, wanderin' around at night in camp clothes."

"I never thought of that."

"Wait after taps until your whole bunk's asleep, see, then sneak on down to the camphor locker an' meet me there. The duty counselor won't give us no trouble. It's Uncle Sid tonight, an' all he does is sit in the social hall an' write letters."

"I gotcha. Hey, this'll be good."

"The heck it will." Herbie felt a tightening around his heart. "It's a crazy scheme. An' I still think I oughta do it alone, Cliff."

"Well, never mind about that. I'll see you at the camphor locker."

"Now, we don't say nothin' to nobody."

" 'Course. Let's go. It's lunch time."

The boys left the stable and went down the hill arm in arm.

Herbie ate little lunch. He sat dreamily at the table, composing in his mind the letter to be left in the safe, explaining that the money was only being borrowed. Immediately after the meal he rushed to the empty office of the camp newspaper and wrote out the note on the rheumatic typewriter, hitting each key painfully with one finger.

All day he turned the midnight sortie over and over in his mind, and like a snowball it seemed to pick up perils and terrors with each turning. The ultimate object, the building of the ride for the Mardi Gras, seemed centuries away. He half hoped that Cliff would beg off—and he half hoped that he wouldn't, and that it would all prove a glorious adventure with fame and triumph as the prize. In this irresolute state he counted the hours as they dragged toward sunset, and he did some remarkably absent-minded things during the day, such as putting a pair of trousers on backward after his afternoon swim, and eating a whole plateful of the odious creamed mackerel known as "Gussie's Goo" for dinner, while his bunkmates regarded him incredulously. Herbie hunted up Cliff in the evening during letter-writing period and threw out veiled "feelers" about the difficulty and danger of the excursion, but Cliff persisted in talking calmly of other things. If he had had a change of heart, he was concealing it.

Night came. The bugle blew taps, and the camp was darkened. Herbie, curled tensely in his cot, glanced at the phosphorescent numerals of his wristwatch, a handsome two-dollar birthday gift that he had never expected to put to such suspenseful use. It read ten minutes after ten. From now on every moment counted; already he had been cheated of ten precious minutes out of the nine allotted hours by a laggard bugler.

And now a new aggravation cropped up. His bunkmates were wakeful and talkative. While Herbie wriggled and fretted under his blanket, getting hotter and more impatient every minute, they held a long, thorough inquiry on the question whether Uncle Sid was or was not the worst counselor in the camp (the affirmative won). Then they thrashed out the historic problem, was Jesus Christ a Jew or a Christian (no decision); then they carefully reviewed all the Intermediate girls one by one from the physical, mental, and moral standpoints; and, just when they seemed to be dropping off, Uncle Sid came by with a flashlight and bawled at them for talking after taps, bringing them all wide awake again and starting a fresh discussion of his failings. Luckily this topic had been well worked over once. When the talk finally died away and Herbie cautiously slipped out of the bunk, his watch read ten minutes to eleven.

Cliff, a shadowy figure already dressed in city clothes, was pacing in front of the camphor locker when Herbie arrived.

"Holy cats, I thought you'd given up," said Cliff.

"Not me." By the light of Cliff's flash, Herbie groped into the locker and donned his city clothes, choking over the camphor fumes.

"Howdja get the lock open, Cliff?"

"The wood's rotten. Pried it loose with a stone."

"We gotta hammer it up again."

"Yeah, in the morning when we get back."

"'Ja bring money?"

"Five dollars. 'Ja bring the note to stick in the safe?"

"Yeah. Got it in my back pants pocket. Don't lemme forget it."

"You bet I won't."

Skulking from shadow to shadow, the two boys went up the hill to the stable. At the top of the rise Herbie paused and looked back at the sleeping camp, two rows of black little boxes by the moonlit lake. The cold night wind stirred his hair. A sense of the enormity of the law-breaking on which they were embarked overwhelmed him.

"Cliff, fer the last time—lemme go this alone. You ain't gonna get nothin' out of it but trouble."

"Come on, we got no time to talk," answered his cousin.

They avoided the light that streamed from the windows of the guest house and reached the gloomy stable. The door opened at a push with a startling creak. Clever Sam neighed and stamped.

"Hey, take it easy, Sam, it's us," whispered Cliff. Nimbly he led the horse out of his stall and saddled him.

"Come on, Herbie, climb on the bench and get on behind me," he said, and jumped into the saddle. Herbie felt as though he were being carried away on a powerful black tide, against which it was useless to struggle. He ascended via the bench to his risky perch in back of Cliff. His cousin walked the horse outside, closed the stable with a shove of one strong arm, and turned the animal's head toward the gate.

"Gee-up," he said, "we got a long way to go."

Clever Sam pranced to one side and to the other, then broke into a quiet trot. With no further antics he carried his double burden out through the gate and, at a click of Cliff's tongue, quickened his pace and set off toward the highway.

Clip-clop, clip-clop, jounce, jounce, jounce, jounce, down the deserted dirt road in the moonlight went the two boys on their aged, ramshackle steed. Clever Sam's gait was stiff and bumpy. Cliff rode to it well, but his cousin did not. Herbie clutched Cliff's middle and tried not to think about the pounding at his posterior. The insides of his legs began to feel warm. Then they grew hot. Then they became fiery. Then they were raw steaks broiling on either side of a red-hot grill sliding up and down, up and down between them—

"Cliff," faintly, "this is murder."

"Oh, sorry, Herbie. Can't you post?"

"Wha—" (bounce) "what's post?"

"Every time the horse goes up, *you* go up. Every time he comes down, *you* come down. See, like me."

Herbie flung himself up and down in time with his cousin a few moments, lost the rhythm, came down when Clever Sam was going up, struck hard, and tumbled off the horse into the road. Cliff and the animal vanished into the night.

Herbie stood up, brushed the dirt off his back, rubbed his sore head, and groaned, "Oh, Lord, whose idea was this?"

His cousin came trotting back to him and held out his hand.

"Here, stick your foot in the stirrup. I'll pull you up."

Herbie obeyed. With a wrench of his arm in its socket that made a dull horrid noise, he was back in his place behind Cliff. His clothes were damp inside with sweat; the night air chilled him.

"I guess trotting is tough on you, Herbie. I'll see if I can get him to single-foot."

They started off again. But Clever Sam, for all his rich background, had evidently never heard of single-footing. Cliff's efforts to lead him into the gait resulted in an even rougher and more ungainly trot. Herbie felt as though he were being punished for all the sins he had ever committed. From the waist down he seemed to be in flames.

"Ohhhh, Cliff!"

"Hm. I'm afraid to gallop. Well, I *know* he can lope. Hey, Sam—ck, ck."

The horse faltered and subsided into an easy rocking motion that was balm to Herbie.

"That's wonderful, Cliff. That's great. Whew!"

And so they loped out to the highway. When Cliff spied the broad ribbon of concrete, he pulled Clever Sam up. The boys jumped to the ground. While Herbie staggered here and there, trying to restore his legs to their normal functioning, his cousin led the horse off the road and went out of sight among thick shrubs and trees. After two minutes he reappeared.

"Whadja do with him, Cliff?"

"Tied him up good an' told him to stay put. He'll be O.K. Nobody won't find him."

Two cars flashed by in succession along the highway.

"Come on," said Cliff. "One o' them mighta taken us."

The boys ran to the main road and stood waiting. Soon a pair of headlights gleamed in the distance. They waved their hands eagerly as the car bore toward them, but it roared past. Then all was silence and cloudy moonlight.

"Not so good," said Herbie.

"What time is it?"

"Five to twelve."

"Boy. It's gonna be close."

Another pair of headlights appeared, far off.

"I got a feeling," said Herbie. "This is it."

It was. The car slowed at their summons and stopped a few feet past them. The cousins scampered toward the door held open for them.

"Hop in, fellows," shouted a husky voice.

The next instant Herbie felt himself yanked by the arm into the bushes. His cousin, Cliff, held his upper arm in a pincers grip, and was dragging him farther into the gloom of the woods.

"Hey, what's goin' on?"

"Sh-h." Cliff pulled the fat boy with him into the middle of some thick bushes, unmindful of scratched skin and ripping clothes, and crouched. "Dincha see the car when we got up close? The guy's a state trooper!"

Talking it over

1. *a.* Explain Herbie's idea for the Mardi Gras. In order to carry out the idea, what problems will have to be solved?

b. Why does Herbie choose Elmer to discuss his plan with?

2. *a.* What crime does Herbie plan to commit? Why? Give as many reasons as you can.

b. Why does Cliff decide to help Herbie?

c. How can you tell that Elmer would like to see Herbie win? (*cont.*)

3. *a.* What are some of the problems involved in Herbie's plan to "borrow" the money he needs? Which of these problems are solved in this chapter? How?

b. What is the first serious setback to Herbie's plan?

⇄ **Words in action**

You may use your Glossary or a dictionary to help you answer the questions, but try context clues first.

1. When the boys are discussing the meaning of *Mardi Gras,* Lennie wrinkles his brow **judiciously.** Which of the following words has a meaning related to *judiciously?* (*a*) joke (*b*) join (*c*) judge (*d*) juggle (*e*) jump

2. Herbie, who knows what *Mardi Gras* means, offers the information **diffidently.** Which of the following words has a meaning related to *diffidently?* (*a*) different (*b*) hesitating (*c*) dictatorial (*d*) difficult (*e*) heroic

3. When Herbie eats the creamed mackerel as if he likes it, his bunkmates stare at him **incredulously.** Does this mean (*a*) that they believe what they see, or (*b*) that they cannot believe it?

4. When Herbie says positively that he is going to get the necessary fifty dollars, he speaks **defiantly.** Be prepared to read this statement defiantly: "I don't care whether you approve or not. I'm going to do it anyway."

5. When Herbie sees his plan as foolish, he walks up and down, kicking **disconsolately** at stones and straws. Demonstrate Herbie's action.

How would you do it differently if you were kicking **defiantly?**

2. A Midnight Adventure

HERBIE'S breath failed him for a moment. Then he gasped, "Whew! Thanks, Cliff. I never noticed. It's lucky—"

"Sh-sh! For cryin' out loud!"

The boys heard the car door closing. Then came the steps of the trooper, crunching on twigs and leaves. A flashlight beam poked here and there between the shadowy trees.

"All right, kids! You needn't be afraid of me. Come on out." The trooper's raised voice was coming from some distance. The boys did not speak or stir. "All I want to know is what you're doing out on the road so late at night. If you're in trouble, I'll help you."

More cracking of twigs under heavy boots. The flashlight beam hit the bushes in which the boys were hiding, but only a thin gleam filtered through to them. It moved and left them in blackness.

"Come on, now. I can find you easily enough if I want to."

Pause. Stamping, cracking, beating of bushes, and gyration of flashlight beam. Then:

"O.K. Spend the night in the woods if you prefer. I have a whole highway to patrol. I'm offering you a lift, but have it your own way. I'm leaving."

The steps moved off. The car door opened and slammed, and the motor roared up and faded away. Cliff began groping out of the bushes. His cousin seized him by the slack of the jacket.

"Are you nuts? Bet he's pullin' a trick. Stay right here."

They waited ten minutes by the glowing dial of Herbie's wristwatch.

Peculiar noises from the trees—cracks, groans, sighs, hoots—startled them now and again. Crickets were making music with full orchestra. After a while ants began to dispute the terrain with them.

"Hey," said Cliff, scratching and slapping himself, "do we lay here all night, or what?"

"All right, let's peek now," whispered Herbie.

The boys made their way to the road. Their two heads poked out of the brush, and suddenly drew in again like a pair of snail's horns.

"He—he's still watchin' for us," Herbie murmured. "We'll be stuck here forever."

The boys had seen a car parked by the roadside, its headlights agleam, not fifty feet from them.

"I dunno. It didn't look exactly like the same car." Cliff slowly poked his head out again. "Nope. It ain't the same." He stepped boldly into the light. "It's a Buick. There's a fat guy in it. Come on!"

The boys approached the automobile. The inside light was burning, and they could see plainly a stout, grizzled man in a creased green suit, with a pallid face and stubbly jaws, slouched at the wheel, his eyes closed. Half a cigar, ashy and no longer burning, protruded from his mouth. One hand in his lap held a flat brown bottle.

"Asleep," said Cliff.

"Maybe he's sick or somethin'," said Herbie, and rapped on the driver's window. The fat man started and opened his eyes. He rolled the window down.

"Whaddya want?" he said hoarsely and sleepily.

"If you're goin' to New York, mister, could we have a hitch?" said Herbie.

The fat man squeezed his eyes, shook his head, and rubbed both hands over his face. "Sure, sure, hop in," he said, and threw open the back door. "Glad you woke me. I pretty near fell asleep three times at the wheel. Hadda stop for a doze for a minute. Like to have company to talk to on these long runs. Keeps me awake."

The cousins gratefully nestled in the back seat amid boxes, books, and luggage. They noticed a powerful smell in the car, but said nothing. The driver started up the car, shifted gears, and suddenly snapped the motor off and turned on the boys with narrowed bloodshot eyes.

"Hey! What are a coupla kids like you doing out on the road at midnight, anyhow?"

Cliff and Herbie looked at each other helplessly.

"Well, talk, boys. Where are you from?"

"Camp Manitou," Herbie managed to say.

"What's that?"

"Boys' camp near here."

"Where you going?"

"New York, like we said."

"Why?" said the man, with a squint of drunken cunning.

"My brother's dying."

The driver's suspicious look altered. He spoke more softly.

"Oh. Well, now. Who's this other boy?"

"He's my brother."

Herbie could feel Cliff jump slightly.

"What? He don't look like he's dying."

"He ain't. He's O.K. He's my brother Cliff. My brother Lennie is dying."

"What from?"

"He got run over. My pa sent us a telegram to come home right away."

"Why aren't you on a train?"

"Ain't no train till morning. We figured we could hitch and maybe get there sooner in case Lennie dies. Mr. Gauss gave us permission. He even drove us out to the highway."

"Who's Mr. Gauss?"

"He owns the camp. You can call him up an' ask him, only please, mister, hurry."

The driver said to Cliff, "Is all this true?"

"Why should Herbie lie?" said Cliff.

The driver pondered a moment. He picked up the brown bottle, twisted off the metal cap, and took a drink. Herbie pulled out a handkerchief and sniffled. Luckily he had been required to weep in the last camp show. His imitation was polished.

"Gosh, mister, call up my father an' reverse the charges if you wanna. His name's Jacob Bookbinder, we live in the Bronx, an' the number's Dayton 6174. Or let us outta the car an' we'll get another hitch. We gotta get goin'. How do we know Lennie won't be dead when we get there?" His grief became louder.

"Well, hold on, boy. I'll take you where you're going. I just don't want to be mixed up in trouble, see? I got enough of my own. Heck, I'll drive you right to the door. I go through the Bronx. Sit way back in that seat and relax."

He started up the car and they went rocketing into the night. Herbie tried to continue the sniffling, but it was hard work. His fiction had conjured up the vivid picture of Lennie Krieger on a bed of pain, which was rather pleasant than otherwise. He soon left off, seeing that the fat man was convinced.

During the next hour and a half they learned that the driver was a **Mr. Butcher**, of Albany. That by profession he was a seller of dolls, wholesale. That the doll business was terrible. That he intended someday to get into a "line" which didn't require a weekly trip to New York. That his wife was a sour old crab, and thought all he did in New York was have gay times with girls, which was a lie. That there was a new doll in his "line," the latest thing, which not only cried and closed its eyes but drank water and did astonishing things thereafter. That this doll, "Weepy Willie," was at present the bread and butter of Mr. Butcher. The boys received this information in an unceasing narrative poured into their ears, punctuated by wheezes, gasps for breath, and occasional sputtering. They gleaned additional facts by observation, such as that Mr. Butcher liked to drive his Buick at seventy-five miles an hour, not slowing for curves; that he was very thirsty, for he kept swallowing drinks from the brown bottle; and that he was still sleepy, for now and then his head would slump on his chest, the automobile would careen, and Mr. Butcher would wake up and snatch the wheel just in time to keep his Buick from climbing a tree. The boys did not at all share Mr. Butcher's sleepiness—they had never, in fact, been more wide awake. After they rounded one sharp curve on two screaming wheels, Cliff suggested in pantomime to Herbie that they open the door and jump from the car. Herbie's whitish face turned a shade whiter, and he shook his head emphatically. His lack of color might have been due to the closeness of the air in the car. All the windows were shut, and a musty mixture of the aromas of old cigars, strong drink, and what can only be described as Mr. Butcher himself, saturated the atmosphere. Once or twice as they sped through the darkness Herbie had the feeling that he was in a nightmare, and that Mr. Butcher would melt away at the sound of a bugle. The next moment a near-collision shaking him to his innermost parts would convince him that it was all excessively real.

But it was not written that Herbie and Cliff should perish that night on the Bronx River Parkway. After a dozen narrow escapes from tragedy, Mr. Butcher and his chariot came whistling into the city streets at a speed that made the boys' hair stand on end. The fat man turned around casually to ask where Homer Avenue was, while his car raced between the "El" pillars of White Plains Road. "Look *out!*" yelled Cliff, and Mr. Butcher looked out, and swerved the car away from a pillar which was about to fold car and occupants to its bosom.

But after all these horrors he kept his word, depositing the boys at Herbie's very doorstep. By this time he was mellow, and swore that if he had had a couple of sons like Cliff and Herbie instead of one sour-faced daughter, the image of her mother, his whole life might have been different. He bade the boys a loving farewell, pressed a "Weepy Willie" doll on them, and drove off to an unknown destiny. Perhaps he is motoring back and forth wildly between New York and Albany to this day. You will be passed by many a car on that highway that could easily have Mr. Butcher at the wheel. But alas, it is all too likely that his lucky charm ran out, and that he now sleeps under flowers.

Herbie looked at his watch and gasped, "Cliff, look!" and extended his arm. It was a quarter to two. Their benefactor had come nearly a hundred miles in an hour and a half. The wonder of gasoline, that gives wheezy fat men the swiftness of eagles!

"We're lucky we got here alive," said Cliff, still breathing hard.

Herbie looked at the dark apartment house where his mother and father were sleeping. Set down suddenly at dead of night in his old haunts, he felt more than ever that he was in a dream. It was unbelievable that he could mount a flight of steps, ring a bell, and embrace his mother amid the old furniture. In his mind she and the apartment were still a hundred miles away. He shook his head to clear away these dizzying ideas, dropped "Weepy Willie" in the gutter, and said, "Let's go, Cliff. We got a good chance to make it now."

The boys scampered through the electric-lit silent streets to the Place.

"Will there be anyone there?" said Cliff.

"Just one engineer tendin' the machines," replied Herbie between gasps. "They make ice all night. But he'll be down the other end from the office. Once we get past him he won't hear us."

"Maybe we better jump him and tie him up."

"If it's Irving we better not. Irving is twice as big as Uncle Sandy."

Cliff got a vivid impression of an Irving twelve feet high, and abandoned the notion of binding and gagging him.

"Hey, what's this?" A block from the Place, Herbie stopped short, and pointed at the building in dismay.

"Whatsamatter?"

"The office. It's lit up. Somebody's there!"

Cliff saw that the little high window of the office, facing the street, was a square of bright yellow.

"Maybe it's the engineer, Herbie."

"Engineers ain't allowed in the office. Who could be there two o'clock in the morning?"

"Might as well find out," said Cliff. He sprinted for the Place, followed by his laboring cousin. Standing beneath the office window, he placed both hands on the sill, jumped up, peered inside for a moment, and dropped back to the ground.

"Who is it?" panted Herbie as he came up.

"Mr. Krieger," said Cliff, "an' that guy Powers. They're foolin' around with some big books."

"We're skunked," said Herbie. "How can we get to the safe with them there?"

"I dunno." Cliff went to the wooden door beside the window and pressed his ear against it. "Hey, you can hear 'em."

Herbie followed his example. The voices of the two men came through the partition, muffled but understandable. Powers sounded very angry.

"—all right. You should have had those figures in a file for me when I came to your house."

"Not much longer. Soon go cup coffee. Not sure what figures Burlingame wanted. Could be this, could be that—"

"Any businessman knows what a potential buyer wants! Profit and loss statement, depreciation figures, inventories, book value—good grief, man, what would *you* want to know before buying an ice plant?"

"Not so fast buying. Burlingame say blue paper maybe good. I sit right there next to you when he say, and——"

"Never mind the blasted blue paper. Burlingame will give us a cash offer conditional on Bookbinder agreeing to sell. When Bookbinder hears the cash figure he'll sell, blue paper or no. It's going to be plenty high."

"You not know Jake. Jake not sell no million years. Jake want better poor but own boss. Here, all inventory figures."

"Good. How about profit and loss for the past ten years?"

"Take five more minutes——"

"Confound it, Krieger, this is ridiculous. Where's the file of annual statements? That's all I need."

"Jake got. Accountant got, too. Not in office. Just books. Simple arrangement."

"Why man, haven't you enough interest in your own firm to keep a file of the annual statements in your home? Dragging me down here in the middle of the night——"

"Please. All very last minute. I say this way, peaceable. You telephone me suddenly want all kind figures. One—two—three. Got to have eight o'clock tomorrow morning. Who got all figures in head? Little by little we got all nearly now, just a few——"

"I'm sorry. I'm tired and nervous. Is there a place around here where we can get coffee right now? Then we can come back and clean this up."

"Why not?"

Herbie, straining his ear against the door though not comprehending the conversation, heard Mr. Krieger shout, "Irving! Me and Mr. Powers go cup coffee. Back ten minutes." He heard a faint "O.K." from the interior of the building. The doorknob started to turn, an inch from Herbie's nose. Like cats the boys darted around the corner of the building, and watched the men come out of the office, cross the avenue, and walk out of sight down a side street.

"What now?" whispered Cliff.

"We got ten minutes. You still game?"

"Come on."

"Good. You boost me through."

But as they emerged from the alley Herbie had another idea. "Wait a second," he said, and cautiously tried the office door. It opened.

He and Cliff slipped inside and closed the door as softly as against velvet cushions. They could hear Irving walking around on the brine tank, and the hissing suction of the pipe taking impure water from the cores of the ice cakes. The safe, the object of their fantastic journey, stood squat and ugly before them.

"O.K., you keep watch," whispered Herbie. "Here goes."

Cliff shuttled between the door leading to the interior of the Place and the window on the street, while Herbie carefully turned the dial. On his first try the safe failed to open.

"Must of done it wrong," he muttered, and ran through the numbers of his birthday again; three spins to the right, two to the left, and one to the right. The safe did not yield. Herbie was distraught.

"Hey, Cliff, it don't work."

"You sure you done the combination right?"

"Well, see, I dunno. All I know is the numbers. I tried three turns, two turns, an' one turn—hey, wait, I got it. I bet you have to start by turnin' the dial to the *left*. I been startin' to the right."

"Make it fast, whatever you do."

More frantic twisting. Then: "Cliff, it still don't open."

"Holy smoke, Herbie, I thought you knew the combination."

"Well, I do know the numbers, but jiminy, I dunno which goes how. I figured sure it would be three turns, two turns, an' one turn, like the locker in gym."

"Herbie, them guys'll be back in a coupla minutes."

"I'll try startin' with four turns." Despairingly he whirled the dial, pressed the handle, and tugged at the door. It swung open so easily he fell to the floor.

"Attaboy, Herbie. Hurry!"

The cash box was behind the other tin box labeled "J.B." Herbie pulled the latter off the shelf and laid it on the seat of the chair. He took out the cash box, placed it on the desk, and opened it. It was full of five, ten, and twenty dollar bills.

"Cliff, there's hundreds!"

"How much you gonna take?"

"Exactly what I gotta borrow. Fifty. Not a penny more," said Herbert primly, and selected two twenties and a ten.

"Herbie! Herbie! Here come them two guys!" Cliff's whisper was strident. "I didn't see 'em comin' till just now. They're on top of us! We can't make it out the door!"

"Follow me, Cliff!"

Herbie plunged through a thick door opposite the street entrance with Cliff at his heels. The boys came into a long, high, terribly chilly room filled with gleaming blue piles of ice cakes. Huge bare electric bulbs were placed here and there in the ceiling. Beside the door, right over the boys' heads, hung the stiff frozen body of a calf, head down, its tongue hanging out, its dead eyes staring at them.

"There's another door outta this icebox," whispered Herbie. "Irving's down by it now. In a minute we'll be able to get out."

"It's freezing in here."

"Yeah, sure is. Gimme a boost, Cliff."

He stepped on Cliff's clasped hands and looked warily into the office through a tiny pane of glass set high in the wall. He saw Krieger and Powers come into the office and register amazement at the sight of the open safe and cash box.

"Irving! Irving! Irving!" shouted Krieger. An immense bald man in ragged blue overalls, his face streaked with black grease, came pounding into the office.

"Look what happened while we gone!" Krieger exclaimed, pointing at the safe. "Didn't you see or hear anything?" (Mr. Krieger reversed the case of almost all other human beings. Under great stress he spoke more clearly than usual.)

"No, sir, Mr. Krieger," said the giant, his eyes popping with surprise, "I been busy suckin' the cores on number eight. You know that makes a lotta noise. I didn't hear a thing."

"I told you keep an eye on the office. Run quickly, call a policeman."

"Yes, sir." Irving lumbered out through the street door.

"Hey, Herbie, I'm gettin' tired holdin' you up," said Cliff softly. His cousin's heel was digging painfully into his interlaced fingers. The damp cold of the storehouse was making his arms

ache. "Can't we sneak out the other door now?"

"They'll be listenin' for every sound now. Wait a second," whispered Herbie.

He heard Powers exclaim, "Look! They took Bookbinder's box!" The young man ran his hand along the empty shelf.

"Don't understand something. Why they don't take all the money?" said Krieger, counting the cash hurriedly. "Only got fifty, and leave behind—"

"What does that matter? Listen to me! Does Bookbinder have photostats of that blue paper?"

"No photostats. One paper always right here in safe, better so—"

"Then the memorandum is gone," said Powers, "and Bookbinder is through." He shook his head. "Tough luck for Bookbinder—I hate to see it happen this way—"

"Mr. Powers look please."

Krieger pointed to the box labeled "J.B." lying on the chair. Both men stared at it. Then they looked each other in the eye. Then both lunged for the box. Krieger got his hands on it first and hugged it.

"What you think? Honest man. Thirty years in the ice business. Never funny business. Jake Bookbinder my partner—"

In the ice room Cliff was staggering under his burden and shivering. His numb fingers were giving way. "Herbie, I gotta let go for a minute."

"One second more, Cliff!"

"Listen to me, Krieger," said Powers, speaking quickly and earnestly, "the best favor you can do Bookbinder—"

Crash! Herbie thudded to the floor as Cliff's fingers refused to obey him any longer.

"*Now* we're in it. Come on!" Herbie picked himself up and charged down a narrow corridor between blue walls of ice. He turned sharply to the right as they came to a break in the pile of cakes, and rushed through another foot-thick refrigerator door, followed by the other boy. The warm air of the engine space smote their faces. They were at one end of the brine tank, at the point where the crane dumped finished ice. The crane stood ten feet away over number eight row, loaded with dripping, yard-long rectangular cans.

"Stay right by this door, Cliff, I'll be back in a second!"

Herbie ran over the loose boards covering the tank to the crane, making a wild clatter, and yanked a chain that hung down between the two middle cans. The crane began to move ponderously toward Cliff, with a great clanking and groaning. Krieger could be heard shouting, "I hear them! Out by the tank!" and there was a running of feet. Herbie came back to Cliff, barely ahead of the moving crane, and gasped, "Now's our chance. Come on!" He pulled his cousin back through the refrigerator door and raced between the ice piles to the other door that opened to the office. Behind them they heard the crane crash into the end of its framework, and the excited voices of Krieger and Powers echoing through the tank room.

"Pray to God," whispered Herbie, and opened the door. The office was empty. The boys were out in the street and around in the darkness of the alley in an instant. From the building they could still hear faintly the shouts of the two men. Herbie peered around the corner of the building for a moment and saw Irving with a policeman a block away, running toward the Place down the middle of the street.

"Here comes the cop," he said, and added disdainfully, "He ain't half as big as Irving."

"Boy, Herbie, I thought we were cooked."

The boys slipped down the alley, crossed a vacant lot filled with rubbish behind the Place, and turned left into a shorter alley between two store buildings. They emerged on a street of small shops, a block away from the ice plant. There was an elevated subway station at one end of the street.

"Herb, how about the subway?"

"They might see us goin' up the steps, but we better try it. They'll have more cops around here in a minute."

Winded and leg-weary, the cousins ran up the steep staircase of the elevated at a rate that threatened to burst Herbie's heart in his chest. Luck was with them. They had scarcely staggered through the turnstiles when a Pelham Bay local train, all but empty, lurched into the station. They boarded it. The doors closed, and the train carried them off to safety with squeals and screams.

The boys sat in a stupor of fatigue and relief while the train passed two stations. Then Cliff said dully, "What time is it anyhow? Five o'clock?"

Herbie looked at his wristwatch and silently held it out toward his cousin. It read five minutes past two.

"What? You sure it ain't stopped?"

Herbie held the timepiece to his ear and heard a healthy, regular ticking. "That's all it is, five after two."

"Gosh, twenty minutes, just twenty minutes since Mr. Butcher dropped us off!"

The boys silently marveled at the strange ways of time. Twenty crowded minutes of adventure and peril had seemed longer to them than many hours.

"Hey, you know what?" said Cliff slowly, his mind emerging from the fog of danger. "We still got a chance to make it back to camp."

"Yeah, a good chance!" said Herbie, with a lift of surprise and pleasure. "I sure never thought we would. Come, we'll get off next station."

The boys jumped up from their straw seats and stood with noses pressed impatiently against the glass of the car door. As soon as the train stopped they were out of it and trampling headlong down the staircase with a great noise. For a while the focus of their minds had narrowed to the single urgent problem of not getting caught. Now it broadened again to include the purpose of their trip, which began to seem miraculously close to accomplishment. They had more than four hours to get back to Manitou.

The train thundered away over their heads, and they stood on a quiet, empty, gloomy boulevard. Two blocks away a patrolman was strolling with his back toward them, swinging his night stick. So silent was the sleeping city that the boys could hear the metallic click and scrape of his heels on the sidewalk. Across the street a man in a gray shirt and brown cap dozed at the wheel of a dilapidated taxicab. The vehicle had been hand-painted bright blue, in an unsuccessful attempt to hide the fact that it had first seen the light around 1921.

"That's what we want," said Herbie, "if it runs."

They crossed the street and woke the

driver by climbing into the back of the taxi and slamming the door.

"Uh-huh, where to?" said the driver, sitting erect with a jerk.

"We wanna go where the Bronx River Parkway starts," said Herbie.

"Huh?" The man looked around at his passengers, with big eyes that grew bigger as he saw two lads in knee-pants. "What you boys want in my cab?"

"I told you, mister, we wanna go to the Bronx River Parkway."

"Why, boy, that cost you three dollars."

"Show him the money, Cliff."

Cliff briefly waved a five-dollar bill before the driver's eyes, and returned it to his pocket.

"Say, what you boys up to this time o' night? You runnin' away from home?"

"Yeah. We got a stepfather beats up our mother. We're runnin' away to our uncle in Albany. His name is—is Butcher."

The man laughed. "Name's Butcher. I see. You lie pretty good, boy. You jest make it up?"

Herbie regarded the driver uncertainly, then joined the laugh and said, "Just made it up."

"Boy, I don't care why you wanna go to Bronx River Parkway. I got a cab, you got money, an' I'm open for business. We're off."

It turned out that the sky-blue wreck could travel fast enough, though not without horrible jolting and grinding. The man let them out at the foot of the Parkway in little less than half an hour. Cliff handed him the five-dollar bill, and the boys waited in some trepidation for their change. Not another car or human being was in sight near the bril-

liantly lit highway entrance. The driver saw their troubled expressions and chuckled.

"You hear lotta bad talk 'bout cullud people, don't you, boys?" He held two single bills out to Cliff, who clasped them gratefully. "Jes' 'member, now, a cullud man done you a favor once an' didn't ask you no questions." He waved, and the blue relic rattled away.

Herbie's watch read fifteen minutes before three. There remained four and a quarter hours to reveille.

"Cliff, we're gonna come through easy," he said. The cousins began walking confidently, almost cockily, along the highway.

It is not advisable to tempt fate with such remarks. Five, ten, fifteen minutes wore away. Only two cars had passed, and the drivers had ignored the boys.

"Someone better pick us up soon," said Cliff.

"Shucks, we got hours yet," bravely answered his cousin.

The boys trudged on. They spoke little about the thrilling passages of the night. In the anticlimax to the tension of their escape both began to feel shaky and scared as they moved slowly along the margin of the broad, vacant highway. The road was filling up with fog, and becoming increasingly murky between the pools of light around the widely spaced lamps. It was, in truth, a lonely place for two footsore, sleepy boys.

Another half hour passed, with every minute a dragging torment, and still they were walking.

"Cliff—Cliff, I gotta sit down."

Herbie sank to the side of the road-way and rested his damp head on his knees. His cousin remained standing beside him. "Sure. Take it easy, Herbie."

"We ain't gonna make it. Why did I ever get you into this? You'll get kicked out of camp an' everything on accounta me—"

"Wait a second. Here comes another car."

"He won't pick us up. No one won't pick us up. We'll have to walk back all the way to Manitou. It serves me right, but you—"

Fate, however, chose to joke with Herbie again. The car stopped, and the boys gratefully scrambled in.

The driver was as different from their first benefactor, Mr. Butcher, as he could have been without being of another species than the human; in fact, had he been a full-grown hog the difference might arguably have been less wide. He was emaciated, his body was bowed over the wheel like a half hoop, and he had a small, round, smooth pink face like a baby's, except for a few strands of gray hair creeping down from under his hat, a long pointed nose, and steel-rimmed glasses such as seldom decorate a baby. His suit was a gray affair that hung shapelessly on him, with here and there a ridge or corner of bone showing under the cloth.

"Where to, fellows?" He spoke in a high, weak voice.

"We're goin' just outside Panksville, but as far as you're goin'll be swell, mister."

"Going right past there. Expect to be in Hudson by seven," said the apparition, and shifted gears with a skinny hand that seemed likely to snap in the process. It did not, however; and the car, a bulky old Pierce Arrow, inhaled a deep draught of gasoline and snorted away into the fog.

The driver spoke no more, nor did he look at his passengers after taking them into the vehicle. He drove with desperate concentration. Steering the big auto required the leverage of his whole body. He would fly up in the air when the car passed over a bump, and would clutch the wheel like a jockey hanging to the reins of a stallion. Herbie watched this strange struggle, fascinated. It was the first time he had ever realized that an automobile was a thing mightier than its driver. The wise men who build these terrors in Detroit have bridled them with gears and reined them with levers and throttled them with pinhole breathing to a point where they seem harmless to an ordinary man. Herbie's new chauffeur, however, was so far below average human weight and strength that the monster, shackled as it was, could still give him a fight—and it did fight, with the senseless bitterness of metal and grease come to life. But Herbie's fund of fear, indeed of all emotions, was almost spent. He observed the battle with waning interest when it grew clear to him that the driver, by however thin a margin, maintained the upper hand. He felt Cliff's head on his shoulder; his cousin had dropped asleep. He resolved to keep his own eyes open, not trusting the silent skeleton at the wheel. But he had been awake now for twenty hours, and had performed more violent exercise in that time than in twenty previous months. . . .

The car stopped with a jolt that shook both boys awake. Opening their eyes, they were amazed to see a bright pink sky and clear daylight.

"Panksville, boys," piped the driver.

The car stood at the crossroads of the dusty village, in front of Scudder's General Store.

"Gee, thanks a lot, mister. We were sleepin'," said Herbie, stretching. "We can get off here, but we're going about a mile further down this road."

"Oh, yes? I'll be happy to take you there." The car started again.

Herbie looked at his watch and showed it to his yawning cousin. Five minutes past six.

"We made it," he whispered.

"Did you boys have a good nap?" said the driver in his creaky voice.

"Yeah, swell," said Herbie.

"Sorry I didn't talk to you, but driving is hard work for me. I can't see well, and this car's hard to handle. You must be going to one of these camps out here."

Herbie felt a prickling of his skin, and said, "Uh—yeah, that's right."

"Penobscot?"

The boys exchanged wary glances.

"No," said Herbie.

"Must be Manitou, then. Charming gentleman, Mr. Gauss. Very pleasant to deal with, always. You boys are fortunate to be at such a splendid—"

The car went whooping around a curve and tried to take charge and dive into a ditch. No helmsman in a hurricane ever fought harder with a wheel than this featherweight driver did, and he was panting when he brought the engine back under control.

"You see—huff—what I mean, boys? Huff, I really should use the train, but in my work I just can't. Well! Here's your road."

Herbie wanted to find out what sort of work this reedy creature did, but he wanted much more strongly to vacate the vicinity of anybody who knew Mr. Gauss. The boys jumped from the car. "Thanks, mister."

"Quite welcome, boys," answered the frail man, and drove away.

Herbie imagined he had seen the last of him. He was mistaken; but neither men nor boys can see into the future much beyond the bend of the next forty-eight hours.

Cliff ran into the woods and came out leading a very stiff-legged and balky Clever Sam. The animal was obviously outraged at having been tied up in dew and darkness all night. He grunted, neighed, pulled his head this way and that, and bucked.

"This ain't gonna be good," said Herbie.

"No, it ain't," agreed his cousin, and mounted to the saddle. Clever Sam looked around at him, then walked to a thick old oak tree and, leaning against it at a sharp angle, rubbed the boy off his back. Cliff dropped harmlessly to the ground and stood up at once. Clever Sam began cropping goldenrod with sullen glances from under his knobby brows at his ex-rider.

"Cliff, it's twenty after. The bugler gets up at ten of."

Cliff approached the horse again cautiously. "I think maybe he'll be O.K. now. I don't blame him. Hey, Sam, I'm sorry. I wouldn't of done it if I didn't have to. We gotta get back to camp fast. Be a good guy."

He got back into the saddle. The horse raised his head and stood quietly, until Herbie drew near. Then he flattened his ears, whinnied, and stamped his hoofs.

"He's got it in for you, too, Herbie."

"What'll he do to me?" said Herbie fearfully.

"You'll just have to climb aboard an' find out."

Assisted by his cousin, Herbie managed to heave himself up on the horse's back. He grasped Cliff around the waist and awaited the worst. The worst turned out to be fairly bad. Clever Sam set forth toward camp at a ragged, violent trot, with an amazing amount of up-and-down movement. His flanks bobbed like buoys in a storm, and the worst of the bobbing took place between Herbie's chubby thighs. Cliff tried in vain to induce Clever Sam to lope, to gallop, and finally, when Herbie began to groan like a dying man, even to walk. The horse maintained exactly the same excruciating pace from the highway to the stable. The slapping, scraping, pounding, and burning that Herbie endured is beyond the power of words to tell.

Herbie's watch read twenty minutes to seven, and Cliff was just backing Clever Sam into his stall, when Elmer Bean walked into the stable. The handy man staggered with astonishment when he saw the two haggard, dirty boys in their city clothes, but when Herbie handed him the fifty dollars he was constrained to sit, trembling a little, on the bench.

"I said I'd get it, and I got it," said Herbie.

"Where the blazes you guys been?"

"What difference does that make? Anyway, we can build the ride now, can't we?"

"I guess so, but—where'd you git it, Herb? Know somebody in another camp?"

"What's the difference? See you later, Elmer. We gotta get back into our bunks before reveille. Come on, Cliff!"

"You didn't—you didn't steal it, fellers?"

"Heck no!" said Herbie over his shoulder with immense righteous indignation. "We borrowed it."

The boys ran down the hill. The camp was as still as a row of pyramids. In fifteen minutes it would be swarming with life. Keeping to the bushes to evade possible early risers, Cliff and Herbie made their way to the camphor locker, doffed their clothes, and pressed the spring lock back into place loosely.

"We better come back an' hammer it later. We'll wake 'em up," said Cliff, pushing at the nails with his fist. He glanced at his cousin for approval, and saw Herbie standing with a horror-stricken look on his face.

"Cliff," he said hollowly. "You know what! I forgot to leave the note in the safe saying we borrowed the money. So we stole it after all. We stole the money, Cliff!"

"Aw, they'll get it back with interest, won't they?"

"Yeah, but meantime—meantime we're just plain crooks."

"For cryin' out loud, let's worry about that later. We gotta get into our bunks."

Clad in brief white drawers, the two boys crept up behind the bungalows, avoiding Company Street, and each tiptoed into his own bunk. As Herbie slid into his cot it squeaked, and he heard Uncle Sid make the familiar snores and snuffles that preceded his waking. The boy closed his eyes and pretended unconsciousness. In a minute the make-believe was a reality; he was fast asleep. When the squalling bugle, ten minutes later, brought all his bunkmates tumbling out of bed, it failed to awake him. He lay like one dead.

"All right, boys," said Uncle Sid. "Flophouse reveille for Herbie Bookbinder."

"A pleasure," exclaimed Lennie. He and Eddie Bromberg sprang to the ends of Herbie's cot and upset it sideways. The sleeper sprawled to the floor and opened red, bleary eyes.

"Top o' the morning, General Garbage!" said Lennie.

"Get a move on," said Uncle Sid. "You'd think you hadn't slept at all."

Herbie groaned, picked his bruised, partly skinned, dog-tired body off the floor, and stumbled out with the other boys to greet the new day—with fifteen minutes of setting-up exercises.

Talking it over

1. *a.* Describe the three drivers with whom Herbie and Cliff ride.

   b. In what ways are the boys lucky in their various rides?

2. *a.* Why does borrowing money from his father's safe turn out to be more difficult than Herbie expected?

   b. Describe in detail how the boys accomplish their purpose without being captured.

3. What part of the boys' original plan was not taken care of? Why is this omission important?

4. *a.* Explain what Mr. Krieger and Mr. Powers are talking about when the boys overhear them. What does Mr. Powers want to do? Why are the men in the office at this hour?

   b. Who is Jake? What is the meaning of Mr. Krieger's statement, "Jake want better poor but own boss"?

   c. To whom does the initialed box belong? Why is it so important? Who gets possession of the box?

   d. How much importance do you think the conversation between Mr. Krieger and Mr. Powers will have in the story as a whole? Would you expect to hear of these men again?

Words in action

Use the Glossary or a dictionary to look up words you don't know.

1. Here are four words that look somewhat alike. What do their meanings have in common?

   benefactor   **beneficial**
   benefactress   **benefit**

2. Which of the following people who appear in Chapter 2 were Herbie and Cliff's **benefactors?** Be ready to explain why. (*a*) Mr. Butcher (*b*) Irving (*c*) Mr. Krieger (*d*) Mr. Powers (*e*) Jake (*f*) taxi driver (*g*) unidentified driver

3. In this chapter, which of these people do the boys have to **evade?** Be able to explain. (*a*) a highway policeman (*b*) Mr. Butcher (*c*) Irving (*d*) Mr. Krieger (*e*) Mr. Powers (*f*) a city policeman (*g*) a taxi driver (*h*) an unidentified driver

4. Which one of the men with whom the boys ride can be compared to an **apparition?**

5. Which of the following words used to describe the driver help explain why he seemed like an apparition? (*a*) pink-faced (*b*) emaciated (*c*) high-voiced (*d*) gray-haired (*e*) featherweight (*f*) reedy

3. The Ride

MR. GAUSS came shuffling absently across the girls' lawn later that same morning, moodily weighing the advantages and disadvantages of using only three buses instead of four to carry the children to the railway station the following week. He had just about decided that the saving of money was worth the bitterness that would be caused by the overcrowding when a surprising sight drove the matter from his mind. Two parallel lines of fresh white lumber stretched from the top of the hill a quarter of the way down. There was a great pile of boards and cans where the lines began, and his handy man and three boys were working like ants around the pile. As he watched, two of the boys, Herbie and Ted, left the pile carrying four boards together by the ends. They walked down the hill, laid the boards so as to lengthen the lines, and scampered uphill again.

"Here, here!" exclaimed the camp owner, approaching and waving a reproachful forefinger before him, his usual battle emblem. "What on earth is the meaning of all this?"

Herbie, Ted, and Cliff dropped their work and clustered around Elmer, as though for protection.

"It's for the Mardigrass, Mr. Gauss —er, Skipper," said Herbie eagerly.

"Boy's got an idea for some kind of ride," said Elmer Bean. "I think it'll be O.K."

"Yes, but—who gave anyone permission to build this thing? And where did all this material come from? Why, it looks like a hundred dollars' worth. Who's paying for all this, I want to know?"

Herbie looked appealingly at the handy man, who said, "Well, sir, it's like this. I know Tom Nostrand down to the Panksville Lumber Yard, see, an' I tole him about this idea this boy had. He's a pretty good guy, an' he gave me this stuff. See, he has no kids hisself, and he's pretty soft where kids are concerned."

This was not a complete lie. It had turned out that fifty dollars was not much more than half of what was needed to buy the materials from the lumber yard. Elmer had wheedled the stuff at a short price from Tom Nostrand in the manner just described. In recounting the tale to Mr. Gauss he simply took the precaution of omitting the detail of the mysterious cash the boys had given him.

Mr. Gauss was partly placated by the answer, to the extent that he knew he was not out of pocket. But he grumbled, "What sort of silly ride is it?"

Herbie started to describe his project with hot enthusiasm, but before the Skipper's fishy stare and pursed lips his force waned quickly, and he ended by stammering, apologizing, and not making much sense.

"Anyway, Uncle Sandy said," Herbie concluded lamely, "we could try anything we wanted. Can't we?"

"I never heard worse foolishness," said Mr. Gauss. "And to think of wasting all this fine material on such a harebrained scheme! Elmer, I'm disappointed in you. You shouldn't encourage them. These boards will do nicely to repair the canoe dock. Better haul them down there right away. The grease can go in the garage. You needn't do the repairs, of course, till after the season."

"You mean," exclaimed Herbie in dismay, "we don't get to build our ride, after everything we done?"

"Not done, did—past tense," said Mr. Gauss. "Of course not, Herbie. I'm sorry, but it'll never work. You should thank me for preventing you from wasting your time."

Herbie's stiff, exhausted body failed him. He fell to the ground and cried.

"Now, now, none of that," said Mr. Gauss, a little flustered. "Be a man, Herbie. Get up."

The boy stifled his sobs in an elbow, but did not stir.

"Why, look, Mr. Gauss," said the handy man, "I don't guess I can do what you said."

"What's this?" The camp owner glared at the mutineer.

"Well, see, I got that stuff offa Tom Nostrand fer the kids. Now, if we jest use it fer camp repairs, why, we gotta pay fer it, if we're honest. So if I do what you said, I'll have to tell Tom an' you'll get a bill fer the stuff tomorrow. A hunnerd dollars. Er do you want me to be dishonest an' not tell him 'bout it?"

With three children listening, the question was an embarrassing one for Mr. Gauss. "That's got nothing to do with it. I simply thought, as long as the stuff is here—of course I don't want to pay for it. The canoe dock doesn't need repairs that badly."

"Why, sir, we can use it to repair the dock all right," said Elmer, "*after* the Mardigrass. See, the wood'll still be here. It won't be new, but it'll be good. Tom Nostrand won't have no use for it, see, *once we build Herbie's ride.*"

This presentation of the case licked the camp owner. As the price of getting a hundred dollars' worth of lumber for nothing, he probably would have permitted the boys to build an altar to Baal or any other heathen god.

"Well, I've never been one to interfere with the children's pleasures," he said, "so long as they're not hurtful. Go ahead, boys, waste your time, so long as you're having fun. That's what camp is for. You have my permission to build your ride." He swept a happy smile over the group, like a water hose washing away any possible ill feeling, and his rotund back parts swayed rhythmically as he ascended to the camp office.

The beaver is the handy comparison when hard work is to be described, but has a beaver ever equaled what Herbie did that day? The fat boy had hardly slept for thirty-six hours and his body was one great ache, yet in that condition he did the longest, hardest day's work of his life. Cliff was in a bad case, too, but he was stronger than his cousin, and he had not taken the battering from Clever Sam that still throbbed in Herbie's muscles and bones. As Herbie toiled and sweated, carrying out Elmer Bean's directions, a red mist swam before his eyes. His feet and hands blistered. Often it seemed to him that his arms would refuse to come away from his sides when he willed them to. Yet somehow, stumbling and slipping, he did whatever he was told.

Ted was an early recruit to the labor. He came with Lennie to jeer, and remained to work. Later in the morning,

Felicia, hearing the spreading news of her brother's project, came and joined the labor gang. By lunch time both camps were gratefully gnawing this bone of novelty, and Herbie had acquired a quick notoriety, not exactly favorable. A few boys and girls appreciated the daring of the scheme and predicted it would work, but the popular reaction was one of ridicule. Some fine jokes were passed about "General Garbage's ride." Herbie, Cliff, and Ted came late into the dining hall, having received permission to be absent from the regular marching lines, and a spontaneous cheer arose from the seated campers:

"Here comes boloney
Riding on a pony.
Hooray, General Garbage!"

But Herbie was too tired to care. He fell into his seat, happier for the rest than for the food, and dozed through most of the meal.

Strangely enough, he revived in the afternoon. His joints grew limber, his eyes cleared, and he made merry remarks to cheer on his fellow workers. The handy man left him in charge while he went to do other chores, and was surprised at his return two hours later to find the rails laid to the edge of the water. Then came the tedious task of securing the boards to each other and to the ground, a drudgery in which the children were still engaged when they heard the call for the evening meal. Herbie went to his bunk to change his clothes, still feeling spry, but he sat on his bed to take off his socks, and instantly toppled over and fell asleep. His "second wind" was gone. His bunkmates could hardly jar him

into opening his eyes. Uncle Sid, with unusual wisdom, decided to let him be. Herbie lay as he was until midnight, when he awoke ragingly hungry and thirsty. He crept up to the dining hall by the light of the moon, and foraged in the dark kitchen until he came upon one of the long loaves of bread that served an entire bunk at a meal. He ate the whole loaf, washing it down with six glasses of water from the dishwasher's faucet, and decided that the most delicious food in the world was bread and water. Then he returned to his bunk, undressed, and slept like a brass idol until reveille.

He woke to a new day, refreshed and easier in his limbs, but low spirited. The weather was sultry. Felicia retired from the gang early in the morning, made faint by the heat. The handy man and the three boys labored on at the Ride with streaming brows, wet bodies, and slippery palms. Herbie had not in his life done such honest work. He discovered gratefully that work was the River of Forgetfulness of the storybooks, a plunge into which caused the past to disappear, if only for a while.

Deep in his heart was the guilty knowledge that his gigantic enterprise was built upon a theft. Herbie had excused the deed to himself with the device of the note; but he had failed to leave the note. The same boyish logic which had persuaded him that stealing explained by a note really wasn't stealing now prodded him with a spiky warning of evil consequences. He tried to reassure himself that once he returned the money he would be cleared, but meantime he felt himself a sinner. Would not the wrath come down on him before the Ride was finished? Would he ever have his chance to pay the money back? These painful thoughts came to him when he opened his eyes in the morning, and stayed with him until he joined Elmer on the hill. They vanished in the hammering, the dragging, the sawing, and the greasing.

Later that afternoon the Ride was ready for its first trial. The rowboat, secured by a slip knot to a stake in the ground, rested at the top of the greased rails. Clever Sam, harnessed for towing, stood by in the custody of Cliff. A distinguished group, including Mr. Gauss, both head counselors, Yishy Gabelson, Uncle Sid, and all of Herbie's bunk, as well as a number of girls, were looking curiously at the contraption and at the four sweat-streaked, grease-covered figures who had created it. The watchers talked in low tones, and sometimes they laughed, as Elmer Bean and his assistants puttered.

At last the handy man brushed the hair from his eyes, rose from his kneeling position beside the boat, and said, "She's ready. Who rides down in 'er first?"

"Me," said Herbie jealously and loudly, expecting a chorus of other volunteers, and surprised to hear his voice ring out alone.

"Why does anyone have to take a chance?" demanded Mr. Gauss. "Let it go and see what happens."

"Lot easier," said the handy man, "if someone's in 'er to paddle 'er back to shore. Wouldn' mind goin' myself. Oughta be fun."

"It's my idea, ain't it?" said Herbie. "I wanna go. Please, Mr. Gauss."

Uncle Sandy said with a slight smile, "I really don't believe it's dangerous, Skipper."

"All right, Sandy, on your say-so.

But the life of that boy is my responsibility, you know. People don't think of those things."

Herbie climbed into the boat, his pulse thumping, and established himself on a front seat, clutching a long yellow paddle.

"Sit in the bottom, Herb," said Elmer. "You might fly out that way."

The boy obeyed.

"And put aside that paddle. Might knock out a few teeth if she bumps."

Herbie dropped the paddle as though it were hot.

"All set, Herb? She's gonna rip when I yank this line." The handy man's hand was on the running end of the slip knot.

"All"—Herbie swallowed to clear an unexpected dryness—"all set."

"Here you go!" Elmer pulled the slip-knot free.

The boat did not move at all.

A few snickers were heard. The handy man said, "That's nothin'. She's sot down in the grease," and pushed the boat with his foot. It slid a few inches and came to a halt with a slushy noise. Herbie looked around at the handy man. His expression was piteous—but we are a cruel species. When the spectators saw his face, there was a roar of laughter.

"Hey, Robert Fulton,[7] give up!"

"Oh, boy, what a great idea!"

"Water's kinda dry, ain't it, Herbie?"

"Don't that speed make you dizzy?"

"Go back to your garbage, General!" (This last gem contributed by Lennie.)

"Well, Yishy, guess you have nothing to worry about," one of the bigger girls giggled. It was known that Yishy

---

[7]**Robert Fulton,** inventor who designed a steamboat and ran it successfully in 1807.

was contriving an elaborate freak show, and except for this crazy undertaking of Herbie's his claim for the prize seemed without much competition. The stout Super-senior, six feet tall and with the shadow of a mustache on his swarthy upper lip, smiled quietly. He felt sorry for the small boy who had sought to challenge him so desperately and foolishly.

"What's the matter, Elmer?" Herbie cried.

The handy man was scratching his head. "Dunno, Herbie, I swear," he said. "That boat ought to be barrelin' down the hill. Unless—I tell you what, the grease is so fresh and thick, maybe it ain't slicked down good yet. Y'know, like fresh snow. Hey, Ted, Cliff! Give us a hand."

Elmer and the two boys began shoving the boat down the incline. They had only pushed it a few steps when it acquired its own momentum and ran away from under their hands.

"There she goes now, Herbie!" cried the handy man.

There she went without a doubt. Accelerating at every yard, the rowboat was soon speeding. Herbie's dark head could barely be seen above the gunwale, looking straight ahead as the boat slid downward. Faster and faster the strange vehicle rattled along the slippery rails. In a few moments it whizzed over the bank, and struck the water with a towering splash. The spectators sent up a real cheer this time, for it was a thrilling thing, after all, to see a boy's wild dream come true. But the cheer died when the splash subsided. Herbie and the yellow paddle remained floating on the water. The rowboat had disappeared.

Mr. Gauss became violently agitated. "Someone save that boy! I knew this was sheer folly! Don't let that paddle drift away! Dismantle this thing immediately! Find the rowboat!" he shouted, waving his arms in many directions and running two full circles around the stupefied handy man. While he was engaged in this useful activity, Uncle Sandy, Ted, and Cliff trampled down the hill, and Clever Sam loped after Cliff, trailing his towing harness. When this strange rescue cavalcade reached the shore, it became evident that lifesaving would not be part of its duties. Herbie floundered to shallow water and began wading sadly ashore, dragging the paddle. Behind his back the rowboat rose to the surface with bloated laziness and rolled over, its greased bottom, adorned with two parallel rails, rocking gently just above the water. The whole scene was a study in the ludicrous, worthy to be sketched by a good-natured painter and titled "Failure."

The feelings of the drenched boy as he stumbled ashore under the eyes of most of the girls' camp, which had gathered at the news of the mishap, cannot in charity be examined. But Ted and Cliff heard him muttering fiercely, "I deserve it! Deserve it! Deserve worse than that," over and over, as he doggedly sloshed up the hill, declining assistance.

"Don't take it too hard, Herb," said Uncle Sandy, striding beside him. "All of us have ideas that don't come off. It was a swell try."

Herbie did not answer.

"What happened, Herb?" said Elmer Bean, coming down to meet him.

"Elmer, the doggone boat just hit the water an' kept goin' straight down." Herbie leaned on the handy man's arm for a moment, pulled off a shoe, and poured a stream of muddy water out of it. He did the same with the other shoe, and padded along the grass in his waterlogged stockings, holding the shoes in one hand. "Somethin's wrong with the whole business, Elmer. There's a curse on me. It ain't never gonna work."

"Don't give up that easy, Herb."

"I ain't givin' up easy. But you can't fight a curse. I got all this comin'."

They were at the top of the slide now, and the large semicircle of spectators stared silently at the boy. He was brought too low to be an object of jokes. Felicia pushed to the front of the crowd and cried, "Herbie, are you all right?"

"Sure I'm all right. Water don't hurt nobody," the sopping boy answered shortly, and turned away from her.

Mr. Gauss's arms were still waving, but more slowly and in fewer directions as he drew near. "Splendid camp spirit, Herbie. You're taking defeat like a man. Not injured a bit, are you? You look just fine. No need to notify your parents, I'm sure. Why upset them? All you need is dry clothes and a nice hot supper. Yes, yes, Herbie, you deserve honorable mention for your idea. It is not a failure, my boy. Look on it as a success, a moral success in which you learned many lessons."

Few things could have been less palatable to Herbie at this point than a dose of Gaussian victory.

"Guess I'll go change my clothes," he mumbled. As he turned to the narrow path to Company Street, he saw Lucille Glass standing close behind Mr. Gauss, peeping at him with round, sympathetic eyes. She gave him her most winning smile and nodded en-couragement. But suddenly she seemed only a gawky little girl in white blouse and blue bloomers, with carroty hair. She had a great many freckles, and when she smiled her upper row of teeth showed crooked, one on each side being set far back in the gum. The thought that for this creature's favor he had undergone all his vain giant labors was preposterous to Herbie. He could not summon up an answering smile. He trudged away, stooped and dripping. The last thing he heard was the camp owner's order, "Start the dismantling right after supper, Elmer. I want this lawn clear by morning," and Elmer's reply, a morose "Um."

Mr. Gauss sat on the veranda of the guest house that evening, listening with pleasure to the sawing, ripping, and banging in the darkness on the hill. To the uninitiated it was harsh noise, but to him it was a sweet song of lumber acquired free of charge. He mused awhile on the amazing burst of energy of young Herbie Bookbinder, which had brought into being the useless structure now being demolished. Boys were powder kegs, he concluded, veritable powder kegs. The quietest of them could go off with a great bang when properly ignited. Why would boys never show such fine spirit in the little tasks he set them? Mr. Gauss sighed, and slapped a mosquito into the hereafter. Another hummed up to take vengeance. Mr. Gauss was in no mood for the nightly duel with the fauna of Manitou. He rose and retreated to his room, where he fell asleep with the sound of hammer and crowbar still in his ears, and a vision of a neat pile of boards in his mind's eye.

In the morning he was awakened by a hail outside his window: "Mr. Gauss!

Hey, Mr. Gauss!" Rolling his reluctant body out of bed, he noticed with blinking surprise that the battered one-legged tin clock on his dresser read only ten minutes after seven. Nobody ever disturbed him until eight.

"Take a look out here, Mr. Gauss!"

The voice was the handy man's. Mr. Gauss shuffled to the window, looked out at the lawn, and came wide awake with astonishment and anger. Herbie's Ride stretched down to the water exactly as before. The rowboat was fastened with a slip knot again at the top of the slide, with Clever Sam happily cropping grass nearby. Ted, Cliff and Herbie sat on the seats of the boat. Elmer stood up in it, with the running end of the knot in his hand. As soon as the handy man saw Mr. Gauss's head he shouted, "She's O.K. now, Mr. Gauss. Watch us go!"

"Elmer, I forbid you!" yelled Mr. Gauss, but even as he uttered the words the handy man pulled the line free and dropped to a seat. The rowboat began sliding. A quarter of the way down the hill it picked up speed, and raced. Just as it came to the water's edge it seemed to jump upward. The boys raised canvas flaps on either side of the gunwales to protect themselves from the splash. The boat flew off shore, hit the water as gracefully as a gull, with a small burst of spray, and coasted to a halt. As soon as the splattering was over the boys dropped the flaps, took up paddles, and waved them gleefully at Mr. Gauss.

The camp owner, trembling with mingled relief and annoyance, dressed and hurried out to the slide. When he arrived the rowboat was already back at the top, and Cliff was releasing Clever Sam from the tow.

"Next ride fer you, Skipper!" said the handy man, saluting him gaily.

"Elmer, my orders were distinctly—"

"Shucks, Mr. Gauss, I knew fer sure you din' wanna make them kids unhappy after all that work, not if we could help it. There's four o' them, see, an' we want 'em to come back next year, don't we? Well, there wasn't nuthin' wrong with the old slide, 'cept I fergot to put in the old ski-jump tilt to the bottom, see? Boat was headin' straight down when it hit water 'stead o' comin' in belly up like a bird. We fixed it easy last night. Jest a little scaffoldin' an' a short ramp."

"Please, Mr. Gauss," said Herbie, looking at him with dog's eyes, "take a ride. We tried it eight times already. It's great. You'll be our first real passenger."

"Very well, Herbie," Mr. Gauss smiled broadly and patted his head. "You have real camp spirit. My hat is off to you." He stepped majestically into the boat and sat. Elmer released the rope and Mr. Gauss had the luxury of a fine thrilling ride, and not a drop of water splashed on him, either. Ted in the bow, and Herbie in the stern, swiftly paddled the boat to the pebbly beach, and helped the camp owner alight. Mr. Gauss watched admiringly as the boys pulled the boat into place on a greased ramp, fastened the towing harness of Clever Sam to the mooring ring in the stern, and guided it up into place on the up-tilted rails at the foot of the Ride. The horse began dragging the boat up the hill smoothly and easily.

There is no arguing with success, and Mr. Gauss knew it. "Herbie, I congratulate you," he said, walking up behind the lad. "You have performed a wonder, my boy."

"I ain't the one. Elmer an' Cliff an' Ted—mostly Elmer—they done it. I can't even do half as much work as Ted. I'm just no good at it."

"But you, my boy, you had the vision. The vision and the enterprise. Did I build Camp Manitou, my boy? Why, I did not nail one stick to another. Yet it is my camp. And this is your ride. Herbie's Ride."

Herbie would have thanked Mr. Gauss to compare his ride to something better than Camp Manitou, but he realized that the camp owner was exerting himself to be pleasant. So he said, "Sure glad you enjoyed it, Mr. Gauss—er, Skipper," and hurried away up the hill.

Talking it over

1. What problem would Herbie have had to face if the lumber had been used for dock repair instead of for the ride?

2. *a.* How does Elmer persuade Mr. Gauss to permit the building of the ride?

   b. What further evidence can you give that Elmer understands Mr. Gauss's character?

3. *a.* What does Herbie's hard work on the ride tell you about him?

   b. What do you learn about Herbie from the way he reacts to the teasing of the other campers?

   c. How do the results of the trial ride affect Herbie? Why?

4. *a.* Try to imagine what Elmer, Herbie, and Herbie's friends say and do between the time when Mr. Gauss orders the ride dismantled and the time when the camp owner begins hearing "sawing, ripping, and banging in the darkness on the hill." What do the sounds actually mean?

   b. Explain how Elmer changes the way the ride is constructed in order to make it successful.

Words in action

The author makes some interesting comparisons in *Herbie's Ride.*

1. He says of Mr. Gauss, "He swept a happy smile over the group, like a water hose washing away any possible ill feeling." In this remark, what two things are being compared? What is similar about these two things?

2. When the author describes Herbie as sleeping "like a brass idol," does he mean (*a*) that Herbie looks like a statue made of brass, or (*b*) that Herbie is sleeping so soundly he hardly seems alive?

3. Felicia hears about her brother's project and joins the labor gang. By lunch time, both boys and girls at the camp are "gnawing this bone of novelty." What are the boys and girls actually doing at lunch time?

4. Lucille's hair is described as "carroty." Is the author referring to (*a*) the color of her hair, (*b*) the way she wears it, or (*c*) whether it is straight or curly?

4. The Triumph of Herbie

AND SO it was that Herbie's Ride came into being after all. Four days ago it had been a cloudy notion in a young boy's mind, a ridiculous dream of a rowboat on wheels coasting downhill. Now, real and working, the slide dominated the landscape of the girls' camp. Elmer added a handsome frill: an archway at the top, bearing the words "HERBIE'S RIDE" cut out of a semicircular frame of cardboard in letters a foot high, with bright red electric lights behind it. Delighted with his handiwork, he drove hastily into town and returned with an electric interrupter switch which he attached to the lights. When dusk fell and the boys and girls turned out in gay costumes for Mardi Gras, this sign, flashing on and off, on and off, was a striking sight. It was the first thing visitors saw, driving into the camp or crossing from the boys' grounds to the girls' lawn. There was nothing as splendid anywhere else in Manitou. When the other booths, games, rides, and entertainments had hardly been visited, a line of twenty children and adults already stretched before the Ride.

Directly under the archway stood Herbie in Elmer's sailor cap and blouse. The cap tended to drop down over his ears, and the blouse was loose enough to have held Cliff inside it, too, but the nautical effect was fine nevertheless. At first Herbie made a few efforts in the way of a cry: "Step right up, folks, best ride you ever been on! Slip down the slide on the slippery slope for only a quarter, twenty-five cents, the fourth part of a dollar," and so forth. But within a few minutes, with two dozen paid passengers waiting their turns, more coming each moment, and a large crowd watching the Ride and exclaiming in admiration, the cry seemed unnecessary, and he gave it up.

Thereafter the night was one of swimming pleasure for him. Money and congratulations poured in. Many passengers came up the hill from their first ride and walked into line for another. The Ride went smooth as oil. Ted and Felicia stayed in the rowboat, paddling it back to shore. Cliff and Clever Sam accomplished recovery with more and more ease as the evening wore on. Herbie collected fares and stored them in a cigar box, and tied up and released the boat with a slip knot, as Elmer had taught him. All four children felt the luxurious pride of participation in a great success, and even Clever Sam was in mellow good humor, and accepted much petting and light thwacks from the onlookers with friendly rolls of the eyes.

In this hour of exalted happiness Herbie's conscience packed up and departed. He amassed fifty dollars in less than two hours. The "borrowing" episode would be erased from the Book of Sins in the morning. The curse was forgotten. All was well. "Boy, you win Skipper sure!" was said to him perhaps a hundred times. Vision and enterprise had carried the day. Heaven had decided mercifully that stealing wasn't really stealing sometimes, and had suspended the Eighth Commandment for Herbie Bookbinder's benefit. What a wonderful old world it was, to be sure!

Yes, and even Lucille came around. Herbie's triumph had been in swing for

three hours, and he was quite drunk with praise and profits, when he felt a timid tug at his oversize sleeve.

"Congratulations, Herbie," said a caroling voice.

The boy looked round at a beautiful little red-headed pirate dressed in a ragged gold shirt, a crimson sash, and short black trousers carefully torn at the bottom. She carried a little dagger and wore a black silk patch over one eye, but the other eye shone with enough admiration and love for two. Herbie, who had thought yesterday he was cured of his romantic affliction, suddenly wondered if he really was. Lucille, the radiant Lucille, was humbling herself to him, and it was a sweet sensation.

" 'Lo, Lucille. 'Scuse me a minute."

He made change for a batch of eight passengers as they boarded the boat, and flourished the cigar box so that Lucille had a long look at its overflowing green and silver contents. Then he pulled the rope with careless ease, and the boat thundered away down the slope.

"Gosh, Herbie." The girl's voice was awed, crushed. "However did you think up such a thing? You're wonderful!"

"Aw, Elmer Bean an' Cliff done it all. I ain't so hot," said Herbie. He paused, glanced at her hand and, as it were, took aim. Then he slowly added, *"I can't even dip."*[8]

The pirate's cheeks all at once became the color of her sash. She pulled the patch off her face, evidently judging she needed both eyes for the work at hand, and said softly, looking at him with innocent appeal, "Herbie, I'm

sorry I been so bad to you. You know what, I haven't even talked to Lennie all night. Except once he wanted to take me on your ride, an' I said I wanted to go alone."

Herbie's congealed affections were melting in the warmth of her voice, low, musical, almost whispering. But he called up the memory of his injuries and said indifferently, "Wanna ride now?"

"Yes, Herbie."

"O.K. You kin go free. An' you don't hafta wait in line."

The flashing sign showed surprise, darkness, disappointment, darkness, then a winsome smile that remained on the girl's face through several flashes. "Won't you come with me?"

"Heck, no, Lucille. See, I gotta take care o' the finances."

"Oh. Maybe after a while you'll come to the dancing at the social hall. I'd like to dance with you."

"Maybe."

Lucille fell silent, and watched Clever Sam towing the rowboat back to the top. Herbie made a great show of counting the money—there was a hundred seven dollars now—and wished Lucille would grovel a little more; but she didn't. So he said at last, "How's the rest of the Mardigrass, Lucille? I ain't had a chance to see it."

"Terrible. Everybody says your ride is the only good thing."

"How's Yishy's freak show?"

The girl sniffed contemptuously in answer.

"What's Lennie doing?"

"Oh, he's got a baseball suit on with 'New York Yankees' on it, an' a pillow in his stomach, an' goes around saying he's Babe Ruth. What a dumb idea!"

Herbie silently compared this inspi-

[8] *"I can't even dip."* Herbie is referring to the night he made a fool of himself at the dance.

ration with his own, and concluded that there were rare moments when brawn did not automatically rule the world. It did not occur to him that Lennie, at least, had not stolen the baseball suit.

The rowboat came creaking to the top of the slide. Herbie lashed it to the stake as Cliff freed Clever Sam. Then he gallantly handed Lucille into the boat, while several boys and girls waiting in line squealed a protest. Felicia, sitting in the bow, looked around, and said, "Humph! Starting all over again." She threw down her paddle and stepped out of the boat.

"Hey, Fleece, where you goin'?" said Herbie.

"As long as we're getting romantic again," snapped his sister as she stalked away, "I'm going to dance for a while at the social hall."

"Never mind, Herbie." Ted spoke up from the stern. "I can handle it myself."

"Thank you for the ride, Herbie. I hope I'll see you later," said Lucille demurely. Now the other passengers piled in, thrusting money at the boy. Lucille all the while gazed up at him worshipfully. Herbie felt foolish and happy and warm, and at the pinnacle of life and time. It was with reluctance that he tripped the rope and sent the boat rumbling downhill with its lovely burden.

Not long afterward three prolonged blasts of Uncle Sandy's whistle echoed through the camp, signaling the end of the Mardi Gras. Grumbling, a line of about a dozen passengers disbanded, all of them campers awaiting a second or third ride, except for a stout lady from the village with a dismal white-headed child. Herbie counted the receipts again while Ted beached the boat and Cliff returned the horse to the stable. Felicia came up from the dance in a glowing, happy mood. When all the colleagues were gathered again under the flashing sign, Herbie announced gaily the income from their labors: a hundred thirteen dollars and fifty cents.

"Holy smoke, we're rich," said Ted.

"How do we divvy it?" said Felicia.

"First of all I owe seventy-five bucks for materials," said Herbie. The others nodded. "That still leaves almost forty bucks, or ten bucks apiece."

Mr. Gauss appeared out of the darkness, smiling broadly. He was carrying half a dozen cigar boxes similar to the one in Herbie's hands.

"Well, well, the gold mine," he said cheerfully. "Let me have your box, Herbie. I'll keep it in the safe overnight for you. I'm doing the same for all the boys that made any real money."

"Gee, thanks, Mr. Gauss," said Herbie, huddling the box protectingly against his side, "but I can take care of it O.K."

"Nonsense, my boy. We don't want to tempt sneak thieves, you know." He grasped the box firmly and pried it out of Herbie's arms. "The safe is the only place for so much money as you made. I'll send for you first thing in the morning and return it to you. Congratulations, all of you!" He walked off toward the guest house.

"Good-by, hundred thirteen bucks," croaked Ted, loud enough for the camp owner to hear him, but Mr. Gauss padded obliviously away.

"G'wan," said Herbie. "He wouldn't take that money for himself."

"He couldn't!" said Felicia.

Cliff said, "Even Mr. Gauss ain't that low. He'll give us some back, anyway."

"O.K., o.k.," said Ted, "I been at this camp a long time. If we see a nickel o' that dough again, it'll be a miracle."

"He's *gotta* gimme back the seventy-five bucks for material!" said Herbie. "I owe it."

"Don't be silly," exclaimed Felicia fretfully. "What are you boys talking about? He's got to give us back *all* of it. You talk as though there was a question about it. Is he a robber? It's our money, not his. How can he possibly keep a penny of it?"

Ted looked sidelong at her out of one eye, like a rooster. "This is my sixth year at Manitou," he said. "Inside that box is money, an' outside that box is Mr. Gauss. All there is between 'em is a lid. It ain't enough. . . . Well, it was fun anyhow." He shrugged. "More fun than I ever had in this hellhole. Thanks for lettin' me in on it, Herb."

"Aw, yer crazy, Ted," Herbie began, but the bugle sounded retreat, and on this foreboding note of Ted's they were compelled to part.

A few minutes later the boys of Bunk Thirteen sat around on their cots in pajamas, awaiting Uncle Sandy's announcement of the Skipper-for-a-Day.

"Who you gonna appoint for Uncle Sandy, Herb?" said Lennie deferentially.

"Heck, Lennie, I ain't won yet."

"You won. Nobody else can possibly win."

The other boys voiced a chorus of assents to this. They were proud of Herbie now. Boys from other bunks were shouting congratulations through the screen.

"Well, let's wait till he announces it, anyhow," said Herbie.

Uncle Sid said, "I'm proud of you, Herbie, I really am. What you did was remarkable. You have a great future."

He puffed anxiously at a forbidden cigarette held in the hollow of his hand. Poor Uncle Sid was actually tense and nervous on Herbie's behalf.

A preliminary blast of Uncle Sandy's unmistakable whistle came from outer darkness, and cut dead all conversation. His voice boomed out of a megaphone.

"Now the announcement you've all been waiting for. The judges—Aunt Tillie, the Skipper, and myself—had a tough time deciding among the many excellent entries, two in particular that you all know about.

"The Skipper of the Day is"—a long agonizing pause; then hurriedly — "Yishy Gabelson for his freak show, with special honorable mention to Herbie Bookbinder for his excellent ride. That's all."

But that was not all. Cries from every bungalow along Company Street tore the night.

"Boo!"

"Gyps!"

"Robbers!"

"General Garbage won!"

"Crooks!"

The whistle blew furiously several times and quieted the din.

"Now, cut that out!" roared the head counselor. "You're not at home yet, you're still in camp. It isn't what you want, it's what we decide that goes here!"

This was a provocative announcement that Uncle Sandy might have spared himself. But he was angry, and feeling guilty, too, to tell the truth, so he acted with poor judgment.

"Yah!"

"Boo!"

"Ssss!"

"You bet it ain't what we want!"

"It ain't *never* what we want!"

"Let's hang Uncle Gussie to a sour-apple tree!"

These and forty other insolent cries were flung through the screens. Confused and at a loss, Uncle Sandy stepped back into his tent. Meantime, Ted in Bunk Thirteen jumped from his bed and seized a tin pan and spoon from his hiking pack.

"Don't worry, General," he grated to the dumfounded, pallid Herbie. "This is one time Uncle Gussie don't get away with it."

"Ted! You come back here!" exclaimed Uncle Sid, but Ted was already outside and marching up Company Street alone, beating the tin pan rhythmically and shouting, "We want Herbie! We want Herbie!" This was all the spark that was needed. In a twinkling twenty boys were in the street banging resounding objects—a glass, a drum, a tin canteen, and even a washtub were among them—and chanting, "We want Herbie!" The counselors were powerless to stop the eruption, and none of them particularly wanted to stop it. By the time the howling crowd of boys in pajamas had reached Uncle Sandy's tent their number included almost the whole camp. They milled under the large white electric light that hung on a pole at the end of the street, and chanted and yelled in a way to frighten the cloud of bugs that danced overhead.

Inside the hot yellow tent sat Mr. Gauss and the two head counselors, with sullen expressions.

"I say again, Sandy," spoke out the camp owner, "are you going to do nothing about this breakdown of discipline?"

"Skipper, I'm just one man. The counselors should have stopped it before it got started. Evidently they feel the same way I do, and I—"

The bulky form of Yishy Gabelson catapulted into the tent, crowding it uncomfortably.

"Uncle Sandy, Mr. Gauss, you can't do it to me. Them guys out there are ready to jump me. You know that kid won!" stammered the Super-senior, in a sweat.

"Now, Yishy, don't be childish," said Mr. Gauss. "Your freak show was admirable. And anyway, you know it's impossible to let an Intermediate be Skipper. It's too risky."

"You shoulda thought of that when you made up the contest!" shouted Yishy. "You shoulda said no Intermediates allowed to compete. It's too late to go makin' up rules now, Mr. Gauss. That kid won and you know it. You can do what you like, but I ain't gonna be your Skipper. I'm no crook!"

He bolted from the tent and the three judges heard him yell above the din that greeted him, "I *tole* 'em! I tole 'em I wouldn't take it!" Thereupon the jeers changed to shouts of approval, and merged into a tremendous chant: "We want Herbie! We want Herbie!"

"It seems to me, Mr. Gauss," said Uncle Sandy, wiping his thick glasses with a handkerchief and laying emphasis on the camp owner's last name, "that we have a choice of calling off Campers' Day or giving Skipper to Herbie Bookbinder."

"Nonsense. They'll forget all about it after a night's sleep. We'll give them ice cream for lunch," said Mr. Gauss.

"So far as I'm concerned," said Aunt Tillie sourly, "the boy obviously did win. I simply went along with the Skipper's insistence that we needed an older boy to run the camp."

"You haven't got the older boy any more," observed Uncle Sandy.

"We want Herbie! We want Herbie!" came with undiminished gusto from outside, accompanied by bangs, rattles, clanks, and stamping.

Mr. Gauss looked from one head counselor to another. He saw two decidedly hostile faces.

"In view of the fact that I have no support from you, who should give it to me," he said, "I seem compelled to abandon the only sensible policy. Do as you please, Uncle Sandy, on your own responsibility. I have no more to say."

"Do we call off the Campers' Day, sir, or give Skipper to the boy?"

"I have no more to say."

Uncle Sandy stepped out of the tent. The mob of boys sensed news, and the chant died. The head counselor squinted around at the strange sight of his campers herded together in night clothes, in complete disorder. In the center of the crowd Herbie Bookbinder loomed high, naked except for white drawers, perched on the shoulders of Yishy and three other Seniors. When Sandy saw the fat boy thus glorified, he burst out laughing. "Come down, Herbie, you win. You're Skipper!" he shouted, and continued his good-natured guffawing.

Great yells of triumph went up. Though the boys knew nothing of what had passed in the tent, they gathered from Uncle Sandy's manner that the change was as welcome to him as to them, and they pressed around him to shake his hand and pound him lovingly with their fists. The four Seniors who were holding Herbie up commenced

dancing, and nearly dropped the hero of the evening several times. Cries of congratulation, good wishes, and admiration came up to the erstwhile General Garbage from every side, and they were all addressed to "Herbie."

Under no circumstances but these could he have received such an ovation, which exceeded anything that Lennie or Yishy had ever received for athletic prowess. He had become the symbol of resistance to Mr. Gauss, and in his victory every boy felt the throwing off of the yoke from his own shoulders. It was a brief temporary success, to be sure—tomorrow the heavy Gauss rules and edicts would be in force as always —but once, at least once, Uncle Gussie had been forced to give ground. "Hooray for Herbie! Hooray for Herbie!" cheered the boys, with all their hearts and lungs.

And Herbie, bouncing and swaying on his perilous perch under the glare of the lamp amid the darting insects, surrounded by a host of friendly, admiring, upturned faces, his ears ringing with cheers and praise, felt warm tears of joy and wonder trickling down his face. None of his many daydreams of triumph had ever been as sweet as this. "There is no man that has not his hour, and no thing that has not its place." General Garbage, the fat, the unathletic, the despised, had come into his hour at last.

⟳ **Talking it over**

1. *a.* How does the success of the ride affect Lucille?

b. How is Herbie affected by her attitude?

2. *a.* What is Mr. Gauss's viewpoint on the matter of the boxes? Does it seem reasonable?

b. Among Herbie's colleagues, what differences of opinion are held about the safety of the money? Why does Ted have doubts?

3. *a.* How do you account for the rating Herbie gets in the contest?

b. What is the reaction of the campers? Why?

c. How do you explain their success in winning the argument?

4. *a.* Why do the campers suddenly like Herbie so much?

b. How do their feelings affect Herbie?

⇄ **Words in action**

1. Ted, Felicia, and Cliff are called Herbie's **colleagues.** Do they work *with* him, *for* him, or *against* him?

2. With the help of the Glossary, determine what these three words have in common: **colleague, collaborate, collaborator.** Could Elmer be called a collaborator? Why or why not?

3. Proud of the success of his ride, and charmed by Lucille's wish to renew their friendship, Herbie feels himself at the **pinnacle** of life. Is Herbie happy or unhappy at this time? Does Herbie ever expect to be happier? Do you know of a time when he *is* happier? Explain.

4. Uncle Sandy's announcement that what the campers wanted didn't count was **provocative.** Which meaning of *provocative* best fits the situation?

5. In what way is Mr. Gauss's choice of Yishy provocative?

5. Disaster

HERBIE WOKE before reveille next day from a most horrible dream. The morning was misty gray outside the dripping screens. His bunkmates lay sleeping all around him. Uncle Sid snored in a fitful, choking way. The crickets were silent. Streamers of mist floated through the screens and hung inside the bungalow, thick to the eye and clammy when they brushed the skin. Herbie shuddered as the events of the dream came back to him, hanging in his memory like the streamers of mist.

He had murdered a man and buried him in the vacant lot behind the Place. Who the man was, he could not remember, but the murder had been done and covered up long ago and he had almost forgotten it. Then for some reason his father had decided to dig a hole behind the Place, and had selected the very spot where the body lay buried. His father, Mr. Krieger, and Mr. Powers had begun digging vigorously, and soon had a deep brown hole which grew deeper every moment. With increasing panic, Herbie, watching them excavate, had realized that the corpse must soon be found. And suddenly, with a ghastly shock of terror that was so powerful it woke him up, he remembered he had left a clue on the body that would instantly identify him as the murderer. As Herbie sat up in bed, still horrified, he strained to recall what the clue had been, and finally caught the fading image of it, though it made no sense. It was the cigar box in which he had kept the fares collected at the Ride.

So vivid had the nightmare been that the drowsy boy actually began reviewing all the events of the night of his trip to the city to see if he had really killed someone, and it was with some relief that he came wider awake and dismissed the absurd fancy. The thought of the cigar box now grew stronger in his mind. He spent some time in imaginary arguments with Mr. Gauss; the camp owner tried to keep the money on various pretexts which Herbie scornfully exploded one by one. Then he dwelled on the glories of the previous night, and pictured some of the pleasures of his forthcoming day as lord of the camp. Little by little his mood of guilty foreboding caused by the dream faded, as the morning mist dissipated before the rising sun. When the bugle blew after what seemed a very long time, he was as cheery as the newly awakened ones, and jumped from bed faster than any of them.

"Hey, Herbie, whaddayou gettin' up for? You're Uncle Gussie," said Lennie, yawning.

"He is not," Uncle Sid put in promptly, rubbing a blue bristling jowl with the back of his hand. "Campers' Day doesn't start until ten o'clock."

"Sure, otherwise the counselors would hafta stand inspection," sneered Ted as he stepped into ragged, dirty slippers. "Mr. Gauss made up that rule after the first year—leave it to Uncle Gussie. Boy, that was fun when the counselors hadda sweep the floor an' all. Campers' Day ain't no good now."

"Shut up and get out to drill, all of you," said Uncle Sid, and fell back on his cot with closed eyes as the boys trooped out the door.

An hour later during breakfast the head counselor walked by the table of Bunk Thirteen and said casually, "Herbie, come to my tent after breakfast.

Uncle Sid, have one of the other boys make Herbie's bed."

"Yes, sir," said Uncle Sid.

Herbie looked modestly into his plate while his bunkmates regarded him respectfully and enviously.

"Hey, Herb, who ya gonna make head counselor?" said Lennie, ladling a generous portion of scrambled eggs into the fat boy's plate. Don't forget your old pals. We been old pals for years, Herbie, you know we have."

"You?" said Ted, wrinkling his thin beak at Lennie in disgust. "After the way you haunted him all summer, how can you have the nerve to wanna be Uncle Sandy? 'Bout all he could appoint you is Clever Sam."

The other boys chortled.

"That's well said," remarked Uncle Sid. "As a matter of fact, Lennie, I appoint you to make Herbie's bed. And if it's Frenched or tricked up in any way, you'll spend the next two days on your cot."

"Why would I French it? I'm glad to make Herbie's bed," said Lennie, with a rather frightening simulation of gladness on his face. "We're old pals, Herbie an' me. Ain't we, Herbie? Remember old Mrs. Gorkin's class, huh, Herbie? That was fun, wasn't it? Hey, I wonder what our fathers are doing now, down at the Place."

Herbie, choking a little at the mention of the Place, pretended to have a mouthful of eggs, and answered Lennie with a meaningless grunt. The other boy continued his demonstrations of friendship throughout the meal, and left his eggs untasted in his eagerness to remind Herbie of their many sentimental ties. Herbie tried his best to say nothing in reply.

"Boy, Herb, with you as Skipper an'

me as Sandy, what stunts we couldn't work up, huh? We could really put this camp on its ear. We'll give 'em the old Homer Avenue treatment!"

Herbie stood. " 'Scuse me, Uncle Sid, could I leave the table early? I think maybe Uncle Sandy'll want to see me as soon as possible."

"Of course, go right ahead—Skipper!" said Uncle Sid, smiling.

"Don't forget, Herbie," called Lennie after him. "You an' me'll stick together, huh? Old Herbie an' Lennie! A coupla regular guys from Homer Avenue!"

Lennie's new-found affection somehow depressed Herbie. As he made his way through the dining room he was the target of dozens of friendly hails; but he did not enjoy the homage quite as much as he might have. It all reminded him too forcibly of an incident he had observed a week ago. Daisy, the miserable, abhorred Daisy, an embittered failure in athletics and in day-to-day life with his fellows, had enjoyed a brief reign of dazzling popularity when the mail brought him a package containing four salamis. From the respect and cordiality lavished on him one might have thought Daisy had suddenly grown two feet taller. His head turned by the intoxication of being loved, poor Daisy had seized a knife and forthwith sliced up and given away all four salamis piece by piece to a swarm of outstretched hands. The last slice gone, he had just as suddenly shrunk to normal size, and Herbie recalled vividly the picture of the thin bespectacled boy, sitting alone on his expensive brass-bound trunk, the greasy knife still in his hand, peering around at the empty bungalow. What was so different, Herbie wondered, between

Daisy with his salamis and General Garbage as Skipper? These were sad ideas to be thinking at the height of good luck and, like all cynicism, only partly true. Daisy's glory had been brief because it was all salami and no achievement. But the fact is, in this summer Herbie had come far in knowledge of certain ways of the world. He was to come farther before sunset.

He knocked diffidently on the pole at the entrance to Uncle Sandy's tent. A hearty voice summoned him inside.

"Hi, Herb. Sit down." Uncle Sandy pointed with a smoking pipe to a three-legged stool beside his narrow desk. The desk was a piece of beaverboard supported by four planks. "First of all, congratulations. You're a remarkable kid."

"If not for Elmer Bean an' my cousin Cliff, I wouldn't be nothin'. I had good luck," said Herbie as he sat.

"I know that. The fact that you know it too, is good. But nobody ever makes a success without luck and help. You deserve your reward."

"Thanks, Uncle Sandy."

"Now, let's move fast." The head counselor thrust a typewritten list and a pencil into his hand. "I've always run Campers' Day on the level, Herb, as much as—hm—as much as I was allowed to. That's why it's been a success. You go through that list and tick off the boy you want to be the counselor in each bunk."

"Yes, sir." Herbie studied the sheet and made slow, careful marks.

"By the way, who's going to be me?"

Herbie answered at once, "Cliff."

Uncle Sandy grinned. "Well, this is the one day Uncle Sandy'll be able to ride Clever Sam. I think Cliff'll be fine." He glanced over Herbie's shoulder, nodding. "Good. Good choices. Ted for Uncle Sid, eh? Fine. Poor Ted hasn't been a counselor in all his years." He returned to writing at his desk. In a few minutes Herbie handed the sheet to him. The head counselor examined it and gave it back. "You haven't filled in names for the doctor and nurse."

"Nurse?" Herbie scratched his head and stared.

"We always do that for laughs. Put down anybody who'll look funny in a nurse's uniform. Yishy would be fine, but you've got him as Uncle Peewee."

Herbie thought a moment; then he scrawled on the paper and passed it to the head counselor, who looked at it and laughed aloud. The writing read:

Doctor—*Daisy Gloster*
Nurse—*Lennie Krieger*

Uncle Sandy glanced at the large cheap watch hanging on a nail over his bedside. "Nine twenty-five. Mr. Gauss wants to see you at nine-thirty, Herbie. Better run on up the hill. Come back here when you're through."

"What's he want to see me about?"

The head counselor kept his eyes on his desk. "Can't say. About the money from the Ride, possibly. Hurry, boy."

There was in Uncle Sandy's manner a sudden aloof cautiousness that Herbie didn't like. He left the tent and trotted up the hill, feeling the gloom of his dream stealing upon him again. He came to the steps of the guest house panting and red-faced, and as he paused for breath he was surprised to see Yishy Gabelson issue from the doorway of the camp office, shaking his head and grinding his teeth.

"Oh, that—! Oh, that fat old—!" muttered the Super-senior, using two epithets from the very bottom of the

barrel of bad language. "Oh, that—!" he added, using one even worse, and actually strange to Herbie's ears.

"Hey, Yishy, what's the matter?" cried Herbie anxiously, as the other strode past him unseeing. Yishy glanced around at him, startled.

"What are you still doing here? You know what's happened."

"No, I don't," quavered Herbie.

"WHAT? You mean he *hasn't* spoken to you about the money, yet?"

Herbie's stomach contracted into a stony lump. "No, Yishy, honest."

"Oh, that old liar!" Yishy staggered, put his hand to his forehead, and groaned. "Oh, that—! That—!" He repeated one old epithet and a brand-new one. Then he stumbled off down the hill, blaspheming and shaking his fists in the air. Herbie looked after this wild sight in wonder, and trudged unhappily up the steps and into the office.

An even greater surprise awaited him. Mr. Gauss was smiling as usual behind his desk, and seated near him on a dirty old plush chair—Herbie almost fainted as he beheld the man—was the emaciated driver, skinny and queer as ever, who had given him and Cliff the hitch from New York to Panksville!

"Ah, good morning, Herbie," Mr. Gauss beamed. "And let me introduce you to Mr. Drabkind. Mr. Drabkind, this is one of our finest, cleverest, most outstanding campers, Herbie Bookbinder—I'm proud to say, also a pupil at my school."

Mr. Drabkind extended a bluish hand to Herbie. The boy grasped the cold fingertips, pumped them once, and dropped them. The thin man peered at him through glasses thick as the bottoms of bottles.

"I don't see too well," he apologized in his unforgettable reedy voice, "but it seems I've met you, Master Bookbinder, rather recently."

Herbie shrugged and tried to still the quivering of his knees. "I don't see how that's possible," said Mr. Gauss, looking hard at Herbie. "Do you, Herbert?"

Herbie shook his head, unable to utter a sound.

"You must be mistaken, Mr. Drabkind," said the camp owner. "This is your first visit here this summer. Unless," he added archly, "Herbie has been out traveling, unbeknownst to me."

Was it a cat-and-mouse game, Herbie wondered through the fog of fear that enveloped his mind? He waited for the blow, if one was to fall.

"Well, I see so many boys—so many boys," sighed Mr. Drabkind. He sat in the chair again, his frame curved like a wilting flower. "Though I don't somehow remember him as being in a crowd."

"No, you wouldn't. Our Herbert stands out very much from the crowd," said Mr. Gauss, and both men giggled politely and, Herbie thought, somewhat eerily. There was a short silence.

"Well, Mr. Gauss, we may as well come to the point," piped the frail man. "I can't stay long, you know."

"Herbie, you don't know who Mr. Drabkind is, do you?" said Mr. Gauss, looking down at his fingertips clasped before him.

As emphatically as he could, Herbie shook his head again.

"Of course he wouldn't," said Mr. Drabkind. He took a card from a black wallet and handed it to Herbie. The boy read:

| Henry Junius Drabkind |
| Field Representative |
| Berkshire Free Camp Fund |

"Mr. Drabkind represents one of the worthiest causes I know of, Herbert," said Mr. Gauss. "The Berkshire Free Camp gives several hundred poor city boys just the same kind of wonderful vacation you're having—well, of course, not as fine as we can give you in Manitou, but for a charity camp, as I say, a wonderful vacation."

"Thanks in good part to men like you, Mr. Gauss—*and* to boys like Master Bookbinder," interposed the wispy Mr. Drabkind.

Mr. Gauss directed a mechanical nod and smile at the visitor.

"Now, Herbie, if you had been here in previous years you'd know that we take a collection every summer for the Free Camp. We who are fortunate enough to have parents who can pay to give us a wonderful vacation at Manitou ought to help the boys who are not so lucky—don't you agree?"

Though not understanding the camp owner's drift, Herbie sensed that it would be better for him not to agree. But there seemed no help for it. He nodded.

"Fine. You see, you don't have to work very hard, Mr. Drabkind, to make a boy of the mental caliber of Herbert Bookbinder understand a simple matter. . . . Then I take it, Herbie, you approve of what I have done in writing this check."

He held toward the boy a green slip. Herbie did not take it, but read the writing. The check was made out to the Berkshire Free Camp Fund, in the sum of two hundred dollars. He looked questioningly at Mr. Gauss.

"That sum of two hundred dollars, Herbie, represents the total earnings of your Ride, Yishy Gabelson's Freak Show, Gooch Lefko's House of Mirrors, and—ah—thirty-five dollars and fifty cents out of my own pocket. There were other little booths that took in some money, but they were not important enough, I feel, to be invited to share in this privilege. . . . Were you about to say something, Herbie?"

The boy had indeed opened his mouth to protest. But he glanced fearfully at Mr. Drabkind, shut it again without a word, and shook his head.

"Ah, then to go on. You understand, Herbie, that the money you earned at the Ride came out of the campers' pockets to begin with. You had the glory of—shall I say—assembling it. And I want to know, will you join Yishy, Gooch, and myself in contributing your collection to Mr. Drabkind's poor boys?"

Torn between anguish at the thought of losing the seventy-five dollars he must have to wipe out the theft, and fear that Mr. Drabkind would recognize his voice and betray him, Herbie was the most miserable boy in those mountains. How could he risk having Mr. Gauss, and thereafter his parents, learn that he had been picked up hitchhiking on Bronx River Parkway on the night of the robbery at the Place? His head buzzed with rage, frustration, and dread.

"Well, Herbie, shall I assume you approve, and hand Mr. Drabkind this check?" said Mr. Gauss, waving the fatal document in the direction of the thin man. "Yishy and Gooch have already gladly, I may say enthusiastical-

ly, contributed their entire earnings. It's all up to you now."

Herbie thought of Yishy's actions, which had been enthusiasm of a sort, but hardly a glad enthusiasm. It was clear to him that Mr. Gauss must have told Yishy that he, Herbie, had already contributed his hundred and thirteen dollars.

What had actually happened was that Yishy, backed into the same corner that Herbie was in now, but not having his situation complicated by terror of Mr. Drabkind, had ventured an objection: "Shucks. I dunno. You mean to say Herbie Bookbinder's gonna give every nickel he made?" To this Mr. Gauss had replied, "I certainly would not ask you to do so if that were not the situation." Yishy had surrendered with a surly "O.K., then," and rushed from the office, to encounter Herbie in the way we have seen. Now, to be strict, Mr. Gauss had perhaps lied to Yishy. But he had phrased his answer carefully, and if caught in the apparent discrepancy, would have at once explained that his reply meant that he intended to *ask* Herbie to give all his money, just as he was asking Yishy.

The gray world of half truth, in which our gray Mr. Gausses spend their gray hours, fumbling for little gray advantages! Mr. Gauss's purpose in this complicated maneuver was simply to save himself about fifteen dollars, and at the same time gain a little prestige. The collection for the Free Camp in previous years had always netted about the same amount—fifty dollars—to which Mr. Gauss added fifty out of the camp treasury to make the round sum of a hundred. This equaled the regular contribution of Penobscot and other institutions of the size of Manitou. When

Mr. Gauss had collected the cigar boxes the previous evening, he had fully intended to return the money to the boys. But next morning the Tempter brought Mr. Drabkind. It occurred to the camp owner, upon a rapid mental calculation, that he could double the Manitou contribution and lessen the usual cost to himself by the simple device of inviting the three most successful Mardi Gras enterprises to donate their earnings. He justified the act to himself and to Uncle Sandy by pointing out that the money was not "really" Herbie's, Yishy's, or Gooch's, but had come out of the payments of the campers. In any case (he declared in explaining the scheme to the head counselor) the boys would be given a free choice of contributing or declining to do so, therefore no objection could possibly be made. Uncle Sandy, a weary workhorse who knew his master well, bent a little lower under the burden of the summer and said nothing. He was counting the hours to his release. Only forty-eight remained.

And so Herbie was offered the free choice of contributing or not. With the check written out and hovering a few inches from the charity collector's hand, with two grown men cajoling him and prodding him, he had the choice of consenting to something practically done, or trying to reverse events at the last instant, thus bringing on himself the odium of being uncharitable. There was the added pressure, though Mr. Gauss cannot be blamed for it, of possible recognition by Mr. Drabkind at any moment. Wonderful to relate, the boy in these circumstances still managed to produce an ounce of resistance. He tried to disguise his voice by pitching it very high, and almost neighed, "Do I have to give all of it?"

"Pardon me?" said Mr. Gauss.

Herbie repeated, "Do I have to give all of it?" still sounding more like Clever Sam than himself. Mr. Drabkind looked amazed at the sound, but there was no light of remembrance in his expression, which was all that mattered to the boy.

"Why, no, Herbert, of course you don't," said Mr. Gauss, also puzzled by the queer tones, but attributing them to nervousness. "Let me be perfectly clear on that point. You don't have to give one single solitary penny, Herbert. I know you received your materials for nothing through Elmer Bean's friend, otherwise I would of course suggest deducting about seventy-five dollars for expenses. But you may have all your money back if you wish." He held the check pinched between thumbs and forefingers as though to tear it down the middle. "Say the word, and I'll send Mr. Drabkind away without this check. Say the word, and I'll give Gooch and Yishy their money back, too, and simply say, 'Herbie Bookbinder has different ideas about charity than the rest of us.' Say the word, Herbie, and the Free Camp gets not one cent of yours. It's all up to you, as I have said before. Shall I tear the check up or shall I hand it to Mr. Drabkind?"

Herbie, loaded down with his own lies, weakened by his fears of the gaunt man who had come back from his buried night of crime to haunt him, pressed without mercy by Mr. Gauss, caved in. He shrugged and nodded his head. At once the camp owner put the check in the hand of the charity collector.

"Thank you, Herbert!" he exclaimed.

"You're the sort of young man I've always thought you were."

"And let me thank you, Master Bookbinder," shrilled Mr. Drabkind, folding the check carefully into his black wallet, "in the name of two hundred poor boys who will benefit by your—"

But Herbie was tottering out through the doorway. He bore a face of such utter tragedy that the camp owner felt an unfamiliar momentary sensation in his heart: doubt of his own rectitude.

"Herbie, come back here!" he called. "You shouldn't go like that." The boy tramped down the steps and did not turn back.

"Well, thank you once more, Mr. Gauss, for an extraordinarily generous contribution and good-by," said Mr. Drabkind hurriedly. "Admirable boy, that Master Bookbinder. Admirable camp you run, indeed, Mr. Gauss. No, please don't trouble to see me out; my car's only a few feet from the house. Good-by, good-by," in his haste, jamming his hat on his head and putting his wallet in his pocket, the willowy charity collector omitted to shake the camp owner's hand and took a quick departure.

When Herbie arrived back at Uncle Sandy's tent, it was five minutes to ten. Cliff was already there, dressed in the head counselor's famous old blue sweater and gray baseball cap, holding his megaphone and wearing the whistle, emblem of boys' camp sovereignty, on a thong around his neck. Sandy was earnestly giving him a multitude of last-minute suggestions as he struggled into a gray and green jersey of Cliff's that was laughably small on him. Herbie stood around feeling dull and useless.

"How 'bout me, Uncle Sandy?" he said at last.

"Why, you really have nothing to do, Herb, except be boss—just like the Skipper. Cliff does all the work," said the head counselor with a grin at his own wit. He took a pair of large green sun glasses and Mr. Gauss's feather headdress from the shelf. "Put these on. Then just walk around, looking important. All right, Cliff, it's ten o'clock. Take over."

The head counselor and his successor went outside. Herbie threw aside his costume and lay on the cot face upward. The sun fell in a flecked orange square on the canvas above his eyes. The air was hot in the tent. He heard the familiar three blasts of the whistle that summoned the bunks into two lines along Company Street, the running of feet on gravel, the slamming of many doors, and a thousand squeals and yelps of mirth as the campers saw the counselors in their silly boys' clothes. The entire joke seemed flat and stale to the Skipper-for-a-Day. He put his hand to his eyes and involuntarily moaned. He was a wretch who had stolen money from his own father, and could never pay it back.

"All right, fellows!" he heard Cliff shout. "Now I want you to show some real camp spirit when you greet Uncle Gus—I mean the Skipper. Here he comes now—our own dear Skipper."

Herbie rose heavily and dashed the tears from his face. He donned the glasses and the feather headdress as he walked to the entrance of the tent. He contorted his body so that he jutted to a remarkable extent before and behind. Then he stepped out into the sunshine, and waddled majestically down Company Street, holding up the corners of his mouth in a fixed smile with two forefingers, and pointing his feet outward like a duck's.

The campers screamed and danced, and so did the counselors. Several of them fell to the ground and rolled around, giggling. Uncle Sandy, standing among the boys of Bunk Thirteen, maintained a straight face for perhaps ten seconds, then burst out in helpless bellow after bellow which touched off a perfect riot of hilarity. Herbert waggled his behind impassively as he strolled between the lines, nodding his head here and there. When he reached the end of the street he vanished in the direction of the lake, leaving the camp still in disorderly convulsions of mirth.

He was not seen again that merry morning, for he spent it lying on a flat rock near the shore, hidden by the underbrush. A lonesome, quiet situation, you might say, yet he had plenty of company. Misery sat at the fat boy's right hand, and Shame at the left; and they made the morning mighty lively for Herbie between them.

Talking it over

1. *a.* Why does Herbie have the dream about murdering someone?

b. What detail in it suggests the kind of disaster he meets?

2. Why does Lennie's change of attitude depress Herbie? How does Herbie take revenge on Lennie?

3. *a.* In his conference with Mr. Gauss and Mr. Drabkind, Herbie is placed in a dilemma: a situation requiring him to choose between two actions, neither of which is good. What is Herbie's dilemma?

b. Why can't Herbie ask for enough money to pay his debt?

4. In what way does Herbie show talent as an actor?

5. What does this chapter add to your understanding of Mr. Gauss?

Words in action

The word *disaster* is made up of the negative prefix *dis-* plus a form of the Latin word *astrum,* meaning "star." In ancient times, people believed that the position of the stars in the sky influenced their lives. Especially important was the appearance of the sky at the moment of a person's birth. A person born at a time when the stars were in a "lucky" combination could count on good fortune all his life. But a person born under an unlucky combination was "ill-starred."

You will probably recognize other words which are based on *astrum*. Decide which of the words listed would best complete each sentence below. You may refer to a dictionary if you need to.

**aster   astronaut   astronomy
astrology   asterisk**

1. We were thrilled to hear the voice of the ———— being transmitted from the orbiting satellite.

2. Mary consulted a magazine on ———— to find her birth sign.

3. When he saw the ————, Jeremy looked on the bottom of the page for a footnote.

4. The directions on the package of ———— seeds tell when to plant them.

5. People who study ———— are interested in facts about the stars but don't try to tell fortunes from them.

S O THE DAY of Herbie's greatest success turned into the bitterest of his young life, because the fruit of triumph had a rotten core. Probably he should have hardened his heart and enjoyed himself, but he could not. Remorse ate him. To a better judge of crime—let us say, a policeman—this remorse might have seemed some days late in setting about its gnawing, but to Herbie his offense had been no offense until Mr. Gauss deprived him of the means to repay with interest the "borrowed" money.

Now, here the boy showed himself of pretty good mettle, for he wasted little breath blaming the camp owner, but took the disaster on his own conscience. A thousand weaklings, of either sex and all ages, will commit a misdeed which they plan to make up for later. Then if someone happens to prevent them from covering, they will throw all the blame for the original offense on that someone, and hold themselves virtuous. If you have not seen this happen yet, watch the feeble ones around you today and tomorrow. Herbie digested the thought of his own wickedness all during Campers' Day, and had a colicky time of it, and never sought the relief of saying "It's really Gauss's fault."

Herbie and Cliff were eating lunch in grandeur at the head counselor's table. They still wore their costumes. Herbie's many-colored feather headdress provided a gay touch to the bleak dining hall.

"What are we gonna do during rest hour?" said Herbie to his cousin.

"Don't we have to stay in our bunks, same as always?" said Cliff.

"What, and us the bosses of the camp? Cliff, you don't use your head sometimes."

The boys both gloated over the prospect of not being compelled to spend the hour after lunch on their cots in silence with shoes and stockings off.

"Hey, know what, Herb?" Cliff suddenly smiled. "Let's go up the hill an' say good-by to Elmer Bean an' Clever Sam. We won't hardly get to see 'em tomorrow, everything'll be so rushed goin' to the train."

"Good," said Herbie. "Why don't we go right now? I ain't hungry."

A tumult of whistles, jeers, and flirtatious calls distracted them. Lennie, his face red, was sidling into the dining room in his white nurse's cap and gown. Baseball sneakers and stockings completed his costume and added to its foolishness. He was looking here and there, trying to smile and flinging an occasional answer to the jibes.

Herbie said, "Where the heck has he been, comin' in so late?"

"Aw, the poor guy's been hidin'. He probably didn't even hear the bugle," said Cliff.

Herbie and Cliff quitted their table of honor and walked through the huge bare wooden hall to the door—and behold, there was no commotion, nobody cracked jokes, and scarcely any campers turned away from the important business of stuffing Spanish omelet into their mouths. Herbie had wisely ceased his waddling after the first great hit; by now it would have been a wearisome jest. Cliff, as Uncle Sandy, had at no time caused much amusement. Lennie had made a sensation where the cousins went unnoticed, for the reason that impersonation is only entertaining when someone is degraded by it.

The boys were halfway up the hill when they met Elmer Bean rattling down with three enormous coarse cloth bags piled in a wheelbarrow. Cliff greeted him, with, "Hi, Elmer! Last laundry, huh?"

"Last everythin', fellers. This time tomorrer yer free men. This time a week from now I am." The handy man braced himself, brought the plunging wheelbarrow to a stop, and leaned against one of the bags. "You guys are the big shots o' the camp, huh?"

"Thanks to you," said Herbie.

"Herb, there's somethin' I wish you'd do fer me on yer twenty-first birthday."

"What, Elmer?"

"Write an' tell me where you guys got that fifty bucks."

Herbie looked sick all at once. Cliff quickly said, "Clever Sam up in the stable, Elmer?"

"He was when I last saw him. Gonna kiss 'im good-by?"

Cliff smiled bashfully.

"Hey, Elmer," said Herbie, "how 'bout us guys writin' to you? Will you write back?"

The handy man laughed. He looked around at the panorama of lake and bungalows, at the trees with creepers along their trunks already flaming in premature autumn colors, and at the two grotesquely dressed boys. The feathers of Herbie's headdress wagged in a breeze that had turned chilly. Elmer felt an impulse of pity for the small fat boy, whom he was sure he would never see after tomorrow, and whom he regarded as such an odd, self-tormenting mixture of good and bad.

"I tell yer, Herb," he said, "I been shipmates with guys that I swore I'd write to regular when I got transferred, see? My first coupla years I did write, too, maybe one or two times, but it wasn't no good. You think a letter's gonna be somethin', see, but it ain't nothin'. You were shipmates once, and now yer on other ships an' it's all different. I dunno why."

"I just thought maybe a letter just once in a long while," persisted the boy. "You know, after all we done on the Ride together an' all—"

"Why, sure, Herb, write if you feel like it." The handy man hesitated a moment, then blurted, "Don't be surprised if you git an answer that looks like you wrote it yourself in the fifth grade. I don't write such a hell of a lot, Herb."

"I'll write, too, Elmer," said Cliff.

Both boys looked intensely unhappy.

"Look, fellers," said the handy man, "don't let old Gauss work on yer feelin's next year, see? You know—remember good old Elmer, remember good old this, good old that? I sure would like to see you again, an' I'll be here too, like as not, 'cause I ain't good fer much else, but don't come back, fellers. What's better than bein' free? Yer free when you git outta school, free fer a whole summer, see, and old Gauss gets you marchin' an' workin' again. And you sing them songs, an' you git choked up an' you think you love camp. I know all about them songs. In the Navy we called 'em shippin'-over music. They played 'em whenever the recruitin' officer come to sign us up fer another hitch. I got all the orders an' salutin' an' bugles I ever want in the Navy. And git this straight, I'm *proud* I was a sailor—but they paid me, see, and what's more important I was doin' somethin'. I was on a ship to defend the country. I wasn't fattenin' up no old turkey like Gauss. Don't come back, guys. I like you both swell. Cliff, yer O.K., yer a real guy." He took the boy's hand and shook it. "Herb—I dunno what to tell you, Herb. You might be a very big guy someday, an' then again I dunno. Herb, is yer father alive?"

Herbie nodded. The question touched off a storm of emotion, and he dared not speak.

"Listen, feller, do what yer father tells you, see? In a coupla years yer gonna start thinkin' he's all wet about everything. Maybe you do now. Well, I'm tellin' you, Herb, do whatever yer father says. A guy like you needs his pa."

The handy man patted Herbie's shoulder. Then he bent and picked up the handles of the wheelbarrow.

"We had fun, didn't we, guys? There ain't never been nothin' like Herbie's Ride in this camp, and there ain't never gonna be again. It took the three of us, see, an' Herbie bein' jealous over Lucille, an' all. Them things only happen once." He started to wheel away his burden, and said over his shoulder, "Sure, write to me here at Panksville. Only like I say, don't mind none about the way I spell an' write. I ain't nothin' but a country boy."

He went off down the hill, leaning backward to keep the wheelbarrow from running away, his yellow hair flying.

The boys walked to the stable in silence. As they came to the door Cliff said, "Clever Sam must be asleep. Can't

hear him movin' at all." The boys went inside and, to their astonishment, found the stall empty.

"Maybe he's outside eatin' grass," Herbie suggested.

"Elmer said he was in here," Cliff said anxiously, but he went outside and looked in the practice ring. The horse was not there, nor anywhere in sight.

"Hey, Herbie, whaddya suppose has happened to him?"

"I dunno. Maybe he wandered off down the road."

"Clever Sam don't wander. He likes the barn better'n any place. Listen, there's somethin' wrong. Let's go down and tell Elmer."

The boys descended the hill at a run. With each step they bounded twice as far as they would have on level ground, and felt fleet as stags. Pounding around the corner of a bungalow into Company Street they came to a quick halt, for there was Clever Sam in the middle of the gravel path, surrounded by laughing, chattering boys. He was walking slowly, his head hanging in a woebegone way, the reins dragging from his bridle, and on his side there was whitewashed in crude letters, "HERBIE THE SISSY."

"Come on, Herb," exclaimed Cliff. He plunged into the crowd, followed by his cousin, and elbowed his way to the horse. He put his arm around Clever Sam's neck, saying, "Whoa, boy. What're they doin' to you? O.K., boy."

Hearing Cliff's voice, the animal raised his head, neighed, and nuzzled against him. Herbie, coming up to Clever Sam, saw that his skin had been whitewashed on his other side too, with the words, "SKIPPER GARBAGE."

The laughter and jokes subsided. A

few boys sneaked away from the fringe of the group into bungalows. Curious noses pressed against screens up and down the street.

"O.K.," said Cliff to the crowd. "Who done it?"

"Not me." "I don't know." "I just got here." "The horse just came walkin' along." These and answers like them came in a chorus. But the boys looked at each other with knowing smiles. Uncle Sandy appeared in the doorway of Bunk Twelve, still dressed as Cliff. He observed the scene and said nothing. Cliff glanced hesitantly at the head counselor, then at the crowd.

"First I'm gonna take care o' this poor horse, then I'll come back and find out who done it."

He was leading the horse to the road up the hill, and was just passing Bunk Thirteen. Lennie stepped out of the doorway, picked up the edges of his white nurse's skirt, and made a clumsy curtsy.

"Why, Mr. Head Counselor, is there somethin' the matter?" he said in effeminate tones.

Herbie, walking beside his cousin, whispered, "Lookit his left arm, Cliff."

Cliff saw a streak of whitewash running from the wrist to the elbow. Lennie noticed where his eyes were directed and rubbed his right hand along the streak, smiling insolently at the other boy.

"O.K., Lennie, you done it, huh?" said Cliff.

"Who's Lennie? I'm Nurse Geiger, dearie," Lennie twittered. "That little fat Skipper next to you appointed me, dincha, Skipper Garbage?"

Cliff took his arm from Clever Sam's neck and walked close to Lennie. The watching boys became quiet. Several counselors were on the outskirts of the group now, but none interfered.

"All right, Lennie. You're gonna come with me and clean off that horse."

"Why, Uncle Sandy," said Lennie in falsetto, "I'm a nurse. I treat human beings, not horses."

Cliff sprang at Lennie, wrapping his arms around him, and toppled him to the ground, falling on top of him. In a moment he was seated astride Lennie, pinning his arms with his knees.

"You gonna clean that horse?"

Lennie, astounded at being on his back, but not at all cowed, said, "Dear me, Uncle Sandy, how rough you play!"

A ringing slap across his face followed. Cliff's expression was peculiarly solemn, except at the instant of the slap, when he bared his teeth.

"Now you gonna clean that horse?"

Lennie heaved his body upward and threw Cliff off him. Both boys sprang to their feet. Lennie raised his fists in fighting position and danced angrily.

"Jump a guy when he ain't lookin' for it, huh?" he growled. "O.K., Cousin Garbage, come an' get murdered!"

One of the counselors shouted, "Uncle Sandy, shall I stop it?"

Uncle Sandy, still leaning in the doorway of Bunk Twelve only a few feet away, said, "If you mean me, my name is Cliff until five o'clock. Looks like Uncle Sandy's trying to maintain discipline in this camp by force. He'd better make it stick."

Lennie punched Cliff lightly in the chest. Cliff put up his hands awkwardly and stood with legs spread wide apart. Three times more Lennie hit him, none very hard blows, and at last Cliff countered with a long swing that missed Lennie by a foot. The pugilist in the nurse's uniform laughed aloud and punched Cliff's head with all his might. Cliff staggered, and then jumped on Lennie and bore him to the dirt exactly as he had done before. Seated on top of him he began cuffing the athlete's face with echoing slaps that could have been heard in the nearby hills.

"Will you clean that horse? Will you clean that horse? *Will* you clean that horse?"

Lennie struggled and squirmed, but could not unseat his foe. Cliff's eyes were bloodshot and he made the same painful face each time he hit Lennie, as though an aching tooth were giving him twinges. Slap! Slap! Slap! Slap! Lennie made two supreme efforts to throw off his tormentor, arching his back and twisting, but Cliff clung to his seat. Slap! Slap! Lennie flattened to the ground.

"I'll clean him!" came a muffled shout from the model of Character.

At once Cliff stood, helped Lennie to his feet, and put out his hand to him.

"Friends, Lennie?" he said.

The athlete's gown was more black than white, and crumpled and torn. His hair hung in his eyes, and his cheeks showed fiery marks from the persuasion he had undergone. He glanced at Cliff from under contracted brows, looked around at the spectators, then touched Cliff's hand with his own and ran into his bungalow.

"I'm bringin' the horse to the stable," Cliff called after him. "Come on up with me."

"I'll come when I'm good and ready," a surly voice answered from the bungalow.

Cliff pointed at one of the counselors in boys' clothes. "You, Peanuts Wishnik. If he ain't at the stable in ten minutes, you bring him up, please."

"Sure, Uncle Sandy," came the grinning reply.

But Lennie arrived at the stable under his own power only a minute or two after the cousins and the dispirited horse. Cliff had already begun to scrub Clever Sam with a large brush and a bucket of soapy warm water. He passed these implements to Lennie without a word, and while the athlete glumly set about erasing his mischief, Cliff walked to the head of the horse and embraced him.

"You'll be O.K. now, Clever Sam," he said. "Well, so long. Good luck." He patted the animal's nose and walked out of the stable.

Herbie hurried after him, exclaiming, "Holy cats, ain't you gonna say no more good-by to the horse than that?"

Cliff regarded his cousin with dulled eyes. "What else should I say?"

"Well, I thought you liked that horse."

"Well, I do."

"Shucks, tell him you're sorry you're leavin' him, an' you'll miss him, an' all that. Hey, didn't you ever read that poem, 'An Arab's Farewell to His Steed'? I bet it's fifteen stanzas long. That guy really says good-by to the horse."

Cliff said, "Yeah, we read it in 6B. That's just a poem." He looked at the ground for a few moments. Then he added, "Herb, do me a favor, huh? Go down an' tell Uncle Sandy that I wanna be excused. You can give the orders from now on. There's only a coupla more hours, anyhow."

He turned on his heel and walked back to the stable. Herbie stood irresolutely for a while, but curiosity overcame him. He went to the door and peeped in. Lennie was drying his hands on some old newspapers and walking toward the door with a surprised smile. And Cliff, with a much happier smile, was lovingly, silently washing Clever Sam.

It has been said already that Mr. Gauss was in the habit of vanishing for the duration of Campers' Day. The explanation he gave to himself and the counselors was that much as he regretted missing the fun, it was inconsistent with his "symbolic prestige" to join in the horseplay.

Mr. Gauss made a great thing of his symbolic prestige. In his speech to the counselors at the start of each season he always trotted out the phrase and delivered a painstaking exposition of it. The gist of his annual remarks was that in his position of director he was not merely Mr. Gauss the man but a symbol of Camp Manitou, and as such he had to behave, and had to ask the counselors to behave, in ways that would constantly maintain his symbolic prestige. In coarse English this meant that the counselors were to show respect for him even if they didn't feel it. It was a sound administrative rule, and may be met with in all walks of life. Now, the truth is that Mr. Gauss's disappearance on Campers' Day was not entirely a matter of symbolic prestige. He could not swim and had a strong natural fear of the water; consequently he dreaded a ducking. This fact, however, was not mentioned.

The camp owner was lounging on his bed in the guest house, propped up with pillows, clad only in the inevitable khaki shorts, peacefully sipping iced coffee, and leafing through a four-week-old Sunday book-review section of the New York *Times*, when there came a knock at the door. He glanced at his clock. It lacked an hour of five, when Campers' Day would officially end and it would be safe for him to sally forth.

"Who is it?" he called crossly.

The voice of the handy man said, "Mrs. Gloster just drove in with her chauffeur. He's parkin' the car an' she's sittin' on the veranda. Thought you'd like to know."

Mr. Gauss leaped off the bed exclaiming, "Thanks, Elmer. Tell her I'll be right down, will you?"

"Um," said the voice.

Mrs. Gloster was the mother of the unfortunate Daisy, and also of four girls, all of whom were campers. She was the richest of all the Manitou parents, and her patronage had brought in its wake perhaps a dozen children. This may explain why Mr. Gauss began dressing with a comical haste that would seriously have injured his symbolic prestige, had there been any onlookers. He flung on his best white flannel trousers, and a snowy short-sleeved shirt, and white socks, and freshly chalked white shoes that he had been saving for the homeward journey. He hastily combed his few strands of hair, crouching to see his image in the tilted mirror of the cheap dresser, and ran out of the room, snatching his green sun glasses from a shelf as he passed through the door.

Mrs. Gloster, a thin, small, bright-eyed lady wearing a smart gray traveling suit, sat in a wicker armchair on the veranda, smoking a cigarette and tapping her foot. Each year it was her practice to drive up to camp and take her children home by automobile to save them from the dirty, stuffy train ride which all the other children endured. She dropped the cigarette and crushed it with her toe as the camp owner approached.

"My dear Mrs. Gloster, how do you manage to keep so young? I declare you look more like one of my counselors than the mother of five wonderful children."

Mrs. Gloster beamed. Her husband, immersed in the textile trade, paid her a huge allowance but no compliments.

"You look splendid yourself, Mr. Gauss. I can't understand how the responsibility for so many children agrees with you, but evidently it does. May I see Raymond now?" (Raymond was Daisy's name in the outside world.)

Mr. Gauss peeked apprehensively through a window of the veranda. The wall clock in the camp office read four-twenty.

"Ah—wouldn't you like to see the girls first? They're right here, you know. Then a little later—perhaps after dinner—a visit to the boys' camp?"

The wealthy lady made no objection. Mr. Gauss summoned a passing girl counselor and sent her flying to call the Gloster girls. Four squealing, giggling children came tumbling up the veranda steps a few minutes later. Unluckily for Mr. Gauss, all they could talk about was Raymond's comic appearance as the camp doctor. Poor Daisy had thrown heart and soul into the impersonation, which gave him something to do at last, and had caused a near riot of hilarity in the girls' camp by bursting in on the lunch hour brandishing a stethoscope and a hypodermic needle, and trying to inoculate everyone against "Gaussitis." This description of her son in such fettle doubled Mrs. Gloster's anxiety to see him at once.

"Oh, it must be a perfect scream. Do let's go down the hill now, Mr. Gauss," she said.

Mr. Gauss looked through the window again. Twenty minutes to five.

"I'll be delighted, of course, to escort you down to the boys' camp. Just let's have a nice refreshing cup of tea first. You've been through a long, hot drive—"

"Better hurry, Ma," broke in one of the girls. "Campers' Day is over at five o'clock."

The mother said, "Why, Mr. Gauss, let's just skip the tea," but Mr. Gauss was already dancing backward through the entrance.

"It won't take a minute, not a minute," he insisted archly, wagging a finger at her as he disappeared. Nevertheless, he hoped it would take twenty. He told the cook, a weary, gray-haired woman in a white smock, to serve tea for two on the veranda, and came outside again, confident of the usual delay of a quarter of an hour. But it happened that the cook was brewing some for herself, and, impatient at the interruption, hurried to bring out the tea so as to be able to drink her own at leisure. Mr. Gauss was flabbergasted to see a tray, tea service for two, and the cook emerge from the door some forty seconds after himself. The mother gulped her tea in a few moments and set down her cup and saucer with a meaningful clink. Mr. Gauss dawdled. Mrs. Gloster curtly sent her daughters scampering off to their bungalows. She stood, straightened her skirt, pulled in her belt, and walked to the steps of the veranda. Still Mr. Gauss sipped and sipped. And well he might. It lacked twelve minutes to five.

"You know," he sighed, "I wonder sometimes whether lovely ladies of social position like yourself, Mrs. Gloster, don't miss some of the quiet pleasures of life as you dash through the mad whirl. Now, a cup of tea, with me, is a ritual."

"Mr. Gauss, you may teach manners to my children, but I'm a little old for correction. Your ritual is taking an awfully long time."

The camp owner perceived that he had blundered. He clattered the cup and saucer to the table and rose. "My dear Mrs. Gloster, by all means let us go. I had no idea—really, you quite misunderstood me. I wish all our parents had one-tenth the polish and gracefulness of yourself. If I made an unfortunate choice of language I regret it, but what I meant—" He smoothed the path down the hill with many apologies and blandishments.

The camp was empty of boys, and silent. The slant afternoon sun cast parallel rays between the walls of the bungalows across the deserted gravel street.

"Why, Mr. Gauss, where can the boys be?"

"Ah—down at the waterfront, I believe."

Said the mother with a delighted cry, "Oh, they're ducking Uncle Sandy!" (The girls had told her about it.) "Come, come, we must see that!"

She took the camp owner's arm and dragged him along the path. When they came to the shore, they saw a group of Seniors and Super-seniors marching up the dock, carrying the horizontal limp form of Uncle Sandy high in the air, and chanting,

> *"In the water he must go,*
> *He must go, he must go.*
> *In the water he must go,*
> *My fair Sandy."*

The rest of the campers lined the beach in disorder, cheering and laughing. Herbie Bookbinder, in green glasses and feather headdress, stood at the end of the dock with folded arms. The Seniors brought Uncle Sandy before him. Yishy cried, "What'll we do with him, Skipper?"

Herbie proclaimed, "Cliff Block, you have appeared on Company Street in clothes too small for you. In the water you must go!"

At once the Seniors grasped the unresisting head counselor by the arms and legs, swung him back and forth twice, then pitched him in. The splash wet them all. The spectators cheered.

Mrs. Gloster clapped her hands. "What fun! I don't see Raymond. I hope he's here." She lifted her voice and called, "Ray-*mond!* Where are you?" This served to turn everybody's eyes on her—and on Mr. Gauss. Raymond answered thinly, from far down the beach, "Here I am, Mother!"

But his cry was ignored. Herbie came striding down the dock shouting, "There's Herbie Bookbinder, men, wearing white flannels before sundown. Grab him!"

The thought of seizing Mr. Gauss was so audacious that the whole camp gasped. But the Seniors, with whoops and howls, came trampling after the fat boy, their steps drumming on the hollow wooden dock. The camp owner quailed, but stood his ground. A few feet from him the boys stopped short, and began fidgeting and murmuring.

"Now, lads," said Mr. Gauss, smiling with all his might, "you know an old Manitou tradition excludes the real Skipper from Camper's Day. I wish I could join the fun, but as you see I'm here with a lady, and I'm afraid I can't join you."

Mrs. Gloster exclaimed quickly, "Oh, please don't let me interfere," and fell away from his side several paces, leaving him quite alone, and raising an uneasy laugh among the boys.

"Grab him, I say!" shouted Herbie. But no one moved toward the camp owner.

"Now, Herbie," said Mr. Gauss, "you've had your fun and you've done very well, I understand. And it's five o'clock, so let's have no more of this foolery. Hand me that headdress. You're just Herbie Bookbinder again."

Herbie glanced at his watch, and brandished it for all the larger boys to see.

"It's *three minutes to five,*" he bawled, "and I'm still Mr. Gauss by Mr. Gauss's own rules. And I say throw Herbie Bookbinder in the lake!"

The close-pressed ranks of the Seniors divided as a smaller figure thrust to the front. It was Ted, his long beak quivering, his birdlike eyes glaring. "Didn't you big lugs hear the Skipper's orders?" he roared. "Come on, let's get him!" He dived for Mr. Gauss's legs.

And Mr. Gauss, in his panicky fear of the water, made a dreadful mistake. He turned and ran.

Instantly he had twenty pursuers. The yellowest hound will chase anything that flees. With yaps and hoots, the Seniors ran after him and laid violent hands on him before he had gone ten yards. In a moment he was struggling in the air, held aloft by a dozen pairs of strong arms.

"In the water he must go, My fair Gussie!" chanted his captors.

Alas for symbolic prestige! Mr. Gauss did not react well in this adversity. As the boys bore him toward the water he squirmed, bucked, and yelled, "Sandy! Sandy! Blow your whistle! Stop them! Put me down, you foolish boys! SAN-DEE!"

To the boys his behavior seemed queer, for they knew nothing of his terror of the water. But in becoming a wriggling victim Mr. Gauss lost any chance he might have had of rescuing himself, and became a simple figure of fun. Uncle Sandy was in a poor position to come to his aid. He was himself clambering up the ladder out of the lake. It is true that he was nearly up on the dock when the bearers of Mr. Gauss were still far from the edge. He might perhaps have jumped forward, dripping as he was, and saved his master by shouting and charging at the group. But strange to tell, as soon as his nearsighted eyes took in what was happening he lost his footing on the ladder— through sheer surprise, he swore a hundred times in after years—and fell back into the water helplessly.

Mr. Gauss entered the most forceful objections to the very last—objections in the form of kicks, punches, shrieks, threats, and an amount of writhing that was remarkable in a man of his years and weight. A few feet from the edge of the dock the boys actually lost their hold on the legs of the white-clad, struggling figure. Mr. Gauss gained temporary footing on the wooden dock and balked like a maddened elephant. But immediately a cluster of boys' arms whisked his feet into the air once more. And with no further ado, omitting the ceremony of swinging, his captors rushed him to the edge and dumped him in.

The camp owner struck the water stomach first with a horrid *splat,* and

sank out of sight. He bobbed up again in a few seconds, gurgling, and flailing so furiously that he seemed to have ten arms and legs.

"It's five o'clock, guys! Campers' Day is over!" yelled Herbie, dashing his feather headdress to the dock. "Run like crazy!"

All the boys stampeded up the path away from the lake. So quickly did they evacuate that by the time Uncle Sandy hauled his bedraggled, shuddering, choking employer up the ladder, the camp owner had but one spectator of his misery—Mrs. Gloster, who was leaning against a tree, holding her sides in an agony of giggling. Mr. Gauss mechanically picked up the feather headdress from the dock and put it on his head.

"Ye gods, Skipper, what are you doing?" exclaimed Uncle Sandy.

The camp owner looked at him fog-gily, then snatched the headdress off. He became aware of Mrs. Gloster's laughter, echoing across the water. He smiled and walked down the dock, his shirt clinging, his white flannel trousers making slushy noises with each step. "You see, Mrs. Gloster," he said as he approached the lady, with a gay laugh that was rather horrible to hear, "we do inculcate the democratic spirit at Manitou."

On Company Street there was light, and gladness, and joy, and honor. Herbie Bookbinder and Cliff Block were marched up and down by a select committee of eminent athletes—not including Lennie—with placards around their necks proclaiming that they had received the sublime and ultimate glory of Manitou: in the last hours of the summer, they had been initiated into the Royal Order of Goofer-dusters.

⟳ **Talking it over**

1. *a.* What is an impersonation? What is usually the purpose of an impersonation?

b. When the campers laugh at Lennie's appearance as a nurse, whom are they making fun of? When they laugh at Herbie's imitation of Mr. Gauss's walk, whom are they making fun of?

2. Consider Lennie's actions on Camper's Day. What do they reveal about him? What traits do Lennie and Mr. Gauss have in common?

3. *a.* What are Mr. Gauss's reasons for not taking part in Camper's Day? How does he happen to approach the dock?

b. Why is Mr. Gauss so much interested in Mrs. Gloster? How does she feel toward him?

c. Explain why Mr. Gauss receives no assistance from Uncle Sandy when he needs it.

4. Why are Herbie and Cliff made members of the Royal Order of Goofer-dusters?

THE GLASS of the train window was cold against Herbie's forehead as he took his last long look at the hills among which Camp Manitou was hidden. Not only regret kept his eyes fastened on the pleasant scenes he was leaving, but embarrassment, for tears were running down his cheeks. He had quite broken down on the railway platform when Uncle Irish had led both camps in the singing of "Bulldog, Bulldog," as the train appeared around a bend in the distance and came puffing toward them, growing bigger with each puff. The pathos had overwhelmed him, but he had managed to repress the water in his eyes until he could scramble into a seat in the railroad car and turn his face to the window. Now he was giving way freely.

Cliff, who knew his cousin's weakness well enough after years of hearing him snivel in the darkness of movie houses, sat beside him as a screen. Cliff was not moved by the departure. The one thing he regretted in all of Manitou was Clever Sam, and in washing the horse he had expressed his emotion fully. His common sense told him that Clever Sam could find no place in the city, and since the separation was not to be avoided, he saw no sense in crying over it.

Herbie was enjoying his grief so much that he was disappointed when it started to wane like the glow from an ice-cream soda, after only a few minutes. He began using devices to work it up and keep it alive, such as humming "Bulldog, Bulldog" and taps dismally to himself, and reviewing every detail of his final hours at camp. He did no such thing when he was overcome upon leaving his parents two months ago, but was glad to be distracted from his emotion as soon as possible. True sorrow is painful. Sham sorrow compares to it as riding down a roller coaster does to falling off a roof. The thrill is there, but not the cost.

The pictures Herbie recalled were pathetic enough to keep the waterworks pumping for a while.

After the revenge on Mr. Gauss and the inconceivable grandeur of becoming a Gooferduster, he had wandered down to the deserted lake front to enjoy the last sunset and to think melancholy thoughts. Mindful of a last-minute comparison of sunburns in the bunk before dinner, when he had turned out several shades paler than the others, Herbie sat on a rock by the still water, took off his shirt, and bared his chest to the yellow rays of the descending sun. A year of exposure to such feeble light would not have tanned him one atom, but he felt like a brawny outdoors man in doing it, and economical, too. While others were frittering away these precious last seconds of sunlight, he was using them.

As he sat gazing at the lake and trying to screw his mood up to a sublime level, he perceived something strange. Felicia and Lucille were in a canoe together, paddling slowly around the promontory that hid the girls' dock from view. Canoeing at sunset was a delight usually reserved for counselors off duty, but evidently Aunt Tillie had decided to bestow it on the girls this last evening in order to seal the book of summer with a pleasant memory, for here came several other canoes behind the first, fanning out on the lake this way and that.

"Hi, Fleece! Hi, Lucille!" Herbie called, waving his arms. His voice carried easily over the water. The girls saw him and began paddling vigorously toward him.

The boy was at a loss to understand this new companionship between his sister and his love, for in the tug of war over Lennie they had come to despise each other with feminine vigor. Neither of them had ever admitted that there had been a contest, but it had been a real, bitter struggle all the same. As the canoe drew near he could hear them chatting amiably. The mystery was partly cleared when the canoe grated to a stop on the shore a few feet from him, and Yishy Gabelson stepped out of the bushes to haul the canoe high out of the water and graciously help Felicia alight.

The fact is that a last-minute romance had kindled between his sister and Yishy at the Mardi Gras dance, and it burned the more brightly for the shortness of time left to enjoy it. Yishy was almost three years older than she, perhaps not so handsome as Lennie, but in every other way more suited to her. She had arranged this rendezvous with her new cavalier by an exchange of notes, and had selected Lucille to share her secret. She sensed that the red-haired girl really wanted to shift her affections back to the aggrandized Herbie, and therefore was likely to be discreet. This was a correct guess. The conversation in the canoe consisted of a hundred eloquent ways of expressing loathing for Lennie, and alternate praises of Herbie and the hulking Super-senior. The girls almost loved each other by the time the canoe grounded.

Buttoning on his shirt, Herbie ran to the canoe and took the hand that Lucille shyly extended to him. Yishy and Felicia were already strolling down the beach, holding hands and murmuring.

"Won't they catch you?" said Herbie. "You can't come to the boys' beach."

"It's your sister's idea. What difference does it make now, anyway?"

Herbie remembered with a lifting of the heart that at this time tomorrow all the laws of Gauss would be as dead as the codes of Egypt.

"Well, I'm sure glad I was sittin' here."

"So am I."

He led Lucille to his favorite rock, and they sat side by side. His hand rested over hers. It felt cool and small. The sun was going down in immense splashes of red and gold over the whole sky.

"Herbie, I've been very bad to you."

"Aw, it's O.K."

"I like you a thousand times better'n Lennie."

"I like you a million times better'n anybody—'cept my father an' mother."

These declarations might have seemed to a cold onlooker to be deficient in poetry, but they were musically sweet and thrilling to both sweethearts. A delicious silence ensued, and Herbie, forgetting the guilt and misery of his recent money transactions, felt that the world was an almost unbearably lovely and happy place.

The train, bouncing suddenly as it rounded a curve, cracked Herbie's nose against the window with much force, bringing sincere tears to his eyes to reinforce the pumped-up ones. The lake scene disappeared under the impact of pain and would not come back into his imagination. He tried to recapture the solemn awe of the passing of time which he had felt as he lay on his cot in the darkness listening to the wailing bugle notes of the last taps, but this effort was a failure, too. He was all cried out. Regretfully he passed a handkerchief over his eyes and turned his face back to the crowded, noisy car.

"Say, Herb," said Cliff promptly—he had been waiting for his cousin to pull himself together—"what are you gonna do about the money?"

This was the reality that Herbie had been avoiding with his eyes turned to the romantic past. An ill, ugly feeling came over him. The train was carrying him to face his father. Only a few hours intervened before that dreaded meeting.

"What can I do?"

"Gonna tell your father?"

Herbie slouched and mumbled, "Dunno."

"You shouldn't of let Gauss talk you outta that money."

"I know I shouldn't of."

"Rotten ol' Gauss."

"Aw, why blame him? I shouldn't of stole it, that's all."

"Well, heck, you didn't think it was stealing."

"I was crazy."

The train was speeding through forests and fields, but the city seemed close to Herbie. He could almost smell asphalt, auto fumes, and the acrid electric air of the subway. He fished a cardboard box out of his pocket and opened it. A little rose-colored lizard looked out at the boys with bulging, steady eyes. The pouch under its throat palpitated.

"He's cursin' you," said Cliff.

"He's cursin' because he's goin' to the city."

"I like the city."

"Why?"

"Oh, I dunno. I just like it. You can play ball when you feel like it, not when some counselor says so, and there's good movies and everythin'."

"Yeah—and school."

"Well, school is pretty awful," Cliff admitted.

The lizard reached up one claw and made a half-hearted attempt to get out of the box. Herbie pushed it back, shut the lid, and returned the box to his pocket.

"He'll be dead when you get home, Herbie."

"Naw, he'll be O.K. I'll put him in a goldfish bowl. I want somethin' to remind me of the country."

Uncle Sandy's whistle blew, loud and out of place in the narrow car.

"All Gooferdusters report to the lounge!"

The cousins rose, self-conscious in the extreme newness of their distinction, and walked down the aisle and through the dusty green curtains into the lounging room. The black leather seats were already filled with Manitou nobility. A few boys were perched on the edge of the metal washbasins. Uncle Sandy leaned against a mirror on the wall, smoking his pipe.

The Gooferdusters consisted of a few of the younger counselors who had once been eminent campers, also all the leading athletes like Yishy, Gooch Lefko, and Lennie, and a few boys like Herbie and Cliff who had won unusual attention in one way or another. For example there was Willie Sutro, who was an Intermediate of the most ordinary sort, except that he came from

Toledo, Ohio. Since everybody else in camp was from New York, Willie enjoyed a sort of geographical glamour that had won him speedy election to the Gooferdusters.

It is impossible to describe how wonderful it was considered at Manitou to be a Gooferduster, and luckily it is not necessary. There is no community, no walk of life, no age group without its Gooferdusters, and every reader knows exactly how fine it is to be in the elect circle, and how sad it is to be out. No matter what they are called—circles, clubs, societies, sororities, or what you please—they are all Gooferdusters, and their virtue lies in this, that they enable a few people to come together and agree solemnly among themselves that they are better than other people. This verdict is usually accepted by the unlucky outsiders. At the last judgment all this shall pass away, and we shall every one of us become Gooferdusters.

Uncle Sandy put away his pipe, drew himself up, and raised his right hand in the secret salute of the Gooferdusters.

"*Sinai*, Gooferdusters," he intoned.

"*Sinai*, Goofermaster," responded the others, imitating his salute.

The head counselor dropped his hand, and with it his priestly attitude, and became casual.

"Now, fellows, you know it's the ancient Gooferduster custom to meet for the last time on the train. The old members tell the new members who were elected this year the great secret —the real meaning of the password 'Sinai.' I suppose you neophytes all think it means the same as Mount Sinai, in the Bible." Uncle Sandy grinned knowingly.

The new members looked abashed, and the old members exchanged glances of superior wisdom.

"Well, it doesn't. It's spelled S-Y-N-Y. Syny, S-Y-N-Y. . . . And now the Gooferdusters will whisper the real meaning to the neophytes."

Gooch Lefko pulled Herbie toward him by an arm, bent, and enunciated hoarsely in his ear, "S-Y-N-Y. *See You Next Year.* Syny!"

"Syny!" Herbie whispered in return, feeling that this was expected of him. But his heart wasn't in the ritual, and the disclosure of the awful mystery gave him no thrill. Cliff's unpleasant reminder of the stolen money was haunting him.

"O.K., fellows," said Uncle Sandy. "Now, remember, this is a secret that will never be mentioned again until the train ride home next year, on your honor, now. Well, boys, you're the cream of Manitou and it's been a great season, hasn't it? It sure has. So thanks again for your swell coöperation and —SYNY!" He gave the secret salute once more, and all the Gooferdusters responded with the gesture and the password.

Herbie looked around at the cream of Manitou. A week ago he had had no more thought of being included in this high caste than of becoming President. These superior beings who ran, jumped, swam, and threw balls so well were the giants of the earth, and he was of the stunted herd. Now, in their city clothes, crowded into this lounge, they looked very much like a group of trolley-car riders after school hours. Once off the grounds of Manitou, the glitter of the Gooferdusters was fading remarkably.

Uncle Sandy paused in stepping through the curtains and said, "You

Gooferdusters have exclusive use of the lounge for the next quarter hour. Then break it up." He went out. One of the counselors offered cigarettes around; two of the Super-seniors accepted them and puffed awkwardly. The athletes began talking about the Senior girls in sniggering tones. Somebody twitted Yishy about Felicia. He made a sullen answer, and Herbie felt his face grow hot.

"Let's get outta here, Cliff."

The cousins were the first to leave the aristocratic meeting. As they walked down the swaying aisle to their seats, friendly jokes and greetings were thrown at them, for their exploits were fresh in the campers' minds. But Herbie found little pleasure in the popularity. The campers were beginning to look different. He was used to seeing these faces on brown, half-naked bodies. Overdressed, muffled in voluminous city clothes, choked up with clean collars and dangling ties, they wore a new aspect. Herbie was not the only one to sense the change. Throughout the car conversation had lost the free, bantering tone of summer days and had become uneasy, bashful, or too loud. The common fate which had bound the boys was dissolving.

"I wish to heck this ride was over," said Herbie, dropping into the seat heavily.

"So do I," said Cliff. "Gee, it was such fun comin' out, too."

Herbie leaned back on the head cushion and dozed. It was not a refreshing nap, but a sickly half-sleeping, half-waking condition wherein he dreamed a dozen times of the stern face of his father listening to his confession.

"Lunch, Herbie."

The boy opened his eyes and saw Uncle Sid standing in the aisle, holding a wrapped sandwich and a container of milk toward him. Cliff was already removing the paper from his sandwich. Herbie took the food and thanked the counselor. Looking out of the window, he saw by the landscape that they were much nearer the city. There was no wilderness any more. Highways with well-tended shrubbery and groups of houses or entire villages, neat and civilized, were moving quickly across the view. A clutching fear killed his appetite. He bit the sandwich once and laid it aside. He managed to sip most of the milk, but each swallow was an effort.

Oddly enough, there was nothing for him to fear. Jacob Bookbinder did not know of his deed, and would surely give him an affectionate welcome. But Herbie felt the strongest possible aversion to the prospect of looking his father in the face. Jumping up from his seat, he walked to the rear platform of the car and paced back and forth in the roaring, drafty space, ransacking his brain for a way out of the trap which was closing on him.

Mingled with the frantic search for an escape was wonderment at his own criminal foolishness for running into this dead end. The midnight trip to the city, the robbery, the triumph of the Ride, all seemed more fantastic, less substantial now than many dreams he could remember. Could it all have happened? Could he, Herbie Bookbinder, Class 8B-3, have done these things? He had nothing to show for them. All had vanished, leaving a tortured conscience and the certainty that, after all, fifty dollars had been taken from the safe of the Place—taken by him. He turned hither and yon like a scared mouse, alone there on the platform, and beat his forehead with his fists.

A half hour passed and he returned to his seat, pallid and gloomy.

"Know what, Cliff?" he said.

"What?" said Cliff, looking up from a tattered copy of *Weird Tales,* in which he was happily perusing a narrative entitled, "Blood-Drinkers of the Sepulcher."

"I figured out what I'm gonna do about the money."

"Oh, what?" said Cliff, laying the magazine aside and looking at his cousin with interest.

"I'm gonna pay it back," said Herbie dramatically.

"Yeah, but how?"

"I know what yer gonna say, I ain't got the money. Well, I'm gonna save it. I figure I get about a quarter a week for candy an' sodas. Well, I don't have to eat 'em, do I? A quarter a week is thirteen dollars a year. In four years I'll have fifty-two dollars. Then I'll walk up to my pop and give him the money an' tell him everything that happened."

Cliff said at once, "You mean you ain't gonna tell your father for four years?"

"I just explained to you," said Herbie in exasperation, "that I wanna punish myself an' pay back the money. Maybe I can go without movies, too, an' save it up in three an' a half years. But I wanna pay it back, see? It don't do no good to tell without payin' it back, does it?"

Cliff was silent.

"Well, whaddya think?" said Herbie, after waiting half a minute.

"Well, it's an easy way out," said his cousin.

Herbie grew very angry. "What's so easy about it?" he snapped. "Goin' without candy or a soda for four years! You call that easy?"

"Yeah, but meantime you don't have to tell your father," said Cliff. "That's what you want, ain't it?"

"O.K., smart guy. Tell me this. What would *you* do if you was me?"

Cliff considered the question. "I dunno. I think maybe I'd just forget the whole thing."

"Aha!" said Herbie with vast sarcasm. "I suppose that ain't an easy way out!"

"Sure. It's a lot easier'n your way. If I was too scared to tell, why should I fool around with skippin' candy an' sodas? That don't make it right."

"But I *am* gonna tell—after four years," said Herbie, almost in a frenzy at Cliff's stupidity.

"O.K., Herbie. If you think yer doin' right, maybe you are. I don't know nothin'. Me, I'd either tell or shut up, that's all."

"Honest, Cliff, if you can't understand that what I'm doin' is right you're dumb. Just plain, thick dumb. Dumb!"

"I never said I was as smart as you," Cliff answered without rancor.

"You make me sore. 'Scuse me, I'm gonna sit somewheres else."

Herbie rose, stalked to a narrow empty half seat in the back of the car, pushed a tennis racket off it, and sat, fuming at the denseness of his cousin. The scheme he had evolved seemed to him to have every conceivable merit. It was noble. It was self-sacrificing. It required four years of spectacular saintliness. And it spared him the distressing necessity of confessing the robbery an hour from now. If Cliff had said aloud what both boys knew in their hearts—that Herbie would gradually forget about the four-year plan once the first meeting with his father was safely passed—Herbie could have shouted him down. As it was, Cliff had spoiled the charm of the scheme, leaving Herbie to wrestle with the question and arrive at no conclusion. At this hour Herbie almost hated his cousin. He did not speak to him during the rest of the ride.

The scenery changed to small, scattered suburbs, then to large, closely settled ones. Apartment houses, those brick hives that indicate the presence of city dwellers as surely as wigwams indicate Indians, began to fly past in increasing numbers. Herbie's spirits sank lower and lower. Soon he was gazing at a succession of Bronx back yards. The scenery began to appear familiar indeed. He looked sharp, and caught a glimpse of the Place, with the faded red and white sign painted across the top of its long side, "Bronx River Ice Company." Then the train dived into the tunnel to go under the East River.

It was exceedingly strange to have the two worlds of Manitou and the Bronx collide. Vivid memories revived of his eavesdropping on the business meeting, and his discovery of the combination of the safe. Uncle Sandy began shouting orders about leaving the train, but Herbie heard them vaguely through a swarm of memories and regrets. The scene of the eavesdropping arose in his mind as though it were happening outside the black window before his eyes. He could see his father turning the dial of the safe, hear him saying with sarcastic bitterness, "You'll be interested to know, Mr. Powers, that the combination is my son Herbie's birthday, 1-14-17. I gave him that little honor because with his small hands he

smeared the plaster for the cornerstone when he was three years old. . . ."

The train slowed. Campers began tumbling over each other, reaching for parcels, putting on coats, shaking hands, exchanging last-minute gifts and jokes, retrieving books, rackets, bats, banners, crudely carved wooden canes and dishes, strips of white birch bark, footballs, basketballs, volleyballs, baseballs, tennis balls, and all the other debris of summer. Uncle Irish started up "Bulldog, Bulldog," but it went mighty dismally, a few discordant voices chiming in with his dogged bellowing while the others were raised in impudent chatter or in more impudent jeers. Uncle Sandy blew his whistle and started to yell a last order, but at the same moment the train came into the lighted platform with jerks, crashes, and hisses, and nobody heard what he said. The cars were still moving slightly when a couple of the more daring boys opened the doors and leaped out with hurrahs. Uncle Sandy galloped after them. The train stopped. Boys came frothing out of one car and girls out of another. A cordon of counselors hurriedly lined up and shunted the rejoicing mob through the gate into a roped-off area of the huge Terminal concourse, where the sign

CAMP MANITOU

hung again as it had hung two eternal months ago. Eager-eyed parents crowded against the ropes, and greetings and cries tore the air as the children appeared.

There was one boy who neither rejoiced nor was eager as he was carried along in the tumultuous rush from the train. Herbie scanned the ranks of par-

ents and could find neither of the familiar faces he longed, yet dreaded to see. One event he noticed which startled him. It was Mr. Gauss being embraced directly under the banner by a big blond-haired, black-browed woman of middle age, who wore a silver-fox cape around her shoulders, though the weather was warm, with a purple orchid pinned to the fur. She hugged Mr. Gauss, who was half a head shorter than she, with one hand. With the other she held a tall, pale girl of about thirteen by the elbow. Herbie had heard legends about Mrs. Gauss from Ted. She had stayed at Manitou during the first two summers, and caused mass resignations of the girl counselors during both seasons; and since that time had gone to California each summer to visit her parents, taking her daughter Flora with her. Nevertheless, it was clear to see that both mother and daughter were human beings. It seemed most odd to Herbie that Mr. Gauss should possess such natural ties. Herbie never felt the same way about Mr. Gauss after this moment. He was only a man, after all. Looking at the brawny, flamboyant Mrs. Gauss and the pale, nervous daughter, Herbie dimly sensed that it was even possible that Mr. Gauss, like all the boys who hated him, could suffer.

"Herbie! Herbie! Here we are, over here!" It was his mother's voice, cutting through the noise of fourscore other reunions. Herbie turned and spied a lady's dowdy brown hat which he knew at the back of the crowd, and a hand waving in a familiar way above the hat. He plunged toward these symbols of home. Then came a jumble of kissing, hugging, and excited greetings with both his parents, and in the turmoil he hugged and kissed Felicia, too, though he had seen her on the platform a few minutes ago. To repeated inquiries of the mother the children protested that they felt swell and had had a swell time and everything was swell. The family walked out of the Terminal to the automobile, Mrs. Bookbinder plying Herbie with questions at every step about his great last-minute glory at camp. She listened to his account with greedy happiness. As he spoke Herbie often glanced sideways at his father. Jacob Bookbinder looked older and more tired than Herbie remembered him, and after the first greetings he paid little attention to the children, walking beside them in a silent study.

When they reached the car and his father unlocked the door, Herbie could resist no longer. He broke off his narrative to his mother and said, "How's everything at the Place, Pop?"

Mr. Bookbinder paused with his hand on the lock. He looked at the boy, compressed his lips, and smiled wryly over his son's head at the mother. Then he opened the door and climbed into the automobile.

Herbie turned to his mother in wonderment. She patted him on the back and said with a forced grin, "Come, come, get into the car."

Silently the children and Mrs. Bookbinder entered the automobile, and silently the father started up the motor and began driving through the thick traffic.

"But what about the Place?" said Herbie, in a sudden chill of fear that ran to his fingers and toes.

"Papa has sold the Place," said Mrs. Bookbinder.

Talking it over

1. *a.* What plan does Herbie think up for paying back the money? Why does he regard his plan as noble? What does the plan accomplish for him?

b. What is Cliff's opinion of the plan? Why does he feel this way? What is likely to happen to the plan?

c. Explain why Herbie becomes so angry when Cliff disagrees with him.

2. *a.* What change takes place in the boys on the way home?

b. Why do they begin to have a different feeling toward each other?

3. *a.* What shocking news awaits Herbie at home?

b. What first tells him that something is wrong?

Words in action

Here is a paragraph which uses five difficult words found in Chapter 7. How are the words in bold type alike in meaning? Use the Glossary for help in answering.

"To be voted into membership in the Royal Order of Gooferdusters was a **distinction.** The club was an organization of high **caste, exclusive** in its membership. Cliff and Herbie were **aggrandized** by their initiation into this **aristocratic** group."

Is this a serious description of the Gooferdusters or is it meant to be funny?

A FTER this shocking announcement, the drive to the Bronx was grim. Mr. and Mrs. Bookbinder did not speak. Felicia, after a flutter of astonishment, looked dreamily out of the window at the traffic, the stony streets, and the high dirty buildings, and bethought her of the manly figure of Yishy Gabelson. Herbie's thoughts were in turmoil; he longed to know more, but dreaded to ask.

"Why is Papa selling the Place, Mama?" the boy inquired after a long silence, trying to sound very young and innocent.

"Well, Herbie, there was a robbery at the Place."

"Oh," said Herbie with wide eyes, "and did the robbers steal all the money and that's why we have to sell it?"

Mrs. Bookbinder shook her head gently at her son's childishness. "No, my boy, they didn't take much money. But they took certain very important papers, and without them—well, Papa knows what he's doing. It'll all be for the best."

Herbie immediately recalled the wrangle of Krieger and Powers, on the night of his expedition, over the box marked "J.B." containing the blue memorandum.

"When — when did Papa sell the Place?"

"It was decided yesterday. Thursday the men are coming to our house to sign all the contracts."

Mr. Bookbinder broke his silence to observe with rough sarcasm, "Tell the boy the terms of the settlement, and what my salary will be, and everything else. Why must you talk to the children about it at all?"

"Herbie is our boy. Naturally he's interested," retorted the mother, with unusual spirit. "I think it's fine that he shows an intelligent interest."

"Papa," said Herbie timidly, "what'll happen to the crooks if they catch them?"

"They should be burned or hanged!" shouted his father, honking his horn furiously at a truck that suddenly lurched out of a side street in front of them. "But the least they'll get is ten years in prison, I hope."

"What if they were kids?"

His father threw a swift keen glance at the boy on the seat behind him, and turned his eyes back to the street. "Kids? Kids rob the Place? What kids?"

"Well, you know about—about the Creek Gang,"[9] Herbie stammered. "They got pistols an' knives an' I bet burglar tools—an' they hang around near the Place—"

"Grandma stories!" said his father.

"But if it was kids," Herbie persisted with a feeling that he was stretching his luck to pursue the topic, "would they go to jail for ten years, too?"

"If they were young kids they'd go to reform school. That's the same as prison. But this robbery wasn't done by kids," said Jacob Bookbinder curtly.

"You know, Jake, maybe Herbie has hit on something," said the mother. "That would explain a silly thing like taking the box with the blue paper and leaving most of the cash. Who but kids would—"

"What are you now, a policewoman? The police say definitely it was done by two men. What would kids be doing there three o'clock in the morning? How could kids break into a safe?"

Felicia said, "It could have been young fellows fifteen or sixteen. I know one who could easily stay up all night —and strong enough to break open a safe with his bare hands, almost."

"I suppose you mean Yishy Gabelson," said Herbie.

"Never mind who I mean," Felicia answered, reddening with pleasure at hearing the ineffable name spoken aloud.

"Do me a favor, all of you, and stop talking about the robbery and the Place," said the father.

Conversation languished. Mrs. Bookbinder tried to start the topic of camp life once more, but both her children gave short, absent-minded answers to her questions. She desisted after a while. The family finished the ride in somber quiet.

As soon as they came home, Herbie rushed to the telephone in the kitchen while the rest of the family went to the bedrooms. He spoke in a near-whisper.

"Intervale 6465 . . . . Hello, Cliff? This is Herbie. Hey I'm sorry I got sore on the train. . . . Well, O.K., thanks, Cliff. . . . Listen, how about doing me a favor? Can you meet me over in front of Lennie's house in fifteen minutes? . . . Yeah, it's important, Cliff." He lowered his voice so that he just breathed the next words. "It's about the money. . . . O.K. So long."

Herbie tiptoed out of the kitchen and softly opened the front door. "Where do you think you're going?"

The classic challenge of mothers rang out clear. Herbie did not have one foot outside, which would have justified a quick escape on the pretense of not

---

[9] **Creek Gang.** The children in Herbie's neighborhood believe that young hoodlums hang out near the creek.

having heard the question. He was fairly halted. His mother stood in the hallway, regarding him mistrustfully.

"I'm just goin' over to Lennie's for a minute."

"To Lennie's? You're home two minutes and you're ready to run out! Aren't you glad to be home?"

"Sure. It's great to be home. It's swell, Mom. Only Lennie has something of mine I wanna get. I'll be right back." He risked a dive through the doorway and got away successfully.

Lennie lived on Homer Avenue two blocks further away from the school, in an apartment house of the same size, shape, age, and dinginess as the Bookbinder abode. Herbie ran the two blocks and arrived perspiring and blowing. Cliff was not there. The fat boy paced back and forth before the entrance. Two minutes later Cliff came in sight around the corner, and Herbie scampered to meet him.

"Holy smoke, what took you so long? Listen—" Herbie breathlessly summarized the news about the Place. Cliff was thunderstruck.

"Gosh, Herb, it's all our fault. On accounta us your father's gonna sell the Place!"

"I know," said Herbie despairingly. "Come on, now!" He pulled his cousin by the hand into the building and skipped up the stairs.

"What do we do here?" Cliff panted as he followed him.

"First let's see who's home."

They trampled up to the third landing and Herbie rang a bell. In a moment the door was opened by Lennie. The athlete scowled when he saw who his visitors were.

"Whadda you guys want?"

"Aw, we're lonesome for camp," said Herbie. "We were walkin' by and figured we'd come up an' talk about good old Manitou."

Lennie's expression became much pleasanter and he made way for the cousins to enter.

"Boy, you're lonesome, too, are you?" he said. "I'm about ready to bust out an' cry. Go on into the parlor." He followed the others, adding, "When I think I gotta live a whole winter in this dump! Boy, remember them ball fields an' that lake? I wish camp was all year round."

"Me, too," said Herbie. He looked around inquisitively at the Krieger home, where he was an infrequent visitor. It much resembled his own in dimensions and furnishings, except that clothing, magazines, and newspapers were scattered about, and dust lay in films on tables and chair arms. (Mrs. Bookbinder never tolerated such details, and never failed to refer to them scornfully when the Krieger establishment was mentioned.)

"Your folks home, Lennie?" said Cliff.

"Naw. My mother brought me home an' went right out shoppin'. Herb, you know about the robbery an' about the Place being sold?"

"Yeah, ain't that terrible?" said Herbie.

"I dunno. My mother says the robbers only got fifty bucks. An' she says we're gettin' a terrific lot o' money for the Place, an' it's a good thing we're sellin' it. Hey, whaddya think we're gettin'? Five million dollars?"

"Nearer ten million," said Herbie. "That's a mighty big place."

"It sure is. Say, we'll be rich, Herb. When our fathers die we can own speedboats an' live in Florida, an' all that stuff. Boy, that's what I want, a speedboat."

"That's a heck of a thing to say," put in Cliff. "You want your father to die?"

"Don't be a sap," Lennie said angrily. "But nobody don't live forever, do they? Yer just sore 'cause you ain't in on this dough like Herb an' me."

"All right, don't you guys start fightin' again," said Herbie. He added craftily, "Unless you wanna do an Indian leg wrestle or somethin'. Bet Cliff can take you, Lennie."

"Bet he can't!"

Lennie still resented the beating he had received from Cliff. He knew that his opponent had won with the abnormal strength of fury, and believed that in an unemotional state Cliff was no match for him. "Come on, Cliff, lay down," he urged. "Two out of three, Indian leg wrestle."

Cliff threw a questioning look at his cousin and understood that this was what Herbie wanted. "Well, o.k.," he said, reclining in the middle of the floor. "But no bets, Herbie. This guy was the best Indian leg wrestler in camp, pretty near."

"Hey, Lennie, I'm gonna get a glass of water." Herbie rose from his chair as Lennie eagerly dropped to the floor beside his erstwhile conqueror.

"Sure, go ahead," said the athlete. As Herbie left the room the wrestlers were raising and dropping opposed legs in the traditional manner and counting, "One, two. . . ."

Herbie prowled through the apartment, looking under beds, and in closets, ransacking drawers, and climbing up to examine shelves. From the parlor came the noises and grunts of combat. He searched for perhaps five minutes, then all at once discontinued

his quest and returned to the parlor. The two boys stood toe to toe, flushed and breathing hard, locked in a hand wrestle. As Herbie entered, Lennie pulled Cliff sharply to one side and threw him to the floor. He laughed triumphantly and said to Herbie, "How about that? Three outta three leg wrestle, an' three outta three hand wrestle!"

"I ain't no good at that stuff, I guess," said Cliff good-naturedly, picking himself up.

"You're really great, Lennie," said Herbie. "Hey, come on, Cliff, we better get goin'."

"What's your hurry?" said Lennie, feeling extremely pleased with life. "Stick around. There's some jello in the icebox. We can have some fun."

"Naw, thanks, they're waitin' for me at home," said Herbie. "We were just passin' by."

He took Cliff by the arm and walked out of the room. Lennie went with them to the door.

"Well, come around again. It's pretty dead here after camp."

"We sure will, Lennie," said Herbie. As the cousins walked down the stairs, Lennie shouted after them, "So long, Herb the millionaire!"

"So long, Speedboat Lennie!" Herbie called back. They heard the athlete laugh and close the door.

"Well, whadja find, Herbie?" exclaimed Cliff.

"*It's there, Cliff.* That box marked 'J.B.' is there in a closet."

Cliff whistled. The boys went out to the street and walked in the direction of Herbie's home. The fat boy's face was pale and his brows knitted.

"Cliff, my father said if kids done the robbery they go to reform school for ten years. Reform school is a prison for kids."

"Yeah, but if we *confess* we done it, do we still go to reform school?" said Cliff, looking as worried as his cousin.

"Why not? The police are lookin' for us, Cliff. They think we were two big guys. I dunno, maybe if we tell we only get five years."

"Herb, I'll do whatever you say."

They were approaching Mr. Borowsky's candy store. Herbie fished two dimes out of his pocket.

"I don't figure they got fraps in reform school," he observed, with a laugh of theatrical bravado. "Wanna join me in a last frap?"

Cliff gasped, "You gonna tell?"

"I ain't gonna tell about you. All you done was help me, anyhow. I'm gonna say I done it myself."

"O.K., Herb. That's swell of you."

Herbie was slightly disappointed in Cliff's answer. He had expected some sort of argument, a heroic insistence on sharing the punishment, but none was forthcoming. Cliff believed that Herbie should own up, and also felt that the robbery was entirely his cousin's responsibility. So he approved gratefully of Herbie's decision.

The boys ate their fraps without a word. Herbie assumed an expression of magnificent mournfulness, in imitation of Robin Hood just prior to his hanging, as played by Douglas Fairbanks.[10] Now that the resolve was taken he felt a martyr. He even looked forward to reform school with a little curiosity and excitement. A vision of vast barred steel gates closing on him, not to be opened for five years, came into his mind, pathetic and thrilling. It was a

fall, but a tremendous, showy fall. He would write constantly to his family and to Lucille. She would wait for him. He would emerge in five years and proceed to become a great man: a general or a Senator. He would show the world how Herbie Bookbinder could rise above reform school!

"Ain't no use scrapin' that dish any more, Herb," said Cliff. "It's dry."

Herbie realized that his spoon had been rasping futilely in the shallow tin dish while he had been lost in dreams.

"O.K. Here we go." He stood up and walked out of the candy store. His steps were not sprightly.

"Want me to come up with you?" said Cliff.

"It don't matter," said the self-condemned boy. He felt the same sense of unreality creeping over him that he had experienced on the moonlit night when he and Cliff had mounted rickety old Clever Sam to start their journey to New York.

"Well, I won't come then," said Cliff.

"Guess I'd rather be alone, at that," Herbie remarked absently.

Cliff held out his hand. "Good luck, Herbie," he said. "Maybe it'll all come out O.K."

The fat boy clasped his cousin's palm. This was the first time the boys had shaken hands in the memory of either; they were too close for such a gesture, ordinarily. It made them both self-conscious.

"So long, pal," said Herbie. "I ain't afraid. Whatever happens, I'll face it. Don't you worry about old Herbie. I can take my medicine. Thanks for helpin' me an' everything. So long, pal."

He wanted to say "pard," which seemed to belong with the rest of this speech, but he felt the word would

10**Douglas Fairbanks,** a popular movie actor (1883-1939).

sound odd amid the stones and bricks of Homer Avenue, so he compromised on "pal." Cliff was not at all as good as Herbie at improvising dramatic dialogue. He answered, "Yeah. Well, g'bye," dropped his cousin's hand, and walked down the avenue, hastening a little in embarrassment.

Aflame with virtue and determination, Herbie scampered up the stairs to the Bookbinder apartment. He came upon his father and mother in the parlor, deep in a financial discussion, with ledgers, notebooks, yellow bank statements, and impressive engraved certificates spread around them on the floor and furniture. His father was writing in a notebook propped on his knees. As the boy entered he looked up.

"Well?" he said. "We're busy."

One glance at his parent's deep-lined, grey, unhappy face, and Herbie's resolution burned blue and flickered out. "Uh, sorry, Pa," he said. "I was gonna bang around on the piano. 'Scuse me." He sneaked from the room.

That night Cliff telephoned him to ascertain whether he was on his way to reform school. Herbie said with some shame that he "hadn't had a chance yet" to make his confession. The next night, and the next after that, he was forced to give the same report to his wondering cousin. It was not true, of course; he had dozens of chances. But the grim aspect of his father scared him off each time he nerved himself to approach.

Thursday came, and Thursday afternoon, and Herbie had not yet taken his medicine, and Jacob Bookbinder was still in the dark. The father, dressed in his best clothes, was pacing back and forth in the parlor, pausing now and again to thump miserable discords on the piano. His son stood in the dining room, contemplating a table spread for tea and laden with pastries and layer cakes. He was not hungry. His gaze was far away. He was, in fact, trying to persuade himself that perhaps it would be a good thing if the Place were sold for five million dollars, after all; that perhaps it would be wrong of him to interfere at this late hour. He was very nearly convinced, too.

His mother came in. She wore a big green apron over the black silk dress reserved for occasions of great pomp. Her face looked much less faded than usual, and the double string of amber beads, unmistakable sign of stirring events, dangled over the apron.

"All right, you can forget about helping yourself. We're having important company in a minute. Go on downstairs and play for an hour."

"Ma, is the company comin' about buyin' the Place?"

A bark from Mr. Bookbinder in the parlor. "Tell that boy to get out of the house!" And a crash of a fist's breadth of notes on the piano.

Mrs. Bookbinder looked anxiously at Herbie. "You heard Papa. Run along."

"Where's Felicia?" With the fateful moment at hand, Herbie suddenly wanted to spar for a few more seconds.

"She's at Emily's. Go, I say. This is no time for you to be in the house."

Herbie slowly walked down the hallway to the outside door. He put his hand on the knob. Then he turned and just as slowly walked into the parlor.

"Pa."

His father was looking out of the window. He whirled at the sound of Herbie's voice.

"*Will* you go downstairs, boy?"

"Pa, are you looking for a green tin box marked 'J.B.'?"

The father stared at him in stupefaction. Then he ran at the boy and gripped his shoulders brutally.

"What are you talking about? Yes, I'm looking for such a box. It was stolen."

Herbie's shoulders were full of pain. He was more frightened than he had ever been in his life. But he caught his breath and said, "I saw it Monday in Mr. Krieger's house. In a bedroom closet. Under a pile of old shoes. I figured it would be there because I myself—"

"Are you crazy, boy? Do you know what you're saying?"

The doorbell rang. Father and son heard the door opened at once, and the voice of Mrs. Bookbinder in words of welcome, and several men's voices. The father seized Herbie's right hand and dragged him into the dining room. Mrs. Bookbinder came in with Powers, Krieger, and the lawyer Julius Glass, Lucille's father. There was also a tall, broad-shouldered, bald stranger. He had pouchy little eyes, and wore stiff dark clothes. Mr. Glass, who was holding a thick brief case under one arm, said as they entered, "Mr. Burlingame, I'd like you to meet Mr. Bookbinder, the manager of Bronx River."

The stranger put out his hand and said with a cold smile, "Delighted. You have a reputation in the industry."

Bookbinder took the extended hand and shook it. His eyes were on his partner. Krieger avoided the glance.

"If you gentlemen will excuse me for a moment, I'd like to have a word alone in the next room with Mr. Krieger."

Powers, whose face was strained and lined, quickly said, "Mr. Bookbinder, I hope there's nothing to be said now that can't be said in front of all of us. We've made a deal with Mr. Burlingame, and it's impossible to go back on it. The present occasion is a formality. For all intents and purposes Bronx River is now the property of Mr. Burlingame, you know."

"All right," said Jacob Bookbinder calmly. But Herbie knew he was not calm, for he was crushing the boy's hand, and trembling a little.

"Krieger, have you got the box with the blue paper?"

Krieger looked at him agape. No words issued from the open mouth.

"What on earth do you mean by such a question?" Powers said hurriedly. "You know perfectly well the box was stolen."

"My boy Herbie here says he saw the box in a closet in Krieger's home."

There was a confusion of exclamations by everyone in the room.

MR. POWERS: *"He's crazy. Let's get on with our business."*

MRS. BOOKBINDER: *"Herbie, I told you to go downstairs."*

MR. KRIEGER: *"Haybie mistake. I got a box, nothing like blue paper box."*

LAWYER GLASS: *"What does this boy know about the whole business, anyway?"*

HERBIE: *"That's right. I did see it."*

The above remarks came all at once in loud tones, and nobody understood anybody else.

Mr. Burlingame's voice emerged, deep and irritated, from the babble. "See here, gentlemen, I had the clear assurance of all of you yesterday that the matter of the so-called blue paper had been amicably settled, and that all of you wanted to sell. If there is still a shadow of doubt on this transaction, why, I—"

"There's no doubt whatever," said Powers. "Mr. Glass, let's get on with the contracts, shall we? The blue paper is stolen and gone."

"It ain't stolen," Herbie insisted loudly.

All the adults stared at him now.

"How do you know so much, young man?" said the lawyer impatiently.

"Because I stole the fifty dollars from the Place myself. And I didn't take no box!"

Now the fat was in the fire. In the hubbub of questions and cries, Mrs. Bookbinder ran to the boy's side and put her arm around him.

Haltingly at first, and then with a freer flow as the grown-ups grew silent with amazement, Herbie told the story of his midnight adventure. He confessed to the eavesdropping that had given him the idea. He explained his motive of getting money to build the Ride. He emphasized that he had intended to return the money, describing the note he had written but failed to leave, and he narrated the treachery of Mr. Gauss, without trying to excuse himself on that account. He omitted the parts played by Cliff and Clever Sam, and he did not mention the scene between Krieger and Powers which he had witnessed from the refrigeration vault. It took him many minutes to unburden himself. Midway, his father dropped his perspiring hand and leaned with both elbows behind him on the buffet, regarding his son with a mixture of perplexity and anger which did not increase the boy's ease. The others listened in various attitudes of astonishment, now and then stopping the boy with brief questions. Lawyer Glass did most of the question-

ing. At last Herbie carried his confession to the end, concluding breathlessly, "So that's how I done it, an' I'm glad I told, even if I do hafta go to reform school now. *But I didn't take no box.*"

Mrs. Bookbinder, eyes wet and face flushed, pulled him close against her side and said, "You won't have to go to reform school."

The men looked at each other wonderingly.

Powers spoke first. "I think the boy has imagined the whole thing. He supposes he's being a hero. It's an utterly incredible story."

Jacob Bookbinder had not taken his eyes off his son. Now he said in a hoarse, harsh voice, "Herbie, you have been the laziest boy in the Bronx all your life. If you did all those crazy things, what did you do them for?"

Herbie glanced at the lawyer, blushed, and transferred his gaze to the floor.

"Come, come, boy," said Mr. Glass, "nobody will hurt you if you speak the truth—speak the truth. Why did you do all this?"

Still no answer.

"Tell us, Herbie, please," said his mother softly. "You must tell us."

Herbie saw no way out. Scarlet-faced, he blurted, "All right. I wanted to make a hit with Lucille Glass."

All the grown-ups except Powers burst out laughing. It may seem surprising that they did so at such a grim time, but that is how people are. Anyone who has attended a funeral knows of the boisterous laughter in the coaches coming from a cemetery. It is a safety-valve action. The hilarity faded quickly, and Jacob Bookbinder said, "Now, if he didn't take the box, the next question is, where is it?"

"When I was hidin' in the ice room," said Herbie, "I seen Mr. Krieger an' Mr. Powers standin' in front o' the open safe, arguin' over it. Mr. Krieger was holdin' the box—"

Krieger interrupted, his voice shrill. "All right, wait, all honest men. I know facts, explain better. Yes, sure I keep box. Protect you, Jake, only protect you. Powers like iron, say burn up paper one two three. Blue paper safe now because I protect—"

"Krieger, you're a dirty liar!" shouted Powers, pounding the dining-room table so that the dishes rattled and two éclairs rolled to the floor. Mrs. Bookbinder instinctively dived for the éclairs, exclaiming, "Please, gentlemen, the child, the child!"

"Herbie, go to your room and get undressed," said his father. It was bright and early in the afternoon, and the order boded ill. Herbie started to slink from the room.

Mr. Burlingame ran a flat palm once over his naked pate and picked up his hat from a chair. "Mr. Bookbinder, you have a remarkable son, remarkable. Will you please understand, gentlemen, that Interborough withdraws completely from this negotiation? We don't want to buy Bronx River on any terms. The best of luck to all of you."

Powers jumped in front of him, barring his exit from the dining room, and also preventing the boy from leaving. Herbie fell back into a corner and tried to look invisible.

"Mr. Burlingame, that memorandum of my father's is meaningless. Glass says so, and Sullivan of Guarantee Building and Loan says so. I can prove it in court. This business of the robbery is a silly misunderstanding. You can't withdraw from a closed deal, sir, just

because of the wild talk of a boy."

Mr. Burlingame donned his hat and pulled it down firmly. "Bob, the Bronx River property is not wanted without the good will and continued management of Bookbinder, as I told you. And Interborough doesn't buy a property with the slightest question as to title. I knew your father, Bob. He wouldn't have been pleased with this day's work. Kindly excuse me."

Powers stepped aside. Mr. Burlingame went out. Young Powers' handsome face became greenish-pale. He dropped into a chair, and covered his eyes with one hand, pressing his thumb and finger into the corners.

"Oh, come, Bob," said Mr. Glass, stepping quickly to his side and putting a hand on his shoulder, as the outer door was heard closing. "It's nothing that serious—nothing that serious."

Powers looked up at the rotund lawyer. His shoulders drooped. Tears stood in his eyes. Herbie had never before seen a man show visible grief. He stared at the scene from his corner between the bureau and the wall.

"Property is property," added the attorney, patting Powers' shoulder. "Property is property. Your interest in Bronx River is still worth fifty thousand, easily."

"Find me a buyer for thirty," said Powers in a choked voice. "Why do you suppose I've been pushing this thing, Louis? I've got to have thirty thousand dollars cash. Oh, what a mess!"

The lawyer nodded gravely. He said in tones that Herbie could barely hear, "Bob, is it that Montauk business I advised you against?"

Powers answered with a short nod. Mr. Glass pulled down the corners of his mouth, and looked at Bookbinder.

"What's done is done. How about it?" he said. "Here's your chance to corner all the equity cheaply. Will you buy Bob Powers out for thirty?"

Herbie's father turned his palms outward in the eternal gesture which means "No weapons" among savages and "No funds" among civilized men. The lawyer glanced toward Mr. Krieger, but the partner was looking steadily out of the window, keeping his face hidden from the others.

"Herbie!" said Jacob Bookbinder all at once, as his eyes chanced on his son. The fat boy jumped, and ran for the door. "I told you ten minutes ago to go to your room and get undressed. Now do as I say or—"

But Herbie heard no more. His scuttling little legs had already carried him out of the dining room and into the bedroom, where he closed the door after him.

Talking it over

1. *a.* Why does Herbie set up his meeting with Cliff at Lennie's house? How does Cliff help?

b. What more do you learn about Lennie's character at this time?

c. How realistic are the boys in estimating the price for which the Place will be sold? Explain.

2. *a.* Why has Mr. Bookbinder agreed to the sale of the business?

b. Explain Herbie's delay in confessing. What finally brings him to the

point? How does he approach the subject?

3. How are the following listeners affected by Herbie's story? (*a*) Mr. Bookbinder (*b*) Mr. Krieger (*c*) Bob Powers (*d*) Mr. Burlingame (*e*) Mr. Glass (*f*) Mrs. Bookbinder

Words in action

In the following items, both choices refer to correct definitions of the word in bold type, but only one of these definitions fits the situation in the story. Choose the one you think is right.

1. When Krieger and Powers **wrangled,** did they (*a*) tend horses, or (*b*) quarrel angrily?

2. When Mrs. Bookbinder put on the dress she usually wore for **stirring** events, was she (*a*) planning to do some cooking, or (*b*) expecting some important guests?

3. When Herbie's intention to repay the money became **futile,** was it (*a*) useless or (*b*) unimportant?

4. When **boisterous** laughter followed Herbie's announcement that he loved Lucille, was the amusement (*a*) violent and rough, or (*b*) noisily cheerful?

5. When Herbie told his version of the midnight events at the Place, his father stared at him in **stupefaction.** Was Mr. Bookbinder (*a*) in a dazed or senseless condition, or (*b*) greatly amazed?

6. If both Herbie and Mr. Glass could be described as **rotund**, does that mean that both (*a*) were plump or (*b*) had rich, full voices?

A FEW MINUTES later Mrs. Book-binder came into Herbie's room. She found her son in crisp fresh yellow pajamas, lying face downward on his bed. She sat beside him softly and caressed his shoulder, saying, "What's the matter, Herbie?"

The boy turned over and sat up. He was dry-eyed, but his look was despairing.

"Matter? Holy smoke, Mom, that's a heck of a question."

"You won't go to reform school, my boy. Mr. Glass is a big man. He'll go to the police and explain the whole thing. Nothing will happen to you."

"Yeah. Maybe not." Herbie appeared not at all reassured as he drew up his knees, rested his elbows on them, and placed his chin in his hands. "But I stole, didn't I?"

"Herbie, what happened to the note?"

"What note?"

"The note you said you were going to leave in the safe, promising to return the money. Did you really write one, or was that a lie?"

"Sure I wrote it," said Herbie indignantly. "I'd of left it, too, if Mr. Krieger an' Mr. Powers hadn't come back so soon that night. They drunk their coffee awful fast, that's all I gotta say."

"Well, where is it now?"

"I dunno. I had it in my suit in one o' the pockets. I guess maybe it's still there."

Mrs. Bookbinder rose and searched the pockets of his jacket.

"What's this?" she said, pulling out the cardboard box.

"Gosh! I bet he's dead!" Herbie jumped up, took the box, and opened it. The lizard was stirring. He picked up the little pink reptile by its tail and set it on the bed. Frightened by the sudden change, the lizard stood still, it's chin-pouch palpitating. Herbie lay beside the creature and studied it. Mrs. Bookbinder, muttering about the things boys brought into the house, went through the pockets of Herbie's trousers. From a back pocket she extracted a crumpled sheet of yellow paper.

"That's it," said Herbie, looking up as he heard the paper crackle. Mrs. Bookbinder unfolded the paper, smoothed it and read:

```
W E ARE THECREEK GANG AND 1 OF
OUR GANG NEEDS AN OPERATION
          $50
THAT COSTS $%) SO ARE BORROWING
NOT STEALING $%) $%) $50 FROM
YOUR SAFE.  YOU'LL GET THE $50
BACK BY MAIL NEXT WEEK WITHOUT
FAIL SO DON'T CALL THE POLICE
ORNOTHING BECUASE YOU'LL GET
THE   %$) $50 BACK   . WITH
INTEREST MAKING IT $&% $75.
          the creek gang.
```

When the mother had absorbed the contents of this interesting document, she ran to Herbie and interrupted his study of natural history to hug and kiss him.

"God bless you, my boy. You meant well."

"Yeah," said Herbie, enduring the affection without response.

"Why did you sign it the Creek Gang?"

"What was I gonna do?" said Herbie, talking as best he could with his head muffled against his mother's bosom. "Sign my own name? I just wanted Pop to know he was gonna get paid back."

"That's right, of course. It was all that rotten Mr. Gauss's fault. I'll never send you back to that terrible camp."

Herbie broke from her arms just in time to save the lizard from diving over the edge of the bed. He placed the creature carefully in the middle of the bedspread.

"Where's Pop?" he inquired uneasily.

"Still busy with the men." The mother sat on the bed once more.

"Ma, hasn't Pa got thirty thousand dollars to buy out that rotten Mr. Powers?"

"Hush, what business is that of yours? What do you know about money? It'll be healthier for you to keep your nose out of Papa's affairs from now on. . . . You listen to me, I want to talk to you about—"

"But is Mr. Powers still here? What's happening, Ma? Gosh, I wanna know—"

"Mr. Glass is on the telephone in the kitchen, talking to I don't know who. That's none of your affair. What I want to know, Herbie is—are you really—I don't know what to say. Interested in this Lucille Glass?"

Herbie barely nodded. He stroked the lizard's back with one finger.

"Don't you think you're a little young to be—interested—in girls?"

Another nod, even barer.

"Mind you, I have nothing against Lucille. She's a nice little girl, although she's very spoiled. And I must say I don't see that she's pretty. But I suppose you think she is."

A slight motion of the head, which might be a nod or the bobbing occasioned by a deep breath.

"Well, there's no harm in it. Just so long as you understand that it doesn't mean anything at all, and that you'll both forget all about it in a couple of weeks."

Herbie and the reptile in equal states of immobility.

"You do understand that, don't you?"

Herbie found himself wishing his mother would go to the market, or to the movies, or on any other mission that would require her immediate removal from the room.

"I'm telling you this just for your own good, my boy. Lucille is much too old for you, first of all. When you're sixteen and a half, she'll be sixteen. A boy that age is still a baby. A girl of sixteen can get married. I married Papa when I was seventeen."

Herbie picked up the lizard in his palm and gave him an intense inspection.

"Well, what have you got to say, Herbie?"

The boy said "Mmmm" in a dry tone that conveyed no meaning at all.

"Good," said the mother quickly, "I'm glad you agree with me. You're a sensible boy."

She fell to patting Herbie's hair. He ignored the caresses and concentrated on the lizard. Restored to air and light, the animal had become more lively. It scuttled around in the boy's palm and tried to climb up his curving fingers. Herbie felt sorry for the rosy, gold-spotted creature, which seemed so out of place in the narrow Bronx bedroom. The lizard brought back visions of the bright broad skies of Manitou, and the fields, and the lake, and the mossy rocks along the shore where the boy had captured his living souvenir. How cramped and small the apartment seemed to Herbie, and the street outside the window, too! Everything in the city seemed to have shrunk to half its size during the summer.

"Guess I'll turn you loose in the lots," Herbie said to the lizard. "I shouldn't of brought you here."

The door of the bedroom was thrown open. Mr. Bookbinder stood in the doorway. At once the mother rose and placed herself between him and the boy.

"Where are the men?" she said.

"They've gone. Glass bought out Powers. We have a new partner."

Mrs. Bookbinder was staggered by the development. "Glass!" she ejaculated.

"He was on the telephone fifteen minutes with his wife, explaining the proposition to her. Don't worry, he's a clever man. Thirty thousand for Powers' share! Leave it to a lawyer to smell a bargain."

"And—and the blue paper?"

"Glass accepts it. He's going to draw it up in legal form. He's a gentleman, always was. Powers is out—finished."

The mother pulled herself together and seized on the amazing news as a means to her end. "Well, so it all comes out fine! Congratulations, Jake! What are we waiting for? Let's all go out and celebrate!"

The father's expression changed. "This boy, too?" he said, in a tone that caused Herbie to cower.

"Why not? Look at this letter. He meant well, Papa, all the time. Hasn't he been punished enough, worrying himself sick?"

She held out the Creek Gang note to him. Mr. Bookbinder read it, crumpled it, and threw it into a corner.

"Leave me alone with him."

"Papa, don't hit him too hard! He meant no harm."

"Leave me alone with him."

Herbie quavered from the bed, "Go ahead, leave us alone, Mom."

"Papa, remember he's just a small boy. Remember!"

Reluctantly the mother left the room. Mr. Bookbinder closed the door and proceeded to give Herbie a tolerably warm licking. Starting with miscellaneous cuffs and clouts, he soon organized the task, sat on the bed, turned the boy over his knees, and drubbed his rear resoundingly and long. He said nothing during the operation. Herbie had resolved to "take it like a man," but his resolution waned halfway through the spanking and he ended by taking it like a boy, with wall-shaking howls. Despite the mother's description of him as a small boy, he was pretty big for this sort of thing, and made a cumbersome figure, draped over his father's knees. Mr. Bookbinder managed well enough, however. Mrs. Bookbinder stood outside the door, trembling from head to foot and wincing each time she heard the whack that signaled another contact between palm and posterior. After perhaps two minutes she could bear no more. She burst into the room, wailing, "All right, all right! Must you murder him?"

"Nobody was ever spanked to death yet," panted the father, but he brought the punishment to a close with a crescendo of thwacks. He rolled the yelling boy back on the bed with surprising gentleness, and walked out, saying, "He can get dressed now, if he wants."

Herbie availed himself of this permission immediately. His mother slowed the dressing process by fussing with his clothes, trying to soften the effect of the licking, until the boy said impatiently, "Gosh, Mom, I ain't been crippled. I can still dress myself." Then she was wounded by the ingratitude, and left him alone. She did not understand that her son was rather glad of the beating than otherwise. The guilt feeling had been dusted out of him. Without reasoning closely, he sensed that the reform-school threat was gone. He feared his father's sternness, but he had faith in his justice, and he knew that if prison had loomed Jacob Bookbinder would not have added a whaling to it. The smarting here and there on his anatomy was unpleasant, but it was a welcome substitute for five years behind bars. He cheered up quickly as he dressed.

He was sliding a brilliant yellow and red tie under his collar when he heard his father say in the next room, "Mom, let's eat at Golden's tonight."

Golden's was the costliest restaurant in the east Bronx. Its windows were always loaded with lusciously rich cakes and pastries. To Herbie's ears, the word *Golden's* always sounded much like "Heaven," and indeed a bit more believable and glamorous. He had eaten there once, and he had only heard about Heaven.

His mother protested, "But Papa, I have a roast."

"You said yourself we ought to celebrate. I think you're right."

A pause. Then his mother's voice, somewhat hesitant. "Herbie, too?"

"Of course Herbie, too. We're not going to treat him like a criminal until he's twenty-one, are we?"

Herbie did a caper before the mirror, and sobered instantly as his father came into the room.

"What's taking you so long to dress?"

"I'm done now, Pa." Herbie knotted his tie with blinding speed.

"Let's go for a walk."

"Yes, Pa." Herbie glanced around the room, and picked the lizard off the floor. "Can I drop this guy on the lots? It ain't right to keep him in no apartment."

The father nodded. As his son followed him to the front door Mr. Bookbinder called, "Mom! Get Felicia and meet us at Golden's at six."

"Fine, fine, fine!" Sounds of drawers sliding and closets opening punctuated each "Fine," as Mrs. Bookbinder hurried to reorganize her costume for dining in public.

Father and son walked a block in silence along Homer Avenue toward the lots.

"Well," said Jacob Bookbinder, as they crossed Cervantes Street, "what did you think of the licking?"

"I deserved it," said Herbie humbly.

"Why?"

"'Cause I stole."

"But you were going to leave that note that Mom showed me. Didn't that make it all right?"

"I thought it did, but it didn't."

"Why not?"

They began to climb the steep, rough rocks of the lot. Herbie was still struggling with the question when they reached the top. The lot was full of dusty weeds that reached almost to his waist, with scattered patches of hardy autumn wild flowers, blue, yellow, and white. Rocks jutted above the vegetation. The boy gratefully sniffed the

strong, sweetish smell of this familiar Bronx greenery. It was not as pretty as a field in the Berkshires, but it was home.

"I dunno, Pa. But the note didn't make it right."

The lizard began wriggling in his palm, as though sensing the nearness of freedom. Herbie stooped and allowed it to run off his hand among the weeds. It was gone immediately.

"So long, Camp Manitou," said Herbie.

"You probably have plenty of fun in these lots, Herbie," said his father.

"Yeah. More fun than any place."

The father took his hand and led him to a rock, where they both sat.

"In the old country I spent all my time in the fields when I was a boy. I loved them."

Herbie tried to picture his father as a boy, but it was impossible. Jacob Bookbinder was as fixed in his present appearance, to the boy's mind, as George Washington in the Stuart portrait that hung in the classrooms at school.

The city noises swam up to them in this solitude, softened by distance.

"Tell me what was wrong with that letter, Herbie."

"Well—I was doin' something bad when I stole, see?"

"Yes."

"And I was only *promisin'* to do somethin' good later to make up for it."

The father looked at him as though he were about to smile. It was the first time Herbie had seen a pleasant light in his parent's eye since the arrival from camp. Thus encouraged, he stammered on, "An'—an' the big catch in that was, how did I know *for sure* I was gonna get a chance to do good? Look

what happened. Mr. Gauss skunked me."

Jacob Bookbinder nodded. Many lines faded from his worn face as he smiled. "So what emerges, Herbie?"

Herbie had been through these dialogue lessons with his father before. He knew that a pithy summary was expected of him. He wrestled with words a moment, and said, "I guess—I guess it ain't never right to do bad now and figure to do good later on."

His father put his arm around the boy's shoulder, briefly squeezed him, and stood. It was a small gesture, but Herbie felt as though he had been set free.

"Let's go to Golden's," was all his father said.　　　　THE END

⟲ **Talking it over**

1. *a.* Why did Herbie bring the lizard home with him?

　b. Why does he forget all about it?

　c. Why does he finally decide to turn it loose in a vacant lot?

2. *a.* Why is the note important to Mrs. Bookbinder? What part of Herbie's story does she seem to be most concerned about?

　b. What is Mr. Bookbinder's attitude toward the note? What do you think concerns him most in relation to Herbie?

3. What solutions are worked out for the business problems?

4. *a.* Why does Mr. Bookbinder punish Herbie?　　　(*cont.*)

b. What is Mrs. Bookbinder's attitude toward the punishment?

c. How does Herbie feel about the penalty?

d. What other form of discipline does Mr. Bookbinder use? What is its purpose? What do you think of it as a method of discipline?

Herbie's Ride: Views and viewpoints

How is the caricature (kar′ ə kə chùr) different from the photograph?

Consider the main characters in *Herbie's Ride*. Some of them seem real and natural. Others are like caricatures, with certain features or traits of character exaggerated.

1. On your paper, write the names of the characters listed below. If the person seems real in the story, write *R* after the name. If he seems more like a caricature, write *C*. Be prepared to explain your decisions. For caricatures, be ready to say what feature or features of the personality are exaggerated.

Mr. Bookbinder	Herbie
Mr. Gauss	Lennie
Elmer	Lucille
Mr. Drabkind	Cliff
Mr. Butcher	Uncle Sandy

2. Mr. Drabkind's name seems to match his personality and appearance. Think of a new last name for some of the other story characters; the name should describe the way the person behaves or a special feature of his personality.

Mr. Gauss   Lucille
Lennie   Cliff

3. If you had to hire a staff for a summer camp and the following people applied, which ones would you hire? Why?

Mr. Bookbinder   Mr. Gauss
Mrs. Bookbinder   Elmer
Mr. Glass   Uncle Sandy
Mr. Powers   Mrs. Gloster
Mr. Krieger

Which person would you appoint as Skipper? Why?

4. When the author first mentions Herbie in his Introduction, he says, "Not much of a hero for an adventure story, you may think." Explain how you feel about Herbie as a hero now.

He was like Herbie

The "overheated imagination" which sometimes got Herman Wouk into trouble when he, like Herbie, was a boy in the Bronx, later led him to write many successful books. He says that the situations in his stories usually come from what he has seen in life, but he invents the plots.

Mr. Wouk edited a humor magazine and wrote two shows while still in school. Later he wrote scripts for radio comedians. *Herbie's Ride* shows his skill in writing stories that make readers laugh.

When World War II broke out, Mr. Wouk wrote and produced radio shows to promote the sale of war bonds. Shortly after Pearl Harbor was bombed, he joined the navy. Although it is not a true story, his novel *The Caine Mutiny* grew out of his experiences aboard ship. This book won the Pulitzer Prize.

Other novels of his are *Aurora Dawn, Marjorie Morningstar, Youngblood Hawke,* and *Don't Stop the Carnival.* Several of his novels, including *The City Boy,* have been made into movies. He has also written three plays and a book about his religion, *This Is My God.*

Every sound you need in order to pronounce English words is represented by a symbol in the Complete Pronunciation Key.

After each symbol are words containing the sound which the symbol stands for. This is the sound you must produce when you see the symbol in the pronunciation of a word.

a

Most symbols are single letters of the alphabet. Some are printed in the usual way. Some have special marks added.

A vowel letter without markings represents the short sound of the vowel. Special marks added to a vowel letter signal other sounds which that vowel letter may represent.

ā
ä

Some symbols are two letters of the alphabet. One of these symbols has a special mark added: T̶H. Can you hear the difference between the sounds represented by the symbols T̶H and th?

ch
th
T̶H

One symbol is not a letter at all. It is called a schwa, and stands for the vowel sound often heard in a syllable that is not accented. The sound represented by the schwa may be *spelled* with any of the five vowel letters, as in the examples.

ə

Most dictionaries include a few foreign words. These special symbols are used to represent sounds which occur in foreign words but not in English.

Y N
œ H

This short key, which appears on each right-hand page of the Glossary, includes the pronunciation symbols you need to refer to most often.

hat, āge, fär; let, bē, tėrm; it, īce; hot, gō, ôrder; oil, out; cup, put, rüle; ch, child; ng, long;
th, thin; T̶H, then; zh, measure; ə represents *a* in about, *e* in taken, *i* in April, *o* in lemon, *u* in circus.

GLOSSARY
COMPLETE PRONUNCIATION KEY

The pronunciation of each word is shown just after the word, in this way: **ab-bre vi ate** (ə brē′vē āt). The letters and signs used are pronounced as in the words below. The mark ′ is placed after a syllable with primary or strong accent, as in the example above. The mark ′ after a syllable shows a secondary or lighter accent, as in **ab bre vi a tion** (ə brē′vē ā′shən).

Some words, taken from foreign languages, are spoken with sounds that otherwise do not occur in English. Symbols for these sounds are given at the bottom of the page as "Foreign Sounds."

a	hat, cap	j	jam, enjoy	u	cup, butter
ā	age, face	k	kind, seek	ù	full, put
ä	father, far	l	land, coal	ü	rule, move
		m	me, am		
b	bad, rob	n	no, in		
ch	child, much	ng	long, bring		
d	did, red			v	very, save
		o	hot, rock	w	will, woman
		ō	open, go	y	young, yet
e	let, best	ô	order, all	z	zero, breeze
ē	equal, see	oi	oil, voice	zh	measure, seizure
ėr	term, learn	ou	house, out		
		p	paper, cup		
f	fat, if	r	run, try	ə represents:
g	go, bag	s	say, yes	a in about
h	he, how	sh	she, rush	e in taken
		t	tell, it	i in April
i	it, pin	th	thin, both	o in lemon
ī	ice, five	ŦH	then, smooth	u in circus

foreign sounds

Y as in French *du*. Pronounce ē with the lips rounded as for English ü in **rule**

N as in French *bon*. The N is not pronounced, but shows that the vowel before it is nasal.

œ as in French *peu*. Pronounce ā with the lips rounded as for ō.

H as in German *ach*. Pronounce k without closing the breath passage.

Pronunciation key from the *Thorndike-Barnhart Advanced Junior Dictionary,* copyright © 1968 by Scott, Foresman and Company.

abandon   apprehend

a ban don (ə ban′dən),   **1.** give up entirely: *She abandoned her hope of becoming a nurse.* **2.** leave without intending to return to; desert: *A good mother will not abandon her baby.* **3.** yield (oneself) completely (to a feeling, impulse, etc.): *abandon oneself to grief.* **4.** freedom from restraint; lack of self-control: *The students cheered with abandon, waving their arms and shouting.* 1-3 *v.,*   4 *n.*

a bash (ə bash′),   embarrass and confuse; make uneasy and somewhat ashamed.   *v.*

ab hor (ab hôr′),   shrink away from with horror; feel disgust or hate for; detest: *Some people abhor snakes.*   *v.,* **ab horred, ab hor ring.**

a bound (ə bound′),   be plentiful: *Fish abound in the ocean.*   *v.*

ab sent ly (ab′sənt lē),   without paying attention to what is going on around one; inattentively.   *adv.*

ab surd (ab sèrd′),   plainly not true or sensible; so contrary to reason that it is laughable; foolish; ridiculous.   *adj.* **—ab surd′ly,** *adv.*

ac cu sa tion (ak′yə zā′shən),   **1.** a charge of having done something wrong, of being something bad, or of having broken the law. **2.** the offense charged.   *n.*

ad e quate (ad′ə kwit),   **1.** as much as is needed; fully sufficient: *His wages are adequate to support three people.* **2.** suitable; competent: *an adequate person for the job.*   *adj.* **—ad′e quate ly,** *adv.* **—ad′e quate ness,** *n.*

ad ver si ty (ad vèr′sə tē),   **1.** condition of unhappiness, misfortune, or distress. **2.** stroke of misfortune; unfavorable or harmful thing or event.   *n., pl.* **ad ver si ties.**

adz or **adze** (adz),   tool somewhat like an ax but with a blade set across the end of the handle and curving inward.   *n.*

af fa ble (af′ə bəl),   easy to talk to; courteous and pleasant.   *adj.* **—af′fa ble ness,** *n.* **—af′fa bly,** *adv.*

af front (ə frunt′),   **1.** insult openly; offend purposely: *The boy affronted the teacher by making a face at her.* **2.** a word or act that openly expresses intentional disrespect: *To be called a coward is an affront to a manly boy.* **3.** offend the modesty or self-respect of: *The people of the village were affronted by the superior airs of the wealthy newcomer.* **4.** a slight or injury to one's dignity. 1,3 *v.,*   2,4 *n.*

a gape (ə gāp′),   **1.** gaping; with the mouth wide open in wonder or surprise. **2.** wide open.   *adv., adj.*

ag gran dize (ə gran′dīz or ag′rən dīz),   increase in power, wealth, rank, etc.; make greater: *The dictator sought to aggrandize himself at the expense of his people.*   *v.*

ag gres sive (ə gres′iv),   **1.** taking the first step in an attack or quarrel; attacking; quarrelsome: *An aggressive country is always ready to start a war.* **2.** *U.S.* active; energetic: *The police are making an aggressive campaign against crime.*   *adj.* **—ag gres′sive ly,** *adv.* **—ag gres′siveness,** *n.*

a ghast (ə gast′),   filled with horror; frightened; terrified.   *adj.*

ag i tate (aj′ə tāt),   **1.** move or shake: *The slightest wind will agitate the leaves of some trees.* **2.** disturb; excite (the feelings or the thoughts of): *She was much agitated by the news of her brother's death.*   *v.*

a jar (ə jär′),   slightly open: *Leave the door ajar.*   *adv., adj.*

al lege (ə lej′),   **1.** assert without proof. **2.** state positively; assert; declare: *This man alleges that his watch has been stolen.*   *v.*

al le vi ate (ə lē′vē āt),   make easier to endure; relieve; lessen: *Heat often alleviates pain.*   *v.*

a loof (ə lüf′),   **1.** at a distance; withdrawn; apart: *One boy stood aloof from all the others.* **2.** unsympathetic; not interested; reserved: *Because of her shyness Jane seemed to be a very aloof girl.* 1 *adv.,*   2 *adj.*

am i ca ble (am′ə kə bəl),   peaceable; friendly.   *adj.* **—am′i ca bly,** *adv.*

an tag o nism (an tag′ə niz əm),   active opposition; conflict; hostility.   *n.*

ante-,   prefix meaning: before, as in *antedate, anteroom.*

an thro pol o gist (an′thrə pol′ə jist),   expert in anthropology.   *n.*

an thro pol o gy (an′thrə pol′ə jē),   science that deals with the origin, development, races, customs, and beliefs of mankind.   *n.*

anti-,   prefix meaning:
1. against; opposed to ——: *Anti-aircraft = against aircraft.*
2. not; the opposite of ——: *Antisocial = the opposite of social.*

an tic i pate (an tis′ə pāt),   **1.** look forward to; expect: *He had anticipated a good vacation in the mountains; but when the time came, he was sick.* **2.** do, make, or use in advance: *The Chinese anticipated some modern discoveries.* **3.** take care of ahead of time: *The nurse anticipated all the patient's wishes.*   *v.*

an tic i pa tion (an tis′ə pā′shən),   act of anticipating; looking forward to; expectation.   *n.*

an ti cli max (an′tē klī′maks),   **1.** an abrupt descent from the important to the trivial. *Example:* "Alas! Alas! what shall I do? I've lost my wife and best hat, too!" **2.** descent (in importance, interest, etc.) contrasting with a previous rise.   *n.*

a pex (ā′peks),   **1.** the highest point; tip: *the apex of a triangle.* **2.** climax.   *n., pl.* **a pex es** or **ap i ces.**

ap pa ri tion (ap′ə rish′ən),   **1.** ghost; phantom. **2.** something strange, remarkable, or unexpected which comes into view.   *n.*

ap praise (ə prāz′),   **1.** estimate the value, amount, quality, etc., of: *An employer should be able to appraise ability and character.* **2.** set a price on; fix the value of: *Property is appraised for taxation.*   *v.* **—ap prais′ing ly,** *adv.*

ap pre hend (ap′ri hend′),   **1.** look forward to with fear; fear; dread: *A guilty man apprehends danger in every sound.* **2.** arrest: *The thief was apprehended and put in jail.* **3.** understand; grasp with the mind: *I apprehended his meaning more from his gestures than from the queer sounds he made.*   *v.*

Glossary entries are based on the *Thorndike-Barnhart Advanced Junior Dictionary,* copyright © 1968 by Scott, Foresman and Company.

550

ap pre hen sion (ap′ri hen′shən),   1. expectation of evil; fear; dread: *The roar of the hurricane filled us with apprehension.*   2. a seizing; being seized; arrest: *apprehension of a thief. n.*

ap pre hen sive (ap′ri hen′siv),   1. afraid; anxious; worried.   2. quick to understand; able to learn.   *adj.*   **—ap′pre hen′sive ly,** *adv.* **—ap′pre hen′sive ness,** *n.*

ap pro pri ate (ə prō′prē it for 1; ə prō′prē-āt for 2,3),   1. suitable; proper: *Plain, simple clothes are appropriate for school wear.*   2. set apart for some special use: *The government appropriated money for roads.*   3. take for oneself: *You should not appropriate other people's belongings without their permission.*   1 *adj.,*   2,3 *v.*

aq ui line (ak′wə lin),   1. of or like an eagle.   2. curved like an eagle's beak; hooked: *an aquiline nose. adj.*

ar bo re al (är bô′rē əl),   1. of trees; like trees.   2. living in or among trees: *A squirrel is an arboreal animal. adj.*

a re na (ə rē′nə),   space where contests or shows take place: *Men fought with lions in the arena of the great amphitheater at Rome. n.*

a ris to crat ic (ə ris′tə krat′ik),   1. belonging to the upper classes; superior in birth, intelligence, culture, or wealth.   2. like an aristocrat in manners; proud. *adj.*

ar tic u late (är tik′yə lit for 1,3; är tik′yə lāt for 2),   1. uttered in distinct syllables of words: *A baby cries and gurgles, but does not use articulate speech.*   2. speak distinctly: *Be careful to articulate your words so that everyone in the room can understand you.*   3. able to put one's thoughts into words: *Julia is the most articulate of the sisters.*   1,3 *adj.,*   2 *v.*

as cer tain (as′ər tān′),   find out; determine: *John telephoned home to ascertain if his father had arrived. v.*

as pect (as′pekt),   1. one side or part or view (of a subject): *We must consider this plan in its various aspects.*   2. look; appearance: *I love the ocean in all its aspects, even its stormy, frightening aspect in winter. n.*

as per i ty (as per′ə tē),   roughness; harshness; severity: *the asperities of a very cold winter. We all noticed the asperity in our teacher's voice. n., pl.* **as per i ties.**

as sent (ə sent′),   1. express agreement; agree.   2. acceptance of a proposal, statement, etc.; agreement: *Jane smiled her assent to the plan.*   1 *v.,*   2 *n.*

as suage (ə swāj′),   1. make easier or milder; quiet; calm: *assuage pain.*   2. satisfy; appease; quench: *assuage thirst. v.*

as sur ance (ə shür′əns),   1. a making sure or certain.   2. positive declaration inspiring confidence: *Mother has given me her assurance that I may go to the circus.*   3. security; certainty; confidence: *We have the assurance of final victory.*   4. self-confidence: *Joe's hard studying has given him considerable assurance in school. n.*

as sure (ə shür′),   1. make sure or certain: *The*

man assured himself that the bridge was safe before crossing it.*   2. tell positively: *The captain of the ship assured the passengers that there was no danger. v.*

as trol o gy (ə strol′ə jē),   study of the stars and planets to reveal their supposed influence on persons, events, etc., and foretell what will happen. *n.*

au da cious (ô dā′shəs),   1. bold; daring.   2. too bold; impudent. *adj.* **—au da′cious ly,** *adv.*

au di ble (ô′də bəl),   capable of being heard; loud enough to be heard: *She spoke in such a low voice that her remarks were barely audible. adj.*

au top sy (ô′top sē),   medical examination of a dead body to find the cause of death. *n.*

a ver sion (ə vèr′zhən),   1. a strong or fixed dislike.   2. unwillingness. *n.*

bait (bāt),   1. anything, especially food, used to attract fish or other animals so that they may be caught.   2. put bait on (a hook) or in (a trap).   3. thing used to tempt or attract.   4. torment or worry by unkind or annoying remarks.   1,3 *n.,* 2,4 *v.*

beige (bāzh),   pale brown; brownish gray. *n., adj.*

be muse (bi myüz′),   confuse; bewilder; stupefy. *v.*

ben e dic tion (ben′ə dik′shən),   1. the asking of God's blessings at the end of a church service.   2. blessing. *n.*

ben e fac tor (ben′ə fak′tər or ben′ə fak′tər),   person who has given money or kindly help. *n.*

ben e fi cial (ben′ə fish′əl),   favorable; helpful; productive of good: *Sunshine and moisture are beneficial to plants. adj.* **—ben′e fi′cial ly,** *adv.*

ben e fit (ben′ə fit),   1. anything which is for the good of a person or thing; advantage.   2. do good to; be good for: *Rest will benefit a sick person.*   3. receive good; profit: *He benefited by the medicine.*   1 *n.,*   2,3 *v.*

bide (bīd),   *Archaic.*   1. dwell; abide.   2. continue; wait. *v.*

blan dish ment (blan′dish mənt),   coaxing; flattery. *n.*

blas pheme (blas fēm′),   speak about (God or sacred things) with abuse or contempt; utter blasphemy. *v.*

bleak (blēk),   1. swept by winds; bare: *bleak and rocky mountain peaks.*   2. chilly; cold: *a bleak wind.*   3. dreary; dismal. *adj.*

blun der (blun′dər),   make a stupid mistake. *v.*

boarding house,   house where meals, or room and meals, are provided for pay.

bode (bōd),   be a sign of; indicate beforehand: *Dark clouds boded rain. v.,* **bod ed, bod ing.**

bode ill,   be a bad sign.

bode well,   be a good sign.

bois ter ous (bois′tər əs),   1. noisily cheerful: *a boisterous game.*   2. violent; rough: *a boisterous wind, a boisterous child. adj.*

bran dish (bran′dish),   wave or shake threat-

hat, āge, fär; let, bē, tèrm; it, īce; hot, gō, ôrder; oil, out; cup, put, rüle; ch, child; ng, long; th, thin; ℟H, then; zh, measure; ə represents *a* in about, *e* in taken, *i* in April, *o* in lemon, *u* in circus.

eningly; flourish: *The knight drew his sword and brandished it at his enemy.* *v.*

bra va do (brə vä′dō), a great show of boldness without much real courage. *n.*

breach (brēch), a breaking (of a law, promise, duty, etc.); neglect: *For me to go away today would be a breach of duty.* *n.*

brit tle (brit′l), very easily broken; breaking with a snap; apt to break: *Thin glass and ice are brittle.* *adj.* —**brit′tle ness,** *n.*

brood (brüd), **1.** think a long time about some one thing. **2.** dwell on in thought: *For years he brooded vengeance.* *v.*

brood on or **over,** **1.** keep thinking about. **2.** hover over; hang close over.

bunt (bunt), **1.** hit (a baseball) lightly so that the ball goes to the ground and rolls only a short distance. **2.** a baseball hit made in this way. 1 *v.*, 2 *n.*

buoy (boi or bü′ē), **1.** a floating object anchored in a certain place on the water to warn or guide. It marks hidden rocks or shallows, shows the safe part of the channel, etc. **2.** a cork belt, ring or jacket to keep a person from sinking; life buoy. *n.*

bur ro (bėr′ō or búr′ō), in the southwestern United States, a kind of small, agile donkey, used to carry camping equipment, etc. *n., pl.* **bur ros.**

ca jole (kə jōl′), persuade by pleasant words, flattery, or false promises; coax. *v.*

cal cu late (kal′kyə lāt), **1.** find out by adding, subtracting, multiplying, or dividing; figure: *calculate the cost of furnishing a house.* **2.** find out beforehand by any process of reasoning; estimate: *calculate the day of the week on which Christmas will fall.* **3.** *U.S. Informal.* plan; intend: *That remark was calculated to hurt someone's feelings.* *v*

cal cu lat ing (kal′kyə lāt′ing), **1.** shrewd; careful. **2.** scheming; selfish. *adj.*

cal i ber or **cal i bre** (kal′ə bər), **1.** diameter, especially inside diameter. **2.** amount of ability: *The president of a railroad or a big factory should be a man of high caliber.* *n.*

cane brake (kān′brāk′), thicket of cane plants. *n.*

can non eer (kan′ən ir′), artilleryman; gunner. *n.*

can tan ker ous (kan tang′kər əs), hard to get along with because ready to make trouble and oppose anything suggested; ill-natured. *adj.*

cap tor (kap′tər), person who takes or holds a prisoner. *n.*

car di nal (kärd′n əl), of first importance; main; chief; principal. *adj.*

car i bou (kar′ə bü), any of several kinds of North American reindeer. *n., pl.* **car i bous** or (*esp. collectively*) **car i bou.**

Caribou (4 ft. high at the shoulder)

car nage (kär′nij), slaughter of a great number of people. *n.*

caste (kast), **1.** a Hindu social class. By tradition, a Hindu is born into the caste of his father and cannot rise from it. **2.** an exclusive social group; distinct class. *n.*

cas u al (kazh′ü əl), **1.** happening by chance; not planned or expected; accidental: *a casual meeting.* **2.** without plan or method; careless: *a casual answer, a casual glance.* **3.** uncertain; indefinite; indifferent; vague. **4.** occasional; irregular. **5.** designed for informal wear: *We dressed in casual clothes for the picnic.* *adj.* —**cas′u al ly,** *adv.*

cat walk (kat′wôk′), a narrow place to walk, as along a bridge or over the stage in a theater. *n.*

cau ter ize (kô′tər īz), burn with a hot iron or a substance that burns or destroys flesh. Doctors sometimes cauterize wounds to prevent bleeding or infection. *v.*

cav a lier (kav′ə lir′), **1.** a courteous gentleman. **2.** a courteous escort for a lady. *n.*

ca vort (kə vôrt′), *U.S. Informal.* prance about; jump around: *The horses cavorted with excitement.* *v.*

cay use (kī yüs′), an Indian pony of the Western United States. *n.*

ce les tial (sə les′chəl), **1.** of the sky; having to do with the heavens: *The sun, moon, planets, and stars are celestial bodies.* **2.** heavenly; divine; very good or beautiful: *celestial music.* *adj.*

chasm (kaz′əm), **1.** a deep opening or crack in the earth; gap. **2.** a wide difference of feelings or interests between people or groups: *The chasm between England and the American colonies grew wider and wider until it finally resulted in the American Revolution.* *n.*

chink (chingk), **1.** a narrow opening; crack; slit: *The chinks between the logs of the cabin let in the wind and snow.* **2.** fill up the chinks in. 1 *n.*, 2 *v.*

cir cu late (sėr′kyə lāt), **1.** go around; pass from place to place or person to person: *Water circulates in the pipes of a building. Money circulates as it goes from person to person.* **2.** be distributed: *A newspaper circulates among people who read it.* **3.** of the blood, to flow from the heart through the arteries and veins back to the heart again. *v.*

clam ber (klam′bər), **1.** climb, using both hands and feet; climb awkwardly or with difficulty; scramble. **2.** an awkward or difficult climb. 1 *v.*, 2 *n.*

clam or (klam′ər), **1.** a loud noise, continual uproar; shouting. **2.** make a loud noise or continual uproar; shout. **3.** a noisy demand or complaint. **4.** demand or complain noisily: *The children were clamoring for candy.* 1,3 *n.*, 2,4 *v.*

cloy (kloi), **1.** weary by too much, too sweet, or too rich food. **2.** weary by too much of anything pleasant. *v.*

co-, prefix meaning:
1. with; together: *Coöperate = act with or together.*
2. joint; fellow: *Coauthor = joint or fellow author.*
3. equally: *Coextensive = equally extensive.*

col lab o rate (kə lab′ə rāt), work together:

Two authors collaborated on that book. *v.*, **col lab o rat ed, col lab o rat ing.**

col league (kol´ēg), an associate; fellow worker: *His colleagues taught his classes while he was ill.* *n.*

com i cal (kom´ə kəl), amusing; funny. *adj.*

com mence (kə mens´), begin; start: *The dedication ceremonies will commence at two o'clock.* *v.*, **com menced, com menc ing.**

com men da tion (kom´ən dā´shən), **1.** praise; approval. **2.** favorable mention; recommendation. **3.** a handing over to another for safekeeping; entrusting. *n.*

com pass (kum´pəs), **1.** instrument for showing directions. **2.** boundary; circumference: *A prison is within the compass of its walls.* **3.** space within limits; extent; range: *The old sailor had many adventures within the compass of his lifetime.* **4.** range of a voice or musical instrument. **5.** circuit; going around. *n.*

Compass for showing directions. It is about the size of a watch. When the needle points to N, the person holding the compass is facing north.

com pat i ble (kəm pat´ə bəl), able to exist together; that can get on well together; agreeing; in harmony: *Health and hard work are compatible.* *adj.* —**com pat´i bly,** *adv.*

com ply (kəm plī´), act in agreement with a request or a command: *We should comply with the doctor's request.* *v.*, **com plied, com ply ing.**

com pound (kom´pound or kom pound´ for 1; kom´pound for 2; kom pound´ for 3,4), **1.** having more than one part: *A clover leaf is a compound leaf.* *"Steamship" is a compound word.* **2.** something made by combining parts; mixture: *A medicine is usually a compound.* **3.** mix; combine: *The man in the drugstore compounds medicines and drinks.* **4.** to increase; multiply. 1 *adj.*, 2 *n.*, 3,4 *v.*

com pre hen sion (kom´pri hen´shən), act or power of understanding; ability to get the meaning: *Arithmetic is beyond the comprehension of a baby.* *n.*

con ceal (kən sēl´), **1.** hide. **2.** keep secret. *v.* —**con ceal´a ble,** *adj.* —**con ceal´er,** *n.*

con ceiv a ble (kən sēv´ə bəl), that can be conceived or thought of; imaginable: *We take every conceivable precaution against fire.* *adj.* —**con ceiv´a bly,** *adv.*

con clude (kən klüd´), **1.** end; finish: *The book concluded happily.* **2.** arrange; settle: *The two countries concluded an agreement on trade.* **3.** find out by thinking; reach (certain facts or opinions) as a result of reasoning; infer: *From the tracks we saw we concluded that the animal must have been a deer.* *v.*, **con clud ed, con clud ing.**

con cus sion (kən kush´ən), **1.** a sudden, violent shaking; shock: *The concussion caused by the explosion broke many windows.* **2.** an injury to the brain, spine, etc., caused by a blow, fall, or other shock. *n.*

con de scend (kon´di send´), **1.** come down willingly or graciously to the level of one's inferiors in rank: *The king condescended to eat with the beggars.* **2.** grant a favor with a patronizing attitude. *v.*

con de scen sion (kon´di sen´shən), **1.** pleasantness to inferiors. **2.** a patronizing attitude. *n.*

con di tion al (kən dish´ən əl), depending on something else; not absolute; limited. *adj.*

con fi den tial (kon´fə den´shəl), **1.** told or written as a secret: *The detective made a confidential report.* **2.** showing confidence. **3.** trusted with secrets, private affairs, etc.: *a confidential secretary.* *adj.*

con fi den tial ly (kon´fə den´shəl ē), in a confidential manner. *adv.*

con firm (kən fėrm´), **1.** prove to be true or correct; make certain: *confirm a rumor. The written order confirmed his telephone message.* **2.** approve by formal consent; approve; consent to: *The Senate confirmed the treaty.* **3.** strengthen; make firmer: *A sudden storm confirmed my decision not to leave.* *v.*

con geal (kən jēl´), **1.** freeze. **2.** thicken; stiffen: *The blood around the wound had congealed.* *v.*

con jure (kən jür´ for 1; kun´jər or kon´jər for 2), **1.** make a solemn appeal to: *By all that is holy, I conjure you not to betray your country.* **2.** compel to appear or disappear by magic words: *Nowadays we do not try to conjure up spirits or devils.* *v.*, **con jured, con jur ing.** **conjure up,** to cause to appear in the mind.

con scious (kon´shəs), **1.** aware; knowing: *He was conscious of a sharp pain.* **2.** able to feel: *After about five minutes he became conscious again.* *adj.*

con se quence (kon´sə kwens), **1.** result; effect: *The consequence of his fall was a broken leg.* **2.** importance: *The loss of that old hat is a matter of little consequence.* **3.** importance in rank or position: *a man of little consequence.* *n.*

con sid er ate (kən sid´ər it), thoughtful of others and their feelings. *adj.*

con strain (kən strān´), **1.** force; compel. **2.** confine; imprison. *v.*

con strict (kən strikt´), draw together; contract; compress: *A rubber band constricts what it encircles.* *v.*

con tem plate (kon´təm plāt), **1.** look at for a long time; gaze at. **2.** think about for a long time; study carefully: *I will contemplate your proposal.* **3.** meditate: *All day he did nothing but contemplate.* **4.** have in mind; intend: *She is contemplating a change of work.* *v.*

con tempt (kən tempt´), the feeling that a person, act, or thing is mean, low, or worthless; scorn; a despising: *We feel contempt for a liar.* *n.*

con temp tu ous (kən temp´chü əs), showing contempt; scornful: *a contemptuous look.* *adj.* —**con temp´tu ous ly,** *adv.*

con tort (kən tôrt´), twist or bend out of shape; distort: *The clown contorted his face.* *v.*

con trive (kən trīv´), **1.** invent; design: *con-*

---

hat, āge, fär; let, bē, tėrm; it, īce; hot, gō, ôrder; oil, out; cup, pút, rüle; ch, child; ng, long; th, thin; ŦH, then; zh, measure; ə represents *a* in about, *e* in taken, *i* in April, *o* in lemon, *u* in circus.

trive a new kind of engine. **2.** plan; scheme; plot: *contrive a robbery.* **3.** bring about. *v.*

con verge (kən vėrj′), **1.** tend to meet in a point. **2.** turn toward each other: *If you look at the end of your nose, your eyes converge.* **3.** come together; center: *The interest of all the students converged upon the celebration.* **4.** cause to converge. *v.*, **con verged, con verg ing.**

cope (kōp), fight with some degree of success; struggle on even terms; deal successfully: *She was too weak to cope with the extra work.* *v.*, **coped, cop ing.**

cor rupt (kə rupt′), **1.** evil; wicked. **2.** make evil or wicked: *Bad company may corrupt a good boy.* **3.** influenced by bribes; dishonest: *a corrupt judge.* **4.** bribe. **5.** damaged by inaccurate copying, insertions, alterations, or the like: *The manuscript is so corrupt that parts of it make no sense at all.* **6.** considered inferior by some because of change in meaning or form, or deviation from standard usage: *Some Indians speak corrupt Spanish.* **7.** rotten; decayed. 1,3,5-7 *adj.*, 2,4 *v.* —**cor rupt′er,** *n.* —**cor rupt′ly,** *adv.* —**cor rupt′ness,** *n.*

coup (kü), a sudden, brilliant action; unexpected, clever move; master stroke. *n., pl.* **coups** (küz).

cow (kou), make afraid; frighten. *v.*

cow er (kou′ər), **1.** crouch in fear or shame. **2.** draw back tremblingly from another's threats, blows, etc. *v.*

cowl ing (koul′ing), a metal covering over the engine of an airplane. *n.*

coy (koi), **1.** shy; modest; bashful. **2.** pretending to be shy. **3.** *Archaic.* reluctant; slow. *adj.*

craft y (kraf′tē), skillful in deceiving others; sly; tricky: *a crafty fox, a crafty villain.* *adj.*, **craft i er, craft i est.** —**craft′i ly,** *adv.*

crane (krān), **1.** machine with a long, swinging arm, for lifting and moving heavy weights. **2.** a large wading bird

Crane for lifting

with very long legs and a long neck. **3.** stretch (the neck) as a crane does, in order to see better. 1,2 *n.*, 3 *v.*, **craned, cran ing.**

crave (krāv), **1.** long for; yearn for; desire strongly: *The thirsty man craved water.* **2.** ask earnestly; beg: *crave a favor.* *v.*, **craved, crav ing.**

cre den tials (kri den′shəlz), letters of introduction; references: *After showing his credentials, the new inspector was allowed to see the bank's records.* *n.pl.*

cred u lous (krej′ə ləs), too ready to believe; easily deceived. *adj.* —**cred′u lous ly,** *adv.*

cre scen do (krə shen′dō), **1.** any gradual increase in force or intensity: *The hurricane reached its crescendo at midnight.* **2.** in music, a gradual increase in force or loudness. *n., pl.* **cre scen dos.**

cru ci fy (krü′sə fī), **1.** put to death by nailing or binding the hands and feet to a cross. **2.** treat severely; torture. *v.*, **cru ci fied, cru ci fy ing.**

cruise (krüz), **1.** sail about from place to place on pleasure or business; sail over or about: *The destroyer cruised along the shore looking for enemy submarines.* **2.** journey or travel from place to place. **3.** fly in an airplane at the speed of maximum efficiency. *v.*

cul mi na tion (kul′mə nā′shən), **1.** the highest point; climax. **2.** a reaching of the highest point. *n.*

cum ber some (kum′bər səm), hard to manage; clumsy; burdensome: *The armor worn by knights seems cumbersome to us today.* *adj.*

cun ning (kun′ing), **1.** clever in deceiving; sly: *a cunning villain.* **2.** slyness in getting what one wants; cleverness in deceiving one's enemies: *A fox has a great deal of cunning.* **3.** skillful; clever: *The old watch was a fine example of cunning workmanship.* 1,3 *adj.*, 2 *n.* —**cun′ning ly,** *adv.*

cu ra tor (kyu rā′tər), person in charge of all or part of a museum, library, etc. *n.*

cu ri ous (kyur′ē əs), **1.** eager to know: *a curious student.* **2.** too eager to know; prying: *The old woman is too curious about other people's business.* **3.** strange; odd; unusual: *a curious old book.* *adj.* —**cu′ri ous ly,** *adv.*

cus tom ar i ly (kus′təm er′ə lē or kus′təm ar′ə lē), in a customary manner; usually. *adv.*

cyn i cal (sin′ə kl), **1.** doubting the sincerity and goodness of others. **2.** sneering; sarcastic. *adj.* —**cyn′i cal ly,** *adv.* —**cyn′i cal ness,** *n.*

cyn i cism (sin′ə siz əm), **1.** cynical quality or disposition. **2.** a cynical remark. *n.*

daft (daft), **1.** silly; foolish. **2.** crazy; insane. *adj.* —**daft′ly,** *adv.* —**daft′ness,** *n.*

dark (därk), **1.** without light; with very little light: *a dark night.* **2.** absence of light. **3.** night; nightfall. **4.** not light-colored: *a dark complexion.* **5.** secret; hidden: *a dark plan.* **6.** evil; wicked: *a dark deed.* **7.** gloomy; dull; dismal: *a dark day.* **8.** sad; sullen; frowning: *a dark face.* 1,4,5-8 *adj.*, 2,3 *n.* —**dark′ly,** *adv.* —**dark′ness,** *n.*

de bris or **dé bris** (də brē′), **1.** scattered fragments; ruins; rubbish. **2.** a mass of fragments of rock, etc.: *the debris left by a glacier.* *n.*

de ceased (di sēst′), dead. *adj.*
the deceased, a (particular) dead person.

de cep tion (di sep′shən), **1.** act of deceiving. **2.** state of being deceived. **3.** thing that deceives; illusion. **4.** trick meant to deceive; fraud; sham. *n.*

de crep it (di krep′it), broken down or weakened by old age; old and feeble. *adj.*

ded i cate (ded′ə kāt), **1.** set apart for a sacred or solemn purpose: *The land on which the battle of Gettysburg was fought was dedicated to the memory of the soldiers who had died there.* **2.** give up wholly or earnestly to some person or purpose. **3.** address (a book, poem, etc.) to a friend or patron as a mark of affection, respect, gratitude, etc. *v.*

de duc tion (di duk′shən), **1.** act of taking away; subtraction. **2.** amount deducted. **3.** inference from a general rule or principle. *Example:*

All animals die; a cat is an animal; therefore, a cat will die. **4.** conclusion: *Sherlock Holmes made brilliant deductions.* *n.*

def er en tial (def′ər en′shəl), showing deference; respectful. *adj.* —**def′er en′tial ly,** *adv.*

de fi ance (di fī′əns), a defying; a standing up against authority and refusing to recognize or obey it; open resistance to power: *He shouted defiance at the enemy.* *n.*

de fi ant (di fī′ənt), showing defiance; challenging; openly resisting. *adj.* —**de fi′ant ly,** *adv.*

de fi cient (di fish′ənt), **1.** incomplete; defective. **2.** not sufficient in quantity, force, etc.: *This milk is deficient in fat.* *adj.*

de flate (di flāt′), **1.** let air or gas out of (a balloon, tire, football, etc.); collapse. **2.** reduce the amount of; reduce: *deflate prices, deflate currency.* *v.*, **de flat ed, de flat ing.**

de form i ty (di fôr′mə tē), **1.** part that is not properly formed. **2.** condition of being improperly formed. **3.** ugliness. *n., pl.* **de form i ties.**

deft (deft), skillful; nimble: *The fingers of a violinist are deft.* *adj.* —**deft′ly,** *adv.*

de grade (di grād′), **1.** reduce to a lower rank; take away a position, an honor, etc., from: *The captain was degraded for disobeying orders.* **2.** make worse; lower; debase: *You degrade yourself when you tell a lie.* *v.*

del i ca cy (del′ə kə sē), **1.** delicate quality or nature; slightness and grace: *the delicacy of lace, the delicacy of a flower, the delicacy of a baby's skin.* **2.** fineness of feeling for small differences; sensitiveness: *delicacy of hearing or touch.* **3.** thought or regard for the feelings of others. **4.** a choice kind of food; a dainty. *n., pl.* **del i ca cies.**

de lir i ous (di lir′ē əs), **1.** temporarily out of one's senses; wandering in mind; raving. **2.** wildly excited. *adj.* —**de lir′i ous ly,** *adv.*

de louse (dē lous′ or dē louz′), remove lice from. *v.*, **de loused, de lous ing.**

de mer it (dē mer′it), **1.** fault; defect. **2.** mark against a person's record for poor work or unsatisfactory behavior. *n.*

de mure (di myür′), **1.** artificially proper; assuming an air of modesty; coy: *the demure smile of a flirt.* **2.** serious; thoughtful; sober: *The Puritan maid was demure.* *adj.* —**de mure′ly,** *adv.* —**de mure′ness,** *n.*

dense (dens), **1.** closely packed together; thick: *a dense fog, a dense growth of weeds.* **2.** stupid. *adj.*, **dens er, dens est.** —**dense′ly,** *adv.* —**dense′ness,** *n.*

de pre ci a tion (di prē′shē ā′shən), **1.** a lessening or lowering in value. **2.** a loss figured as part of the cost in doing business. **3.** a speaking slightingly of; a belittling. *n.*

der e lict (der′ə likt), **1.** abandoned; deserted; forsaken: *a derelict ship.* **2.** a ship abandoned at sea. **3.** any worthless, deserted person or thing. 1 *adj.*, 2,3 *n.*

de sist (di zist′), stop; cease. *v.*

des o late (des′ə lit), **1.** barren; laid waste;

devastated: *desolate land.* **2.** not lived in; deserted. **3.** left alone; solitary; lonely. **4.** unhappy; wretched; forlorn. *adj.*

de spair (di sper′ or di spar′), **1.** loss of hope; state of being without hope; hopelessness; a feeling that nothing good can happen: *Despair seized us as we felt the boat sinking under us.* **2.** person or thing that causes despair. **3.** lose hope; be without hope: *The doctors despaired of saving the sick man's life.* 1,2 *n.*, 3 *v.*

de spair ing (di sper′ing or di spar′ing), feeling, showing, or expressing despair; hopeless. *adj.* —**de spair′ing ly,** *adv.* —**de spair′ing ness,** *n.*

de vice (di vīs′), **1.** a mechanical invention used for a special purpose. **2.** plan; scheme; trick: *By some device or other he got the boy to let him into the house.* *n.*

de vise (di vīz′), think out; plan; contrive; invent: *The boys devised a scheme for earning money during the summer vacation.* *v.*, **de vised, de vis ing.**

de void (di void′), lacking (*of*): *devoid of sense.* *adj.*

di a lect (dī′ə lekt), **1.** form of speech characteristic of a fairly definite region or class, that varies from the standard language. **2.** one of a group of closely related languages. **3.** words and pronunciations used by certain professions, classes of people, etc. *n.*

dic ta tor (dik′tā tər), person exercising absolute authority; especially, a person who seizes control of a government. *n.*

dic ta to ri al (dik′tə tô′rē əl), **1.** of or like that of a dictator: *dictatorial government.* **2.** domineering; overbearing: *The soldiers disliked the dictatorial manner of that officer.* *adj.* —**dic′ta to′ri al ly,** *adv.*

dif fer en ti ate (dif′ər en′shē āt), **1.** make different: *Consideration for others differentiates good manners from mere politeness.* **2.** perceive the difference in; make a distinction between. *v.*, **dif fer en ti at ed, dif fer en ti at ing.**

dif fi dent (dif′ə dənt), lacking in self-confidence; shy. *adj.* —**dif′fi dent ly,** *adv.*

di lap i dat ed (də lap′ə dāt′id), falling to pieces; partly ruined or decayed through neglect: *a dilapidated house.* *adj.*

di lem ma (də lem′ə), situation requiring a choice between two evils; any embarrassing or perplexing situation; a difficult choice: *Her dilemma was whether to go to the party in her old dress or to stay at home.* *n.*

di men sion (də men′shən), **1.** measurement of length, breadth, or thickness. **2.** size; extent. **3.** characteristic; quality. *part.*

di min u tive (də min′yə tiv), small; little. *adj.*

dirk (dėrk), **1.** dagger. **2.** stab with a dirk. 1 *n.*, 2 *v.*

dis a gree ment (dis′ə grē′mənt), **1.** difference of opinion. **2.** quarrel; dispute. *n.*

dis ci pline (dis′ə plin), **1.** training; especially,

---

hat, āge, fär; let, bē, tèrm; it, īce; hot, gō, ôrder; oil, out; cup, pùt, rüle; ch, child; ng, long; th, thin; ᴛн, then; zh, measure; ə represents *a* in about, *e* in taken, *i* in April, *o* in lemon, *u* in circus.

training of the mind or character. **2.** the training effect of experience, hardship, etc. **3.** a trained condition of order and obedience. **4.** order among school pupils, soldiers, or members of any group: *When the fire broke out, the pupils showed good discipline.* **5.** train; bring to a condition of order and obedience; bring under control. **6.** punishment; chastisement. **7.** punish: *discipline a child for bad behavior.* 1-4,6 *n.,* 5,7 *v.,* **dis ci plined, dis ci plin ing. —dis′ci plin er,** *n.*

dis clo sure (dis klō′zhər), **1.** act of making known. **2.** thing disclosed. *n.*

dis con so late (dis kon′sə lit), without hope; forlorn; unhappy; cheerless. *adj.* **—dis con′so late ly,** *adv.* **—dis con′so late ness,** *n.*

dis cord ant (dis kôrd′nt), **1.** not in harmony: *a discordant note in music.* **2.** not in agreement. **3.** harsh; clashing: *Many automobile horns are discordant.* *adj.* **—dis cord′ant ly,** *adv.*

dis creet (dis krēt′), careful and sensible in speech and action; wisely cautious; showing good sense. *adj.* **—dis creet′ly,** *adv.*

dis crep an cy (dis krep′ən sē), lack of consistency; difference; disagreement: *The lawsuit was lost because of discrepancies in the statements of the witnesses.* *n., pl.* **dis crep an cies.**

dis dain (dis dān′), **1.** look down on; consider beneath oneself; scorn: *The honest official disdained the offer of a bribe.* **2.** act of disdaining; feeling of scorn: *That selfish boy treated his younger brothers with disdain.* 1 *v.,* 2 *n.*

dis em bod y (dis′em bod′ē), separate (a soul, spirit, etc.) from the body: *Ghosts are usually thought of as disembodied spirits.* *v.,* **dis em bodied, dis em bod y ing. —dis′em bod′i ment,** *n.*

dis il lu sioned (dis′i lü′zhənd), having lost faith in ideas or hopes previously held. *adj.*

dis in te grate (dis in′tə grāt), break up; separate into small parts or bits. *v.,* **dis in te grat ed, dis in te grat ing.**

dis mal (diz′məl), **1.** dark; gloomy: *A damp cave or a rainy day is dismal.* **2.** dreary; miserable: *Sickness or bad luck often makes a person feel dismal.* *adj.* **—dis′mal ly,** *adv.*

dis man tle (dis man′tl), pull down; take apart. *v.,* **dis man tled, dis man tling.**

dis per sal (dis pėr′səl), act of scattering or state of being scattered: *the dispersal of a crowd.* *n.*

dis pir it (dis pir′it), to lower the spirits of; depress; discourage; dishearten: *A week of rain dispirited us all.* *v.* **—dis pir′it ed ly,** *adv.*

dis posed (dis pōzd′), willing; inclined. *adj.*

dis sim i lar i ty (di sim′ə lar′ə tē), lack of similarity; unlikeness; difference. *n., pl.* **dis sim i lar i ties.**

dis si pate (dis′ə pāt), **1.** spread in different directions; scatter. **2.** disappear or cause to disappear. **3.** spend foolishly; waste on things of little value. *v.,* **dis si pat ed, dis si pat ing.**

dis tinc tion (dis tingk′shən), **1.** difference: *What is the distinction between ducks and geese?* **2.** point of difference; special quality or feature. **3.** honor: *The soldier served with distinction.* **4.** mark or sign of honor: *He won many distinctions for bravery.* *n.*

dis tin guished (dis ting′gwisht), **1.** famous; well-known: *a distinguished artist.* **2.** having the appearance of an important person. *adj.*

di ver sion (də vėr′zhən), **1.** a turning aside: *High tariffs often cause a diversion of trade from one country to another.* **2.** amusement; entertainment; pastime: *Golf is my father's favorite diversion.* *n.*

doc u men ta ry (dok′yə men′tə rē), **1.** consisting of documents; in writing, print, etc.: *The man's own letters were documentary evidence of his guilt.* **2.** presenting or recording factual information in an artistic fashion: *a documentary film.* **3.** a documentary motion picture. 1,2 *adj.,* 3 *n., pl.* **doc u men ta ries.**

dog ged (dôg′id), stubborn; persistent; not giving up: *In spite of failures he kept on with dogged determination to succeed.* *adj.* **—dog′ged ly,** *adv.* **—dog′ged ness,** *n.*

dom i nate (dom′ə nāt), **1.** control or rule by strength or power: *A man of strong will often dominates others.* **2.** rise high above; hold a commanding position over: *The mountain dominates the harbor.* *v.,* **dom i nat ed, dom i nat ing.**

dregs (dregz), **1.** solid bits of matter that settle to the bottom of a liquid. **2.** the most worthless part: *Thieves and murderers are the dregs of humanity.* *n.pl.*

drib ble (drib′l), **1.** flow or let flow in drops, small amounts, etc.; trickle: *Gasoline dribbled from the leak in the tank.* **2.** let saliva run from the mouth: *The baby dribbles on his bib.* **3.** move (a ball) along by bouncing it or giving it short kicks. *v.* **—drib′bler,** *n.*

drought (drout), a long period of dry weather; continued lack of rain. *n.*

drub (drub), **1.** beat with a stick; whip soundly. **2.** defeat by a large margin in a fight, game, contest, etc. *v.,* **drubbed, drub bing. —drub′ber,** *n.*

drub bing (drub′ing), **1.** a beating. **2.** a thorough defeat. *n.*

drudg er y (druj′ər ē), hard, uninteresting, or disagreeable work. *n., pl.* **drudg er ies.**

du ra tion (dù rā′shən or dyù rā′shən), length of time; time during which anything continues. *n.*

ebb (eb), **1.** a flowing of the tide away from the shore; fall of the tide. **2.** flow out; fall: *We waded farther out as the tide ebbed.* **3.** a growing less or weaker; decline. **4.** point of decline: *His fortunes were at an ebb.* **5.** grow less or weaker; decline: *His courage began to ebb as he neared the haunted house.* 1,3,4 *n.,* 2,5 *v.*

ec sta sy (ek′stə sē), **1.** state of great joy; thrilling or overwhelming delight; rapture. **2.** any strong feeling that completely absorbs the mind; uncontrollable emotion. *n., pl.* **ec sta sies.**

ed i bil i ty (ed′ə bil′ə tē), fitness for eating. *n.*

e dict (ē′dikt), a public order or command by some authority; decree. *n.*

ee rie (ir′ē), **1.** causing fear; strange; weird. **2.** timid because of superstition. *adj.,* **ee ri er, ee ri est. —ee′ri ly,** *adv.* **—ee′ri ness,** *n.*

ef fem i nate (ə fem′ə nit), lacking in manly qualities; showing weakness or delicacy that is not manly. *adj.* —**ef fem′i nate ly,** *adv.*

e jac u late (i jak′yə lāt), say suddenly and briefly; exclaim. *v.*, **e jac u lat ed, e jac u lat ing.**

e lat ed (i lā′tid), in high spirits; joyful; proud. *adj.* —**e lat′ed ly,** *adv.*

e ma ci ate (i mā′shē āt), make unnaturally thin; cause to lose flesh or waste away: *A long illness had emaciated the invalid.* *v.*, **e ma ci at ed, e ma ci at ing.**

em bark (em bärk′), **1.** go on board ship. **2.** set out; start: *After leaving college, the young man embarked upon a business career.* *v.*

em bit ter (em bit′ər), cause to feel bitter or hostile: *The old man was embittered by the loss of his money.* *v.* —**em bit′ter ment,** *n.*

e merge (i mėrj′), come out; come up; come into view: *The sun emerged from behind a cloud. Many facts emerged as a result of the investigation.* *v.*, **e merged, e merg ing.**

em i nent (em′ə nənt), **1.** distinguished; exalted: *Washington was eminent both as general and as President.* **2.** conspicuous; noteworthy: *The judge was a man of eminent fairness.* *adj.*

em phat i cal ly (em fat′ik lē), in a forceful manner. *adv.*

en coun ter (en koun′tər), **1.** meet unexpectedly: *I encountered an old friend on the train.* **2.** a meeting; unexpected meeting. **3.** meet with (difficulties, opposition, etc.). **4.** meet as an enemy; meet in a fight or battle. **5.** a meeting of enemies; fight; battle. 1,3,4 *v.*, 2,5 *n.*

en gulf (en gulf′), swallow up; overwhelm; submerge: *A wave engulfed the small boat.* *v.*

en ig mat ic (en′ig mat′ik), like a riddle; baffling; puzzling; mysterious. *adj.*

en join (en join′), **1.** order; direct; urge: *Parents enjoin good behavior on their children.* **2.** issue an authoritative command. *v.*

e nor mi ty (i nôr′mə tē), **1.** extreme wickedness; outrageousness: *The cruel murderer was put to death for the enormity of his crime.* **2.** an extremely wicked crime; outrageous offense. *n.*

en sign (en′sīn or en′sən for 1; en′sən for 2), **1.** flag; banner. **2.** *U.S.* a navy officer ranking next below a lieutenant, junior grade. An ensign is the lowest commissioned officer in the navy. *n.*

en sue (en sü′), **1.** come after; follow. **2.** happen as a result: *In his anger he hit the man, and a fight ensued.* *v.*, **en sued, en su ing.**

en ter prise (en′tər prīz), **1.** an important, difficult, or dangerous undertaking. **2.** an undertaking; project: *a business enterprise.* **3.** readiness to start projects; courage and energy in starting projects. *n.*

en trance (en trans′), **1.** put into a trance. **2.** fill with joy; delight; charm. *v.*, **en tranced, en tranc ing.** —**en tranc′ing ly,** *adv.*

en vel op (en vel′əp), **1.** wrap; cover: *The baby was so enveloped in blankets that we could hardly see its face.* **2.** surround: *Our soldiers enveloped the enemy and captured them.* **3.** hide; conceal: *Fog enveloped the village.* *v.*, **en vel oped, en vel op ing.**

ep i thet (ep′ə thet), **1.** a descriptive expression. **2.** word or phrase expressing abuse or contempt. *n.*

e qua to ri al (ē′kwə tô′rē əl or ek′wə tô′rē əl), **1.** of, at, or near the equator. **2.** like conditions at or near the equator: *The heat this week was almost equatorial.* *adj.*

eq ui ty (ek′wə tē), **1.** fairness; justice. **2.** what is fair and just. **3.** *Informal.* amount that a property is worth beyond what is owed on it. *n., pl.* **eq ui ties.**

e quiv a lent (i kwiv′ə lənt), **1.** equal in value, measure, force, effect, meaning, etc.: *Nodding your head is equivalent to saying yes.* **2.** something equivalent. 1 *adj.*, 2 *n.*

er rant (er′ənt), **1.** traveling in search of adventure; wandering; roving. **2.** wrong; mistaken; incorrect. *adj.*

er rat i cal ly (ə rat′ik lē), in an irregular or uncertain manner. *adv.*

erst while (ėrst′hwīl′), **1.** *Archaic.* some time ago; in time past; formerly. **2.** former; past. 1 *adv.*, 2 *adj.*

e rup tion (i rup′shən), **1.** a bursting forth. **2.** a throwing forth of lava, etc., from a volcano or of hot water from a geyser. **3.** a breaking out in a rash. **4.** outbreak; outburst. *n.*

es pi o nage (es′pē ə nij or es′pē ə näzh), use of spies; especially, the use of spies by one country to find out the military, political, etc., secrets of another; spying. *n.*

es teem (es tēm′), **1.** have a very favorable opinion of; regard highly: *We esteem courage.* **2.** a very favorable opinion; high regard: *Courage is held in esteem.* 1 *v.*, 2 *n.*

es trange (es trānj′), **1.** turn (a person) from affection to indifference, dislike, or hatred; make unfriendly; separate: *A quarrel had estranged him from his family.* **2.** keep apart; keep away. *v.*, **es tranged, es trang ing.**

es trange ment (es trānj′mənt), **1.** an estranging. **2.** being estranged: *A misunderstanding between the two friends had caused their estrangement.* *n.*

et i quette (et′ə ket), **1.** conventional rules for conduct or behavior in polite society. **2.** formal rules or conventions governing conduct in a profession, official ceremony, etc.: *medical etiquette.* *n.*

e vac u ate (i vak′yü āt), **1.** leave empty; withdraw from: *After surrendering, the soldiers evacuated the fort.* **2.** withdraw; remove: *Efforts were made to evacuate all foreign residents from the war zone.* *v.*, **e vac u at ed, e vac u at ing.**

e vade (i vād′), get away from by trickery; avoid by cleverness: *The thief evaded his pursuers and escaped.* *v.*

e volve (i volv′), develop gradually; work out. *v.*, **e volved, e volv ing.**

ex-, prefix meaning: **1.** out of; from; out, as in *exclude, exit, export.*

---

hat, āge, fär; let, bē, tèrm; it, īce; hot, gō, ôrder; oil, out; cup, pút, rüle; ch, child; ng, long; th, thin; ᴛʜ, then; zh, measure; ə represents *a* in about, *e* in taken, *i* in April, *o* in lemon, *u* in circus.

2. utterly; thoroughly, as in *excruciating, exasperate.*

3. former; formerly, as in *ex-member, ex-president, ex-soldier.*

ex alt (eg zôlt′), **1.** raise in rank, honor, power, character, quality, etc.: *We exalt a man when we elect him President of our country.* **2.** fill with pride, joy, or noble feeling: *An exalted mood is one in which we think noble thoughts. v.*

ex as per ate (eg zas′pər āt), irritate very much; annoy extremely; make angry; vex. *v.,* **ex as per at ed, ex as per at ing.**

ex as per a tion (eg zas′pər ā′shən), extreme annoyance; irritation; anger. *n.*

ex ces sive (ek ses′iv), too much; too great; going beyond what is necessary or right. *adj.*

ex ces sive ly (ek ses′iv lē), too much; too greatly. *adv.*

ex clude (eks klüd′), **1.** shut out; keep out. **2.** drive out and keep out; expel: *Perfect faith excludes doubt. v.*

ex clu sive (eks klü′siv), **1.** each shutting out the other. "Tree" and "animal" are exclusive terms; a thing cannot be both a tree and an animal. **2.** shutting out all or most: *This club is exclusive; only seniors can belong to it.* **3.** very particular about choosing friends, members, patrons, etc. *adj.* —**ex clu′sive ness,** *n.*

ex er tion (eg zėr′shən), effort: *The exertions of the firemen kept the fire from spreading. n.*

ex pe di en cy (eks pē′dē ən sē), **1.** usefulness; suitability for bringing about a desired result; desirability or fitness under the circumstances: *Consider expediency as well as truth in what you say.* **2.** personal advantage; self-interest: *The crafty lawyer was influenced more by expediency than by the love of justice. n., pl.* **ex pe di en cies.**

ex posed (eks pōzd′), **1.** left unprotected; uncovered. **2.** open to view; not concealed. *adj.*

ex po si tion (eks′pə zish′ən), **1.** a public show or exhibition. A world's fair is an exposition. **2.** a detailed explanation. **3.** speech or writing explaining a process or idea. *n.*

ex po sure (eks pō′zhər), a laying open or subjecting to the influence or action of something. *n.*

ex pul sion (eks pul′shən), **1.** an expelling; forcing out: *expulsion of air from the lungs.* **2.** a being expelled or forced out: *Expulsion from school was his punishment for bad behavior. n.*

ex tra cur ric u lar (eks′trə kə rik′yə lər), outside the regular course of study. *adj.*

eye wit ness (ī′wit′nis), person who actually sees or has seen some act or happening, and thus can give testimony concerning it. *n.*

fab u lous (fab′yə ləs), **1.** not believable; amazing. **2.** of or belonging to a fable; imaginary: *The phoenix is a fabulous bird. adj.,* —**fab′u lous ly,** *adv.*

fac ul ty (fak′əl tē), power of the mind or body: *the faculty of hearing, the faculty of memory. Old people sometimes lose their faculties. n., pl.* **fac ul ties.**

false pretenses, *Law.* incorrect or untrue statements made to defraud or cheat.

fal set to (fôl set′ō), an unnaturally high-pitched voice, especially in a man. *n., pl.* **fal set tos.**

fan tas tic (fan tas′tik), **1.** very odd or queer; wild and strange in shape: *The firelight cast weird, fantastic shadows on the walls.* **2.** very fanciful; unreasonable: *The idea that machines could be made to fly seemed fantastic a hundred years ago.* **3.** existing only in the imagination; unreal: *Superstition causes fantastic fears.* **4.** *Informal.* unbelievably good, quick, etc. *adj.* —**fantas′ti cal ly,** *adv.*

fan ta sy (fan′tə sē), **1.** play of the mind; imagination; fancy. **2.** a wild, strange fancy. **3.** picture existing only in the mind; illusion. Fantasies seem real to a delirious person. *n., pl.* **fan ta sies.** Also, **phantasy.**

fat u ous (fach′ü əs), stupid but self-satisfied; foolish; silly. *adj.* —**fat′u ous ly,** *adv.* —**fat′u ous ness,** *n.*

fau na (fô′nə), animals of a given region or time: *the fauna of Australia. n.*

feath er stitch (feᴛʜ′ər stich′), a zigzag embroidery stitch. *n.*

fer vid (fėr′vid), **1.** showing great warmth of feeling; intensely emotional: *a fervid orator.* **2.** intensely hot. *adj.* —**fer′vid ly,** *adv.*

fet tle (fet′l), condition; trim: *The horse is in fine fettle and should win the race. n.*

feud (fyüd), **1.** a long and deadly quarrel between families, tribes, etc., often passed down from generation to generation. **2.** continued strife between two persons, groups, etc. **3.** quarrel. *n.*

flam boy ant (flam boi′ənt), **1.** gorgeously brilliant; flaming: *flamboyant colors.* **2.** very ornate; excessively decorated: *flamboyant architecture.* **3.** bold in putting oneself forward: *a flamboyant person. adj.*

flush (flush), **1.** blush; glow: *The girl flushed when they laughed at her (v.). The flush of sunrise was on the clouds (n.).* **2.** cause to blush or glow: *Exercise flushed his face.* **3.** a sudden rush; rapid flow. **4.** excite; make joyful and proud: *The team was flushed with its first victory.* **5.** a sudden, fresh growth: *April brought the first flush of grass.* **6.** glowing vigor; freshness: *the first flush of youth.* 1,2,4 *v.,* 1,3,5,6 *n.,* —**flush′er,** *n.*

foc us (fō′kəs), **1.** point where rays of light, heat, etc., meet after being reflected. **2.** bring (rays of light, heat, etc.)

Rays of light brought to a focus at F by the lens, L.

to a point: *The lens focused the sun's rays on a piece of paper and burned a hole in it.* **3.** adjust (a lens, the eye, etc.) to make a clear image: *A near-sighted person cannot focus accurately on distant objects.* **4.** the central point of attention, activity etc.: *The new puppy was the focus of attention.* **5.** concentrate: *When studying, he focused his mind on his lessons.* 1,4 *n., pl.* **fo cus es** or **fo ci;** 2,3,5 *v.,* **fo cused, fo cus ing.**

fore bod ing (fôr bōd′ing),   **1.** prediction; warning. **2.** a feeling that something bad is going to happen. *n.*

forge (fôrj),   **1.** place with fire where metal is heated very hot and then hammered into shape. **2.** heat (metal) very hot and then hammer into shape. **3.** make; shape; form. **4.** make or write (something false). **5.** sign (another's name) falsely to deceive. 1 *n.*, 2-5 *v.* —**forg′er**, *n.*

for lorn (fôr lôrn′),   **1.** left alone; neglected; deserted: *The lost kitten, a forlorn little animal, was wet and dirty.* **2.** wretched in feeling or looks; unhappy. **3.** hopeless; desperate. *adj.* —**for lorn′ly**, *adv.* —**for lorn′ness**, *n.*

for mi da ble (fôr′mə də bəl),   hard to overcome; hard to deal with; to be dreaded. *adj.* —**for′mi da bly**, *adv.*

for mu la (fôr′myə lə),   **1.** a set form of words, especially one which by much use has partly lost its meaning: *"How do you do?" is a polite formula.* **2.** rule for doing something, especially as used by those who do not know the reason on which it is based. **3.** recipe; prescription: *a formula for making soap.* **4.** expression showing by chemical symbols the composition of a compound: *The formula for water is* H_2O. **5.** expression showing by algebraic symbols a rule, principle, etc.: $(a+b)^2 = a^2+2ab+b^2$ *is an algebraic formula.* *n., pl.* **for mu las** or **for mu lae**.

for ti tude (fôr′tə tüd or fôr′tə tyüd),   courage in facing pain, danger, or trouble; firmness of spirit. *n.*

fos sil (fos′əl),   **1.** the hardened remains or traces of animals or plants of a former age. Fossils of ferns are found in coal. **2.** forming a fossil; of the nature of a fossil. 1 *n.*, 2 *adj.*

fra cas (frā′kəs),   a noisy quarrel or fight; disturbance; uproar; brawl. *n.*

frag ile (fraj′əl),   easily broken, damaged, or destroyed; delicate; frail. *adj.*

fran tic (fran′tik),   very much excited; wild with rage, fear, pain, grief, etc. *adj.* —**fran′ti cal ly**, *adv.*

frus trate (frus′trāt),   **1.** bring to nothing; make useless or worthless; foil; defeat: *Heavy rain frustrated our plans for a picnic.* **2.** thwart; oppose: *The great artist had never been frustrated in his ambition to paint.* *v.*, **frus trat ed, frus trat ing.**

frus tra tion (frus trā′shən),   a frustrating or being frustrated. *n.*

fur tive (fèr′tiv),   **1.** done stealthily; secret: *a furtive glance into the forbidden room.* **2.** sly; shifty: *The thief had a furtive manner.* *adj.* —**fur′tive ly**, *adv.* —**fur′tive ness**, *n.*

fu tile (fyü′tl),   **1.** not successful; useless: *Many persons have made futile attempts to swim from England to France.* **2.** not important; trifling. *adj.* —**fu′tile ly**, *adv.*

gait (gāt),   kind of steps used in going along; way of walking or running: *He has a lame gait*

because of an injured foot. *A gallop is one of the gaits of a horse.* *n.*

gal lant ry (gal′ən trē),   **1.** noble spirit or conduct; bravery; dashing courage. **2.** great politeness and attention to women. **3.** a gallant act or speech. *n.,-pl.* **gal lant ries.**

Gaul (gôl),   an ancient country in W Europe. It included France, Belgium, the Netherlands, and parts of Switzerland, Germany, and N Italy. *n.*

gaunt (gônt),   **1.** very thin and bony; with hollow eyes and a starved look: *Hunger and suffering make people gaunt.* **2.** looking bare and gloomy; desolate; forbidding; grim: *the gaunt slopes of a high mountain in winter.* *adj.* —**gaunt′ly**, *adv.* —**gaunt′ness**, *n.*

gen ial (jēn′yəl),   **1.** smiling and pleasant; cheerful and friendly; kindly: *a genial welcome.* **2.** helping growth; pleasantly warming; comforting: *genial sunshine.* *adj.* —**gen′ial ly**, *adv.* —**gen′ial ness**, *n.*

ges tic u late (jes tik′yə lāt),   **1.** make or use gestures. **2.** make or use many vehement gestures: *The speaker gesticulated by raising his arms, pounding the desk, and stamping his foot.* *v.*, **ges tic u lat ed, ges tic u lat ing.**

ges ture (jes′chər),   **1.** movement of the hands, arms, or any part of the body, used instead of words or with words to help express an idea or feeling. **2.** make or use gestures. 1 *n.*, 2 *v.*

gid dy (gid′ē),   **1.** having a confused, whirling feeling in one's head; dizzy. **2.** likely to make dizzy; causing dizziness. **3.** rarely or never serious; living for the pleasure of the moment; flighty; heedless. *adj.*

gin ger ly (jin′jər lē),   with extreme care or caution. *adv., adj.* —**gin′ger li ness**, *n.*

girth (gèrth),   **1.** the measurement around anything; *a man of large girth, the girth of a tree.* **2.** measure in girth. **3.** strap or band that keeps a saddle, pack, etc., in place on a horse's back. **4.** fasten with a strap or band. 1,3 *n.*, 2,4 *v.*

gist (jist),   the essential part; real point; main idea; substance of a longer statement. *n.*

glean (glēn),   **1.** gather (grain) left on a field by reapers. **2.** gather little by little or slowly. *v.* —**glean′er**, *n.*

glow er (glou′ər),   **1.** stare angrily; scowl. **2.** an angry or sullen look. 1 *v.*, 2 *n.*

griev ance (grē′vəns),   a real or imagined wrong; reason for being angry or annoyed; cause for complaint. *n.*

grim (grim),   **1.** without mercy; stern; harsh; fierce. **2.** not yielding; not relenting: *a grim resolve.* **3.** looking stern, fierce, or harsh: *Father was grim when he heard about the six broken windows.* **4.** horrible; ghastly: *He made grim jokes about death and ghosts.* *adj.*, **grim mer, grim mest.** —**grim′ly**, *adv.* —**grim′ness**, *n.*

griz zled (griz′əld),   **1.** grayish; gray. **2.** grayhaired. *adj.*

gro tesque (grō tesk′),   **1.** odd or unnatural in shape, appearance, manner, etc. **2.** ridiculous;

hat, āge, fär; let, bē, tèrm; it, ĭce; hot, gō, ôrder; oil, out; cup, půt, rüle; ch, child; ng, long; th, thin; ŦH, then; zh, measure; ə represents *a* in about, *e* in taken, *i* in April, *o* in lemon, *u* in circus.

absurd: *The monkey's grotesque antics made the children laugh.* *adj.* —**gro tesque′ly,** *adv.* —**gro tesque′ness,** *n.*

gun wale (gun′l), the upper edge of a ship's or boat's side. *n.* Also, **gunnel.**

gy rate (jī′rāt), move in a circle or spiral; whirl; rotate: *A top gyrates.* *v.*

hag gard (hag′ərd), **1.** looking worn from pain, fatigue, worry, hunger, etc.; gaunt; careworn. **2.** wild; untamed. *adj.*

hand i cap (han′dē kap), **1.** race, contest, game, etc., in which the better contestants are given certain disadvantages, or the poorer ones certain advantages, so that all have an equal chance to win. **2.** disadvantage or advantage given: *A runner with a 5-yard handicap in a 100-yard race has to run either 105 yards or 95 yards.* **3.** something that puts a person at a disadvantage; hindrance: *A sore throat is a handicap to a singer.* **4.** put at a disadvantage; hinder: *The pitcher was handicapped by a lame arm.* **1,2,3** *n.,* **4** *v.,* **hand i capped, hand i cap ping.**

hap less (hap′lis), unlucky; unfortunate. *adj.*

har ass (har′əs or hə ras′), **1.** trouble by repeated attacks: *Pirates harassed the villages along the coast.* **2.** disturb; worry; torment. *v.*

har bin ger (här′bin jər), one that goes ahead to announce another's coming; forerunner: *The robin is a harbinger of spring.* *n.*

hare brained (her′brānd′ or har′brānd′), giddy; heedless; reckless. *adj.*

har poon (här pün′), a barbed spear with a rope tied to it, used for catching whales and other sea animals. *n.*

har row (har′ō), **1.** a heavy frame with iron teeth or upright disks. Harrows are drawn over plowed land to break up clods, cover seeds, etc. **2.** draw a harrow over (land, etc.). **1** *n.,* **2** *v.*

haunt (hônt), **1.** go often to; visit frequently: *People say ghosts haunt that old house.* **2.** place frequently gone to or often visited: *The swimming pool was the favorite haunt of the boys in the summer.* **3.** be often with; come often to: *Memories of his youth haunted the old man.* **4.** Dialect. ghost. **1,3** *v.,* **2,4** *n.* —**haunt′ing ly,** *adv.*

haz ard (haz′ərd), **1.** risk; danger; peril: *The life of an aviator is full of hazards.* **2.** chance. **3.** take a chance with; risk; venture: *I would hazard my life on his honesty.* **1,2** *n.,* **3** *v.*

hear say (hir′sā′), common talk; gossip. *n.*

heav y (hev′ē), **1.** hard to lift or carry; of great weight: *a heavy load, heavy responsibilities.* **2.** of great amount, force, or intensity; greater than usual; large: *a heavy vote, heavy strain, heavy sea, heavy sleep, heavy rain, heavy meal, heavy crop.* **3.** sorrowful; gloomy: *heavy news.* **4.** grave; serious; sober; somber: *a heavy part in a play.* *adj.* —**heav′i ly,** *adv.* —**heav′i ness,** *n.*

heft (heft), *Informal.* **1.** weight; heaviness. **2.** judge the weight or heaviness of by lifting. **3.** lift; heave. **1** *n.,* **2,3** *v.*

heir (er or ar), **1.** person who receives, or has the right to receive, someone's property or title after the death of its owner; person who inherits

property. **2.** person who inherits anything; person who receives or has something from someone before him. *n.*

helms man (helmz′mən), man who steers a ship. *n., pl.* **helms men.**

hem lock (hem′lok), **1.** *U.S.* an evergreen tree of the same family as the pine, with small cones and drooping branches. Bark from hemlocks is used in tanning. **2.** its wood. *n.*

hi lar i ty (hə lar′ə tē), great mirth; noisy gaiety. *n.*

hom age (hom′ij or om′ij), respect; reverence; honor. *n.*

home com ing (hōm′kum′ing), **1.** a returning home. **2.** a return to a place formerly frequented. *n.*

home spun (hōm′spun′), **1.** spun or made at home. **2.** cloth made of yarn spun at home. **3.** a strong, loosely woven cloth similar to it. **4.** not polished; plain; simple: *homespun manners.* **1,4** *adj.,* **2,3** *n.*

hos pi ta ble (hos′pi tə bəl or hos pit′ə bəl), **1.** giving or liking to give a welcome, food and shelter, and friendly treatment to guests or strangers. **2.** willing and ready to entertain; favorably receptive or open: *a person hospitable to new ideas.* *adj.* —**hos′pi ta bly,** *adv.*

host (hōst), **1.** person who receives another at his house as a guest. **2.** plant or animal in or on which a parasite lives: *The oak tree is the host of the mistletoe that grows on it.* *n.*

hos tile (hos′tl; *sometimes* hos′tīl), **1.** of an enemy or enemies: *the hostile army.* **2.** opposed; unfriendly; unfavorable: *a hostile look.* *adj.*

hu mane (hyü mān′), **1.** kind; merciful; not cruel or brutal: *We believe in humane treatment of prisoners.* **2.** tending to humanize and refine: *humane studies.* *adj.*

hum ble (hum′bəl), **1.** low in position or condition; not important or grand: *a humble log cabin.* **2.** having or showing a feeling that one is unimportant, weak, poor, etc.; modest in spirit; not proud: *Defeat makes people humble.* **3.** make humble; bring down; make lower in position, condition, or pride. **1-2** *adj.,* **3** *v.*

hu mil i ate (hyü mil′ē āt), lower the pride, dignity, or self-respect of: *We felt humiliated by our failure.* *v.,* **hu mil i at ed, hu mil i at ing.**

hyp no sis (hip nō′sis), state resembling deep sleep, but more active, in which a person has little will of his own and little feeling, and acts according to the suggestions of the person who brought about the hypnosis. *n.*

hyp not ic (hip not′ik), **1.** of hypnosis. **2.** easily hypnotized. **3.** person who is hypnotized or easily hypnotized. **4.** causing sleep. **5.** drug or other means of causing sleep. **1,2,4** *adj.,* **3,5** *n.*

hyp no tize (hip′nə tīz), **1.** put into a hypnotic state; cause hypnosis. **2.** *Informal.* dominate or control the will of by suggestion. *v.,* **hyp no tized, hyp no tiz ing.**

hy po der mic (hī′pə dėr′mik), **1.** dose of medicine injected under the skin. **2.** syringe used to inject a dose of medicine under the skin. *n.*

hy poth e sis (hī poth′ə sis), **1.** something assumed because it seems likely to be a true explanation; theory: *Let us act on the hypothesis that he is honest.* **2.** proposition assumed as a basis for reasoning. *n., pl.* **hy poth e ses.**

hy po thet i cal (hī/pə thet/ə kəl), of or based on a hypothesis; assumed; supposed. *adj.* —**hy′po thet/i cal ly,** *adv.*

hys ter i cal (his ter/ə kəl), **1.** unnaturally excited. **2.** showing an unnatural lack of control; unable to stop laughing, crying, etc.; suffering from hysteria. *adj.* —**hys ter/i cal ly,** *adv.*

hys ter ics (his ter/iks), fit of hysterical laughing and crying. *n.pl.*

id i o syn cra sy (id/ē ō sing/krə sē), a personal peculiarity: *Eating no meat was Amy's idiosyncrasy.* *n., pl.* **id i o syn cra sies.**

ig nite (ig nīt/), **1.** set on fire: *You ignite a match by scratching it.* **2.** make intensely hot; cause to glow with heat. **3.** take fire; begin to burn: *Gasoline ignites easily.* *v.,* **ig nit ed, ig nit ing.** —**ig nit/er,** *n.*

ig ni tion (ig nish/ən), **1.** a setting on fire. **2.** a catching on fire. **3.** apparatus for igniting the explosive vapor in the cylinders of an internal-combustion engine. A spark plug is a part of the ignition of a gasoline engine. *n.*

im age ry (im/ij rē), **1.** pictures in the mind; things imagined. **2.** descriptions and figures of speech that help the mind to form forceful or beautiful pictures. Poetry often contains imagery. *n., pl.* **im age ries.**

im be cile (im/bə səl), a very stupid or foolish person. *n.*

im mac u late (i mak/yə lit), **1.** without a spot or stain; absolutely clean. **2.** without sin; pure. *adj.* —**im mac/u late ly,** *adv.*

im merse (i mèrs/), **1.** plunge into a liquid. **2.** involve deeply; absorb: *immersed in business affairs, immersed in debts.* *v.*

im mo bile (i mō/bəl), **1.** not movable; firmly fixed. **2.** not moving; not changing; motionless. *adj.*

im mo bil i ty (im/ō bil/ə tē), a being immobile. *n.*

im pas sive (im pas/iv), **1.** without feeling or emotion; unmoved; indifferent: *He listened with an impassive face.* **2.** not feeling pain or injury; insensible: *The soldier lay as impassive as if he were dead.* *adj.* —**im pas/sive ly,** *adv.*

im pel (im pel/), **1.** drive; force; cause: *Hunger impelled the lazy man to work.* **2.** cause to move, drive forward; push along: *The wind impelled the boat to shore.* *v.,* **im pelled, im pel ling.** —**im pel/ler,** *n.*

im per ma nence (im pèr/mə nəns), quality of not being permanent; condition not intended to last; being temporary. *n.*

im per son ate (im pèr/sən āt), **1.** act the part of: *impersonate Hamlet on the stage.* **2.** pretend to be; mimic the voice, appearance, and manners of. *v.,* **im per son at ed, im per son at ing.**

im per son a tion (im pèr/sən ā/shən), **1.** an impersonating. **2.** a being impersonated. *n.*

im ply (im plī/), indicate without saying outright; express indirectly; suggest: *Silence often implies consent.* *v.,* **im plied, im ply ing.**

im pres sion ist (im presh/ə nist), one who entertains by imitating the speech and actions of famous persons. *n.*

im pres sive (im pres/iv), able to impress the mind, feelings, conscience, etc.: *an impressive sermon, an impressive storm, an impressive ceremony.* *adj.* —**im pres/sive ly,** *adv.* —**im pres/sive ness,** *n.*

im pro vise (im/prə vīz), compose or utter (verse, music, etc.) without preparation: *Fred improvised a new stanza for the school song at the football game.* *v.,* **im pro vised, im pro vis ing.**

in-¹, prefix meaning: not; the opposite of; the absence of, as in *inexpensive, inattention, inconvenient.* Also: **im-,** before *b, m, p;* **ir-,** before *r.*

in-², prefix meaning: in; into; on; upon, as in *inhale, inscribe.* Also: **im-,** before *b, m, p;* **ir-,** before *r.*

in-³, prefix meaning: in; within; into; toward, as in *inborn, indoors, inland.*

in ad e quate (in ad/ə kwit), not adequate; not enough; not as much as is required: *inadequate preparation for an examination.* *adj.*

in ap pro pri ate (in/ə prō/prē it), not appropriate; not suitable; not fitting. *adj.*

in ci sive (in sī/siv), sharp; penetrating; piercing; keen. *adj.* —**in ci/sive ly,** *adv.* —**inci/sive ness,** *n.*

in con ceiv a ble (in/kən sēv/ə bəl), impossible to imagine; unthinkable; incredible. *adj.*

in con sist ent (in/kən sis/tənt), not in agreement or harmony: *The policeman's failure to arrest the criminal was inconsistent with his duty.* *adj.* —**in/con sist/ent ly,** *adv.*

in cred i ble (in kred/ə bəl), seeming too extraordinary to be possible; unbelievable. *adj.* —**in cred/i bly,** *adv.*

in cred u lous (in krej/ə ləs), **1.** not ready to believe; not credulous; doubting. **2.** showing a lack of belief. *adj.* —**in cred/u lous ly,** *adv.*

in crim i nate (in krim/ə nāt), accuse of a crime; show to be guilty: *In his confession the thief incriminated two others who helped him steal.* *v.,* **in crim i nat ed, in crim i nat ing.**

in cul cate (in kul/kāt), impress by repetition; teach persistently: *Week after week she inculcated good manners in her pupils.* *v.,* **in cul cat ed, in cul cat ing.**

in dif fer ence (in dif/ər əns), **1.** lack of interest or attention. **2.** lack of importance: *Where we ate was a matter of indifference.* *n.*

in dif fer ent (in dif/ər ənt), **1.** having no feeling for or against: *indifferent to an admirer.* **2.** impartial; neutral; without preference: *an indifferent decision.* **3.** unimportant; not mattering much: *The time for starting is indifferent to me.* **4.** neither good nor bad; just fair: *an indifferent ballplayer.* *adj.*

---

hat, āge, fär; let, bē, tèrm; it, īce; hot, gō, ôrder; oil, out; cup, pùt, rüle; ch, child; ng, long; th, thin; ᴛʜ, then; zh, measure; ə represents *a* in about, *e* in taken, *i* in April, *o* in lemon, *u* in circus.

in dif fer ent ly (in dif′ər ənt lē),　without interest; as though it doesn't matter. *adv.*

in dig nant (in dig′nənt),　angry at something unworthy, unjust, or mean. *adj.* **—in dig′-nant ly,** *adv.*

in dig na tion (in′dig nā′shən),　anger at something unworthy, unjust, or mean; anger mixed with scorn; righteous anger: *Cruelty to animals arouses indignation.* *n.*

in dis tin guish a ble (in′dis ting′gwish ə-bəl),　that cannot be seen clearly or told apart. *adj.*

in do lent (in′də lənt),　lazy; disliking work. *adj.* **—in′do lent ly,** *adv.*

in dus tri ous (in dus′trē əs),　hard-working. *adj.* **—in dus′tri ous ly,** *adv.*

in ev i ta ble (in ev′ə tə bəl),　not avoidable; sure to happen; certain to come: *Death is inevitable.* *adj.* **—in ev′i ta bly,** *adv.*

in fer (in fėr′),　1. find out by reasoning; conclude: *People inferred that so able a governor would make a good President.* 2. indicate; imply: *Ragged clothing infers poverty.* 3. draw inferences. *v.,* **in ferred, in fer ring.**

in fin i ty (in fin′ə tē),　1. state of being infinite. 2. distance, space, time, or quantity without limits. 3. an infinite extent, amount, or number: *the infinity of God's mercy.* *n., pl.* **in fin i ties.**

to infinity, without limits or bounds; endlessly.

in flamed (in flāmd′),　unnaturally hot, red, sore, or swollen. *adj.*

in for mal (in fôr′məl),　1. not formal; not in the regular or prescribed manner. 2. done without ceremony: *an informal party.* 3. used in everyday, common talk, but not used in formal talking or writing. Such an expression as *funny* for *queer* is informal. *adj.* **—in for′mal ly,** *adv.*

in fre quent (in frē′kwənt),　not frequent; occurring seldom or far apart; scarce; rare. *adj.* **—in fre′quent ly,** *adv.*

in ge nu i ty (in′jə nü′ə tē or in′jə nyü′ə tē),　skill in planning, inventing, etc.; cleverness. *n., pl.* **in ge nu i ties.**

in ha la tion (in′hə lā′shən),　1. act of inhaling. 2. medicine to be inhaled. *n.*

in hale (in hāl′),　draw into the lungs; breathe in (air, gas, fragrance, tobacco smoke, etc.). *v.,* **in haled, in hal ing.**

in hib it (in hib′it),　1. check; restrain; hinder by obstruction or restriction. 2. prohibit; forbid. *v.*

i ni tial (i nish′əl),　1. occurring at the beginning; first; earliest. 2. the first letter of a word. 3. mark or sign with initials. 1 *adj.,* 2 *n.,* 3 *v.,* **i ni tialed, i ni tial ing.**

in quis i tive (in kwiz′ə tiv),　1. curious; asking many questions. 2. too curious; prying into other people's affairs. *adj.* **—in quis′i tive ly,** *adv.* **—in quis′i tive ness,** *n.*

in sist ence (in sis′təns),　1. act of firmly demanding. 2. quality of being insistent. *n.*

in sist ent (in sis′tənt),　1. continuing to make a strong, firm demand or statement: *In spite of the rain he was insistent on going out.* 2. compelling attention or notice; pressing; urgent: *There*

was an insistent knocking on my door. *adj.* **—in sist′ent ly,** *adv.*

in so lent (in′sə lənt),　boldly rude; insulting: *"Shut up!" the insolent boy said to his father.* *adj.* **—in′so lent ly,** *adv.*

in spi ra tion (in′spə rā′shən),　1. influence of thought and strong feelings on actions, especially on good actions: *Some people get inspiration from sermons, some from nature.* 2. any influence that arouses effort to do well: *The captain was an inspiration to his men.* 3. idea that is inspired. 4. suggestion to another; act of causing something to be told or written by another. *n.*

in stan ta ne ous (in′stən tā′nē əs),　occurring, done, or made in an instant. *adj.*

in stinct (in′stingkt),　1. natural feeling, knowledge, or power, such as guides animals; unlearned tendency: *An instinct leads birds to fly.* 2. a natural bent, tendency, or gift; talent: *Dorothy has such an instinct for color that she will study art.* *n.*

in tense (in tens′),　1. very much; very great; very strong: *intense happiness, intense pain, intense light.* 2. full of vigorous activity, strong feelings, etc.: *An intense life is crowded with action, interests, etc.* 3. having or showing strong feeling: *an intense person, an intense face.* *adj.*

in tent (in tent′),　1. very attentive; having the eyes or thoughts earnestly fixed on something; earnest: *an intent look.* 2. earnestly engaged; much interested: *He is intent on making money.* *adj.* **—in tent′ly,** *adv.*

inter-, prefix meaning: 1. together; one with the other: *Intercommunicate = communicate with each other.* 2. between: *Interpose = put between.* 3. among a group: *Interscholastic = between or among schools.*

in ter cept (in′tər sept′),　1. take or seize on the way from one place to another: *intercept a letter or a messenger.* 2. check; stop: *intercept the flight of a criminal.* *v.* **—in′ter cep′tion,** *n.*

in ter ject (in′tər jekt′),　throw in between other things; insert abruptly: *Every now and then the speaker interjected some witty remark.* *v.*

in ter lock (in′tər lok′),　lock or join with one another: *The two stags interlocked their horns.* *v.*

in ter pose (in′tər pōz′),　1. put between; insert. 2. interrupt. *v.,* **in ter posed, in ter pos ing.**

in ter sperse (in′tər spėrs′),　1. vary with something put here and there: *The grass was interspersed with beds of flowers.* 2. scatter here and there among other things: *Bushes were interspersed among trees.* *v.,* **in ter spersed, in ter spers ing.**

in to na tion (in′tō nā′shən),　1. act of intoning: *the intonation of a psalm.* 2. production of musical notes. 3. manner of sounding words. *n.*

in tone (in tōn′),　1. read or recite in a singing voice; chant: *A priest intones part of the service.* 2. utter with a particular tone. *v.,* **in toned, in ton ing.**

in var i a bly (in ver′ē ə blē or in var′ē ə blē),　in an invariable manner; without change; without exception: *Spring invariably follows winter.* *adv.*

in vert (in vėrt´),　1. turn upside down: *invert a glass.* 2. turn around or reverse in position, direction, order, etc. If you invert "I can," you have "Can I?"　*v.*

i ron ic (ĭ ron´ik),　1. expressing one thing and meaning the opposite: *"Speedy" would be an ironic name for a snail.* 2. contrary to what would naturally be expected: *It was ironic that the man was run over by his own automobile. adj.*

ir res o lute (i rez´ə lüt),　unable to make up one's mind; not sure of what one wants; hesitating: *Irresolute persons make poor leaders. adj.* —**ir res´o lute ly,** *adv.* .

ju di cial (jü dish´əl),　1. of or having to do with courts, judges, or the administration of justice. 2. like a judge; suited to a judge; impartial; fair. *adj.* —**ju di´cial ly,** *adv.*

ju di cious (jü dish´əs),　having, using, or showing good judgment; wise; sensible. *adj.* **ju di´cious ly,** *adv.*

ju ris dic tion (jür´is dik´shən),　1. right or power of administering law or justice. 2. authority; power; control. 3. extent of authority: *The judge ruled that the case was not within his jurisdiction. n.*

jus ti fy (jus´tə fī),　1. show to be just or right; give a good reason for: *The fine quality of the cloth justifies its high price.* 2. clear of blame or guilt. *v.,* **jus ti fied, jus ti fy ing.** —**jus´ti fi´er,** *n.*

lab y rinth (lab´ə rinth),　a place through which it is hard to find one's way; maze. *n.*

lag gard (lag´ərd),　1. person who moves too slowly or falls behind; backward person. 2. slow; falling behind; backward. 1 *n.,* 2 *adj.*

lair (ler or lar),　1. den or resting place of a wild animal. 2. hide-out or hide-away. *n.*

lank y (lang´kē),　awkwardly long and thin; tall and ungraceful. *adj.,* **lank i er, lank i est.**

lar ce ny (lär´sə nē),　1. theft. 2. the unlawful taking, carrying away, and using of the personal property belonging to another person without his consent. *n., pl.* **lar ce nies.**

le git i mate (lə jit´ə mit),　1. rightful; lawful; allowed: *Sickness is a legitimate reason for a child's being absent from school.* 2. conforming to accepted standards. 3. logical: *a legitimate conclusion. adj.* —**le git´i mate ly,** *adv.*

len ien cy (lē´nyən sē),　mildness; gentleness; mercy. *n.*

le thal (lē´thəl),　causing death; deadly: *lethal weapons, a lethal dose. adj.*

list less (list´lis),　seeming too tired to care about anything; not interested in things; not caring to be active. *adj.* —**list´less ly,** *adv.*

log ic (loj´ik),　1. science of proof. 2. science of reasoning. 3. book on logic. 4. reasoning; use of argument. 5. reason; sound sense. *n.*

lu di crous (lü´də krəs),　amusingly absurd; ridiculous. *adj.* —**lu´di crous ly,** *adv.*

lu pin or **lu pine** (lü´pən),　any of several plants of the same family as peas and beans, that have long spikes of flowers, radiating clusters of grayish, hairy leaflets, and flat pods with bean-shaped seeds. *n.*

lux u ri ous (lug zhúr´ē əs or luk shúr´ē əs),　1. fond of luxury; tending toward luxury; self-indulgent. 2. giving luxury; very comfortable and beautiful. *adj.* —**lux u´ri ous ly,** *adv.* —**lux u´ri ous ness,** *n.*

lux u ry (luk´shə rē or lug´zhə rē),　1. comforts and beauties of life beyond what is really necessary. 2. thing that one enjoys, usually something choice and costly: *He saves some money for luxuries such as fine paintings.* 3. any means or form of enjoyment. *n., pl.* **lux u ries.**

mag net ize (mag´nə tīz),　1. give the properties of a magnet to. An electric current in a coil around a bar of iron will magnetize the bar. 2. attract or influence (a person): *Her beautiful voice magnetized the audience. v.*

man i fest (man´ə fest),　1. apparent to the eye or to the mind; plain; clear. 2. show plainly; reveal; display. 3. prove; put beyond doubt. 1 *adj.,* 2,3 *v.* —**man´i fest´ly,** *adv.*

man tle (man´tl),　1. a loose cloak without sleeves. 2. anything that covers like a mantle: *The ground had a mantle of snow. n.*

mar tyr (mär´tər),　1. person who chooses to die or suffer rather than renounce his faith. 2. person who suffers great pain or anguish. *n.*

mauve (mōv),　delicate, pale purple. *n., adj.*

mel an chol y (mel´ən kol´ē),　1. sadness; low spirits; tendency to be sad. 2. sad; gloomy. 3. causing sadness; depressing: *a melancholy scene.* 4. sober thoughtfulness. 5. soberly thoughtful. 1,4 *n., pl.* **mel an chol ies;** 2,3,5 *adj.*

me lo de on (mə lō´dē ən),　a small reed organ. *n.*

mem o ran dum (mem´ə ran´dəm),　a short written statement for future use; note to aid one's memory. *n.*

men ace (men´is),　1. threat: *In dry weather forest fires are a great menace.* 2. threaten: *Floods menaced the valley with destruction.* 1 *n.,* 2 *v.,* **men aced, men ac ing.** —**men´ac ing ly,** *adv.*

me tal lic (mə tal´ik),　1. of, containing, or consisting of metal. 2. like metal; characteristic of metal; that suggests metal: *a metallic luster, a metallic voice. adj.*

met a mor pho sis (met´ə môr´fə sis),　1. change of form. Tadpoles become frogs by metamorphosis; they lose their tails and grow legs. 2. the changed form. 3. a noticeable or complete change of character, appearance, or condition. *n., pl.* **met a mor pho ses** (-sēz).

me te or (mē´tē ər),　mass of stone or metal that comes toward the earth from outer space with enormous speed; shooting star. Meteors be-

---

hat, āge, fär; let, bē, tėrm; it, īce; hot, gō, ôrder; oil, out; cup, pùt, rüle; ch, child; ng, long; th, thin; ŦH, then; zh, measure; ə represents *a* in about, *e* in taken, *i* in April, *o* in lemon, *u* in circus.

come so hot from rushing through the air that they glow and often burn up. *n.*

me thod i cal (mə thod′ə kəl), according to a method; systematic; orderly. *adj.* —**me thod′i cal ly,** *adv.* —**me thod′i cal ness,** *n.*

met tle (met′l), disposition; spirit; courage. *n.* **on one's mettle,** ready to do one's best.

mi gra to ry (mī′grə tô′rē), moving from one place to another: *migratory laborers, migratory birds. adj.*

min is cule (min′ə skyül), miniature; extremely small. *adj.*

mis-, prefix meaning:
1. bad, as in *misgovernment.*
2. badly, as in *misbehave, mismanage.*
3. wrong, as in *mispronunciation.*
4. wrongly, as in *misapply, misunderstand.*

mi ser (mī′zər), person who loves money for its own sake; one who lives poorly in order to save money and keep it. *n.*

mis tri al (mis trī′əl), trial having no effect in law because of some error in the proceedings or because the jury cannot reach a verdict. *n.*

mo lest (mə lest′), meddle with and injure; interfere with and trouble; disturb. *v.* —**mo lest′er,** *n.*

mol li fy (mol′ə fī), soften; soothe; pacify. *v.,* **mol li fied, mol li fy ing.** —**mol′li fi ca′tion,** *n.*

mo men tum (mō men′təm), 1. force with which a body moves, the product of its mass and its velocity: *A falling object gains momentum as it falls.* 2. impetus resulting from movement. *n., pl.* **mo men tums, mo men ta** (-tə).

mo not o nous (mə not′n əs), 1. continuing in the same tone. 2. not varying; without change. *adj.* —**mo not′o nous ly,** *adv.*

mood y (mü′dē), 1. likely to have changes of mood. 2. often having gloomy moods: *She has been moody ever since she lost her job.* 3. sunk in sadness; gloomy; sullen: *Maud sat in moody silence. adj.,* **mood i er, mood i est.** —**mood′i ly,** *adv.*

mo rose (mə rōs′), gloomy; sullen; ill-humored. *adj.* —**mo rose′ly,** *adv.* —**mo rose′ness,** *n.*

mo tive (mō′tiv), 1. thought or feeling that makes one act: *His motive in going away was a wish to travel.* 2. that which makes something move: *motive power of steam or electricity.* 1 *n.,* 2 *adj.*

mot tle (mot′l), 1. mark with spots or streaks of different colors. 2. a mottled coloring or pattern. 1 *v.,* **mot tled, mot tling;** 2 *n.*

mot tled (mot′ald), marked with streaks or spots of different colors. *adj.*

muse (myüz), 1. think in a dreamy way; think; meditate: *The boy spent the whole afternoon in musing.* 2. look thoughtfully. 3. say thoughtfully. *v.,* **mused, mus ing.** —**mus′er,** *n.*

mu ti late (myü′tl āt), 1. cut, tear, or break off a part of; injure seriously by cutting, tearing, or breaking off some part. 2. make (a story, song, etc.) imperfect by removing parts. *v.,* **mu ti lat ed, mu ti lat ing.**

mu ti neer (myü′tə nir′), person who rebels against lawful authority. *n.*

muz zle (muz′l), 1. nose, mouth, and jaws of a four-footed animal. 2. cover of straps or wires to put over an animal's head to keep it from biting or eating. *n.*

nar ra tor (na rā′tər), one who tells a story. *n.*

nau sea (nô′shə or nô′sē ə), 1. the feeling that one has when about to vomit. 2. seasickness. 3. extreme disgust; loathing. *n.*

nau ti cal (nô′tə kəl), of or having to do with ships, sailors, or navigation. *adj.* —**nau′ti cal ly,** *adv.*

ne o phyte (nē′ə fīt), 1. a new convert; one recently admitted to a religious body. 2. beginner; novice. *n.*

nest ling (nest′ling), 1. bird too young to leave the nest. 2. a young child. *n.*

nim bly (nim′blē), quickly and lightly. *adv.*

no bil i ty (nō bil′ə tē), 1. people of noble rank. Earls and counts belong to the nobility. 2. noble birth; noble rank. 3. noble character. *n., pl.* **no bil i ties.**

non-, prefix meaning: not; not a; opposite of; lack of; failure of, as in *nonbreakable, nonconformity, nonpayment.*

non cha lant (non′shə lənt or non′shə länt′), without enthusiasm; coolly unconcerned; indifferent. *adj.* —**non′cha lant ly,** *adv.*

Norse (nôrs), of or having to do with ancient Scandinavia, its people, or their language. *adj.*

no to ri e ty (nō′tə rī′ə tē), a being famous for something bad; ill fame. *n.*

no to ri ous (nō tô′rē əs), well-known because of something bad; having a bad reputation. *adj.* —**no to′ri ous ly,** *adv.*

nuz zle (nuz′əl), 1. poke or rub with the nose; press the nose against: *The calf nuzzles his mother.* 2. nestle; snuggle; cuddle. *v.,* **nuz zled, nuz zling.**

o blige (ə blīj′), 1. bind by a promise, contract, duty, etc.; force. 2. put under a debt of thanks for some favor. 3. do a favor: *She obliged us with a song. v.,* **o bliged, o blig ing.**

ob lique ly (ə blēk′lē or ə blīk′lē), in a slanting direction; indirectly. *adv.*

ob liv i ous (ə bliv′ē əs), 1. forgetful; not mindful: *The book was so interesting that I was oblivious of my surroundings.* 2. bringing or causing forgetfulness: *an oblivious slumber. adj.* —**ob liv′i ous ly,** *adv.* —**ob liv′i ous ness,** *n.*

ob ses sion (əb sesh′ən), 1. influence of a feeling, idea, or impulse that a person cannot escape. 2. the feeling, idea, or impulse itself. *n.*

oc to pus (ok′tə pəs), 1. a sea mollusk having a soft body and eight arms with suckers on them. 2. anything like an octopus; powerful, grasping organization with far-reaching influence. *n., pl.* **oc to pus es** or **oc to pi.**

Octopus (from 6 in. to 20 ft. across, depending on the species)

o di ous (ō′dē əs), very

displeasing; hateful; offensive; detestable; repulsive. *adj.* **—o′di ous ly,** *adv.*

o di um (ō′dē əm), **1.** hatred; dislike. **2.** reproach; blame. *n.*

of fence (ə fens′), *Esp. Brit.* offense. *n.*

of fense (ə fens′), **1.** a breaking of the law; sin. **2.** cause of wrongdoing. **3.** condition of being offended; hurt feelings; anger: *He tried not to cause offense. n.*

omis sion (ō mish′ən), **1.** something left out. **2.** a failure to do something; something neglected. *n.*

op ti mis tic (op′tə mis′tik), **1.** inclined to look on the bright side of things. **2.** hoping for the best. *adj.*

or deal (ôr dēl′), a severe test or difficult experience. *n.*

os ten ta tious (os′ten tā′shəs), **1.** done for display; intended to attract notice: *Tom rode his new bicycle up and down in front of Dick's house in an ostentatious way.* **2.** showing off; liking to attract notice. *adj.* **—os′ten ta′tious ly,** *adv.*

out skirts (out′skėrts′), the outer parts or edges of a town, district, etc.; outlying parts. *n.pl.*

pal at a ble (pal′ə tə bəl), agreeable to the taste; pleasing: *That was a most palatable lunch. I find your suggestion extremely palatable. adj.*

pal lid (pal′id), lacking color; pale: *a pallid face. adj.*

pal pi tate (pal′pə tāt), **1.** beat very rapidly: *Your heart palpitates when you are excited.* **2.** quiver; tremble: *His body palpitated with terror.* *v.,* **pal pi tat ed, pal pi tat ing.**

pam per (pam′pər), indulge too much; allow too many privileges to: *pamper a child. v.*

pan de mo ni um (pan′də mō′nē əm), **1.** place of wild disorder or lawless confusion. **2.** wild uproar or lawlessness. *n.*

pan ic (pan′ik), **1.** fear spreading through a multitude of people so that they lose control of themselves; unreasoning fear: *When the theater caught fire, there was a panic.* **2.** sudden fear or terror. *n.*

pan to mime (pan′tə mīm), **1.** a play without words, in which the actors express themselves by gestures. **2.** gestures without words. **3.** express by gestures. *1,2 n., 3 v.*

pan to mim ist (pan′tə mī′mist), actor in a pantomime. *n.*

par a lyt ic (par′ə lit′ik), **1.** having a loss of sensation in any part of the body; unable, or less able, to move a part of the body. **2.** person who is crippled. *1 adj., 2 n.*

parch (pärch), **1.** dry by heating; roast slightly: *Corn is sometimes parched.* **2.** make hot and dry or thirsty. **3.** become dry, hot, or thirsty. *v.*

par tic i pa tion (pär tis′ə pā′shən), a sharing; a taking part. *n.*

pas sion ate (pash′ən it), **1.** having or showing strong feelings. **2.** easily moved to anger.

3. resulting from strong feeling: *He made a passionate speech. adj.* **—pas′sion ate ly,** *adv.*

pa thet ic (pə thet′ik), **1.** pitiful; arousing pity: *A lost child is pathetic.* **2.** emotional. *adj.* **—pa thet′i cal ly,** *adv.*

pa thos (pā′thos), quality in speech, writing, music, events, or a scene that arouses a feeling of pity or sadness. *n.*

pa tron age (pā′trən ij or pat′rə nij), **1.** regular business given to a store, hotel, etc., by customers. **2.** favor, encouragement, or support given by a person. **3.** power to give jobs or favors: *the patronage of a governor, mayor, or congressman. n.*

pa tron ize (pā′trə nīz or pat′rə nīz), **1.** be a regular customer of; give regular business to: *We patronize our neighborhood stores.* **2.** give approval, support, and protection to some person, art, or cause: *patronize the ballet.* **3.** treat others as if they are inferior: *We dislike to have anyone patronize us.* *v.,* **pa tron ized, pa tron iz ing.** **—pa′tron iz′ing ly,** *adv.*

per ceive (pər sēv′), **1.** be aware of through the senses; see, hear, taste, smell, or feel: *Did you perceive the colors of that bird?* **2.** take in with the mind; observe: *I perceived that I could not make him change his mind.* *v.,* **per ceived, per ceiv ing.**

per il ous (per′ə ləs), dangerous. *adj.* **—per′il ous ly,** *adv.*

per plex i ty (pər plek′sə tē), **1.** confusion; being puzzled; a not knowing what to do or how to act. **2.** something that puzzles or bewilders. *n., pl.* **per plex i ties.**

per suade (pər swād′), win over to do or believe; make willing or sure by urging, arguing, etc.: *I knew I should study, but he persuaded me to go to the movies.* *v.,* **per suad ed, per suad ing.**

per sua sion (pər swā′zhən), **1.** a persuading: *All our persuasion was of no use; she would not come.* **2.** power of persuading. **3.** firm belief. **4.** religious belief; creed: *All Christians are not of the same persuasion. n.*

per sua sive (pər swā′siv), able, intended, or fitted to persuade: *The salesman had a very persuasive way of talking. adj.* **—per sua′sive ly,** *adv.* **—per sua′sive ness,** *n.*

per verse (pər vėrs′), **1.** contrary and willful; stubborn: *The perverse child did just what we told him not to do.* **2.** persistent in wrong. **3.** wicked. **4.** not correct; wrong: *perverse reasoning. adj.*

phe nom e non (fə nom′ə non), **1.** fact, event, or circumstance that can be observed: *Lightning is an electrical phenomenon.* **2.** something or someone extraordinary or remarkable: *An eclipse is an interesting phenomenon. n., pl.* **phe nom e na** or (*esp. for def. 2*) **phe nom e nons.**

phleg mat ic (fleg mat′ik), **1.** sluggish; indifferent. **2.** cool; calm: *John is phlegmatic; he never seems to get excited about anything. adj.*

phos pho res cent (fos′fə res′ənt), showing light without burning or by very slow burning that seems to not give out heat. *adj.*

---

hat, āge, fär; let, bē, tėrm; it, īce; hot, gō, ôrder; oil, out; cup, pùt, rüle; ch, child; ng, long; th, thin; ∓H, then; zh, measure; ə represents *a* in about, *e* in taken, *i* in April, *o* in lemon, *u* in circus.

pho to stat (fō′tə stat), **1.** photograph made with a Photostat, a special camera for making copies of maps, drawings, pages of books, etc. **2.** make a photostat of. 1 *n.*, 2 *v.*

pig my (pig′mē), **1.** a very small person; dwarf. **2.** very small. 1 *n.*, *pl.* **pig mies;** 2 *adj.* Also, **pygmy.**

pil fer (pil′fər), steal in small quantities; steal. *v.*

pin na cle (pin′ə kəl), **1.** a high peak or point of rock. **2.** the highest point: *at the pinnacle of his fame.* **3.** put on a pinnacle. 1,2 *n.*, 3 *v.*

pit e ous (pit′ē əs), to be pitied; moving the heart; deserving pity: *The starving children are a piteous sight. adj.*

pit fall (pit′fôl′), **1.** a hidden pit to catch animals in. **2.** any trap or hidden danger. *n.*

pith y (pith′ē), full of substance, meaning, force, or vigor: *pithy phrases, a pithy speaker. adj.*

pla cate (plā′kāt), soothe or satisfy the anger of; make peaceful: *placate a person one has offended. v.,* **pla cat ed, pla cat ing.**

plac id (plas′id), calm; peaceful; quiet: *a placid lake. adj.* —**plac′id ly,** *adv.* —**plac′id ness,** *n.*

plain tive (plān′tiv), mournful; sad. *adj.*

plait (plāt or plat for 1, 2; plāt or plēt for 3, 4), **1.** a braid: *She wore her hair in a plait.* **2.** to braid: *She plaits her hair.* **3.** a flat, usually narrow, fold made in cloth by doubling it on itself; a pleat. **4.** fold or arrange in plaits; pleat: *a plaited skirt.* 1,3 *n.*, 2,4 *v.*

plau si ble (plô′zə bəl), **1.** appearing true, reasonable, or fair. **2.** apparently worthy of confidence but not really so: *a plausible liar. adj.* —**plau′si bly,** *adv.*

pos se (pos′ē), group of men summoned by a sheriff to help him: *The posse pursued the thief. n.*

post-, prefix meaning: after, as in *postgraduate, postwar, postscript.*

po ten tial (pə ten′shəl), **1.** possible as opposed to actual; capable of coming into being or action. **2.** something possible. 1 *adj.*, 2 *n.*

po ten tial ly (pə ten′shəl ē), possibly, but not yet actually. *adv.*

pre-, prefix meaning: before in place, time, order, or rank, as in *prepay, preheat, prewar.*

pre car i ous (pri ker′ē əs or pri kar′ē əs), **1.** dependent on the will or pleasure of another. **2.** not safe or secure; uncertain; dangerous; risky: *A soldier leads a precarious life. adj.* —**pre car′i ous ly,** *adv.* —**pre car′i ous ness,** *n.*

prec i pice (pres′ə pis), a very steep cliff; almost vertical slope. *n.*

pre cise (pri sīs′), **1.** exact; accurate; definite: *The precise sum was 34 cents.* **2.** careful: *Alice is precise in her manners.* **3.** strict: *We had precise orders to come home by nine o'clock. adj.*

pred e ces sor (pred′ə ses′ər), **1.** person holding a position or office before another: *John Adams was Jefferson's predecessor as President.* **2.** thing that came before another. *n.*

prej u dice (prej′ə dis), **1.** opinion formed without taking time and care to judge fairly: *a prejudice against doctors.* **2.** cause a prejudice in;

fill with prejudice: *One unfortunate experience prejudiced him against all lawyers.* **3.** damage; harm; injure. **4.** harm; injury: *I will do nothing to the prejudice of my cousin in this matter.* 1,4 *n.*, 2,3 *v.*, **prej u diced, prej u dic ing.**

pre lim i nar y (pri lim′ə ner′ē), **1.** coming before the main business; leading to something more important: *After the preliminary exercises of prayer and song, the speaker of the day gave an address.* **2.** a step taken to prepare for something: *A physical examination is a preliminary to joining the army.* 1 *adj.*, 2 *n.*

pre oc cu pa tion (prē ok′yə pā′shən), **1.** occupying beforehand. **2.** absorption; taking up all the attention of. *n.*

pre pos ter ous (pri pos′tər əs), contrary to nature, reason, or common sense; absurd; senseless: *It would be preposterous to shovel coal with a teaspoon. adj.* —**pre pos′ter ous ly,** *adv.*

pre rog a tive (pri rog′ə tiv), right or privilege that nobody else has: *The government has the prerogative of coining money. n.*

pres tige (pres tēzh′), reputation or influence based on one's abilities, achievements, opportunities, associations, position, etc. *n.*

pre text (prē′tekst), a false reason concealing the real reason; pretense; excuse: *He used his sore finger as a pretext for not going to school. n.*

pre vi ous (prē′vē əs), coming or going before; that came before; earlier: *She did better in the previous lesson. adj.*

prime¹ (prīm), **1.** chief: *His prime object was to lower the tax rate.* **2.** first in time or order; fundamental. **3.** first in quality; excellent: *prime ribs of beef.* **4.** the best part. 1-3 *adj.*, 4 *n.*

prime² (prīm), **1.** prepare by putting something in or on. **2.** cover (a surface) with a first coat of paint or oil so that paint will not soak in. **3.** equip (a person) with information, words, etc. *v.,* **primed, prim ing.**

prim i tive (prim′ə tiv), **1.** of early times; of long ago: *Primitive people often lived in caves.* **2.** first of the kind. **3.** very simple; such as people had early in human history: *A primitive way of making fire is by rubbing two sticks together.* **4.** original; primary. *adj.* —**prim′i tive ly,** *adv.*

pri or (prī′ər), coming before; earlier: *I can't go with you because I have a prior engagement. adj.* **prior to,** coming before in time, order, or importance; earlier than; before.

proc ess (pros′es or prō′ses), **1.** set of actions or changes in a special order: *By what process or processes is cloth made from wool?* **2.** treat or prepare by some special method: *This cloth has been processed to make it waterproof.* 1 *n.*, 2 *v.*

prod i gal (prod′ə gəl), **1.** spending too much; wasting money or other resources; wasteful. **2.** extremely generous. **3.** person who is wasteful or extravagant; spendthrift. 1,2 *adj.*, 3 *n.*

pro found (prə found′), **1.** very deep: *a profound sigh, a profound sleep.* **2.** deeply felt; very great: *profound despair, profound sympathy.* **3.** going far deeper than what is easily understood; having or showing great knowledge or understanding: *a profound book. adj.* —**pro found′ly,** *adv.* —**pro found′ness,** *n.*

prom on to ry (prom′ən tô′rē),   a high point of land extending from the coast into the water; headland. *n., pl.* **prom on to ries.**

pros e cute (pros′ə kyüt),   **1.** bring before a court of law: *Reckless drivers will be prosecuted.* **2.** carry out; follow up: *He prosecuted an inquiry into reasons for the company's failure.*   *v.,* **pros e cut ed, pros e cut ing.**

pro tract ed (prō trak′tid), lengthened. *adj.*

pro voc a tive (prə vok′ə tiv),   **1.** irritating; vexing. **2.** tending or serving to call forth action, thought, laughter, anger, etc.: *a remark provocative of laughter.* **3.** something that rouses or irritates. **1,2** *adj.,* **3** *n.*

pro voke (prə vōk′), **1.** make angry; vex: *She provoked him by her teasing.* **2.** stir up; excite: *An insult provokes a person to anger.* **3.** call forth; bring about; start into action; cause: *The President's speech provoked much discussion.*   *v.,* **provoked, pro vok ing.**

prow ess (prou′is),   **1.** bravery;   daring. **2.** unusual skill or ability. *n.*

pub li cist (pub′lə sist),   **1.** person skilled or trained in law or in public affairs. **2.** writer on law, politics, or public affairs. **3.** a person in public relations; one who is concerned with giving the public a better understanding of the policies and purposes of an organization. **4.** an agent in charge of publicity for a person, group, etc. *n.*

pu gi list (pyü′jə list),   person who fights with the fists; boxer. *n.*

pun gent (pun′jənt),   **1.** sharply affecting the organs of taste and smell: *a pungent pickle, the pungent smell of burning leaves.* **2.** sharp; biting: *pungent criticism.* **3.** stimulating to the mind; keen; lively: *a pungent wit. adj.*

purse (pėrs),   **1.** a little bag or case for carrying money around with one. **2.** money; resources; treasury. **3.** sum of money: *A purse was made up for the victims of the fire.* **4.** draw together; press into folds or wrinkles: *Grace pursed her lips and frowned.* **1-3** *n.,*   **4** *v.,* **pursed, purs ing.**

pur sue (pər sü′),   **1.** follow to catch or kill; chase. **2.** proceed along; follow in action; follow: *He pursued a wise course by taking no chances.* **3.** strive for; try to get; seek: *pursue pleasure.* **4.** carry on; keep on with: *She pursued the study of French for four years.* **5.** continue to annoy or trouble. *v.,* **pur sued, pur su ing.**

quail[1] (kwāl),   any of various game birds belonging to the same group as fowls and partridges, especially the bobwhite. *n., pl.* **quails** or (*esp. collectively*) **quail.**

quail[2] (kwāl),   be afraid; lose courage; shrink back in fear. *v.*

quar ry (kwôr′ē),   place where stone is dug, cut, or blasted out for use in building. *n., pl.* **quar ries.**

qua ver (kwā′vər),   **1.** shake tremulously; tremble: *The old man's voice quavered.* **2.** a

shaking or trembling, especially of the voice. **1** *v.,*   **2** *n.* —**qua′ver ing ly,** *adv.*

quea sy (kwē′zē),   **1.** inclined to nausea; easily upset: *a queasy stomach.* **2.** tending to unsettle the stomach. **3.** uneasy; uncomfortable. **4.** squeamish. *adj.*

quid (kwid),   **1.** piece to be chewed. **2.** bite of chewing tobacco. *n.*

quirt (kwėrt),   a riding whip with a short, stout handle and a lash of braided leather. *n.*

quiz zi cal (kwiz′ə kəl),   **1.** odd; queer; comical. **2.** that suggests making fun of others; teasing: *a quizzical smile. adj.* —**quiz′zi cal ly,** *adv.*

rack (rak),   **1.** frame with bars, shelves, or pegs to hold, arrange, or keep things on, such as a hat rack or tool rack. **2.** instrument once used for torturing people by stretching them. **3.** hurt very much: *racked with grief. A toothache racked his jaw.* **4.** cause or condition of great suffering in body or mind. **5.** stretch; strain. **1,2,4** *n.,* **3,5** *v.*

ran cor (rang′kər),   bitter resentment or ill will; extreme hatred or spite. *n.*

rasp (rasp),   **1.** make a harsh, grating sound: *The file rasped as he worked.* **2.** a harsh, grating sound: *the rasp of crickets, a rasp in a person's voice.* **3.** utter with a grating sound: *rasp out a command.* **4.** have a harsh or irritating effect (on); grate. **1,3,4** *v.,*   **2** *n.*

re-,   prefix meaning:
1. again; anew; once more, as in *reappear, rebuild, reheat, reopen.*
2. back, as in *recall, repay, replace.* Also, before vowels, **red-.**

re ad mit (rē′əd mit′),   to admit again. *v.*

ream (rēm),   **1.** enlarge or shape (a hole). **2.** remove with a reamer. **3.** to open up, clear. *v.*

re as sur ance (rē′ə shůr′əns),   **1.** new or fresh assurance. **2.** restoration of courage or confidence. *n.*

re as sure (rē′ə shůr′),   **1.** restore to confidence: *The captain's confidence during the storm reassured the passengers.* **2.** assure again or anew. *v.,* **re as sured, re as sur ing.**

re bel lion (ri bel′yən),   **1.** armed resistance or fight against one's government. **2.** resistance or fight against any power or restriction. *n.*

rec on cile (rek′ən sīl),   **1.** make friends again. **2.** settle (a quarrel, disagreement, etc.). **3.** make agree; bring into harmony: *It is impossible to reconcile his story with the facts. v.*

re cruit (ri krüt′),   **1.** a newly enlisted soldier or sailor. **2.** get (men) to join an army or navy. **3.** strengthen or supply (an army, navy, etc.) with new men. **4.** a new member of any group or class. **5.** get (new members). **1,4** *n.,*   **2,3,5** *v.*

rec ti tude (rek′tə tüd or rek′tə tyüd),   upright conduct or character; honesty; righteousness. *n.*

re cu per a tion (ri kyü′pər ā′shən or ri kü′-

hat, āge, fär; let, bē, tèrm; it, īce; hot, gō, ôrder; oil, out; cup, pùt, rüle; ch, child; ng, long; th, thin; ∓H, then; zh, measure; ə represents *a* in about, *e* in taken, *i* in April, *o* in lemon, *u* in circus.

pər ā′shən), recovery from sickness, exhaustion, loss, etc. *n.*

reed y (rē′dē), **1.** full of reeds. **2.** made of a reed or reeds. **3.** like a reed or reeds. **4.** sounding like a reed instrument: *a reedy voice. adj.*

re flect (ri flekt′), **1.** turn back or throw back (light, heat, sound, etc.): *The sidewalks reflect heat on a hot day.* **2.** give back an image; give back a likeness or image of: *A mirror reflects your face and body.* **3.** reproduce or show like a mirror: *The newspaper reflected the owner's opinions.* **4.** think; think carefully: *Take time to reflect before doing important things.* **5.** cast blame, reproach, or discredit: *Bad behavior reflects on home training.* **6.** serve to cast or bring: *A brave act reflects credit on the person who does it. v.*

re flec tive (ri flek′tiv), **1.** reflecting: *the reflective surface of polished metal.* **2.** thoughtful: *reflective look. adj.*

re form (ri fôrm′), **1.** make better; improve by removing faults: *Prisons should try to reform criminals instead of just punishing them.* **2.** become better. **3.** a changing for the better; improvement, especially one made by removing faults or abuses. *1,2 v.,* 3 *n.*

re form a to ry (ri fôr′mə tô′rē), **1.** serving to reform; intended to reform. **2.** an institution for reforming young offenders against the laws; prison for young criminals. 1 *adj.,* 2 *n., pl.* **re form a to ries.**

re fu el (rē fyü′əl), **1.** supply with fuel again. **2.** take on a fresh supply of fuel. *v.*

rel e gate (rel′ə gāt), **1.** send away, usually to a lower position or condition: *to relegate a dress to the rag bag.* **2.** send into exile; banish. **3.** hand over (a matter, task, etc.). *v.,* **rel e gat ed, rel e gat ing.** —**rel′e ga′tion,** *n.*

rel ic (rel′ik), **1.** thing, custom, etc., that remains from the past: *This ruined bridge is a relic of the Civil War.* **2.** something belonging to a holy person, kept as a sacred memorial. **3.** object having interest because of its age or its associations with the past; keepsake; souvenir. *n.*

re luc tant (ri luk′tənt), **1.** unwilling; showing unwillingness. **2.** slow to act because unwilling: *He was reluctant to give his money away. adj.*

re ly (ri lī′), depend; trust. *v.*

re morse (ri môrs′), deep, painful regret for having done wrong. *n.*

re per cus sion (rē′pər kush′ən), **1.** an indirect influence or reaction from an event. **2.** sound flung back; echo. **3.** a springing back. *n.*

re proach (ri prōch′), **1.** blame. **2.** disgrace: *A coward is a reproach to an army.* **3.** object of blame, censure, or disapproval. **4.** expression of blame, censure, or disapproval. *1-4 n., 1,2 v.*

re proach ful (ri prōch′fəl), full of reproach; expressing reproach. *adj.*

re sent ful (ri zent′fəl), feeling resentment; injured and angry; showing resentment. *adj.*

re sent ment (ri zent′mənt), the feeling that one has at being injured or insulted; indignation. *n.*

re serve (ri zėrv′), **1.** keep back; hold back: *reserve criticism.* **2.** set apart: *time reserved for recreation.* **3.** save for use later: *Reserve enough money for your fare home.* **4.** anything kept back for future use. **5.** keeping one's thoughts, feelings, and affairs to oneself; self-restraint; lack of friendliness. **6.** a silent manner that keeps people from making friends easily. *1-3 v., 4-6 n.*

re sil i ent (ri zil′ē ənt), **1.** springing back; returning to the original form or position after being bent, compressed, or stretched: *resilient steel, resilient turf.* **2.** buoyant; cheerful: *a resilient nature that throws off trouble. adj.*

re solve (ri zolv′), **1.** make up one's mind; determine; decide: *He resolved to do better work in the future.* **2.** thing determined on: *He kept his resolve to do better.* **3.** firmness in carrying out a purpose; determination: *Washington was a man of great resolve.* 1 *v.,* **re solved,** **re solv ing;** *2,3 n.*

re sound (ri zound′), **1.** give back sound; echo. **2.** sound loudly: *Radios resound from every house.* **3.** be filled with sound: *The room resounded with the children's shouts.* **4.** be much talked about: *The fame of the first flight across the Atlantic resounded all over the world. v.* —**re sound′ing ly,** *adv.*

re spec tive (ri spek′tiv), belonging to each; particular; individual: *The classes went to their respective rooms. adj.*

re strict (ri strikt′), keep within limits; confine: *Our club membership is restricted to twelve. v.*

re stric tion (ri strik′shən), **1.** something that restricts; limiting condition or rule: *The restrictions on the use of the playground are: No fighting; no damaging property.* **2.** a restricting or being restricted: *This park is open to the public without restriction. n.*

re tal i ate (ri tal′ē āt), pay back wrong, injury, etc.; return like for like: *If we insult them, they will retaliate. v.*

rev eil le (rev′ə lē), a signal on a bugle or drum to waken soldiers or sailors in the morning. *n.*

rev e la tion (rev′əl ā′shən), **1.** act of making known: *The revelation of the thieves' hiding place by one of their own number caused their capture.* **2.** the thing made known. *n.*

rev er ie (rev′ər ē), dreamy thoughts; dreamy thinking of pleasant things. *n.* Also, **revery.**

re vive (ri vīv′), **1.** bring back or come back to life or consciousness: *revive a half-drowned person.* **2.** bring or come back to a fresh, lively condition. **3.** make or become fresh; restore. **4.** bring back to use, fashion, memory, etc. *v.*

rheu mat ic (rü mat′ik), **1.** having rheumatism, a disease with inflammation, swelling, and stiffness of the joints. **2.** caused by rheumatism. **3.** like or characteristic of one who has this disease. *adj.*

rid i cule (rid′ə kyül), **1.** laugh at; make fun of: *Boys ridicule their sisters' friends.* **2.** laughter, words or actions that make fun of somebody or something. 1 *v.,* **rid i culed, rid i cul ing;** 2 *n.*

ri dic u lous (ri dik′yə ləs), deserving ridicule; absurd; laughable. *adj.*

right eous (rī′chəs), **1.** doing right; virtuous; behaving justly. **2.** morally right or justifiable: *righteous indignation. adj.* —**right′eous ly,** *adv.*

rit u al (rich′ü əl), **1.** form or system of solemn

ceremonies. Baptism, marriage, and burial are parts of the ritual of the church. Secret societies have a ritual for initiating new members. **2.** the regular carrying out of certain practices because they seem fitting. *n.*

roan (rōn), **1.** yellowish- or reddish-brown sprinkled with gray or white. **2.** a roan horse. 1 *adj.,* 2 *n.*

ro tund (rō tund´), **1.** round; plump. **2.** sounding rich and full; full-toned: *a rotund voice. adj.*

ru mi nate (rü´mə nāt), **1.** chew the cud. **2.** chew again: *A cow ruminates its food.* **3.** ponder; meditate: *He ruminated on the strange events of the past week.* *v.,* **ru mi nat ed, ru mi nat ing.**

running board, a footboard or step along the lower side of some automobiles.

rus tler (rus´lər), *U.S.* **1.** *Slang.* an active, energetic person. **2.** *Informal.* a cattle thief. *n.*

rust y (rus´tē), **1.** covered with rust; rusted: *a rusty knife.* **2.** made by rust: *a rusty spot.* **3.** colored like rust. **4.** faded: *a rusty black.* **5.** out of practice. *adj.*

sanc ti mo ni ous (sangk´tə mō´nē əs), making a show of holiness. *adj.*

sat u rate (sach´ə rāt), soak thoroughly; fill full: *During the fog, the air was saturated with moisture.* *v.,* **sat u rat ed, sat u rat ing.**

sa vor (sā´vər), **1.** taste or smell; flavor: *The soup has a savor of onion.* **2.** enjoy the savor of; perceive or appreciate by taste or smell: *He savored the soup with pleasure.* **3.** relish; to enjoy with appreciation. **4.** have the quality or nature (*of*): *a request that savors of a command.* 1 *n.,* 2-4 *v.*

sa vour (sā´vər), *Esp. Brit.* savor. *n., v.*

scant y (skan´tē), **1.** not enough: *His scanty clothing did not keep out the cold.* **2.** barely enough; meager: *a scanty harvest. adj.,* **scant i er, scant i est. —scant´i ly,** *adv.* **—scant´i ness,** *n.*

scape goat (skāp´gōt´), person or thing made to bear the blame for the mistakes or sins of others. The ancient Jewish high priests used to lay the sins of the people upon a goat (called the scapegoat) which was then driven out into the wilderness. *n.*

score (skôr), **1.** record of points made in a game, contest, test, etc.: *The score was 9 to 2 in our favor.* **2.** make as points in a game, contest, test, etc. **3.** make points; succeed. **4.** cut; scratch; mark. **5.** group or set of twenty; twenty: *A score or more were present at the party.* 1,5 *n.,* 2-4 *v.*

scores, a large number.

scourge (skėrj), **1.** a whip. **2.** any means of punishment. **3.** whip; punish. **4.** some thing or person that causes great trouble or misfortune. In olden times, an outbreak of disease was called a scourge. **5.** trouble very much. 1,2,4 *n.,* 3,5 *v.*

scut tle (skut´l), scamper; scurry. *v.,* **scut tled, scut tling. —scut´tler,** *n.*

self-re li ance (self´ri lī´əns), reliance on one's own acts, abilities, etc. *n.*

self-re li ant (self´ri lī´ənt), having or showing self-reliance. *adj.* **—self´-re li´ant ly,** *adv.*

se nile (sē´nīl), **1.** of old age. **2.** showing the weakness of old age. **3.** caused by old age. *adj.*

se nil i ty (sə nil´ə tē), **1.** old age. **2.** weakness of old age. *n.*

sen si tive (sen´sə tiv), **1.** receiving impressions readily. **2.** easily affected or influenced. **3.** easily hurt or offended. **4.** of or connected with the senses or sensation. *adj.*

sen su ous (sen´shü əs), **1.** of or derived from the senses; having an effect on the senses: *the sensuous thrill of a warm bath, a sensuous love of color.* **2.** enjoying the pleasures of the senses. *adj.*

sen ti men tal (sen´tə men´tl), **1.** having or showing much tender feeling. **2.** likely to act from feelings rather than from logical thinking. **3.** of sentiment; dependent on sentiment: *She values her mother's gift for sentimental reasons. adj.*

sen ti men tal ist (sen´tə men´tl ist), a sentimental person. *n.*

se quel (sē´kwəl), **1.** that which follows; continuation. **2.** something that follows as a result of some earlier happening; result; consequence; outcome. **3.** a complete story continuing an earlier one about the same people. *n.*

se rene (sə rēn´), **1.** peaceful; calm: *a serene smile.* **2.** clear; not cloudy: *a serene sky. adj.*

shak y (shā´kē), **1.** shaking. **2.** liable to break down; weak. **3.** not to be depended on. *adj.*

sham (sham), **1.** pretense; fraud. **2.** counterfeit; imitation. **3.** pretended: *The soldiers fought a sham battle for practice.* 1,2 *n.,* 2,3 *adj.*

sha man (shä´mən, shā´mən, or sham´ən), a medicine man; a priest-doctor who uses magic. *n.*

shape less (shāp´lis), **1.** without definite shape. **2.** having an unattractive shape. *adj.* **—shape´less ly,** *adv.* **—shape´less ness,** *n.*

sheep ish (shē´pish), **1.** awkwardly bashful or embarrassed: *a sheepish smile.* **2.** like a sheep; timid; weak; stupid. *adj.* **—sheep´ish ly,** *adv.*

sheer (shir), **1.** very thin; almost transparent: *a sheer white dress.* **2.** unmixed with anything else; complete: *sheer weariness.* **3.** straight up and down; steep: *From the top of the wall it was a sheer drop of 100 feet to the water below. adj.*

shrewd (shrüd), **1.** having a sharp mind; clever; showing a keen wit; clever. **2.** keen; sharp. *adj.* **—shrewd´ly,** *adv.*

shrike (shrīk), bird with a strong, hooked beak that feeds on large insects, frogs, and sometimes on other birds. *n.*

shroud (shroud), **1.** cloth or garment in which a dead person is wrapped for burial. **2.** wrap for burial. **3.** something that covers, conceals, or veils: *The fog was a shroud over the city.* **4.** cover; conceal; veil: *The earth is shrouded in darkness.* 1,3 *n.,* 2,4 *v.*

si dle (sī´dl), **1.** move sideways. **2.** move side-

---

hat, āge, fär; let, bē, tėrm; it, īce; hot, gō, ôrder; oil, out; cup, pùt, rüle; ch, child; ng, long; th, thin; ŦH, then; zh, measure; ə represents *a* in about, *e* in taken, *i* in April, *o* in lemon, *u* in circus.

ways slowly so as not to attract attention. *v.*, **si dled, si dling.**

sig nif i cance (sig nif′ə kəns), **1.** importance; consequence. **2.** meaning. *n.*

sim plis tic (sim plis′tik), made extremely simple; changed to a plainer or easier form; made overly simple. *adj.*

sim u la tion (sim′yə lā′shən), **1.** pretense; feigning. **2.** imitation; acting or looking like. *n.*

skep ti cal (skep′tə kəl), of or like a person who questions the truth of theories or apparent facts; inclined to doubt; not believing easily. *adj.* Also, **sceptical.** —**skep′ti cal ly,** *adv.*

sleight (slīt) **of hand,** **1.** skill and quickness in moving the hands. **2.** tricks or skill of a modern magician; juggling.

slip shod (slip′shod′), careless in dress, habits, speech, etc.; untidy; slovenly. *adj.*

smite (smīt), **1.** strike; strike hard; hit hard: *The hero smote the giant with his sword.* **2.** come with force (upon). **3.** affect with a sudden pain, disease, etc. *v.*, **smote, smit ten** or **smit, smit ing.**

smote (smōt), a pt. of **smite.** *v.*

smug (smug), **1.** too pleased with one's own goodness, cleverness, respectability, etc.; self-satisfied. **2.** sleek; neat; trim. *adj.*, **smug ger, smug gest.** —**smug′ly,** *adv.* —**smug′ness,** *n.*

so lid i fy (sə lid′ə fī), **1.** make or become solid; harden. **2.** unite firmly. *v.*, **so lid i fied, so lid i fy ing.**

sol i tude (sol′ə tüd or sol′ə tyüd), **1.** being alone. **2.** a lonely place. **3.** loneliness. *n.*

som ber (som′bər), **1.** dark; gloomy: *A cloudy winter day is somber.* **2.** melancholy; dismal. *adj.*

som bre (som′bər), *Esp. Brit.* somber. *adj.*

soothe (süᴛʜ), **1.** quiet; calm; comfort: *The mother soothed the crying child.* **2.** make less painful; relieve; ease. *v.*, **soothed, sooth ing.**

sor tie (sôr′tē), a sudden attack by troops from a defensive position; raid. *n.*

sov er eign ty (sov′rən tē), supreme power or authority. *n.*

spend thrift (spend′thrift′), **1.** person who wastes money. **2.** extravagant with money; wasteful. **1** *n.*, **2** *adj.*

spig ot (spig′ət), **1.** valve for controlling the flow of water or other liquid from a pipe, tank, barrel, etc. **2.** *U.S.* faucet. **3.** peg or plug used to stop the small hole of a cask, barrel, etc. *n.*

spon ta ne ous (spon tā′nē əs), **1.** caused by natural impulse or desire; not forced or compelled; not planned beforehand: *Both sides burst into spontaneous cheers at the skillful play.* **2.** taking place without external cause or help; caused entirely by inner forces. **3.** growing or produced naturally; not planted, cultivated, etc. *adj.*

spright ly (sprīt′lē), lively; gay. *adj.*

stac ca to (stə kä′tō), **1.** in music, with breaks between the successive tones; disconnected; abrupt. **2.** in a staccato manner. **1** *adj.*, **2** *adv.*

stam pede (stam pēd′), **1.** a sudden scattering or headlong flight of a frightened herd of cattle or horses. **2.** any headlong flight of a large group: *a stampede of a panic-stricken crowd from a burning building.* **3.** scatter or flee in a stam-

pede. **4.** a general rush: *a stampede to newly discovered gold fields.* **5.** make a general rush. **1,2,4** *n.*, **3,5** *v.*

stat ure (stach′ər), **1.** height. **2.** development; physical, mental, or moral growth. *n.*

stat ute (stach′üt), law; decree; formally established rule. *n.*

stealth y (stel′thē), done in a secret manner; secret; sly: *The cat crept in a stealthy way toward the bird.* *adj.* —**stealth′i ly,** *adv.* —**stealth′i ness,** *n.*

ste ve dore (stē′və dôr), man who loads and unloads ships. *n.*

sti fle (stī′fəl), **1.** stop the breath of; smother: *The smoke stifled the firemen.* **2.** be unable to breathe freely. **3.** keep back; suppress; stop: *stifle a cry, stifle a yawn.* *v.*, **sti fled, sti fling.**

stir ring (stėr′ing), **1.** moving; active; lively: *stirring times.* **2.** exciting: *a stirring speech.* *adj.*

strad dle (strad′l), **1.** walk, stand, or sit with the legs wide apart. **2.** have a leg on each side of (a horse, bicycle, chair, ditch, etc.). **3.** *Informal.* avoid taking sides. *v.*

strained (strānd), forced; not natural: *Her greeting was cold and strained.* *adj.*

stran gle (strang′gl), **1.** kill by squeezing the throat to stop the breath. **2.** suffocate; choke: *His high collar seemed to be strangling him.* **3.** choke down; keep back: *Tom strangled an impulse to cough.* *v.*, **stran gled, stran gling.**

stri dent (strīd′nt), making or having a harsh sound; creaking; grating; shrill. *adj.*

stu pe fac tion (stü′pə fak′shən or styü′pə-fak′shən), **1.** dazed or senseless condition; stupor. **2.** overwhelming amazement. *n.*

stu pe fy (stü′pə fī or styü′pə fī), **1.** make stupid, dull, or senseless. **2.** overwhelm with amazement; astound: *They were stupefied by the calamity.* *v.*, **stu pe fied, stu pe fy ing.**

stu por (stü′pər or styü′pər), a dazed condition; loss or lessening of the power to feel: *The man lay in a stupor, unable to tell what had happened to him.* *n.*

suave (swäv), smoothly agreeable or polite. *adj.* —**suave′ly,** *adv.* —**suave′ness,** *n.*

sub-, prefix meaning:
1. under; below, as in *subway, submarine.*
2. down; further; again, as in *subdivide, sublease.*
3. near; nearly, as in *subarctic.*
4. lower; subordinate; assistant, as in *subagent.*
5. of less importance, as in *subhead.*
6. resulting from further division, as in *subatom.*
7. in a comparatively small degree or proportion; somewhat, as in *subacid.*

sub due (səb dü′ or səb dyü′), **1.** conquer; overcome. **2.** tone down; soften; sober. *v.*, **sub dued, sub du ing.**

sub lime (sə blīm′), lofty; noble; majestic; exalted. *adj.*

sub side (səb sīd′), **1.** sink to a lower level. **2.** grow less; die down; become less active; abate; ebb: *The storm finally subsided.* **3.** fall to the bottom; settle. *v.*, **sub sid ed, sub sid ing.**

sub stan tial (səb stan′shəl), **1.** real; actual: *People and things are substantial; dreams and ghosts are not.* **2.** large; important: *John has made* a *substantial improvement in health.* **3.** strong; firm; solid: *The house is substantial enough to last a hundred years. adj.*

sub tle (sut′l),　**1.** delicate; thin; fine.　**2.** faint; mysterious: *a subtle smile.*　**3.** having a keen, quick mind: *She is a subtle observer of slight differences in things.*　**4.** sly; tricky: *a subtle scheme to get some money.*　**5.** skillful; clever; expert. *adj.*

suc ces sion (sək sesh′ən),　**1.** group of things happening one after another; series.　**2.** the coming of one person or thing after another.　*n.*
in succession, one after another.

suc ces sor (sək ses′ər),　one that follows or succeeds another in office, position, or ownership of property; thing that comes next after another in a series.　*n.*

su per (sü′pər),　**1.** *Informal.* extra person or thing. Mobs on the stage are usually made up of supers.　**2.** *Informal.* superintendent.　**3.** *Slang.* excellent.　1,2 *n.,*　3 *adj.*

super-, prefix meaning:
1. over; above, as in *superimpose, superstructure.*
2. besides, as in *supertax.*
3. in high proportion; to excess; exceedingly, as in *superabundant, supersensitive.*
4. surpassing, as in *superman, supernatural.*

su per la tive (sə pèr′lə tiv),　**1.** of the highest kind; above all others; supreme.　**2.** person or thing above all others; supreme example.　**3.** expressing the highest degree of comparison of an adjective or adverb. *Fairest, best,* and *most slowly* are the superlative forms of *fair, good,* and *slowly.*　**4.** the highest degree of an adjective or adverb.　**5.** form or combination of words that shows this degree.　1,3 *adj.,*　2,4,5 *n.*
talk in superlatives, exaggerate.

sup plant (sə plant′),　take the place of; displace or set aside. *v.*

sup ple (sup′əl),　**1.** bending easily.　**2.** readily adaptable to different ideas, circumstances, people, etc.; yielding: *a supple mind. adj.,* **sup pler, sup plest.**

sur ly (sèr′lē),　bad-tempered and unfriendly; rude; gruff.　*adj.,* **sur li er, sur li est.**

sus pend (səs pend′),　**1.** hang down by attaching to something above: *The lamp was suspended from the ceiling.*　**2.** hold in place as if by hanging.　**3.** stop for a while: *suspend work.*　**4.** remove or exclude for a while from some privilege or job: *He was suspended from school for a week. v.*

swale (swāl),　a low, wet piece of land; low place.　*n.*

sym bol (sim′bəl),　something that stands for or represents something else: *The lion is the symbol of courage; the olive branch, of peace. n.*

sym bol ic (sim bol′ik),　**1.** used as a symbol: *A lily is symbolic of purity.*　**2.** of a symbol; expressed by a symbol; using symbols. *adj.*

tal ly (tal′ē),　**1.** anything on which a score or account is kept.　**2.** notch or mark made on a tally.　**3.** number or group used in tallying: *The*

dishes *were counted in tallies of 20.*　**4.** mark on a tally; count up: *tally a score.*　**5.** account; score: *a tally of a game.*　**6.** label; tag.　**7.** entire amount; last in a given amount.　1-3,5-7 *n., pl.* **tal lies;** 4 *v.,* **tal lied, tal ly ing.**

taps (taps),　a signal on a bugle or drum to put out lights at night. *n.pl.*

tat ting (tat′ing),　giving a series of rhythmic taps or raps. From **tattoo** (beat or rap rhythmically). *adj.*

taut (tôt),　**1.** tightly drawn; tense: *a taut rope.*　**2.** in neat condition; tidy: *a taut ship. adj.*

ten et (ten′it),　doctrine, principle, belief, or opinion held as true.　*n.*

ten sion (ten′shən),　**1.** a stretching.　**2.** a stretched condition.　**3.** mental strain: *A mother feels tension when her baby is sick.*　**4.** strained condition: *political tension.*　**5.** stress caused by the action of a pulling force.　*n.*

ten ta tive (ten′tə tiv),　done as a trial or experiment; experimental: *a tentative plan. adj.*

ten u ous (ten′yü əs),　**1.** thin; slender: *the tenuous thread of a spider's web.*　**2.** having slight importance; not substantial: *a tenuous claim. adj.*

ter mite (tèr′mīt),　any of various insects that have a soft, pale body and a dark head. Termites look like white ants. Termites are very destructive to buildings, furniture, provisions, etc.　*n.*

ter rain (te rān′),　land; tract of land, especially considered as to its natural features in relation to its use in warfare.　*n.*

the at ri cal (thē at′rə kəl),　**1.** of or having to do with the theater or actors: *theatrical performances, a theatrical company.*　**2.** suggesting a theater or acting; for display or effect; artificial. *adj.* —**the at′ri cal ly,** *adv.*

the o ry (thē′ə rē),　**1.** explanation based on thought, observation and reasoning: *Einstein's theory of relativity.*　**2.** principles or methods of a science or art rather than its practice: *the theory of music.*　**3.** thought or fancy as opposed to fact or practice.　*n., pl.* **the o ries.**

thong (thông),　**1.** a narrow strip of leather, etc., especially used as a fastening.　**2.** lash of a whip.　*n.*

thwack (thwak),　**1.** strike vigorously with a stick or something flat.　**2.** a sharp blow with a stick or something flat.　1 *v.,*　2 *n.*

thwart (thwôrt),　**1.** oppose and defeat; keep from doing something.　**2.** across; crosswise.　1 *v.,* 2 *adv.*

tol er a ble (tol′ər ə bəl),　**1.** able to be borne or endured.　**2.** fairly good. *adj.* —**tol′er a ble ness,** *n.* —**tol′er a bly,** *adv.*

tor ment (tôr ment′ for 1,5; tôr′ment for 2-4),　**1.** cause very great pain to: *Headaches tormented him.*　**2.** cause of very great pain.　**3.** very great pain.　**4.** cause of very much worry or annoyance.　**5.** worry or annoy very much: *He torments everyone with silly questions.*　1,5 *v.,*　2-4 *n.*

tor men tor or **tor ment er** (tôr men′tər),　person or thing that torments.　*n.*

tor rid (tôr′id),　very hot. *adj.*

---

hat, āge, fär;　let, bē, tèrm;　it, īce;　hot, gō, ôrder;　oil, out;　cup, pùt, rüle;　ch, child;　ng, long; th, thin;　ᵺ, then;　zh, measure;　ə represents *a* in about, *e* in taken, *i* in April, *o* in lemon, *u* in circus.

trag e dy (traj′ə dē), **1.** a serious play having an unhappy ending. **2.** a very sad or terrible happening: *The father's sudden death was a tragedy to his family.* *n., pl.* **trag e dies.**

trans-, prefix meaning:
1. across; over; through, as in *transcontinental.*
2. beyond; on the other side of, as in *transcend.*
3. across, etc.; and also beyond, on the other side of, as in *transmarine, transoceanic,* and many other geographical terms, such as *trans-Adriatic, trans-African.*
4. into a different place, condition, etc., as in *transform, transplant.*

trans fix (trans fiks′), **1.** pierce through. **2.** fasten by piercing through with something pointed. **3.** make motionless (with amazement, terror, etc.). *v.*

tran si tion (tran zish′ən), a change or passing from one condition, place, thing, activity, topic, etc., to another. *n.*

treach er y (trech′ər ē), **1.** a breaking of faith; treacherous behavior; deceit. **2.** treason. *n., pl.* **treach er ies.**

tre men dous (tri men′dəs), **1.** dreadful; awful: *The army suffered a tremendous defeat.* **2.** *Informal.* very great; enormous: *a tremendous house.* **3.** *Informal.* extraordinary: *have a tremendous time.* *adj.* —**tre men′dous ly,** *adv.*

trem or (trem′ər), **1.** an involuntary shaking or trembling: *a nervous tremor in the voice.* **2.** thrill of emotion or excitement. *n.*

trep i da tion (trep′ə dā′shən), **1.** nervous dread; fear; fright. **2.** a trembling. *n.*

tri ple (trip′əl), **1.** having three parts. **2.** three times as much or as many. **3.** make or become three times as much or as many. **4.** hit by which a batter gets to third base in baseball. **5.** make such a hit. 1,2 *adj.,* 4 *n.,* 3,5 *v.,* **tri pled, tri pling.**

tu bu lar (tü′byə lər or tyü′byə lər), shaped like a tube; round and hollow. *adj.*

tu mult (tü′mult or tyü′mult), **1.** noise; uproar. **2.** a violent disturbance or disorder. **3.** confusion; excitement. *n.*

tu mul tu ous (tü mul′chü əs or tyü mul′chü əs), **1.** characterized by tumult; very noisy or disorderly; violent: *a tumultuous celebration.* **2.** greatly disturbed: *tumultuous emotion.* **3.** rough; stormy: *Tumultuous waves beat upon the rocks.* *adj.* —**tu mul′tu ous ly,** *adv.* —**tu mul′tu ous ness,** *n.*

tur bu lence (tèr′byə ləns), turbulent condition; disorder; tumult; commotion. *n.*

tur moil (tèr′moil), commotion; disturbance; tumult. *n.*

ul ti mate (ul′tə mit), **1.** coming at the end; last possible; final: *He never stopped to consider the ultimate result of his actions.* **2.** fundamental; basic. **3.** greatest possible. *adj.*

un-¹, prefix meaning: not; the opposite of, as in *unfair, unjust, unequal.*

un-², prefix meaning: do the opposite of; do what will reverse the act, as in *undress, unlock, untie.*

un a vail ing (un′ə vā′ling), not successful; useless. *adj.* —**un′a vail′ing ly,** *adv.*

un bridge a ble (un brij′ə bəl), not bridgeable; not capable of being crossed. *adj.*

un bur den (un bèrd′n), **1.** free from a burden. **2.** relieve (one's mind or heart) by talking. *v.*

un con scious (un kon′shəs), **1.** not conscious. **2.** not aware. **3.** not meant; not intended: *unconscious neglect.* *adj.* —**un con′scious ly,** *adv.*

un con scious ness (un kon′shəs nis), unconscious condition; lack of consciousness; insensibility. *n.*

un du late (un′jə lāt for 1-4; un′jə lit or un′jə lāt for 5), **1.** move in waves: *undulating water.* **2.** have a wavy form or surface. **3.** cause to move in waves. **4.** give a wavy form or surface to. **5.** wavy. 1-4 *v.,* **un du lat ed, un du lat ing;** 5 *adj.*

un fail ing ly (un fāl′ing lē), always; without fail. *adv.*

un flinch ing (un flin′ching), not drawing back from difficulty, danger, or pain; firm. *adj.* —**un flinch′ing ly,** *adv.*

un gain ly (un gān′lē), awkward; clumsy. *adj.* —**un gain′li ness,** *n.*

un i den ti fied (un′ī den′tə fīd), not identified; not shown or proved the same as something known. *adj.*

un i ni ti at ed (un′i nish′ē ā′tid), **1.** not introduced to something; not given knowledge of something. **2.** not admitted to a group, its special ceremonies or secrets. *adj.*

u nique (yü nēk′), **1.** having no like or equal; being the only one of its kind. **2.** *Informal.* rare; unusual. *adj.* —**u nique′ly,** *adv.* —**u nique′ness,** *n.*

un kempt (un kempt′), **1.** not combed. **2.** neglected; untidy. *adj.*

un tu tored (un tü′tərd or un tyü′tərd), untaught. *adj.*

vain (vān), **1.** having too much pride in one's looks, ability, etc.: *She is vain of her beauty.* **2.** of no use; without effect or success; producing no good result: *I made vain attempts to reach her by telephone.* **3.** of no value or importance; worthless; empty: *a vain boast.* *adj.* —**vain′ness,** *n.*

vale (vāl), *Poetic.* **1.** valley. **2.** the world as a place of sorrow or tears; earthly life: *this vale of tears.* *n.*

var i a tion (ver′ē ā′shən or var′ē ā′shən), **1.** a varying in condition, degree, etc.; change. **2.** amount of change. **3.** a varied or changed form. *n.*

var y (ver′ē or var′ē), **1.** make or become different; change: *The driver can vary the speed of an automobile. The weather varies.* **2.** be different; differ: *The stars vary in brightness.* **3.** give variety to: *vary one's style of writing.* **4.** alternate. *v.,* **var ied, var y ing.** —**var′y ing ly,** *adv.*

ven ture (ven′chər), **1.** a risky or daring undertaking: *His courage was equal to any venture.* **2.** speculation to make money: *A lucky venture in oil stock made his fortune.* **3.** expose to risk or danger: *Men venture their lives in war.* **4.** dare to say or make: *He ventured an objection.* 1,2 *n.,* 3,4 *v.,* **ven tured, ven tur ing.**

ver i ta ble (ver′ə tə bəl), true; real; actual. *adj.* —**ver′i ta ble ness,** *n.*

vex (veks), 1. anger by trifles; annoy; provoke. 2. disturb; trouble. *v.*

vig or (vig′ər), 1. active strength or force. 2. healthy energy or power. *n.*

vig or ous (vig′ər əs), full of vigor; strong and active; energetic; forceful. *adj.* —**vig′or ous ly,** *adv.*

vine yard (vin′yərd), place planted with grapevines. *n.*

vir tue (vėr′chü), 1. moral excellence; goodness. 2. a particular moral excellence: *Justice and kindness are virtues.* 3. a good quality. 4. power to produce effects: *There is little virtue in that medicine.* *n.*

vir tu ous (vėr′chü əs), 1. good; moral; righteous. 2. chaste; pure. *adj.* —**vir′tu ous ly,** *adv.*

vi sion (vizh′ən), 1. power of seeing; sense of sight: *The old man wears glasses because his vision is poor.* 2. act or fact of seeing; sight. 3. power of perceiving by the imagination or by clear thinking: *a prophet of great vision.* 4. something seen in the imagination, in a dream, in one's thoughts, etc.: *The beggar had visions of great wealth.* 5. a very beautiful person, scene, etc. *n.*

vi tal (vī′tl), 1. of life; having to do with life: *vital forces.* Vital statistics give facts about births, deaths, marriages, etc. 2. necessary to life: *Eating is a vital function. The heart is a vital organ.* 3. very necessary; very important; essential: *An adequate army is vital to the defense of a nation.* 4. full of life and spirit; lively. *adj.* —**vi′tal ly,** *adv.*

vo lup tu ous (və lup′chü əs), 1. caring much for the pleasures of the senses. 2. giving pleasure to the senses: *voluptuous music or beauty.* *adj.* —**vo lup′tu ous ly,** *adv.* —**vo lup′tu ous ness,** *n.*

wad dle (wod′l), 1. walk with short steps and an awkward, swaying motion, as a duck does. 2. act of waddling. 3. an awkward, swaying gait. 1 *v.,* **wad dled, wad dling;** 2,3 *n.*

wag gle (wag′l), 1. move quickly and repeatedly from side to side; wag. 2. a waggling motion. 1 *v.,* **wag gled, wag gling;** 2 *n.*

waif (wāf), 1. person without home or friends; homeless or neglected child. 2. anything without an owner; stray thing, animal, etc. *n.*

wan (won), 1. pale; lacking natural color. 2. looking worn or tired; faint; weak. *adj.,* **wan ner, wan nest.** —**wan′ly,** *adv.* —**wan′-ness,** *n.*

wane (wān), 1. become smaller; become smaller gradually: *The moon wanes after it has become full.* 2. decline in power, influence, importance, etc.: *Many great empires have waned.* 3. decline in strength, intensity, etc.: *The light of day wanes in the evening.* *v.,* **waned, wan ing.**

war i ly (wer′ə lē or war′ə lē), cautiously; carefully. *adv.*

war y (wer′ē or war′ē), 1. on one's guard against danger, deception, etc.: *a wary fox.* 2. cautious; careful: *He gave wary answers to all of the stranger's questions. adj.*
wary of, cautious about; careful about.

weal (wēl), streak or ridge on the skin made by a stick or whip; welt. *n.*

well-dis posed (wel′dis pōzd′), 1. well-meaning. 2. having a favorable or kindly feeling (toward). *adj.*

whee dle (hwē′dl), 1. persuade by flattery, smooth words, caresses, etc.; coax: *The children wheedled their mother into letting them go to the picnic.* 2. get by wheedling: *They finally wheedled the secret out of him.* *v.,* **whee dled, whee-dling.**

wheeze (hwēz), 1. breathe with difficulty and a whistling sound. 2. a whistling sound caused by difficult breathing. 3. make a sound like this: *The old engine wheezed, but it didn't stop.* 4. say with a wheeze. 1,3,4 *v.,* **wheezed, wheez ing;** 2 *n.*

whif fle (hwif′əl), blow in puffs or gusts. *v.,* **whif fled, whif fling.**

wilt (wilt), 1. become limp and drooping; wither. 2. lose strength, vigor, assurance, etc. 3. cause to wilt. *v.*

wince (wins), draw back suddenly; flinch slightly: *The boy winced at the sight of the dentist's drill.* *v.,* **winced, winc ing.**

wind swept (wind′swept′), exposed to the full force of the wind. *adj.*

wing man (wing′man′ or wing′mən), a pilot who flies at the side and to the rear of a group leader. *n.,pl.* **wing men.**

win some (win′səm), charming; attractive; pleasing. *adj.* —**win′some ly,** *adv.*

wist ful (wist′fəl), 1. longing; yearning: *A child stood looking with wistful eyes at the toys in the window.* 2. pensive; melancholy. *adj.* —**wist′ful ly,** *adv.* —**wist′ful ness,** *n.*

worm (wėrm), an instrument for extracting a wad or ball from a muzzle-loading gun. *n.*

wor ry (wėr′ē), 1. feel anxious or uneasy: *She will worry if we are late.* 2. cause to feel anxious or troubled: *The problem worried him.* 3. seize and shake with the teeth; bite at; snap at: *A cat will worry a mouse.* *v.,* **wor ried, wor ry ing.**

wran gle (rang′gəl), 1. dispute noisily; quarrel angrily: *The children wrangled about who should sit in front.* 2. a noisy dispute; angry quarrel. 3. argue. 4. in the western United States, herd or tend (horses, etc.) on the range. 1,3,4 *v.,* **wran gled, wran gling;** 2 *n.*

wry (rī), turned to one side; twisted: *She made a wry face to show her disgust.* *adj.* —**wry′ly,** *adv.*

ze nith (zē′nith), 1. the point in the heavens directly overhead. 2. the highest point: *At the zenith of its power Rome ruled all of civilized Europe.* *n.*

---

hat, āge, fär; let, bē, tėrm; it, īce; hot, gō, ôrder; oil, out; cup, put, rüle; ch, child; ng, long; th, thin; ᴛH, then; zh, measure; ə represents *a* in about, *e* in taken, *i* in April, *o* in lemon, *u* in circus.

INDEX OF LITERARY TYPES

NOVEL
Herbie's Ride, 452.

POETRY
Achilles Deatheridge, 156; *Advice to Travelers,* 167; *Angus McGregor,* 342; *The Builders,* 341; *Charley Lee,* 266; *Dog, Midwinter,* 177; *Foul Shot,* 224; *The Giraffe,* 44; *Hunger,* 402; *Jail,* 253; *Limericks,* 27; *The Meadow Mouse,* 360; *Money,* 419; *Some Brown Sparrows,* 450.

SHORT STORY
All Summer in a Day, 14; *The Bear Hunt,* 52; *Beginning of Wisdom,* 188; *Beware of the Dog,* 254; *Death of a Tsotsi,* 352; *G. Trueheart, Man's Best Friend,* 20; *Ha'penny,* 396; *Harvey Kendall, A Father Who Grew Up,* 362; *Introducing Ellery's Mom,* 28; *Joey's Ball,* 344; *Just Try to Forget,* 149; *Millie,* 226; *Necktie Party,* 269; *The Nest,* 140; *Not Too Hard,* 241; *The Old Cardinal Spirit,* 232; *The Old Dog,* 320; *Orphan Pup,* 169; *Prairie Kid,* 425; *Stainless Steele,* 409; *The Torn Invitation* (excerpt), 117; *The Way Up,* 158; *Wine on the Desert,* 332.

SONG LYRIC
Eleanor Rigby, 178; *God Bless' the Child,* 420.

INDEX OF SKILLS

WORD ATTACK (CONTEXT): Handbook, 67-79. *Application:* 19, 144, 148, 187, 252, 268, 327-328, 351, 358-359, 377-379, 401, 448, 539. See also Teacher's Guidebook.

WORD ATTACK (STRUCTURE): Handbook, 80-94. *Application:* 144, 166, 358-359, 375, 377-379, 448, 482, 508.

See also Teacher's Guidebook.

WORD ATTACK (SOUND): Handbook, 95-108. *Application:* 377-379. See also Teacher's Guidebook.

WORD ATTACK (DICTIONARY): Handbook, 290-299. *Application:* 19, 144, 155, 176, 358-359, 377-379, 400-401, 408, 448, 468, 482, 499, 508, 529. See also Teacher's Guidebook.

INFERENCES: Handbook, 109-120. *Application:* 18, 25, 51, 61, 143, 154-155, 157, 166, 186-187, 199, 231, 239, 251-252, 253, 264, 267-268, 281, 323, 327, 331, 339, 341, 351, 375, 400, 407, 424, 436-437, 490, 499, 508, 519, 529, 545. See also Teacher's Guidebook.

PURPOSE: Handbook, 121-137. *Application:* See Teacher's Guidebook.

CENTRAL IDEA: Handbook, 201-221. *Application:* 19, 43, 167, 200, 239, 252, 273, 288, 341, 358, 361, 400, 407, 419, 421.

RELATIONSHIPS: Handbook, 300-317. *Application:* 177, 179, 199, 264-265, 289, 323, 340, 376, 448, 467, 499, 508, 519, 529, 539, 545. See also Teacher's Guidebook.

INVENTORY: Handbook, 380-393. *Application:* See Teacher's Guidebook.

JUDGMENTS: 18, 35, 45, 143, 148, 155, 157, 166, 175-176, 179, 200, 231, 251, 281, 288, 289, 323, 331, 339, 351, 358, 376, 407, 424, 437, 448, 451, 499, 546. See also Teacher's Guidebook.

SENSORY IMAGES: 19, 26, 45, 340, 343, 361.

FIGURATIVE LANGUAGE; SYMBOLISM: 26, 35, 45, 166, 167, 199-200, 225, 253, 268, 351, 375, 490.

1 2 3 4 5 6 7 8 9 10 11 12 13 14 15 16 17 18 19 20 21 22 23 24 25   AC 82 81 80 79 78 77 76 75 74